166.

SOIL CONDITIONS AND PLANT GROWTH

JEAN BAPTISTE DIEUDONNE BOUSSINGAULT
1802–1887

The Founder of Modern Agricultural Chemistry

Soil Conditions and Plant Growth

NINTH EDITION

by E. WALTER RUSSELL

C.M.G., M.A., PH.D.

Director, East African Agriculture and Forestry Research Organisation
Formerly Reader in Soil Science at the University of Oxford

FIRST TO SEVENTH EDITIONS

BY SIR E. JOHN RUSSELL

D.SC., F.R.S.

Formerly Director of the Rothamsted Experimental Station
and of the Imperial Bureau of Soil Science, Harpenden
President of the British Association, 1949

LONGMANS

LONGMANS, GREEN AND CO LTD
48 Grosvenor Street, London W.1
Associated companies, branches and representatives
throughout the world

First published (in Monographs in Biochemistry) by E. J. Russell   *1912*
Second Edition   *1915*
Third Edition   *1917*
Fourth Edition (in Rothamsted Monographs on Agricultural Science)   *1921*
Fifth Edition   *1927*
Sixth Edition   *1932*
Seventh Edition   *1937*
Eighth Edition rewritten and revised by E. W. Russell   *1950*
Ninth Edition   *1961*
Fourth Impression   *1966*

NINTH EDITION © E. W. RUSSELL 1961

Made and Printed in Great Britain by
Jarrold and Sons Ltd., Norwich

PREFACE TO THE NINTH EDITION

WHEN SIR JOHN RUSSELL was about to retire from the Directorship of Rothamsted Experimental Station in 1943, he asked me to take over full responsibility for the future editions of this book, and he gave me authority to make whatever alterations I considered desirable to help it fulfil its original function of presenting an up-to-date account of our knowledge of the soil as a medium for plant growth. I made full use of this liberty in preparing the Eighth Edition, re-writing and re-casting almost the whole text with the exception of Chapter I, which has hardly been altered since the first edition. I tried, however, to keep within the general framework that Sir John Russell gave the book when it was first published in 1912 and which he maintained until he handed it over to me.

This is the first time that a new edition of this book has been issued with only parts of the book properly revised. Our understanding of many of the topics discussed has increased sufficiently rapidly in the last ten years to make it impossible to bring the text up to date by altering a sentence here or there. I have preferred to carry out a thorough revision of as many sections as I had the time and opportunity to do, and leave the rest little altered. Thus, I have thoroughly revised most of the sections in Chapters V to XVI and all Chapter XXVI. A few sections in other chapters have also been re-written, but otherwise the text has been left unaltered except where a statement was definitely false or misleading.

One of the functions of this book has been to give a critical account of our present knowledge, and for this reason references have been quoted, wherever possible, for all the statements made. This has always been one of the essential features of the book in the past and I consider that it should remain so in the future. I have, however, been obliged to give references to work which is familiar to me, knowing that often the reference is neither the earliest nor necessarily the most suitable to the subject. This has been forced on me partly because of the immensity of the literature in Soil Science, but partly also because library facilities in East Africa are much more restricted than in the United Kingdom. Hence I hope that any worker whose work I have overlooked, but ought to have been quoted, will forgive my omission but let me know, so I can correct the omission in the next edition.

This revision had only just been started when I resigned from the Readership in Soil Science at the University of Oxford to come out to

East Africa. Much of the revision has, however, been done when I have
been back in Oxford on leave, and I am very much indebted to
Professor G. E. Blackman for allowing me to make full use of the facilities of his department, and to his staff for the generous help they have
always given me.

It is also a great pleasure to acknowledge the unfailing help I have
received from my friends and colleagues whenever I have asked it of
them. I cannot possibly make adequate acknowledgement to all of them,
though I would like to make personal acknowledgements to the following.
The late Dr. R. Kenworthy Schofield with whom I had the privilege of
having numerous discussions on parts of Chapters VII and XXVI,
and Drs. J. M. Bremner, G. W. Cooke, R. Greene-Kelly, D. S. Jenkinson,
G. E. G. Mattingly, J. Meiklejohn, P. S. Nutman and R. G. Warren
of Rothamsted. Finally, I am greatly indebted to my wife for preparing
the Author Index.

E. W. RUSSELL

East African Agricultural and Forestry
Research Organisation
Kikuyu, Kenya

CONTENTS

PLATES

xiii

CHAPTER I

HISTORICAL AND INTRODUCTORY

IN ALL AGES the growth of plants has interested thoughtful men. The mystery of the change of an apparently lifeless seed to a vigorous growing plant never loses its freshness, and constitutes, indeed, no small part of the charm of gardening. The economic problems are of vital importance, and become more and more urgent as time goes on and populations increase and their needs become more complex.

There was an extensive literature on agriculture in Roman times which maintained a pre-eminent position until comparatively recently. In this we find collected many of the facts which it has subsequently been the business of agricultural experts to classify and explain. The Roman literature was collected and condensed into one volume about the year 1240 by a senator of Bologna, Petrus Crescentius, whose book[1] was one of the most popular treatises on agriculture of any time, being frequently copied, and in the early days of printing, passing through many editions—some of them very handsome, and ultimately giving rise to the large standard European treatises of the sixteenth and seventeenth centuries. Many other agricultural books appeared in the fifteenth and early sixteenth centuries, notably in Italy, and later in France. In some of these are found certain ingenious speculations that have been justified by later work. Such, for instance, is Palissy's remarkable statement in 1563: "You will admit that when you bring dung into the field it is to return to the soil something that has been taken away. . . . When a plant is burned it is reduced to a salty ash called alcaly by apothecaries and philosophers. . . . Every sort of plant without exception contains some kind of salt. Have you not seen certain labourers when sowing a field with wheat for the second year in succession, burn the unused wheat straw which had been taken from the field? In the ashes will be found the salt that the straw took out of the soil; if this is put back the soil is improved. Being burnt on the ground it serves as manure because it returns to the soil those substances that had been taken away." But for every speculation that has been confirmed will be found many that have not, and the beginnings of agricultural chemistry must be sought later, when men had learnt the necessity for carrying on experiments.

[1] *Ruralium commodorum libri duodecim*, Augsburg, 1471, and many subsequent editions.

The Search for the "Principle" of Vegetation, 1630–1750

It was probably very early discovered that manures, composts, dead animal bodies, and parts of animals, such as blood, all increased the fertility of the land; and this was the basis of the ancient saying that "corruption is the mother of vegetation". Yet the early investigators consistently ignored this ancient wisdom when they sought for the "principle" of vegetation to account for the phenomena of soil fertility and plant growth. Thus the great Francis Bacon, Lord Verulam, believed that water formed the "principal nourishment" of plants, the purpose of the soil being to keep them upright and protect them from excessive cold or heat, though he also considered that each plant drew a "particular juyce" from the soil for its sustenance, thereby impoverishing the soil for that particular plant and similar ones, but not necessarily for other plants. Van Helmont (1577–1644) regarded water as the sole nutrient for plants, and his son thus records his famous Brussels experiment: "I took an earthen vessel in which I put 200 pounds of soil dried in an oven, then I moistened with rain-water and pressed hard into it a shoot of willow weighing 5 pounds. After exactly five years the tree that had grown up weighed 169 pounds and about three ounces. But the vessel had never received anything but rain-water or distilled water to moisten the soil when this was necessary, and it remained full of soil, which was still tightly packed, and, lest any dust from outside should get into the soil, it was covered with a sheet of iron coated with tin but perforated with many holes. I did not take the weight of the leaves that fell in the autumn. In the end I dried the soil once more and got the same 200 pounds that I started with, less about two ounces. Therefore the 164 pounds of wood, bark, and root arose from the water alone."[1]

The experiment is simple and convincing, and satisfied Robert Boyle,[2] who repeated it with "squash, a kind of Indian pompion" and obtained similar results. Boyle further distilled the plants and concluded, quite justifiably from his premises, that the products obtained, "salt, spirit, earth, and even oil (though that be thought of all bodies the most opposite to water), may be produced out of water". Nevertheless, the conclusion is incorrect, because two factors had escaped Van Helmont's notice—the parts played by the air and by the missing two ounces of soil. But the history of this experiment is thoroughly typical of experiments in agricultural chemistry generally: in no other subject is it so easy to overlook a vital factor and draw from good experiments a conclusion that appears to be absolutely sound, but is in reality entirely wrong.

[1] *Ortus medicinae*, pp. 84–90. *Complexionum atque mistionum elementalium figmentum*, Amsterdam, 1652.
[2] *The Sceptical Chymist*, Pt. II, 1661.

Some years later J. R. Glauber[1] set up the hypothesis that saltpetre is the "principle" of vegetation. Having obtained saltpetre from the earth cleared out from cattle sheds, he argued that it must have come from the urine or droppings of the animals, and must, therefore, be contained in the animal's food, i.e. in plants. He also found that additions of saltpetre to the soil produced enormous increases in crop. He connected these two observations and supposed that saltpetre is the essential principle of vegetation. The fertility of the soil and the value of manures (he mentions dung, feathers, hair, horn, bones, cloth cuttings) are entirely due to saltpetre.

This view was supported by John Mayow's experiments.[2] He estimated the amounts of nitre in the soil at different times of the year, and showed that it occurs in greatest quantity in spring when plants are just beginning to grow, but is not to be found "in soil on which plants grow abundantly, the reason being that all the nitre of the soil is sucked out by the plants". J. A. Külbel,[3] on the other hand, regarded a *magma unguinosum* obtainable from humus as the "principle" sought for.

The most accurate work in this period was published by John Woodward[4] in a remarkable paper. Setting out from the experiments of Van Helmont and of Boyle, but apparently knowing nothing of the work of Glauber and of Mayow, he grew spearmint in water obtained from various sources with the following results among others:

Source of water	Weight of plants		Gained in 77 days	Expense of water (i.e. trans-piration)	Proportion of increase of plant to expense of water
	When put in	When taken out			
	grains	grains	grains	grains	
Rain-water . .	$28\frac{1}{4}$	$45\frac{3}{4}$	$17\frac{1}{2}$	3004	1 to $171\frac{23}{85}$
River Thames . .	28	54	26	2493	1 to $95\frac{23}{26}$
Hyde Park conduit .	110	249	139	13140	1 to $94\frac{74}{139}$
Hyde Park conduit plus $1\frac{1}{2}$ oz. garden mould .	92	376	284	14950	1 to $52\frac{182}{284}$

Now all these plants had abundance of water, therefore all should have made equal growth had nothing more been needed. The amount of growth, however, increased with the impurity of the water. "Vegetables", he concludes, "are not formed of water, but of a certain

---

[1] *Des Teutschlandts Wohlfart (Erster Theil), das dritte Capittel. De concentratione Vegetabilium, Miraculum Mundi*, Amsterdam, 1656.
[2] *Tractatus quinque medico-physici*, 1674 (Alembic Club reprint, Edinburgh, 1907).
[3] *Cause de la fertilité des terres*, Bordeaux, 1741.   [4] *Phil. Trans. Roy. Soc.*, 1699, **21**, 382.

peculiar terrestrial matter. It has been shown that there is a considerable quantity of this matter contained in rain, spring and river water, that the greatest part of the fluid mass that ascends up into plants does not settle there but passes through their pores and exhales up into the atmosphere: that a great part of the terrestrial matter, mixed with the water, passes up into the plant along with it, and that the plant is more or less augmented in proportion as the water contains a greater or less quantity of that matter; from all of which we may reasonably infer, that earth, and not water, is the matter that constitutes vegetables."

He discusses the use of manures and the fertility of the soil from this point of view, attributing the well-known falling off in crop yield when plants are grown for successive years on unmanured land to the circumstance that "the vegetable matter that it at first abounded in being extracted from it by those successive crops, is most of it borne off. . . . The land may be brought to produce another series of the same vegetables, but not until it is supplied with a new fund of matter, of like sort with that it at first contained; which supply is made several ways, either by the ground's being fallow some time, until the rain has poured down a fresh stock upon it; or by the tiller's care in manuring it." The best manures, he continues, are parts either of vegetables or of animals, which ultimately are derived from vegetables.

In his celebrated text-book of chemistry, H. Boerhaave[1] taught that plants absorb the juices of the earth and then work them up into food. The raw material, the "prime radical juice of vegetables, is a compound from all the three kingdoms, viz. *fossil* bodies and putrified parts of *animals* and *vegetables*". This "we look upon as the *chyle of the plant*; being chiefly found in the first order of vessels, viz. in the roots and the body of the plant, which answers to the stomach and intestines of an animal".

For many years no such outstanding work as that of Glauber and Woodward was published, if we except Stephen Hales's *Vegetable Staticks* in 1727, the interest of which is physiological rather than agricultural.[2] Advances were, however, being made in agricultural practice. One of the most important was the introduction of the drill and the horse hoe by Jethro Tull, an Oxford man of a strongly practical turn of mind, who insisted on the vital importance of getting the soil into a fine, crumbly state for plant growth. Tull was more than an inventor; he discussed in most picturesque language the sources of fertility in the soil.[3] In his view it was not the juices of the earth, but the very minute particles of soil loosened by the action of moisture, that constituted the

---

[1] *A New Method of Chemistry*, London, 1727.
[2] He shows, however, that air is "wrought into the composition" of plants.
[3] *Horse Hoeing Husbandry*, London, 1731.

"proper pabulum" of plants. The pressure caused by the swelling of the growing roots forced these particles into the "lacteal mouths of the roots", where they entered the circulatory system. All plants lived on these particles, i.e. on the same kind of food; it was incorrect to assert, as some had done, that different kinds of plants fed as differently as horses and dogs, each taking its appropriate food and no other. Plants will take in anything that comes their way, good or bad. A rotation of crops is not a necessity, but only a convenience. Conversely, any soil will nourish any plant if the temperature and water supply are properly regulated. Hoeing increased the surface of the soil or the "pasture of the plant", and also enabled the soil better to absorb the nutritious vapours condensed from the air. Dung acted in the same way, but was more costly and less efficient.

So much were Tull's writings esteemed, Cobbett tells us, that they were "plundered by English writers not a few and by Scotch in whole bandittis".

The position at the end of this period cannot better be summed up than in Tull's own words: "It is agreed that all the following materials contribute in some manner to the increase of plants, but it is disputed which of them is that very increase or food: (1) nitre, (2) water, (3) air, (4) fire, (5) earth."

The Search for Plant Nutrients

I. THE PHLOGISTIC PERIOD, 1750–1800

Great interest was taken in agriculture in this country during the latter half of the eighteenth century. "The farming tribe", writes Arthur Young during this period, "is now made up of all ranks, from a duke to an apprentice." Many experiments were conducted, facts were accumulated, books written, and societies formed for promoting agriculture. The Edinburgh Society, established in 1755 for the improvement of arts and manufactures, induced Francis Home[1] "to try how far chymistry will go in settling the principles of agriculture". The whole art of agriculture, he says, centres in one point: the nourishing of plants. Investigation of fertile soils showed that they contain oil, which is therefore a food of plants. But when a soil has been exhausted by cropping, it recovers its fertility on exposure to air,[2] which therefore supplies another food. Home made pot experiments to ascertain the effect of various substances on plant growth. "The more they (i.e. farmers) know of the effects of different bodies on plants, the greater chance they have to discover the nourishment of plants, at

---

[1] *The Principles of Agriculture and Vegetation*, Edinburgh, 1757.
[2] Recorded by most early writers, e.g. Evelyn (*Terra, a philosophical discourse of earth*, 1674).

least this is the only road." Saltpetre, Epsom salt, vitriolated tartar (i.e. potassium sulphate) all lead to increased plant growth, yet they are three distinct salts. Olive oil was also useful. It is thus clear that plant food is not one thing only, but several; he enumerates six: air, water, earth, salts of different kinds, oil, and fire in a fixed state. As further proof he shows that "all vegetables and vegetable juices afford those very principles, and no other, by all the chymical experiments which have yet been made on them with or without fire".

The book is a great advance on anything that had gone before it, not only because it recognises that plant nutrition depends on several factors, but because it indicates so clearly the two methods to be followed in studying the problem—pot cultures and plant analysis. Subsequent investigators, J. G. Wallerius,[1] the Earl of Dundonald[2] and R. Kirwan[3] added new details but no new principles. The problem, indeed, was carried as far as was possible until further advances were made in plant physiology and in chemistry. The writers just mentioned are, however, too important to be passed over completely. Wallerius, in 1761, professor of chemistry at Upsala, after analysing plants to discover the materials on which they live, and arguing that *Nutritio non fieri potest a rebus heterogeneis, sed homogeneis*, concludes that humus, being *homogeneous*, is the source of their food—the *nutritiva*—while the other soil constituents are *instrumentalia*, making the proper food mixture, dissolving and attenuating it, till it can enter the plant root. Thus chalk and probably salts help in dissolving the "fatness" of the humus. Clay helps to retain the "fatness" and prevent it being washed away by rain: sand keeps the soil open and pervious to air. The Earl of Dundonald, in 1795, adds alkaline phosphates to the list of nutritive salts, but he attaches chief importance to humus as plant food. The "oxygenation" process going on in the soil makes the organic matter insoluble and therefore useless for the plant; lime, "alkalis and other saline substances" dissolve it and change it to plant food; hence these substances should be used alternately with dung as manure. Manures were thus divided, as by Wallerius, into two classes: those that afford plant food, and those that have some indirect effect.

Throughout this period it was believed that plants could generate alkalis. "Alkalis", wrote Kirwan in 1796, "seem to be the product of the vegetable process, for either none, or scarce any, is found in the soils, or in rain water." In like manner Lampadius thought he had proved that plants could generate silica. The theory that plants agreed

[1] *Agriculturae Fundamenta Chemica: Akerbrukets Chemiska Grunder*, Upsala, 1761.
[2] *A Treatise Showing the Intimate Connection that Subsists between Agriculture and Chemistry, etc.*, London, 1795.
[3] *The Manures most advantageously applicable to the various sorts of soils and the cause of their beneficial effects in each particular instance*, 4th ed., London, 1796.

in all essentials with animals was still accepted by many men of science; some interesting developments were made by Erasmus Darwin.[1]

Between 1770 and 1800 work was done on the effects of vegetation on air that was destined to revolutionise the ideas of the function of plants in the economy of nature, but its agricultural significance was not recognised until later. Joseph Priestley,[2] knowing that the atmosphere becomes vitiated by animal respiration, combustion, putrefaction, etc., and realising that some natural purification must go on, or life would no longer be possible, was led to try the effect of sprigs of living mint on vitiated air. He found that the mint made the air purer, and concludes "that plants, instead of affecting the air in the same manner with animal respiration, reverse the effects of breathing, and tend to keep the atmosphere pure and wholesome, when it is become noxious in consequence of animals either living, or breathing, or dying, and putrefying in it". But he had not yet discovered oxygen, and so could not give precision to his discovery: and when, later on, he did discover oxygen and learn how to estimate it, he unfortunately failed to confirm his earlier results because he overlooked a vital factor, the necessity of light. He was therefore unable to answer Scheele, who had insisted that plants, like animals, vitiate the air. It was Jan Ingen-Housz[3] who reconciled both views and showed that purification goes on in light only, whilst vitiation takes place in the darkness. Jean Senebier at Geneva had also arrived at the same result. He also studied the converse problem—the effect of air on the plant, and in 1782[4] argued that the increased weight of the tree in Van Helmont's experiment (p. 2) came from the fixed air. "Si donc l'air fixe, dissous dans l'eau de l'atmosphère, se combine dans la parenchyme avec la lumière et tous les autres éléments de la plante; si le phlogistique de cet air fixe est sûrement précipité dans les organes de la plante, si ce précipité reste, comme on le voit, puisque cet air fixe sort des plantes sous la forme d'air déphlogistiqué, il est clair que l'air fixe, combiné dans la plante avec la lumière, y laisse une matière qui n'y seroit pas, et mes expériences sur l'étoilement suffisent pour le démontrer." Later on Senebier translated his work into the modern terms of Lavoisier's system.

2. THE MODERN PERIOD, 1800–60

(a) *The Foundation of Plant Physiology.* We have seen that Home in 1757 pushed his inquiries as far as the methods in vogue would permit, and in consequence no marked advance was made for forty years. A

---

[1] *Phytologia, or the philosophy of agriculture and gardening,* London, 1800.
[2] *Experiments and Observations on Different Kinds of Air,* London, 1775.
[3] *Experiments upon Vegetables, discovering their great power of purifying common air in the sunshine and of injuring in the shade and at night,* London, 1779.
[4] *Mémoires Physico-chimiques,* 1782.

new method was wanted before further progress could be made, or before the new idea introduced by Senebier could be developed. Fortunately, this was soon forthcoming, in 1804. To Théodore de Saussure,[1] son of the well-known de Saussure of Geneva, is due the quantitative experimental method which more than anything else has made modern agricultural chemistry possible; which formed the basis of subsequent work by Boussingault, Liebig, Lawes and Gilbert, and, indeed, still remains our safest method of investigation. Senebier tells us that the elder de Saussure was well acquainted with his work, and it is therefore not surprising that the son attacked two problems that Senebier had also studied—the effect of air on plants and the nature and origin of salts in plants. De Saussure grew plants in air or in known mixtures of air and carbon dioxide, and measured the gas changes by eudiometric analysis and the changes in the plant by "carbonisation". He was thus able to demonstrate the central fact of plant respiration—the absorption of oxygen and the evolution of carbon dioxide, and further to show the decomposition of carbon dioxide and evolution of oxygen in light. Carbon dioxide in small quantities was a vital necessity for plants, and they perished if it was artificially removed from the air. It furnished them not only with carbon, but also with some oxygen. Water is also decomposed and fixed by plants. On comparing the amount of dry matter gained from these sources with the amount of material that can enter through the roots even under the most favourable conditions, he concludes that the soil furnished only a very small part of the plant food. Small as it is, however, this part is indispensable: it supplies nitrogen—*une partie essentielle des végétaux*—which, as he had shown, was not assimilated direct from the air; and also ash constituents, *qui peuvent contribuer à former, comme dans les animaux, leur parties solides ou osseuses.* Further, he shows that the root is not a mere filter allowing any and every liquid to enter the plant; it has a special action and takes in water more readily than dissolved matter, thus effecting a concentration of the solution surrounding it; different salts, also, are absorbed to a different extent. Passing next to the composition of the plant ash, he shows that it is not constant, but varies with the nature of the soil and the age of the plant; it consists mainly, however, of alkalis and phosphates. All the constituents of the ash occur in humus. If a plant is grown from seed in water there is no gain in ash: the amount found at the end of the plant's growth is the same as was present in the seed excepting for a relatively small amount falling on the plant as dust. Thus he disposes finally of the idea that the plant *generated* potash.

After the somewhat lengthy and often wearisome works of the earlier

[1] *Recherches chimiques sur la végétation*, Paris, 1804.

writers it is very refreshing to turn to de Saussure's concise and logical arguments and the ample verification he gives at every stage. But for years his teachings were not accepted, nor were his methods followed.

The two great books on agricultural chemistry then current still belonged to the old period. A. von Thaer and Humphry Davy, while much in advance of Wallerius, the text-book writer of 1761, nevertheless did not realise the fundamental change introduced by de Saussure; it has always been the fate of agricultural science to lag behind pure science. Thaer published his *Grundsätze de rationellen Landwirtschaft* in 1809–12: it had a great success on the Continent as a good, practical hand-book, and was translated into English as late as 1844 by Cuthbert Johnson. In it he adopted the prevailing view that plants draw their carbon and other nutrients from the soil humus. "Die Fruchtbarkeit des Bodens", he says, "hängt eigentlich ganz vom Humus ab. Denn ausser Wasser ist er es allein, der den Pflanzen Nahrung gibt. So wie der Humus eine Erzeugung des Lebens ist, so ist er auch eine Bedingung des Lebens. Er gibt den Organismen die Nahrung. Ohne ihn lässt sich kein individuelles Leben denken." Humphry Davy's book[1] grew out of the lectures which he gave annually at the Royal Institution on agricultural chemistry between 1802 and 1812; it forms the last text-book of the older period. Whilst no great advance was made by Davy himself he carefully sifted the facts and hypotheses of previous writers, and gives us an account, which, however defective in places, represents the best accepted knowledge of the time, set out in the new chemical language. His great name gave the subject an importance it would not otherwise have had.[2] He did not accept de Saussure's conclusion that plants obtain their carbon chiefly from the carbonic acid of the air: some plants, he says, appear to be supplied with carbon chiefly from this source, but in general he supposes the carbon to be taken in through the roots. Oils are good manures because of the carbon and hydrogen they contain; soot is valuable, because its carbon is "in a state in which it is capable of being rendered soluble by the action of oxygen and water". Lime is useful because it dissolves hard vegetable matter. Once the organic matter has dissolved there is no advantage in letting it decompose further: putrid urine is less useful as manure than fresh urine, whilst it is quite wrong to cause farmyard manure to ferment before it is applied to the land. All these ideas have been given up, and indeed there never was any sound experimental evidence to

---

[1] *Elements of Agricultural Chemistry*, London, 1813.

[2] Thus Charles Lamb, *Essays of Elia* (1820–3) in the "Old and New Schoolmaster", writes: "The modern schoolmaster is required to know a little of everything because his pupil is required not to be entirely ignorant of anything. He is to know something of pneumatics, of chemistry, the quality of soils, etc. . . ."

support them. It is even arguable that they would not have persisted so long as they did had it not been for Davy's high reputation. His insistence on the importance of the physical properties of soils—their relationship to heat and to water—was more fortunate and marks the beginning of soil physics, afterwards developed considerably by Gustav Schübler.[1] On the Continent, to an even greater extent than in England, it was held that plants drew their carbon and other nutrients from the soil humus, a view supported by the very high authority of J. J. Berzelius.[2]

(b) *The Foundation of Agricultural Science.* Hitherto experiments had been conducted either in the laboratory or in small pots: about 1834, however, J. B. Boussingault, who was already known as an adventurous traveller in South America, began a series of field experiments on his farm at Bechelbronn in Alsace. These were the first of their kind: to Boussingault, therefore, belongs the honour of having introduced the method by which the new agricultural science was to be developed. He reintroduced the quantitative methods of de Saussure, weighed and analysed the manures used and the crop obtained, and at the end of the rotation drew up a balance sheet, showing how far the manures had satisfied the needs of the crop and how far other sources of supply —air, rain and soil—had been drawn upon. The results of one experiment are given in Table 1.[3] At the end of the period the soil had returned to its original state of productiveness, hence the dry matter, carbon, hydrogen and oxygen not accounted for by the manure must have been supplied by the air and rain, and not by the soil. On the other hand, the manure afforded more mineral matter than the crop took off, the balance remaining in the soil. Other things being equal, he argued that the best rotation is one which yields the greatest amount of organic matter over and above what is present in the manure. No fewer than five rotations were studied, but it will suffice to set out only the nitrogen statistics (Table 2), which show a marked gain of nitrogen when the newer rotations are adopted, but not where wheat only is grown.

Now the rotation has not impoverished the soil, hence he concludes that "l'azote peut entrer directement dans l'organisme des plantes, si leur parties vertes sont aptes à le fixer". Boussingault's work covers the whole range of agriculture and deals with the composition of crops at different stages of their growth with soils, and with problems in animal nutrition. Unfortunately the classic farm of Bechelbronn did not remain a centre of agricultural research and the experiments came to an end after the war of 1870. Some of the work was summarised

---

[1] *Grundsätze der Agrikulturchemie in näherer Beziehung auf land- und fortswirtschaftliche Gewerbe,* Leipzig, 1838.

[2] *Traité de chimie,* Brussels, 1838.   [3] *Ann. Chim. Phys.* (III), 1841, **1**, 208.

TABLE 1
Statistics of a Rotation

	Weight in kg. per hectare of					
	Dry matter	Carbon	Hydrogen	Oxygen	Nitrogen	Mineral matter
1. Beets . .	3172	1357·7	184·0	1376·7	53·9	199·8
2. Wheat . .	3006	1431·6	164·4	1214·9	31·3	163·8
3. Clover hay .	4029	1909·7	201·5	1523·0	84·6	310·2
4. Wheat . .	4208	2004·2	230·0	1700·7	43·8	229·3
Turnips (catch crop) . .	716	307·2	39·3	302·9	12·2	54·4
5. Oats . .	2347	1182·3	137·3	890·9	28·4	108·0
Total during rotation . .	17478	8192·7	956·5	7009·0	254·2	1065·5
Added in manure .	10161	3637·6	426·8	2621·5	203·2	3271·9
Difference not accounted for taken from air, rain or soil . . .	+7317	+4555·1	+529·7	+4387·5	+51·0	—2206·4

1000 kg. per hectare = 8 cwt. per acre

TABLE 2
Nitrogen Statistics of Various Rotations

Rotation	Kg. per hectare			
	Nitrogen in manure	Nitrogen in crop	Excess in crop over that supplied in manure	
			Per rotation	Per annum
(1) Potatoes, (2) wheat, (3) clover, (4) wheat, turnips,[1] (5) oats . .	203·2	250·7	47·5	9·5
(1) Beets, (2) wheat, (3) clover, (4) wheat, turnips,[1] (5) oats . .	203·2	254·2	51·0	10·2
(1) Potatoes, (2) wheat, (3) clover, (4) wheat, turnips,[1] (5) peas, (6) rye	243·8	353·6	109·3	18·3
Jerusalem artichokes, two years .	188·2	274·2	86·0	43·0[2]
(1) Dunged fallow, (2) wheat, (3) wheat	82·8	87·4	4·6	1·5
Lucerne, five years	224·0	1078·0	854·0	170·8

[1] Catch crop, i.e. taken in autumn after the wheat.
[2] This crop does not belong to the leguminosae, but it is possible that the nitrogen came from the soil, and that impoverishment was going on.

by J. B. A. Dumas and Boussingault[1] in a very striking essay that has been curiously overlooked by agricultural chemists.

During this period (1830–40) Carl Sprengel was studying the ash constituents of plants, which he considered were probably essential to nutrition.[2] Schübler was working at soil physics, and a good deal of other work was quietly being done. No particularly important discoveries were being made, no controversies were going on, and no great amount of interest was taken in the subject.

But all this was changed in 1840 when Liebig's famous report to the British Association[3] upon the state of organic chemistry, published as *Chemistry in its Application to Agriculture and Physiology* in 1840, came like a thunderbolt upon the world of science. With polished invective and a fine sarcasm he holds up to scorn the plant physiologists of his day for their continued adhesion, in spite of accumulated evidence, to the view that plants derive their carbon from the soil and not from the carbonic acid of the air. "All explanations of chemists must remain without fruit, and useless, because, even to the great leaders in physiology, carbonic acid, ammonia, acids and bases are sounds without meaning, words without sense, terms of an unknown language, which awake no thoughts and no associations." The experiments quoted by the physiologists in support of their view are all "valueless for the decision of any question". "These experiments are considered by them as convincing proofs, whilst they are fitted only to awake pity." Liebig's ridicule did what neither de Saussure's nor Boussingault's logic had done: it finally killed the humus theory. Only the boldest would have ventured after this to assert that plants derive their carbon from any source other than carbon dioxide, although it must be admitted that we have no proof that plants really do obtain all their carbon in this way. Thirty years later, in fact, L. Grandeau[4] adduced evidence that humus may, after all, contribute something to the carbon supply, and his view found some acceptance in France;[5] for this also, however, convincing proof is lacking. But for the time carbon dioxide was considered to be the sole source of the carbon of plants. Hydrogen and oxygen came from water, and nitrogen from ammonia. Certain mineral substances were essential: alkalis were needed for neutralisation of the acids made by plants in the course of their vital processes, phosphates were necessary for seed formation, and potassium silicates for the development of grasses and cereals. The evidence lay in the composition of the ash: plants might absorb anything soluble from the soil,

[1] *Essai de statique chimique des êtres organisés*, Paris, 1841.

[2] *Chemie für Landwirthe, Forstmänner und Cameralisten*, Göttingen, 1832.

[3] There is no record of this Report ever having been presented to the Association.

[4] *C.R.*, 1872, **74**, 988; *Publication de la Station Agronomique de l'Est*, 1872.

[5] See, for example, L. Cailletet (*C.R.*, 1911, **152**, 1215), Jules Lefèvre (ibid., 1905, **141**, 211), and J. Laurent (*Rev. gén. bot.*, 1904, **16**, 14).

but they excreted from their roots whatever was non-essential. The fact of a substance being present was therefore sufficient proof of its necessity.

Plants, Liebig argued, have an inexhaustible supply of carbonic acid in the air. But time is saved in the early stages of plant growth if carbonic acid is being generated in the soil, for it enters the plant roots and affords extra nutrient over and above what the small leaves are taking in. Hence a supply of humus, which continuously yields carbonic acid, is advantageous. Further, the carbonic acid attacks and dissolves some of the alkali compounds of the soil and thus increases the mineral food supply. The true function of humus is to evolve carbonic acid.

The alkali compounds of the soil are not all equally soluble. A weathering process has to go on, which is facilitated by liming and cultivation, whereby the comparatively insoluble compounds are broken down to a more soluble state. The final solution is effected by acetic acid excreted by the plant roots, and the dissolved material now enters the plant.

The nitrogen is taken up as ammonia, which may come from the soil, from added manure, or from the air. In order that a soil may remain fertile it is necessary and sufficient to return in the form of manure the mineral constituents and the nitrogen that have been taken away. When sufficient crop analyses have been made it will be possible to draw up tables showing the farmer precisely what he must add in any particular case.

An artificial manure known as Liebig's patent manure was made up on these lines and placed on the market.

Liebig's book was meant to attract attention to the subject, and it did; it rapidly went through several editions, and as time went on Liebig developed his thesis, and gave it a quantitative form: "The crops on a field diminish or increase in exact proportion to the diminution or increase of the mineral substances conveyed to it in manure." He further adds what afterwards became known as the Law of the Minimum, "by the deficiency or absence of *one* necessary constituent, all the others being present, the soil is rendered barren for all those crops to the life of which *that one* constituent is indispensable". These and other amplifications in the third edition, 1843, gave rise to much controversy. So much did Liebig insist, and quite rightly, on the necessity for alkalis and phosphates, and so impressed was he by the gain of nitrogen in meadow land supplied with alkalis and phosphates alone, and by the continued fertility of some of the fields of Virginia and Hungary and the meadows of Holland, that he began more and more to regard the atmosphere as the source of nitrogen for plants.

Some of the passages of the first and second editions urging the necessity of ammoniacal manures were deleted from the third and later editions. "If the soil be suitable, if it contain a sufficient quantity of alkalis, phosphates, and sulphates, nothing will be wanting. The plants will derive their ammonia from the atmosphere as they do carbonic acid", he writes in the *Farmer's Magazine*.[1] Ash analysis led him to consider the turnip as one of the plants "which contain the least amount of phosphates and therefore require the smallest quantity for their development". These and other practical deductions were seized upon and shown to be erroneous by J. B. Lawes and J. H. Gilbert,[2] who had for some years been conducting vegetation experiments. Lawes does not discuss the theory as such, but tests the deductions Liebig himself draws and finds them wrong. Further trouble was in store for Liebig; his patent manure when tried in practice *had failed*. This was unfortunate, and the impression in England at any rate was, in Philip Pusey's words: "The mineral theory, too hastily adopted by Liebig, namely, that crops rise and fall in direct proportion to the quantity of mineral substances present in the soil, or to the addition or abstraction of these substances which are added in the manure, has received its death-blow from the experiments of Mr. Lawes."

And yet the failure of the patent manure was not entirely the fault of the theory, but only affords further proof of the numerous pitfalls of the subject. The manure was sound in that it contained potassium compounds and phosphates (it ought, of course, to have contained nitrogen compounds), but it was unfortunately rendered insoluble by fusion with lime and calcium phosphate so that it should not too readily wash out in the drainage water. Not till J. T. Way had shown in 1850[3] that *soil precipitates soluble salts of ammonium, potassium and phosphates* was the futility of the fusion process discovered, and Liebig[4] saw the error he had made.

Meanwhile the great field experiments at Rothamsted had been started by Lawes and Gilbert in 1843. These experiments were conducted on the same general lines as those begun earlier by Boussingault, but they have the advantage that they are still going on, having been continued year after year on the same ground without alteration, except in occasional details, since 1852. The mass of data now accumulated is considerable and it is being treated by modern statistical methods. Certain conclusions are so obvious, however, that they can

[1] *Farmer's Magazine*, 1847, **16**, 511. A good summary of Liebig's position is given in his *Familiar Letters on Chemistry*, 3rd ed., 1851, 34th letter, p. 519.
[2] *J. Roy. Agric. Soc.*, 1847, **8**, 226; 1851, **12**, 1; 1855, **16**, 411.
[3] *J. Roy. Agric. Soc.*, 1850, **11**, 313; 1852, **13**, 123.
[4] *Familiar Letters on Chemistry*, 3rd ed., London, 1851.

be drawn on mere inspection of the data. By 1855 the following points were definitely settled:[1]

1. Crops require phosphates and salts of the alkalis, but the composition of the ash does not afford reliable information as to the amounts of each constituent needed, e.g. turnips require large amounts of phosphates, although only little is present in their ash. Some of the results are:

Composition of ash, per cent (1860 crop)—		Yield of turnips, tons per acre (1843)—	
K_2O	44·8	Unmanured . . .	4·5
P_2O_5	7·9	Superphosphate . . .	12·8
		,, + potassic salts	11·9

2. Non-leguminous crops require a supply of some nitrogenous compounds, nitrates and ammonium salts being almost equally good. Without an adequate supply no increases of growth are obtained, even when ash constituents are added. The amount of ammonia obtainable from the atmosphere is insufficient for the needs of crops. Leguminous crops behave abnormally.

3. Soil fertility may be maintained for some years at least by means of artificial manures.

4. The beneficial effect of fallowing lies in the increase brought about in the available nitrogen compounds in the soil.

Although many of Liebig's statements were shown to be wrong, the main outline of his theory as first enunciated stands. It is no detraction that de Saussure had earlier published a somewhat similar, but less definite view of nutrition: Liebig had brought matters to a head and made men look at their cherished, but unexamined, convictions. The effect of the stimulus he gave can hardly be over-estimated, and before he had finished, the essential facts of plant nutrition were settled and the lines were laid down along which scientific manuring was to be developed. The water cultures of Knop and other plant physiologists showed conclusively that potassium, magnesium, calcium, iron, phosphorus, along with sulphur, carbon, nitrogen, hydrogen and oxygen are all necessary for plant life. The list differs from Liebig's only in the addition of iron and the withdrawal of silica; but even silica, although not strictly essential, is advantageous for the nutrition of cereals.

In two directions, however, the controversies went on for many years.

[1] Lawes and Gilbert's papers are collected in ten volumes of *Rothamsted Memoirs*, and the general results of their experiments are summarised by Hall in *The Book of the Rothamsted Experiments*. A detailed investigation of the early experiments of Lawes in their relation to the discovery of superphosphate has been made by Max Speter in *Superphosphate*, 1935, 8.

Farmers were slow to believe that "chemical manures" could ever do more than stimulate the crop, and declared they must ultimately exhaust the ground. The Rothamsted plots falsified this prediction; manured year after year with the same substances and sown always with the same crops, they even now, after a hundred years of chemical manuring, continue to produce good crops, although secondary effects have sometimes set in. In France the great missionary was Georges Ville,[1] whose lectures were given at the experimental farm at Vincennes during 1867 and 1874-5. He went even further than Lawes and Gilbert, and maintained that artificial manures were not only more remunerative than dung, but were the only way of keeping up fertility. In recommending mixtures of salts for manure he was not guided by ash analysis but by field trials. For each crop one of the four constituents, nitrogen compounds, phosphates, lime and potassium compounds (he did not consider it necessary to add any others to his manures) was found by trial to be more wanted than the others and was therefore called the "dominant" constituent. Thus for wheat he obtained the following results, and therefore concluded that on his soil wheat required a good supply of nitrogen, less phosphate, and still less potassium:

	Crop per acre bushels
Normal manure	43
Manure without lime	41
„ „ potash . . .	31
„ „ phosphate . . .	26½
„ „ nitrogen . . .	14
Soil without manure	12

Other experiments of the same kind showed that nitrogen was the dominant for all cereals and beetroot, potassium for potatoes and vines, phosphates for the sugar-cane. An excess of the dominant constituent was always added to the crop manure. The composition of the soil had to be taken into account, but soil analysis was no good for the purpose. Instead he drew up a simple scheme of plot trials to enable farmers to determine for themselves just what nutrient was lacking in their soil. His method was thus essentially empirical, but it still remains the best we have; his view that chemical manures are always better and cheaper than dung is, however, too narrow and has not survived.

The second controversy dealt with the source of nitrogen in plants. Priestley had stated that a plant of *Epilobium hirsutum* placed in a small

[1] *On Artificial Manures, their chemical selection and scientific application to agriculture.* Trans. by W. Crookes, London, 1879.

vessel absorbed during the course of the month seven-eighths of the air present. De Saussure, however, denied that plants assimilated gaseous nitrogen. J. B. Boussingault's pot experiments[1] showed that peas and clover could get nitrogen from the air while wheat could not, and his rotation experiments emphasised this distinction. He himself did not make as much of this discovery as he might have done, but later[2] fully realised its importance.

Liebig, as we have seen, maintained that ammonia, but not gaseous nitrogen, was taken up by plants, a view confirmed by Lawes, Gilbert and E. Pugh[3] in the most rigid demonstration that had yet been attempted. Plants of several natural orders, including the leguminosae, were grown in surroundings free from ammonia or any other nitrogen compound. The soil was burnt to remove all trace of nitrogen compounds, while the plants were kept throughout the experiment under glass shades, but supplied with washed and purified air and with pure water. In spite of the ample supply of mineral food the plants languished and died: the conclusion seemed irresistible that plants could not utilise gaseous nitrogen. For all non-leguminous crops this conclusion agreed with the results of field trials. But there remained the very troublesome fact that leguminous crops required no nitrogenous manure and yet they contained large quantities of nitrogen, and also enriched the soil considerably in this element. Where had the nitrogen come from? The amount of combined nitrogen brought down by the rain was found to be far too small to account for the result. For years experiments were carried on, but the problem remained unsolved. Looking back over the papers[4] one can see how very close some of the older investigators were to the discovery of the cause of the mystery: in particular J. Lachmann[5] carefully examined the structure of the nodules, which he associated with the nutrition of the plant, and showed that they contained "vibrionenartige" organisms. His paper, however, was published in an obscure journal and attracted little attention. W O Atwater in 1881 and 1882 showed that peas acquired large quantities of nitrogen from the air, and later suggested that they might "favour the action of nitrogen-fixing organisms".[6] But he was too busily engaged to follow the matter up, and once again an investigation in agricultural chemistry had been brought to a standstill for want of new methods of attack.

[1] *Ann. Chim. Phys.*, 1838 (II), **67**, 5; **69**, 353; 1856 (III), **46**, 5.
[2] J. B. A. Dumas and Boussingault, *Essai de statique chimique des êtres organisés*, Paris, 1841.
[3] *Phil. Trans.*, 1861, **151**, 431; 1889, **180** A, 1; *J. Roy. Agric. Soc.*, 1891, ser. 3, **2**, 657.
[4] A summary of the voluminous literature is contained in Löhnis's *Handbuch der landw. Bakteriologie*, pp. 646 *et seq.*
[5] *Mitt. Landw. Lehranst.*, Poppelsdorf, 1858, **1**. Reprinted in *Zbl. Agrik. Chem.*, 1891, **20**, 837.
[6] *Amer. Chem. J.*, 1885, **6**, 365; **8**, 327.

The Beginnings of Soil Bacteriology

It had been a maxim with the older agricultural chemists that "corruption is the mother of vegetation". Animal and vegetable matter had long been known to decompose with formation of nitrates: indeed nitre beds made up from such decaying matter were the recognised source of nitrates for the manufacture of gunpowder during the European wars of the seventeenth and eighteenth centuries.[1] No satisfactory explanation of the process had been offered, although the discussion of rival hypotheses continued up till 1860, but the conditions under which it worked were known and on the whole fairly accurately described.

No connection was at first observed between nitrate formation and soil productiveness. Liebig[2] rather diverted attention from the possibility of tracing what now seems an obvious relationship by regarding ammonia as the essential nitrogenous plant nutrient, though he admitted the possible suitability of nitrates. Way came much nearer to the truth. In 1856 he showed that nitrates were formed in soils to which nitrogenous fertilisers were added. Unfortunately he failed to realise the significance of this discovery. He was still obsessed with the idea that ammonia was essential to the plant, and he believed that ammonia, unlike other nitrogen compounds, could not change to nitrate in the soil, but was absorbed by the soil by the change he had already described (p. 14). But he only narrowly missed making an important advance in the subject, for after pointing out that nitrates are comparable with ammonium salts as fertilisers he writes: "Indeed the French chemists are going further, several of them now advocating the view that it is in the form of nitric acid that plants make use of compounds of nitrogen. With this view I do not myself at present concur: and it is sufficient here to admit that nitric acid in the form of nitrates has at least a very high value as a manure."

It was not till ten years later, and as a result of work by plant physiologists, that the French view prevailed over Liebig's, and agricultural investigators recognised the importance of nitrates to the plant and of nitrification to soil fertility. It then became necessary to discover the cause of nitrification.

During the 'sixties and 'seventies great advances were being made in bacteriology, and it was definitely established that bacteria bring about putrefaction, decomposition and other changes; it was therefore conceivable that they were the active agents in the soil, and that the

[1] *Instructions sur l'établissement des nitrières, publié par les Régisseurs généraux des Poudres et Salpêtre*, Paris, 1777.
[2] *Principles of Agricultural Chemistry with special reference to the late researches made in England*, London, 1855.

process of decomposition there taking place was not the purely chemical "eremacausis" Liebig had postulated. Pasteur himself had expressed the opinion that nitrification was a bacterial process. The new knowledge was first brought to bear on agricultural problems by Th. Schloesing and A. Müntz[1] during a study of the purification of sewage water by land filters. A continuous stream of sewage was allowed to trickle down a column of sand and limestone so slowly that it took eight days to pass. For the first twenty days the ammonia in the sewage was not affected, then it began to be converted into nitrate; finally all the ammonia was converted during its passage through the column, and nitrates alone were found in the issuing liquid. Why, asked the authors, was there a delay of twenty days before nitrification began? If the process were simply chemical, oxidation should begin at once. They therefore examined the possibility of bacterial action and found that the process was entirely stopped by a little chloroform vapour, but could be started again after the chloroform was removed by adding a little turbid extract of dry soil. Nitrification was thus shown to be due to micro-organisms—"organised ferments", to use their own expression.

R. Warington[2] had been investigating the nitrates in the Rothamsted soils, and at once applied the new discovery to soil processes. He showed that nitrification in the soil is stopped by chloroform and carbon disulphide; further, that solutions of ammonium salts could be nitrified by adding a trace of soil. By a careful series of experiments described in his four papers to the Chemical Society he found that there were two stages in the process and two distinct organisms: the ammonia was first converted into nitrite and then to nitrate. But he failed altogether to obtain the organisms, in spite of some years of study, by the gelatin methods then in vogue. However, S. Winogradsky,[3] in a brilliant investigation, isolated these two groups of organisms, showing they were bacteria. He succeeded where Warington failed because he realised that carbon dioxide should be a sufficient source of carbon for them, so that they ought to grow on silica gel plates carefully freed from all organic matter; and it was on this medium that he isolated them in 1890.

Warington also established definitely the fact that nitrogen compounds rapidly change to nitrates in the soil, so that whatever compound is supplied as manure, plants get practically nothing but nitrate as food. This closed the long discussion as to the nitrogenous food of non-leguminous plants; in natural conditions they take up nitrates only (or at any rate chiefly), because the activities of the nitrifying

[1] *C.R.*, 1877, **84**, 301; **85**, 1018; 1878, **86**, 892.
[2] *J. Chem. Soc.*, 1878, **33**, 44; 1879, **35**, 429; 1884, **45**, 637; 1891, **59**, 484.
[3] *Ann. Inst. Pasteur*, 1890, **4**, 213, 257, 760.

organisms leave them no option. The view that plants assimilate gaseous nitrogen has from time to time been revived,[1] but it is not generally accepted.

The apparently hopeless problem of the nitrogen nutrition of leguminous plants was soon to be solved. In a striking series of sand cultures H. Hellriegel and H. Wilfarth[2] showed that the growth of non-leguminous plants, barley, oats, etc., was directly proportional to the amount of nitrate supplied, the duplicate pots agreeing satisfactorily; while in the case of leguminous plants no sort of relationship existed and duplicate pots failed to agree. After the seedling stage was passed the leguminous plants grown without nitrate made no further progress for a time, then some of them started to grow and did well, while others failed. This stagnant period was not seen where nitrate was supplied. Two of their experiments are given in Table 3.

TABLE 3

Relation between Nitrogen Supply and Plant Growth

Nitrogen in the calcium nitrate supplied per pot, gm. . . .	none	0·056	0·112	0·168	0·224	0·336
Weight of oats obtained (grain and straw) .	$\begin{cases}0{\cdot}361\\0{\cdot}419\end{cases}$	$\begin{cases}5{\cdot}902\\5{\cdot}851\\5{\cdot}287\end{cases}$	$\begin{cases}10{\cdot}981\\10{\cdot}941\end{cases}$	15·997	$\begin{cases}21{\cdot}273\\21{\cdot}441\end{cases}$	30·175
Weight of peas obtained (grain and straw) .	$\begin{cases}0{\cdot}551\\3{\cdot}496\\5{\cdot}233\end{cases}$	$\begin{cases}0{\cdot}978\\1{\cdot}304\\4{\cdot}128\end{cases}$	$\begin{cases}4{\cdot}915\\9{\cdot}767\\8{\cdot}497\end{cases}$	5·619	$\begin{cases}9{\cdot}725\\6{\cdot}646\end{cases}$	11·352

Analysis showed that the nitrogen contained in the oat crop and sand at the end of the experiment was always a little less than that originally supplied, but was distinctly greater in the case of peas; the gain in three cases amounted to 0·910, 1·242 and 0·789 gm. per pot respectively. They drew two conclusions: (1) the peas took their nitrogen from the air; (2) the process of nitrogen assimilation was conditioned by some factor that did not come into their experiment except by chance. In trying to frame an explanation they connected two facts that were already known. M. Berthelot[3] had made experiments to show that certain micro-organisms in the soil can assimilate gaseous nitrogen. It was known to botanists that the nodules on the

---

[1] e.g. Th. Pfeiffer and E. Franke, *Landw. Vers.-Stat.*, 1896, **46**, 117; Thos Jamieson, *Aberdeen Res. Assoc. Repts.*, 1905–8; C. B. Lipman and J. K. Taylor, *J. Franklin Inst., Calif.*, 1924, p. 475.
[2] *Ztschr. Rübenzucker-Ind.*, Beilageheft, 1888.
[3] *C.R.*, 1885, **101**, 775.

roots of leguminosae contained bacteria.[1] Hellriegel and Wilfarth, therefore, supposed that the bacteria in the nodules assimilated gaseous nitrogen, and then handed on some of the resulting nitrogenous compounds to the plant. This hypothesis was shown to be well founded by the following facts:

1. In absence of nitrates peas made only small growth and developed no nodules in sterilised sand; when calcium nitrate was added they behaved like oats and barley, giving regular increases in crop for each increment of nitrates (the discordant results of Table 3 were obtained on unsterilised sand).

2. They grew well and developed nodules in sterilised sand watered with an extract of arable soil.

3. They sometimes did well and sometimes failed when grown without soil extract and without nitrate in *unsterilised* sand, which might or might not contain the necessary organisms. An extract that worked well for peas might be without effect on lupins or serradella. In other words, the organism is specific.

Hellriegel and Wilfarth read their paper and exhibited some of their plants at the Naturforscher-Versammlung at Berlin in 1886. Gilbert was present at the meeting, and on returning to Rothamsted repeated and confirmed the experiments. At a later date Th. Schloesing *fils* and E. Laurent[2] showed that the weight of nitrogen absorbed from the air was approximately equal to the gain by the plant and the soil, and thus finally clinched the evidence.

	Control	Peas	Mustard	Cress	Spurge
Nitrogen lost from the air, mgm.	1·0	134·6	—2·6	—3·8	—2·4
Nitrogen gained by crop and soil, mgm. . . .	4·0	142·4	—2·5	2·0	3·2

The organism was isolated by M. W. Beijerinck[3] and called *Bacillus radicicola*, but is now known as *Rhizobium*.

Thus another great controversy came to an end, and the discrepancy between the field trials and the laboratory experiments of Lawes, Gilbert and Pugh was cleared up. The laboratory experiments gave the correct conclusion that leguminous plants, like non-leguminous

[1] This had been demonstrated by Lachmann (p. 17) and by M. Woronin (*Mem. Acad. Sci.* St. Petersburg, 1866, ser. 7, **10**, No. 6). J. Eriksson in 1874 (Doctor's dissertation, abs. in, *Botan. Ztg.*, 1874, **32**, 381) carried on the investigation, while G. Brunchorst in 1885 (*Ber. Deut. Bot. Ges.*, **3**, 241) gave the name "bacteroids".

[2] *Ann. Inst. Pasteur*, 1892, **6**, 65.

[3] *Bot. Ztg.*, 1888, **46**, 725, 741, 757; 1890, **48**, 837.

plants, have themselves no power of assimilating gaseous nitrogen; this power belongs to the bacteria associated with them. But so carefully was all organic matter removed from the soil, the apparatus and the air in endeavouring to exclude all trace of ammonia, that there was no chance of infection with the necessary bacteria. Hence no assimilation could go on. In the field trials the bacteria were active, and here there was a gain of nitrogen.

The general conclusion that bacteria are the real makers of plant food in the soil, and are, therefore, essential to the growth of all plants, was developed by E. Wollny[1] and M. Berthelot.[2] It was supposed to be proved by E. Laurent's[3] experiments. He grew buckwheat on humus obtained from well-rotted dung, and found that plants grew well on the untreated humus, but only badly on the humus sterilised by heat. When, however, soil bacteria were added to the sterilised humus (by adding an aqueous extract of unsterilised soil) good growth took place. The experiment looks convincing, but is really unsound. When a rich soil is heated some substance is formed toxic to plants. The failure of the plants on the sterilised humus was, therefore, not due to absence of bacteria, but to the presence of a toxin. No one has yet succeeded in carrying out this fundamental experiment of growing plants in two soils differing only in that one contains bacteria while the other does not.

The Rise of Modern Knowledge of the Soil, and the Return to Field Studies

Further investigation of soil problems has shown that they are more complex than was at first supposed. Soils can no longer satisfactorily be divided into a few simple groups: sands, clays, loams, etc., according to their particle size; nor can attention be confined to the surface layer. It is necessary to take account of their history. The properties of a soil depend not only on its parent material but also, as shown by the Russian investigator V. V. Dokuchaev[4] in particular, on the climatic, vegetation and other factors to which it has been subjected.

The relations of the plant to the soil are also recognised as highly complex. The older workers had thought of soil fertility as a simple chemical problem; the early bacteriologists thought of it as bacteriological. E. Wollny[5] and F. H. King[6] showed that the physical

[1] *Bied. Zbl. Agric. Chem.*, 1884, **13**, 796.
[2] *C.R.*, 188, **106**, 569.
[3] *Bull. Acad. Roy. Belgique*, 1886, **2**, 128. See also E. Duclaux, *C.R.*, 1885, **100**, 66.
[4] *Tchernozéme de la Russie d'Europe*, St. Petersburg, 1883.
[5] Papers by himself and his students in *Forschungen auf dem Gebiete der Agrikultur-Physik*, 1878–98.
[6] *The Soil*, New York, 1899.

properties of the soil already studied by Davy and Schübler play a fundamental part in soil fertility. Van Bemmelen showed that soil has colloidal properties, and present-day workers have observed in the soil many of the phenomena investigated in laboratories devoted to the study of colloids. Whitney and Cameron at Washington greatly widened the subject by revealing the importance of the soil solution and introducing the methods and principles of physical chemistry. Russell and Hutchinson at Rothamsted showed that bacterial action alone would not account for the biological phenomena in the soil, but that other organisms are also concerned, and subsequent work in the Rothamsted laboratories and elsewhere has revealed the presence of a complex soil population, the various members of which react on one another and on the growing plant.

The nature of the subject necessitates a departure from the usual procedure. In purely laboratory investigations it is customary to adopt the Baconian method, in which factors are studied one at a time, all others being kept constant except the particular one under investigation. In dealing with soils in natural conditions, however, it is impossible to proceed in this way: climatic factors will not be kept constant, and however careful the effort to ensure equality of conditions there is always the probability, and sometimes the certainty, that the variable factor under investigation is interacting with climatic factors and exerting indirect effects which modify or even obscure the direct effects it is desired to study. Hence, in recent years, statisticians have had to devise methods for dealing with cases where several factors are varying simultaneously.

This increased interest in the soil has shown itself in two directions. The development of soil surveys has encouraged an enormous development of soil studies *in situ*; and the introduction of modern statistical methods has given to field experiments a new value they completely lacked before. In the past, field experiments were always weakened by the unknown errors due to the circumstances that the soil of one plot was never strictly comparable with the soil of another. Modern methods of field plot technique have overcome this difficulty and yield results to which a definite value can be assigned so that the data can be utilised in further investigations.

CHAPTER II

THE FOOD OF PLANTS

GREEN PLANTS SYNTHESISE their food from simple substances taken out of the air and the soil. It is common to speak of these substances as the actual foods: in reality they are the raw materials out of which the food is made. Plants, like all other organisms, have their tissues built out of carbohydrates, fats, proteins and nucleoproteins, and need for the functioning of their tissues a host of enzymes. Hence the plant needs large quantities of carbon, oxygen, hydrogen, nitrogen, phosphorus, and sulphur for building up its tissues; it needs small quantities of at least iron, magnesium, manganese, zinc, copper and boron and usually molybdenum for building up its enzymes; and it needs potassium, sometimes sodium, calcium, chlorine and often other electrolytes for these or other purposes. Other elements, such as silicon and aluminium may be necessary, and are certainly present in the tissues of all plants grown in the field, though they have not been shown to have essential specific effects on the growth and development of the crop. Carbon dioxide and water are probably the sole source of carbon and hydrogen for most plants; ammonium and nitrate ions are an adequate source of nitrogen, though some leguminous and other plants can supplement these with nitrogen from the air; and the other elements are usually taken up from the soil as simple inorganic ions.

Carbon dioxide from the air and simple inorganic ions in the soil can certainly supply all the nutrients needed by the plant. But this does not prove that plants in the field obtain all their nutrients from these sources or that their growth may not be improved if they can take up complex substances of vitamin or hormone-like nature. Claims have, in fact, repeatedly been made that other sources of food are necessary if the crop is to make optimum growth, which is sometimes measured by crop yield and sometimes by improvements in its feeding value. In some conditions plants in fact obtain some of their food from other sources. The outer cells of their roots may contain fungal hyphae which extend around or even through the cells and into the soil. This association between root and fungus can be very strongly developed—as, for example, on forest trees growing on poor soil—giving structures known as mycorrhizas, which are described in more detail in Chapter XIII. The fungus in this association transfers nutrients, in particular nitrogen and phosphate, from the soil to the root cells, handing them on to these cells as complex substances. There is, however, no critical evidence to show that this mechanism plays any important part in the nutrition of crops grown on normal arable soils.

Many experiments have been made to see if the performance of a crop can be improved by supplying it either with vitamins or with plant hormones, but the results so far have been inconclusive. It is well established that isolated organs of a plant—such as excised roots —can only be grown in artificial conditions if some of the B vitamins are present, but this is no evidence that plants are unable to synthesise all the vitamins they need. There is, in fact, no well-established evidence that adding any vitamin or growth promoting factor to the soil ever improves crop production,[1] or has any appreciable effect on the vitamin content of the plant. This is much more dependent on climate and possibly soil than on manuring. Vitamin C contents in particular seem to be high in years of bright sunshine.[2]

The question whether farmyard manure owes its value as a plant food to any so far unrecognised nutrient, needed only in minute quantities, cannot yet be definitely answered, though the experimental evidence is against any such possibility. Provided the soil conditions around the plant roots—as measured by the air and water supply—are favourable, it appears that the value of farmyard manure—as measured by crop yield—depends only on the amount of nutrients it can supply in simple form to the crop. Naturally, the farmyard manure itself often has an important role in creating a favourable air and water régime around the plant roots, but this effect is not of relevance to this particular question. Farmyard manure can, however, be a very valuable carrier of some minor elements, and in particular additions of farmyard manure may be the easiest way of maintaining an adequate supply of available iron to the plant.[3]

The second question—to which extravagant answers have been given by some workers—is whether the feeding value of the crop, either for animals or humans, is affected by the presence of farmyard manure or composts in the soil. The earlier experimental evidence on this

[1] For some evidence that vitamin B₁ may be of value, see J. Bonner and J. Greene, *Bot. Gaz.*, 1938, **100**, 226, and 1939, **101**, 491; but D. I. Arnon, *Sci.*, 1940, **92**, 264; C. L. Hamner, *Bot. Gaz.*, 1940, **102**, 156; W. G. Templeman and M. Pollard, *Ann. Bot.*, 1941, **5**, 133; and D. B. Swartz, *Bot. Gaz.*, 1941, **103**, 366, were unable to confirm this. H. Lundegårdh, *Kgl. Lantbr. Akad. Tidskr.*, 1943, **82**, 99, found some evidence that vitamin B₁ in the presence of phosphate and magnesium might be able to increase yields. For a short review of the literature, see R. L. Starkey, *Soil Sci.*, 1944, **57**, 264. For some evidence that indolyl- or naphthyl-acetic acids may be of value, see G. P. McRostie *et al.*, *Canad. J. Res.*, 1938, **16 C**, 510, for wheat, A. Dunez, *C.R. Acad. Agric.*, 1946, **32**, 736, and 1947, **33**, 548, for wheat and other farm crops, and H. L. Stier and H. G. du Bay, *Proc. Amer. Soc. Hort. Sci.*, 1939, **36**, 723, for tomatoes. H. L. Pearse reviewed this subject in *Imp. Bur. Hort.*, *Tech. Comm.* 12, 1939.

[2] For cow-peas, M. E. Reid, *Bull. Torrey Bot. Cl.*, 1942, **62**, 204; for tomatoes in England, F. Wokes *et al.*, *Nature*, 1947, **159**, 172.

[3] J. Bonner, *Bot. Gaz.*, 1946, **108**, 267.

point was conflicting, possibly because of imperfections in experimental technique, but the few recent accurate experiments that have been made have given no indication that the presence of farmyard manure or compost in a soil has any specific action in increasing the vitamin content[1] or the nutritive value[2] of the plant.

This result appears to be general, for fertilisers also seem to have little effect on the vitamin content of the leaves and roots of crops. However, the carotene and chlorophyll content of grass can be increased a little by nitrogen manuring,[3] as is shown by its darker green colour, and the carotene content of lucerne by boron under some conditions,[4] and of soybean leaves by phosphates.[5] On the other hand, the concentration of vitamin C in the tissues of a crop is often somewhat lowered by any manuring that increases the growth of the crop. Thus L. J. Harris and D. J. Watson[6] found that normal dressings of farmyard manure or sulphate of ammonia lowered the vitamin C content of potato tubers. Again, small potato tubers[7] tend to have higher vitamin C contents than large, and slow-growing leaves of vegetable crops than fast growing. [8]

The plant needs its nutrients for three distinct but overlapping purposes. It must build its protoplasm and form all the enzymes needed for its vital processes and growth, it must build tissues to support and protect its protoplasm, and it must be able to transport nutrients from one organ to another.

The plant's supporting and protecting tissues are built out of polymerised sugar residues such as celluloses, hemicelluloses and pectins, on the one hand, and lignins on the other, though the latter are typically formed as the tissues mature. They also contain inorganic constituents whose functions and chemical combinations are uncertain. Thus graminaceous plants—the grasses and cereals—accumulate considerable quantities of silica in their tissues. Further, many plants accumulate sugars or polymerised sugar residues, for example, starch and insulin, as a food reserve in their tissues, but other substances, such as oils and proteins, may also accumulate in them for the same reason. The enzyme systems in the plant are built up out of proteins and nucleoproteins, and thus contain large proportions of nitrogen and phosphate, with some sulphur. They also require certain metals and other elements, and unless the particular metal needed is present, the

[1] For a review of this subject, see L. A. Maynard and K. C. Beeson, *Nutr. Abstr.*, 1943, 13, 155.
[2] D. I. Arnon, H. D. Simms and A. F. Morgan, *Soil Sci.*, 1947, 63, 129.
[3] B. Thomas and F. E. Moon, *Emp. J. Expt. Agric.*, 1938, 7, 235.
[4] W. L. Powers, *Proc. Soil Sci. Soc. Amer.*, 1939, 4, 290.
[5] W. J. Peterson *et al.*, *Amer. Fert.*, 1948, No. 3, 24.
[6] Unpublished observations.
[7] Unpublished observations of J. Meiklejohn.
[8] S. H. Wittiver, R. A. Schroeder and W. A. Albrecht, *Soil Sci.*, 1945, 59, 329.

enzyme cannot function: only very rarely can that particular metal be replaced by another without destroying, or at least greatly weakening, the effectiveness of the enzyme. The liquid that transports the various nutrients throughout the plant, either from the roots, the green leaves or the storage organs, also contains inorganic ions. These may be nutrient ions, but they are also regulators of the osmotic pressure and hydrogen-ion concentration in the protoplasm, and for these latter functions the particular anions or cations present are of minor importance.

These considerations allow one to understand something about the total nutrient demands of the plant. Rapid growth can only take place when there is an adequate quantity of enzymes present, and hence after the plant has absorbed adequate quantities of the minerals necessary for their functioning. The maximum demand for these minerals therefore occurs when the plant is young, and the supply can be reduced later in the season; for as the cells in which the enzymes are situated age, much or all of these minerals can be transferred to new growing points to build new enzymes there. Further, if some of the minerals needed by the enzymes are in short supply, the older cells containing the enzyme may die prematurely and the limiting element transferred to the growing point. This need not affect the yield of cereals or root crops since it is food reserve material that is harvested, but it can severely limit the yield of pasture and forage crops which are grown for their green, and therefore actively functioning, leaves. Hence, these green crops must be able to obtain an adequate supply of all essential minerals throughout their growing season.

These points are illustrated in Fig. 1, taken from some work of A. E. V. Richardson and H. C. Trumble[1] on the uptake of nutrients, and the rate of growth of barley. Nitrogen, phosphate, potassium and calcium are all taken up rapidly when the plant is small, as measured by the amount of dry matter present, but the rate of uptake falls when the plant is making its dry matter rapidly. The uptake of minerals, however, may continue even if they are not needed by the plant, for plants take up minerals because they are present in the soil solution, and this uptake goes on all through the active life of the roots.

The concentration of cations in some plant tissues, such as the actively functioning leaves and the fruits, tends to be a characteristic of the crop and fairly independent of the soil and manuring. Thus D. J. Watson[2] quotes the results of leaf analyses made on the Rothamsted permanent mangold experiment for the six years 1878–83, which showed that the leaf contained between 300 and 360 milli-equivalents of cations (sodium, potassium, magnesium and calcium) per 100 gm. of dry matter

[1] *J. Dept. Agric. S. Aust.*, 1928, 32, 224.   [2] *Emp. J. Expt. Agric.* 1946, 14, 57.

when the manuring, and in consequence the actual composition of the bases present, was varied within wide limits. D. R. Hoagland and J. C. Martin[1] found that tomato plants contained about 300 milli-equivalents of cations per 100 gm. of dry matter, although the potassium content could vary from 25 to 150 milli-equivalents. Similarly, T. B. van Itallie[2] found that Italian ryegrass contained about 200 milli-equivalents of cations per 100 gm. of dry matter in the leaf and F. E. Bear and A. L. Prince[3] found lucerne contained between 150 and 200 milli-equivalents.

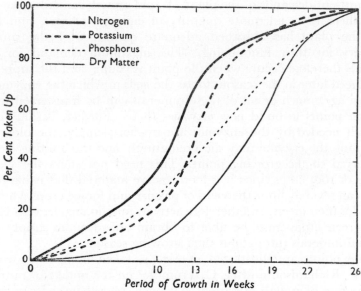

FIG. 1. Uptake of nutrients and production of dry matter in barley.

This constancy, however, is not exact. In the first place young tissues and leaves tend to have a higher ionic concentration in them than the older, and in the second place plants growing in a soil with an appreciable soluble salt content often accumulate considerable quantities of mineral salts in their tissues. As an extreme example some desert plants growing in saline soil can have between 20 and 50 per cent of their dry matter in the form of soluble salts, whereas most crops cannot accumulate more salts than 1–2 per cent of their dry matter.[4]

[1] Soil Sci., 1933, 36, 1. For further examples, see J. T. Cope, R. Bradfield and M. Peech, Soil Sci., 1953, 76, 65.
[2] Soil Sci., 1938, 46, 175.
[3] J. Amer. Soc. Agron., 1945, 37, 217; 1948, 40, 80. For additional data, F. E. Bear, Soils and Fertilizers, 4th ed.
[4] For examples of such plants, see M. M. Shukevich, Trans. Dokuchaev Inst., 1939, 19, No. 2, 39.

In some plants minerals that are no longer needed for metabolic processes are removed from the active tissues and often from the plant. One method is for the excess minerals to accumulate in mature leaves, which then die. But there is also evidence that some of these minerals are excreted by the plant roots. Thus N. T. Deleano and his colleagues at Bucharest[1] have shown that the total amount of potassium in the aerial parts of cereals and tobacco decreases towards the end of their growing season, and this potassium is presumably excreted into the soil as it does not appear in the portion of the root system they were able to separate.[2] Table 4 illustrates this effect for winter wheat growing on a heavy Essex clay,[3] though only the aerial part of these plants has been analysed. The table also shows, what was not illustrated in Fig. 1, that the silica content of the plant is almost directly proportional to the dry matter, and since towards the end of the season the dry matter is increasingly being formed in the grain, a portion of the plant low in silica, the silica content of the straw must be increasing during this period.

TABLE 4

Production of Dry Matter, and Assimilation of Nutrients from the Soil by Wheat growing in the Open Field

Weight in grams of substances in whole wheat plant grown in the field

	Before ear emergence			After ear emergence					
	1st Samp- ling (30.iv)	2nd Samp- ling (21.v)	3rd Samp- ling (4.vi)	4th Samp- ling (18.vi)	5th Samp- ling (2.vii)	6th Samp- ling (16.vii)	7th Samp- ling (23.vii)	8th Samp- ling (30.vii)	9th Samp- ling (6.viii)
Dry matter .	770	2970	6190	9510	12270	14350	15060	14730	14210
Nitrogen .	27	55	80	90	96	110	109	109	109
Potassium .	26	79	140	149	121	103	94	86	75
Calcium .	5·1	12·8	21·6	25·6	26·8	26·5	22·8	22·0	21·6
Phosphorus .	3·2	10·5	18·0	24·4	24·8	27·0	27·8	27·8	27·8
Chlorine .	6·0	15·1	24·2	28·8	33·9	30·5	27·4	23·6	19·3
Silicon . .	8	40	91	125	152	199	206	209	207

[1] Biol. d. Pflanz., 1932, 19, 249; 1933; 20, 179; 1936, 24, 19; also V. G. Bossie, Dissert. d. Pharm. Fak. Bukarest, 1934.
[2] J. D. Sayre, Plant Physiol., 1948, 23, 267, found the same result with maize.
[3] F. Knowles and J. E. Watkins, J. Agric. Sci., 1931, 21, 612. For another example, see E. K. Woodford and A. G. McCalla, Canad. J. Res., 1936, 14 C, 245.

CHAPTER III

THE INDIVIDUAL NUTRIENTS NEEDED BY PLANTS

IN THE FOLLOWING discussion a brief account will be given of the effects of the various nutrients on crop growth. It will usually be assumed that all nutrients are present in adequate supply except the one under discussion. The field symptoms of the various deficiencies will not be described, as full descriptions with coloured plates will be found in several standard works.[1] Nor is it relevant to the general purpose of this book to discuss in any detail the physiological functions of these nutrients in the plant.

NITROGEN

Nitrogen is essential for plant growth as it is a constituent of all proteins and hence of all protoplasm. It is generally taken up by plants either as ammonium or as nitrate ions, but the absorbed nitrate is rapidly reduced, probably to ammonium, through a molybdenum-containing enzyme. The ammonium ions and some of the carbohydrates synthesised in the leaves are converted into amino acids, mainly in the green leaf itself. Hence as the level of the nitrogen supply increases compared with other nutrients, the extra protein produced allows the plant leaves to grow larger and hence to have a larger surface available for photosynthesis, and in fact over a considerable range of nitrogen supply for many crops the amount of leaf area available for photosynthesis is roughly proportional to the amount of nitrogen supplied.

This effect of nitrogen in increasing leaf growth is not its only effect on the leaf, for the higher the nitrogen supply the more rapidly the synthesised carbohydrates are converted to proteins and to protoplasm and the smaller the proportion left available for cell wall material, which is mainly nitrogen-free carbohydrates such as calcium pectate, cellulosans, cellulose and low-nitrogen lignins.

This effect of nitrogen in increasing the proportion of protoplasm to cell wall material has several consequences. It increases the size of the cells and gives them a thinner wall, hence makes the leaves more succulent and less harsh. It also increases the proportion of water[2] and

[1] T. Wallace, *The Diagnosis of Mineral Deficiencies in Plants*, 1943, and Supplement, 1944, London, and *Hunger Signs in Crops*, ed. by G. Hambidge, Washington, 1941.
[2] For an example with mangolds at Rothamsted, see D. J. Watson, *Emp. J. Exp. Agric.*, 1946, 14, 409.

decreases that of calcium[1] to dry matter: the former because proto-plasm has more water and the latter because it has less calcium than cell wall material. Excessive amounts of nitrogen give leaves with such large thin-walled cells that they are readily attacked by insect and fungus pests and harmed by unfavourable weather such as droughts and frosts. A very low nitrogen supply on the other hand gives leaves with small cells and thick walls, and the leaves are in consequence harsh and fibrous. The nitrogen supply has one other noticeable effect on the leaf: it darkens the green colour. The leaves of plants growing with a low level of nitrogen compared with other nutrients are pale yellowish to reddish green, which darken rapidly as the nitrogen supply increases and become very dark green when it is excessive. Further increasing the nitrogen supply to the leaves tends to keep them green for a longer time, and in many cereals it increases the length of the growing season and delays the onset of maturity (see p. 33) presumably also through its effect in keeping the free carbohydrate content of the leaf low.

Crops grown for their carbohydrates, such as the root crops and the cereals, thus only benefit from nitrogen manuring through the in-creased leaf area brought about by the nitrogen, so that the additional yield of carbohydrate is usually less in proportion than the increase in leaf area. The root crops show this effect most strikingly when the length of the growing season is varied. Thus a high level of nitrogen manuring mainly affects the tops on a crop which is only in the ground for a short time, such as white turnips, but has a very considerable effect on both tops and roots on a crop that is in the ground for a long time, such as mangolds, as is shown in Table 5. Late sown sugar-beet also sometimes responds to nitrogen manuring by making a very large increase in leaf growth which is accompanied by a very disappointing yield of root.

The cereal crops of the temperate regions—wheat, barley, oats and rye—grown for grain and not for fodder, only require a moderate supply of nitrogen, for too high a level leads to excessive straw, as shown in Table 6 and in Plate I. These show the yield and the appearance of the wheat crop grown on Broadbalk at Rothamsted—a field that has been in wheat almost continuously since 1843, and the manuring of the plots has been continued unaltered for a long time. The plots shown in Plate I have been manured as follows: Plot 2, 14 tons per acre annually of farmyard manure and Plot 3 unmanured, both since 1843; Plots 5, 6, 7, 8 and 16 all have received annually $3\frac{1}{2}$ cwt. of superphosphate, 200 lb. potassium sulphate, 100 lb. of magnesium sulphate and 100 lb. of sodium sulphate per acre since

[1] For a review of the literature, see K. C. Beeson, *Bot. Rev.*, 1946, **12**, 424.

TABLE 5

Relative Proportions of Roots and Leaves at Harvest under Nitrogenous manuring (Rothamsted)

Yields in tons per acre

Nitrogen in manuring lb. per acre	Rapidly growing crop			Nitrogen in manuring lb. per acre	Slow growing crop[1]		
	White turnips (1845–8)				Mangolds (1906–10)		
	Roots	Leaves	Roots/Leaves		Roots	Leaves	Roots/Leaves
None	8·20	2·70	3·04	None	5·29	1·14	4·64
47	9·90	4·30	2·30	86	17·91	3·80	4·72
137	10·25	6·15	1·67	184	29·32	6·20	4·73

1852 (Plot 16 since 1885) and annual dressings of ammonium sulphate or sodium nitrate to give 45, 90, 135 and 90 lb. per acre of nitrogen since these dates. The excessive development of straw on some of these plots induces a liability of the crop to lodge, and the very high nitrogen dressing on Plot 8 may delay the time the wheat comes to maturity.

TABLE 6

Effect of Increasing Nitrogen Supply on the Growth of Wheat, Rothamsted, 1852–64

Nitrogen in manure, lb. per acre	Yields in 1000 lb. per acre	
	Grain	Straw
None	1·06	1·86
43	1·68	3·03
86	2·18	4·28
129	2·27	4·78
172	2·29	5·22

In practice, however, these harmful secondary effects can be minimised by using suitable stiff short-strawed varieties, for, under most English conditions, the amount of nitrogen a crop will stand is determined by the onset of these secondary effects rather than by the extra yield of grain due to the high manuring ceasing to be economic. These harmful effects, in the case of the cereals, can also be minimised to some extent by applying the high level of nitrogen as late as possible to the crop, for D. J. Watson[2] found that delaying the time at which the nitrogen

[1] This table must be interpreted with some caution, for the relative weight of leaves at harvest on the different treatments may not accurately reflect their relative weights during the growing season.

[2] J. Agric. Sci., 1936, 26, 391.

top dressing was applied barely affected the increment in the grain yield due to the manure, but it appreciably reduced the increment in the straw yield.

The results given for the effect of nitrogen manuring on the cereals of the temperate region—that high nitrogen delays maturity of the crop and encourages growth of the straw relative to the grain—is not true for some tropical cereals such as maize and the sorghums, for with them a high level of nitrogen manuring has just the opposite effect: it hastens the time of flowering and maturity and increases the grain yield relative to the straw. This last point is illustrated in Table 7,

TABLE 7

The Effect of Increasing the Nitrogen Supply on the Yield of Maize, Rice and Wheat in the Nile Delta

(Abu Hammad, 1935 and 1936)

Yields of grain and straw in hundredweights per acre

Nitrogen supplied lb. per acre	Maize			Rice			Wheat		
	Grain	Straw	Grain/Straw	Grain	Straw	Grain/Straw	Grain	Straw	Grain/Straw
0	15·1	38·6	0·39	34·2	40·3	0·85	18·5	27·8	0·67
33	26·0	42·3	0·61	41·4	49·0	0·84	26·2	42·3	0·62
66	33·8	39·8	0·85	44·0	51·1	0·86	30·6	52·5	0·58
99	35·7	11·6	0·06						

derived from the results of some field experiments made on the same farm in the Nile Delta by F. Crowther and his associates.[1] The yield of maize grain can be more than doubled by the nitrogen without the yield of straw being appreciably affected, whereas the result with wheat is comparable with that obtained at Rothamsted and illustrated in Table 6. Rice in this area is intermediate between these two, nitrogen manuring having almost no effect on the ratio of grain to straw, although in parts of India it behaves like wheat.[2] The sorghum dura in the Sudan Gezirah behaves like maize,[3] and other sorghums, the millets, cotton and sunflower have been stated to do likewise, whilst soybeans and buckwheat may behave like rice.[4]

The effect of nitrogen fertiliser on the nitrogen content of the crop depends both on the responsiveness of the crop and on the time the nitrogen is given relative to the development of the crop. If the nitrogen

[1] *Roy. Agric. Soc. Egypt, Bull.* 28, 1937.
[2] R. L. Sethi, K. Ramish, and T. P. Abraham, *Ind. Counc. Agric. Res., Bull.* 38, 1952.
[3] *Agriculture in the Sudan*, ed. J. D. Tothill, London, 1948, p. 474.
[4] M. H. Cailahjan, *C.R. Acad. Sci. U.S.S.R.*, 1945, **47**, 146. F. Crowther (*Roy. Agric. Soc. Egypt, Bull.* 31, 1937) showed that nitrogen manuring hastened the time of flowering of cotton.

fertiliser greatly stimulates crop growth, the nitrogen content of the fertilised crop, expressed as a percentage of its dry or fresh weight, will often decrease, although the total uptake of nitrogen per acre will increase, as is shown in Fig. 2.[1] This is because the extra dry matter which the added nitrogen stimulates the plant to produce has a lower nitrogen content than that produced by a nitrogen-starved plant. As the level of nitrogen supply increases, however, this stimulating effect grows smaller, so the uptake of nitrogen is increasing relative to the additional production of dry matter due to it: the nitrogen content of the dry matter in the crop now begins to rise. But this rise only becomes

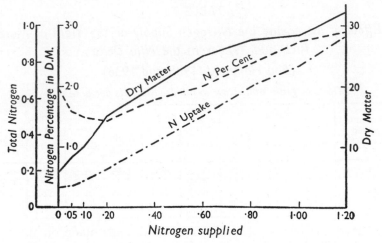

FIG. 2. The effect of increasing the nitrogen supply on the dry matter produced by mustard and on its nitrogen content.

appreciable when the growth of the crop ceases to respond economically to the additional fertiliser.

Nitrogenous fertilisers can often be made to increase the nitrogen content of the crop more economically if they are given sufficiently near harvest for the crop to absorb much of the added nitrogen, but for the synthesised proteins not to have time to increase the growth of the crop appreciably. Thus, by adding a nitrogen fertiliser to a meadow one to three weeks before it is cut, the protein content of the hay will be increased though the yield of hay will barely be affected.[2] During the war the Germans[3] also experimented with this method of converting

[1] For a field example with barley, see E. J. Russell, *Min. Agric.*, *Bull.* 28, 2nd ed., 1933.
[2] H. B. Sprague and A. Hawkins, *New Jersey Agric. Expt. Sta.*, *Bull.* 644, 1938; M. W. Evans, F. A. Welton and R. M. Salter, *Ohio Agric. Expt. Sta.*, *Bull.* 603, 1939; A. H. Lewis, *J. Min. Agric.*, 1939, **46**, 77; *Emp. J. Expt. Agric.*, 1941, **9**, 43; W. S. Ferguson, *J. Agric. Sci.*, 1948, **38**, 33.
[3] See, for example, W. Selke, *Bodenk. PflErnähr.*, 1940, **20**, 1; 1942, **26**, 137, 151; 1943, **32**, 163.

nitrogen fertilisers into protein by applying them to cereal or potato crops at flowering time; they found nitrates were more efficient than ammonia, and that dressings of 40 lb. of nitrogen per acre, or 2 cwt. of nitrate of soda, gave substantial increases in the protein content of the crop.

The average response of crops to additional nitrogen under normal English agricultural conditions is shown in Table 8.[1] It shows that on the average 1 lb. of nitrogen, as sulphate of ammonia, gives about 1 lb. of protein and 10 to 15 lb. of starch equivalent.[2] These nitrogen responses differ from those to potash and phosphate in being relatively independent of climate if the rainfall lies between 22 and 40 inches, but they are reduced in years of considerable drought or excessive rain.

TABLE 8

Increase in the Amount of Crop and Food Value obtained by using 28 lb. of Nitrogen (1·2 cwt. of Sulphate of Ammonia) per acre

Average values for North European conditions

Crop	Crop cwt. per acre	Protein equivalent lb. per acre	Starch equivalent lb. per acre
Potatoes . . .	17	16	360
Kale	35	52	360
Swedes . . .	42	31	330
Mangolds . . .	56	22	360
Sugar-beet roots . .	18	12 ⎫ 34	300 ⎫ 490
Sugar-beet tops . .	20	22 ⎭	190 ⎭
Cereal grain . . .	4	31 ⎫ 37	300 ⎫ 400
Cereal straw . . .	6	6 ⎭	100 ⎭
Meadow hay . . .	6	31	210

Plants can take up their nitrogen either as ammonium or as nitrate ions, and most plants probably can use either equally easily. The main difference between these two ions is that all the nitrate in the soil is dissolved in the soil solution, whilst if the soil contains much clay or humus, much of the ammonium will be present as an exchangeable cation and hence not in solution. Perhaps for this reason a nitrate fertiliser is more rapid acting than an ammonium as it would be present in a higher ionic concentration round the plants' roots. But in most arable soils, added ammonium ions are rapidly oxidised to nitrate, so no matter what form of nitrogen is given, nitrate is the only form

[1] Based on E. M. Crowther and F. Yates, *Emp. J. Expt. Agric.*, 1941, **9**, 77. For other British data, see D. J. Halliday, *Jealotts Hill Res. Sta., Bull.* 6, 1948.

[2] 100 lb. of nitrogen, the amount contained in 1,550 cubic feet of air—the volume of a fair-sized living-room—as sulphate of ammonia can provide enough additional food to feed one person for a year.

present in appreciable concentration in the soil solution for the plant to take up.

Crops that respond to nitrogen manuring commonly take up and fix in their mature tissue between one-third and one-half of the nitrogen added as sulphate of ammonia, and a rather higher proportion of nitrogen added as nitrate; the remainder is lost to the crop and usually to the soil, probably being washed out into the subsoil during wet weather, though its fate has not been too well determined (see p. 315).

PHOSPHORUS

Phosphorus, as ortho-phosphate, plays a fundamental role in the very large number of enzymic reactions that depend on phosphorylation. Possibly for this reason it is a constituent of the cell nucleus and is essential for cell division and for the development of meristem tissue. Its concentration in these tissues can be demonstrated very beautifully if some radioactive phosphorus P^{32} is mixed with the main phosphorus nutrient supply. This radioactive phosphorus behaves exactly like ordinary phosphorus in the plant, except in so far as its radiations may harm the plant tissues if it is present in too high a concentration. These radiations, however, will affect a photographic plate so that this phosphorus can be made to register its position. A radio-autograph of the phosphorus in a young barley plant is reproduced in Plate II, and it shows very clearly that the actively growing meristematic leaf and root cells contain far more phosphorus, in fact from several hundred to several thousand times more, than the cells that have ceased to divide.[1]

Phosphate deficiency is very widespread in the world, and in many countries such as Australia and South Africa crop production is limited over enormous areas by phosphate supply. In the British Isles phosphate deficiency can be very marked on many of the Jurassic clays of the English midlands, on the acid Millstone grits of northern England and in large areas of Northern Ireland.[2] Further, in Great Britain crops are, on the whole, more responsive to phosphate fertilisers in the higher rainfall areas of the west than in the drier regions of the east;[3] though whether this is due to the crops having a higher phosphate demand in wet years, or whether this result is purely a reflection of the tendency for the soils in the moister regions to be more acid, and therefore stronger fixers of phosphate in an unavailable form (see p. 510), than those in the drier areas has not been determined.

Phosphate deficiency differs from nitrogen deficiency in being

[1] R. S. Russell and R. P. Martin, *Nature*, 1949, **163**, 71.
[2] For an excellent description of cases occurring here, see Scott Robertson, *J. Min. Agric. Northern Ireland*, 1927, **1**, 7.
[3] E. M. Crowther and F. Yates, *Emp. J. Expt. Agric.*, 1941, **9**, 77.

extremely difficult to diagnose, and crops can be suffering from severe starvation without there being any obvious signs that lack of phosphate is the cause. By the time the deficiency has been recognised it may be too late to remedy it in annual crops. Thus wheat and barley take up much of their phosphate in the early stages of their growth, and starvation at this period cannot be rectified by a good supply later.[1]

Cereals suffering from phosphate starvation are retarded at every stage of their life-history, from the emergence of the second leaf to the time of ripening. They have a stunted root system and an even more stunted leaf and stem; the leaf colour is a dull greyish-green, a red pigment is often produced in the leaf bases and the dying leaves, and the tillering and the number of tillers bearing seed are depressed. On the other hand, except in extreme cases, the ratio of grain to straw is not affected. On soils badly deficient in phosphate, phosphatic fertilisers hasten the ripening processes, thus producing the same effect as a deficiency of water, but to a less extent. This ripening effect is well shown on the barley plots at Rothamsted: crops receiving phosphates are golden yellow in colour while those on the phosphate-starved plots are still green.

Certain indirect effects also follow: the ear of barley emerges from its ensheathing leaves a few days in advance of those receiving insufficient phosphate, and therefore has a better chance of escaping attack by the larvae of the gout fly (*Chlorops tæniopus* Meig.), which, hatching from their eggs on the top of the topmost leaf, crawl downwards seeking the ear for food.

Root crops suffering from severe phosphate shortage are also very stunted, and the effect of added phosphate can be spectacular. As a matter of history the early workers were so impressed with the great increase in the yield of roots obtained by phosphatic fertilisers that they assumed the phosphate had a specific action in encouraging root development, yet the permanent mangold field at Rothamsted (Barnfield) shows, in fact, that potassium increases the ratio of roots to tops far more than phosphate, and even the potassium effect is probably mainly a reflection of the early increase of leaf area.[2] Phosphate seems to increase leaf area without affecting the power of the leaves to transport carbohydrates to the roots, and it thus differs from nitrogen manuring, which also increases leaf growth but reduces their power of sending carbohydrates to the roots. Thus heavy nitrogen manuring of sugar-beet usually reduces the sugar content of the beet somewhat, although it may increase the amount of sugar produced per acre very considerably. All the experimental evidence available is in accord with

[1] W. F. Gericke, *Bot. Gaz.*, 1925, **80**, 410; W. E. Brenchley, *Ann. Bot.*, 1929, **43**, 89.
[2] D. J. Watson and E. J. Russell, *Emp. J. Expt. Agric.*, 1943, **11**, 49, 65.

this generalisation, and the statements made that crops respond especially well to dressings of phosphate on heavy soils is only a reflection of the low phosphate status of many English clay soils, and is not due to the power of phosphates to mitigate the effects of deficient aeration.

Excess of phosphate over the amount required by the crop sometimes depresses crop yield.[1] This usually occurs on light soils in dry years and has been attributed to the hastening of the maturation processes and consequent reduction of vegetative growth.

Plants take up their phosphorus almost exclusively as inorganic phosphate ions, probably principally as the $H_2PO_4^-$ ion,[2] for they may take this up more easily than the HPO_4^{--}. Other phosphates besides ortho-phosphate act as phosphatic fertilisers, as for example meta- and pyro-phosphates and, though it has not yet been rigorously demonstrated, it is probable that these anions are hydrolysed to the ortho-phosphate before being absorbed.[3] Plants are, however, relatively inefficient users of phosphates in the field, for rarely more than 20 to 30 per cent of the amount supplied as fertiliser is taken up.

SULPHUR

Sulphur is an essential constituent of many proteins and occurs also in the oils produced by certain plants such as the mustard oil of the Brassicae.

One of the first deficiency diseases due to lack of sulphur to be recognised as such was tea yellows, which occurs in parts of Nyasaland;[4] but some of the most striking improvement in the yield of farm crops have been obtained with lucerne. There is a large region in the centre and west of the United States and extending into Canada, where yields of lucerne in particular, and other leguminous crops to a less extent, are limited by the amount of sulphates given in the fertiliser, and increases of yield ranging from 50 per cent to tenfold can be brought about by dressings of 2 to 4 cwt. of gypsum per acre.[5] There are also considerable areas in Australia and New Zealand, and probably in Africa, where the growth of legumes is limited by a lack of sulphur.

POTASSIUM

Potassium is one of the essential elements in the nutrition of the plant, and one of the three that are commonly in sufficiently short

[1] For instances, see E. J. Russell, *J. Inst. Brew.*, 1923, **29**, 631 (barley); J. C. Wallace, *J. Min. Agric.*, 1926, **32**, 893; *Rothamsted Conf. Repts.*, No. 16, 1934 (potatoes).
[2] C. E. Hagen and H. T. Hopkins, *Plant Physiol.*, 1955, **30**, 193.
[3] W. T. McGeorge, *Arizona Agric. Exp. Sta., Tech. Bull.* 82, 1939.
[4] H. H. Storey and R. Leach, *Ann. Appl. Biol.*, 1933, **20**, 23.
[5] See, for example, F. J. Alway (Minnesota), *Proc. 1st Int. Congr. Soil Sci.*, Washington, 1927, **3**, 590; W. Crocker, *Soil Sci.*, 1945, **60**, 149; *Rept. Min. Agric. Dom. Canada*, 1945, 91. For the effect of sulphur on the growth of clover in Florida, see R. W. Bledsoe and R. E. Blaser, *J. Amer. Soc. Agron.*, 1947, **39**, 146.

supply in the soil to limit crop yield; hence it often needs to be added regularly in the fertiliser. Potassium differs from nitrogen and carbon, however, in not being a constituent of the plant fabric. It seems to be important in the synthesis of amino acids and proteins from ammonium ions, for plants growing in solutions high in ammonium and low in potassium can have their tissues killed by the high concentration of the ammonium ions that accumulate in them under these conditions.[1] It is interesting to note that the only other element known that can replace potassium in this function is rubidium.[2] It is also probably important in the photosynthetic process, for potassium shortage in the leaf is commonly considered to lead to low rates of carbon dioxide assimilation,[3] though D. J. Watson[4] has been unable to confirm this on crops grown on the Rothamsted farm: it increased the leaf area and might put up the efficiency of assimilation slightly, but its effect was variable and always much smaller than that of nitrogen. But a discussion on the general effects of potassium deficiency is complicated by the fact that they depend so much on the relative concentration of other elements, particularly sodium and calcium in the plant tissues.[5]

In the field the potassium supply in the soil may be adequate for crops growing under conditions of a low nitrogen and phosphorus supply, but become inadequate if these are increased. Hence, signs of potassium starvation are often seen when only nitrogenous and phosphatic fertilisers are given to a crop; and the most characteristic sign is the premature death of the leaves.

When nitrogen and potassium are simultaneously in short supply, the plants are stunted, their leaves are small and rather ashy-grey in colour, dying prematurely, first at the tips and then along the outer edges, and the fruit and seed is small in quantity, size and weight. These effects are general, and are seen on all soils, but best on light sandy or chalky soils and on certain peaty soils; and it is on these soils that potassic fertilisers are most likely to act on all crops. With large supplies of nitrogen relative to potassium, on the other hand, the leaves are large but relatively inefficient photosynthesisers; hence an abnormal concentration of nitrogen compounds compared to carbohydrate occurs in the leaf, leading to various undesirable effects, such as the greater liability of these leaves to fungus and bacterial diseases, and to a reduced resistance against damage by drought compared with those receiving more adequate dressings of a potassium fertiliser. Thus potassium acts as a corrective to the harmful effects of nitrogen, and

[1] T. W. Turtschin, *Ztschr. Pflanz. Düng.*, 1934, A **34**, 343; M. E. Wall, *Soil Sci.*, 1940, **49**, 393.
[2] F. J. Richards, *Ann. Bot.*, 1941, **5**, 263, who used barley plants.
[3] F. G. Gregory with F. J. Richards, *Ann. Bot.*, 1929, **43**, 119; with E. C. D. Baptiste, ibid., 1936, **50**, 579; O. Eckstein, *Plant Physiol.*, 1939, **14**, 113.
[4] *Ann. Bot.*, 1947, **11**, 375.
[5] For a discussion of these effects, see F. G. Gregory, *Ann. Rev. Biochem.*, 1937, **6**, 557.

is therefore often required for crops receiving high levels of nitrogen manures.

An adequate supply of potassium in the leaf is probably essential for the photosynthetic process to go on efficiently, and results, such as those given in Table 9, have been used to demonstrate the truth of this statement. This table gives the weight of mangold tops and roots

TABLE 9

Action of Potassium Salts on the Yield of Mangolds

Barnfield, Rothamsted, 50 years, 1876–1928[1]

Yields in 1,000 lb. per acre

	Roots			Leaves		
Nitrogen supplied in manure, lb. per acre . . .	none	86	184	none	86	184
Series[2]	O	A	AC	O	A	AC
No potassium salts[3] . .	10·01	15·01	21·26	2·35	5·85	7·37
With potassium sulphate, 500 lb. per acre . .	9·03	30·24	50·51	2·08	6·29	11·65

at harvest obtained on certain plots at Rothamsted, some of which receive potassium, but all of which receive phosphate. It shows that with moderate dressings of nitrogen, given as sulphate of ammonia, potassium doubles the weight of roots, but has only a small effect on the yield of tops. One cannot argue, however, that this increase was necessarily due to the greater efficiency of the leaves, for D. J. Watson[4] has shown that the potassium increased the size of the leaves in the early part of the growing season, though this effect had disappeared by harvest, and that this initial increase was sufficient to account for the differences in the yield of roots without having to assume any effect of potassium on the efficiency of photosynthesis.

A result entirely similar to mangolds is found with sugar-beet. The results of a large series of manurial experiments carried out over the sugar-beet areas of Great Britain are given in Table 10.[5] Nitrogen alone depresses the sugar content, potassium increases it and phosphate has no effect, though these experiments, like that in Barnfield, cannot

---

[1] Excluding 1885 when nitrogenous fertilisers were not applied owing to poverty of crop, and 1908 and 1927 when the crop failed.

[2] Series A as 400 lb. ammonium salts to 1915; 412 lb. sulphate of ammonia since. Series AC as Series A, but in addition 2,000 lb. rape cake.

[3] Series 5 and 6 respectively. Each receives 3½ cwt. per acre of superphosphate each year.

[4] Ann. Bot., 1947, 11, 375.

[5] E. M. Crowther, Roth. Expt. Sta. Rept., 1939–45, revised to include later data.

furnish the information required for their correct physiological interpretation.

Crops differ greatly in their responsiveness to potassium. Many fruit trees—apples, gooseberries, red currants—need ample supplies of

TABLE 10

The Effect of Fertilisers on the Yield of Sugar-beet
Great Britain, 1934–48 (359 experiments)

	Mean yield	Response to		
		Sulphate of ammonia	Superphosphate	Muriate of potash
		4 cwt./acre	6 cwt./acre	2½ cwt./acre
Roots, tons per acre . .	11·2	1·2	0·4	0·5
Sugar, per cent . . .	17·3	—0·4	0·0	0·2
Sugar, cwt. per acre . .	38·8	3·5	1·5	2·1
Tops, tons per acre . .	9·5	2·7	0·3	0·3

potassium for good cropping; beans and potatoes among British field crops, and tomatoes among the glasshouse crops, are all very responsive. Leguminous pasture plants—clovers and lucerne—also seem to need adequate supplies of potassium, particularly if they are to compete successfully with grasses;[1] and for lucerne in addition potassium increases its winter hardiness, possibly because it encourages the plant to store more carbohydrate and protein in its root system.[2]

Excess potassium in the soil, as brought about by too high a level of potassium manuring for example, will reduce very considerably the amount of other cations the crop can take up (see p. 66), and this may lead to crop growth being badly upset by these induced deficiencies of other cations.

CALCIUM

Calcium appears to be essential for the growth of meristems, and particularly for the proper growth and functioning of root tips. It is also present as calcium pectate, which is a constituent of the middle lamellae of the cell walls, and possibly for this reason it tends to accumulate in the leaf.[3]

Calcium deficiency typically occurs on very acid soils, though the

[1] For the Rothamsted experiments on this point, see J. B. Lawes and J. H. Gilbert, *Phil. Trans.*, 1900, **192** B, 156; W. E. Brenchley, *Manuring of Grassland for Hay*, London, 1924.
[2] L. F. Graber *et al.*, *Wisconsin Agric. Expt. Sta., Res. Bull.* 80, 1927.
[3] For a review of the calcium nutrition of plants, see F. Kersting-Münster, *ForschDienst.*, 1938, **5**, 48, and eight papers in *Soil Sci.*, 1948, **65**, 1–128.

harmful effect of acid soils is often due to causes other than calcium deficiency; but it appears to occur also on some alkaline soils low in calcium but high in sodium. In general, however, farm crops are rarely limited by lack of calcium alone, though in this country during the war, cases of potatoes suffering from calcium deficiency were not uncommon on newly ploughed-up common or waste lands if the land had not previously been limed. The calcium status of acid soils undoubtedly is one of the factors that complicates the easy prediction from the pH of the soil alone whether a soil needs liming before a given crop can be grown on it.

Calcium deficiency appears to have two effects on the plant: it causes a stunting of the root system and it gives a fairly characteristic appearance to the leaf. Calcium deficiency also may have an indirect effect on the plant by allowing other substances to accumulate in the tissues so much that they may either lower the vigour or actually harm the plant. Thus a good calcium supply helps to neutralise the undesirable effects of an unbalanced distribution in the soil of nutrients and other compounds that can be taken up by the plant.

High levels of calcium in a soil, such as occur, for example, in some calcareous soils, have no direct harmful effect on most crops, but they may have several undesirable secondary effects. A high level depresses the uptake of magnesium and potassium; and in particular, calcareous soils typically require high levels of potassic fertilisers, a fact very well known on the thin chalk soils of southern and eastern England.

MAGNESIUM

Magnesium is needed by all green plants as it is a constituent of chlorophyll. It also seems to play an important role in the transport of phosphate in the plant, and possibly as a consequence of this it accumulates in the seeds of plants rich in oil, for the oil is also accompanied by an accumulation of lecithin, a phosphate-containing fat.[1] Thus the phosphate content of a crop can sometimes be increased to a higher level by adding a magnesium rather than a phosphatic fertiliser, and it is for this reason that magnesium silicates, such as finely ground serpentine[2] or olivine,[3] are sometimes added to superphosphate to increase its effectiveness.

Magnesium deficiency often occurs on acid sandy soils that are also deficient in calcium, and it is then rectified by using a dolomitic instead of a purely calcareous limestone. But it can also be induced by unbalanced manuring, such as by an excessive use of potassium fertilisers

[1] For a symposium on the role of magnesium in plant nutrition, see *Soil Sci.*, 1947, **63** 1–28.
[2] See, for example, H. O. Askew, *New Zealand J. Sci. Tech.*, 1942, **24** B, 79, 128.
[3] D. U. Druzhinin, *Ztschr. Pflanz. Düng.*, 1936, **45**, 303.

(p. 66), or by the repeated use of grass mulches,[1] and these are common causes of the magnesium deficiency that can sometimes be seen on orchard trees, tomatoes, tobacco, cotton and sugar-beet. This induced deficiency is very dependent on season and does not always reduce the yield, but can be cured, if it is really necessary to use such large dressings of potassic or sodium fertilisers, by adding soluble magnesium salts to the soil or, better still, by spraying them on the crops.

SODIUM

Sodium does not seem to be an essential element for any crop, even for salt marsh plants, yet certain crops undoubtedly grow better in the presence of available sodium supplies than in their absence, the sodium in these cases appearing to carry out some of the functions that potassium usually fulfils. Crops can be divided into four groups with respect to their relative needs of sodium compared to potassium: some need sodium for optimum growth, some benefit if available sodium is present, some can tolerate part of their potassium supply being replaced by sodium and some can make no use of sodium even if the potassium supply is restricted. Table 11[2] shows the groups into which various

TABLE 11

Effect of Sodium applied as a Nutrient on several Crops

Degree of benefit in deficiency of potassium		Degree of benefit in sufficiency of potassium	
1. None to very slight	2. Slight to medium	3. Slight to medium	4. Large
Buckwheat	Barley	Cabbage	Celery
Lettuce	Broccoli	Kale	Mangold
Maize	Brussels sprouts	Kohlrabi	Sugar-beet
Potato	Carrot	Mustard	Swiss chard
Rye	Cotton	Radish	Table beet
Soybean	Millet	Rape	Turnip
Spinach	Oat		
Strawberry	Pea		
Sunflowers	Tomato		
White bean	Wheat		

agricultural crops are believed to fall, though the grouping may depend somewhat on climatic conditions.

The role of sodium in the last group of plants is not known, though one of its effects is to increase the succulence of the plant, that is, the amount of water held by unit dry weight of leaf tissue. This may be

[1] J. B. D. Robinson and E. M. Chenery, *Emp. J. Exp. Agric.*, 1958, **26**, 259.
[2] Taken from P. M. Harmer and E. J. Benne, *Soil Sci.*, 1945, **60**, 137.

the reason why it appears to increase the drought resistance of these plants. It also increases the leaf area of sugar-beet.[1] F. J. Richards[2] suggests another role of sodium in helping crops such as barley to grow in a potassium-deficient soil is that it prevents an accumulation of other cations that may be toxic to the plant, for a deficiency of one cation leads to an accumulation of others.

Sugar-beet and mangolds are probably the most sodium-demanding crops grown in western Europe, and although they need a reasonable potassium supply if they are to make proper growth, yet once this minimum supply has been provided, they require a good supply of sodium if they are to give satisfactory yields. Thus in a large series of manuring experiments on sugar-beet conducted throughout England during 1940–5,[3] the yield of sugar per acre was about 37 cwt. in the absence of potassium or sodium in the fertiliser used; it was increased by 2·8 cwt. an acre by 2 cwt. of muriate of potash, by 5·1 cwt. per acre by 5 cwt. of agricultural salt, and by 5·5 cwt. by the potash and salt together. Thus, here there is a definite need for sodium, and given the sodium there is no need for potassium; but in its absence potassium can in part take its place.

There is very little evidence that adding sodium salts to a soil increases the availability of the soil's potassium supply, nor in fact is there any theoretical reason to think that sodium ions are more powerful extractors of potassium from soils than are actively growing roots or root hairs.

SILICON

Great importance was attached by the older plant physiologists to silicon in the nutrition of the cereals and grasses, it being supposed to give strength to the straw.[4] Field experiments at Rothamsted disproved this view, neither barley straw nor grass being strengthened by manuring with sodium silicate. Certainly these crops contain much silicon in their dry matter, and, as can be seen from Table 4 on p. 29, the silicon content of wheat grown on a clay soil increases linearly with the dry matter. The function the silicon plays in these crops is not known, though F. Wagner[5] found crops grown without soluble silica were much more susceptible to mildew than those that had soluble silica available.

Manuring the soil with sodium silicate can, however, increase crop yields on soils deficient in phosphate, as is shown in Table 12 for barley

[1] J. J. Lehr, *Soil Sci.*, 1942, **53**, 399.   [2] *Ann. Rev. Biochem.*, 1944, **13**, 611.
[3] E. M. Crowther, *Brit. Sugar-Beet Rev.*, 1947, **16**, 19.
[4] For a review of this subject, see *Soils and Fert.*, 1946, **9**, 1; G. J. Raleigh, *Soil Sci.*, 1945, **60**, 133.
[5] *Phytopath. Ztschr.*, 1940, **12**, 427.

TABLE 12

Effect of Silicates on the Growth of Barley, 1864–1900. Rothamsted

	Yield of Dressed Grain, bushels		Yield of Straw, cwt.		Ratio $\dfrac{\text{Total Grain}}{\text{Straw}}$	
	Without Silicate	With Silicate	Without Silicate	With Silicate	Without Silicate	With Silicate
Nitrate only . . .	27·3	33·8	16·2	19·8	85·1	86·6
Nitrate + phosphate .	42·2	43·5	24·6	25·8	87·2	85·8
Nitrate + potassium salts	28·6	36·4	17·9	21·7	80·6	85·0
Nitrate + phosphate + potassium salts . .	41·2	44·5	25·3	27·6	82·7	82·1

at Rothamsted. This result was later obtained for oats in water cultures by C. Kreuzhage and E. Wolff.[1] The phenomena were studied by A. D. Hall and C. G. T. Morison,[2] who concluded that silicates act by causing an increased assimilation of phosphoric acid by the plant, the seat of action being in the plant and not in the soil. O. Lemmermann[3] and R. A. Fisher,[4] however, showed that the main effect of the silicate was to increase the amount of phosphate available in the soil, and that any other effect of silicate is of much less importance.

Great interest was taken in this problem, both in Germany and Japan, because it seemed at one time to open up both the possibility of replacing some of the imported phosphates by home-made silicates. So far the hopes have not materialised.[5]

CHLORIDES

Chlorides are taken up by most plants from the soil solution, and there is no evidence that any soils are so deficient in chlorides for crop failures to occur for lack of it, nor is there any evidence that crops would fail if chlorides were completely absent from the soil.

Some crops, however, often respond to additional dressings of chloride, for example, barley, lucerne and tobacco. Thus small dressings of chlorides appear to increase the yield and improve the texture of the tobacco leaf without affecting its burning qualities,

[1] *Landw. Vers.-Stat.*, 1884, **30**, 161.
[2] *Proc. Roy. Soc.*, 1906, **77** B, 455. See also W. E. Brenchley, E. J. Maskell and K. Warington, *Ann. Appl. Biol.*, 1927, **14**, 45.
[3] *Ztschr. Pflanz. Düng.*, 1929, A **13**, 28. This contains a critical review.
[4] *J. Agric. Sci.*, 1929, **19**, 132.
[5] For further information, see O. Lemmermann and H. Wiessmann, *Ztschr. Pflanz. Düng.*, 1922, A **1**, 185; D. S. Jennings, *Soil Sci.*, 1919, **7**, 210; Th. Pfeiffer, *Mitt. Deut. Landw. Gesell.*, 1923, 196; P. L. Gile and J. G. Smith, *J. Agric. Res.*, 1925, **31**, 247; W. Krüger and G. Wimmer, *Bied Zbl.*, 1928, **57**, 414; *Ztschr. für Zückerind.*, 1927, 127; H. Wiessmann, *Ztschr. Pflanz. Düng.*, 1925, A **4**, 73.

though larger dressings, which still increase the yield, lower this quality.[1]

There is no strong evidence that chloride has any specific effect on plant growth, though it may sometimes hasten maturity. Its main function, for which, however, it is not specific, is as an osmotic pressure regulator and a cation balancer in the cell sap and in the plant cells themselves.

In natural conditions plants receive measurable quantities of chlorides (chiefly sodium chloride) in the rain, and the amount is greater in the wetter western parts of the country than in the east. At Rothamsted the amount of chloride brought down averages 16 lb. per acre per annum and fluctuates between 10·3 and 24·4 lb.;[2] it comes chiefly in the winter months. But nearer the sea the amounts become very high, rising, according to N. H. J. Miller's determinations in rain-water from the Hebrides,[3] to:

	Annual rainfall in.	Chlorine per acre lb.
Laudale . .	76·89	168·5
Butt of Lewis[4] .	40·57	6884·0
Monarch . .	47·21	2723·0
Barrahead[5] .	33·93	5753·0

Trace Elements in Plant Nutrition

Plants need very small quantities of certain elements—the so-called trace or minor elements—for their nutrition, and these include iron, manganese, zinc, copper and boron, whilst molybdenum is beneficial under some circumstances. These elements are called trace elements, because only very small quantities, ranging from a few ounces to a few pounds per acre, are usually needed by the crop; and in fact C. S. Piper and A. Walkley[6] estimate that a full crop of oats only removes about $\frac{1}{4}$ oz. of copper, 1–2 oz. of zinc and 7 oz. of manganese, compared with 7 lb. of phosphorus per acre. But it must be realised that there is no sharp distinction between elements needed in large and small quantities, magnesium and sulphur being two good examples of intermediate elements for many crops. The literature on trace elements is now very extensive, and the reader should refer to recent books and reviews for more detailed discussion on their role in plant nutrition.

[1] J. Amer. Soc. Agron., 1929, 21, 113.
[2] E. J. Russell and E. H. Richards, J. Agric. Sci., 1919, 9, 309.
[3] J. Scottish Met. Soc., 1913, 16, 141.   [4] Collected at 70 feet above sea-level.
[5] Collected at 620 feet above sea-level.   [6] Aust. J. Counc. Sci. Indust. Res., 1943, 16, 217.

A shortage of one or more of these elements usually, but not always, affects the appearance of the plant, giving the leaves a chlorotic, bronzed or mottled colour, or altering its habit of growth, or causing the death of the growing points, so giving the plant a rosette appearance. Plants suffering from trace-element deficiencies need not show any symptoms of the deficiency at all—except in so far as growth is not as good as it might be, or they may only display symptoms for a short period in the growing season. Sometimes the symptoms are sufficiently characteristic for the deficiency to be diagnosed visually,[1] but often they are so indefinite, or even suppressed altogether, that they can only be diagnosed by chemical tests, either by analysing the minerals in the leaf tissue or by applying small quantities of any element suspected of being deficient to selected leaves or shoots of the plant.

Deficiencies of the trace elements need not be made good by adding the deficient element to the soil: it is often more economical either to spray it on the leaves of the plant, or, if it is a tree, to insert pellets containing it under the bark in the trunk. Further trace element deficiencies often occur in soils which contain adequate quantities of the element, but in a form unavailable to the plant. Under these conditions the deficiency cannot usually be made good by adding some of the element to the soil. In general, increasing the acidity of the soil by any means, such as placement of sulphur near the plant for example, will increase the availability of all the trace elements except molybdenum. As a corollary, if an acid soil is suspected of having any trace element in minimal quantities, liming that soil may easily induce a deficiency of that element. Trace-element deficiencies have the characteristic that their severity on a given soil depends very strongly on the season, hence the climate affects either the trace element requirements of the crop or else the availability of their compounds in the soil to the crop.

On many soils, plants suffer from a deficiency of a number of elements simultaneously, though they may only show the symptoms of one, or even of none of them. An observation of W. A. Roach[2] illustrates the complexities arising in such a soil. Potatoes growing on a marsh soil in Kent showed symptoms of manganese deficiency which were cured by spraying with manganese, though this did not affect the yield of the crop. The crop was, however, also suffering from zinc deficiency although no symptoms whatever of this were visible; spraying with zinc improved the yield slightly, but spraying with zinc and manganese gave a very considerable increase in yield and obviously

---

[1] For colour reproductions of some of these symptoms, see *Hunger Signs in Crops*, ed. G. Hambidge, Washington, 1941; T. Wallace, *The Diagnosis of Mineral Deficiencies in Plants*, London, 1943, and *Supplement*, 1944.

[2] *E. Malling Res. Sta. Ann. Rept.*, 1945, 29, 83.

rectified the main cause of the low yields. Roach considers that the yields of many of our orchards are unnecessarily low because of a combined deficiency of several of these elements, none of which is severe enough to cause any visible symptoms. Again, plants can have their vitality lowered by shortages of trace elements without any symptoms of deficiency showing.

Trace elements have another characteristic; namely, that they are normally all very poisonous if present in the soil in an available form in more than very small amounts. Hence, it is very dangerous to apply them indiscriminately at more than very light dressings; though if concealed trace-element deficiencies are found to be widespread it will obviously become important to discover just how high a concentration of a mixture of them can be applied indiscriminately without harming the crop.

IRON

Iron deficiency typically shows up as a chlorosis, particularly on calcareous soils, but not all calcareous soils induce iron chlorosis, and crops differ markedly in their susceptibility to this trouble. Fruit trees and bushes are the crops of most economic importance to be affected in England; but the calcifuge leguminous plants, such as yellow and blue lupins and serradella, as well as many conifers, are also strongly affected. Iron-deficiency chlorosis can also be induced as a result of potassium deficiency, and by over-manuring with phosphates on neutral or calcareous soils; it also occurs on soils high in available zinc and under some conditions high in available manganese and copper.[1]

Lime-induced chlorosis is the commonest of the iron-deficiency chloroses, and it is also one of the most difficult deficiencies to cure. It is probable that the trouble lies both in the inability of the plant to extract sufficient iron from the soil and also in an appreciable proportion of the absorbed iron being in combinations unavailable to the plant cells for their metabolism; for chlorotic leaves do not necessarily have a low total iron content though they have a low soluble iron content. The chemical characteristic of these leaves is that they have a very high potassium and a rather low calcium content, and, in fact, young, chlorotic leaves may cause such a drain on the potassium supplies in the plant that the older leaves will suffer from potassium deficiency as a result. This chlorosis cannot yet always be controlled in practice. Farmyard manure and composts can sometimes be used to carry iron in a form available to the plant, but resistant to immobilisation in the soil; grassing down the land between orchard trees and mowing it

[1] For reviews of this subject, see T. Wallace and E. J. Hewitt, *J. Pomol.*, 1946, **22**, 153; H. D. Chapman, *Ann. Rev. Biochem.*, 1945, **14**, 709.

Plate I

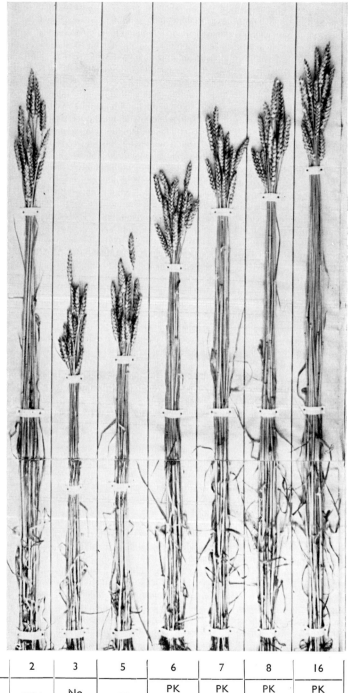

Plot	2	3	5	6	7	8	16
Annual manuring	FYM	No manure	PK	PK 45 lb. N	PK 90 lb. N	PK 135 lb. N	PK 90 lb. N

N given as ammonium sulphate on plots 6, 7, 8 and sodium nitrate on plot 16

The effect of nitrogen fertilisers on the yield of wheat
on Broadbalk in 1943

(p. 31)

Plate II

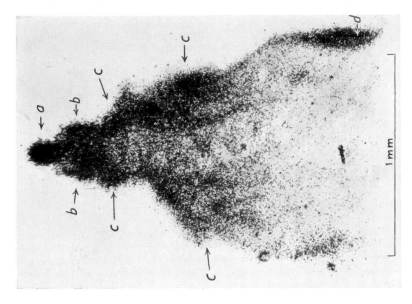

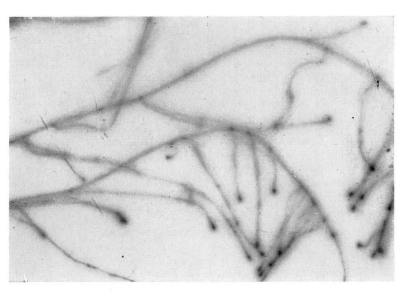

Auto-radiographs of barley plants containing radioactive phosphorus

(*Left*) Showing the concentration of phosphorus in the tips of the growing roots (natural size)
(*Right*) Showing the concentration of phosphorus in the apical meristem (*a*) the leaf primordia; (*b*) the bases of leaf sheaves; (*c*) and (*d*) the initial of adventitious shoots (× 53)

(p. 36)

Plate III

The oxygen and hydroxyl layer containing aluminium in 6-co-ordination

The arrangement of the layers to form a sheet of the mineral pyrophyllite

The oxygen layer containing silicon in 4-co-ordination

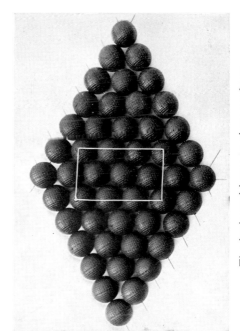

The hydroxyl layer in close packing

(pp. 82–84)

Plate IV

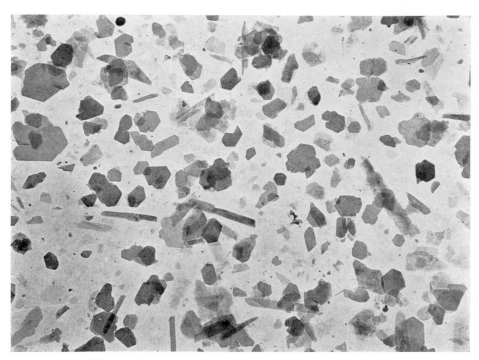

Electron microscope photograph of kaolinite particles
between 0·1 and 0·2 μ (×15,000)

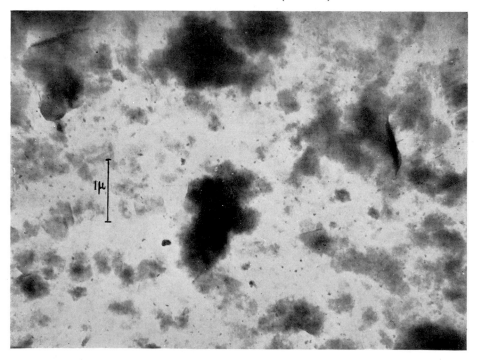

Electron microscope photograph of bentonite particles (×16,000)
These particles are too small and too thin to be resolved, and are mainly aggregated together
in the photograph

regularly, leaving the mown grass on the ground, sometimes cures it, but is a method that is not always applicable: spraying with iron sulphate or inserting pellets of iron citrate or tartrate may also help. The trouble is now usually cured, if it is economically justified, by using a suitable iron chelate.[1]

Iron deficiency can be induced if a crop is growing on a soil containing too high a concentration of many metallic ions. Thus cobalt, copper, chromate, zinc, manganese and lead can all cause plants to show symptoms of iron deficiency as well as those of specific toxicity of these ions.[2] The trouble is sometimes due to an immobilisation of iron within the leaves themselves, for the plant leaves have a very high iron content, yet the trouble can be cured by repeatedly spraying the crop with iron sulphate. Thus, this trouble occurs on some of the zinc-rich soils derived from the dolomitic limestone in the Mendips,[3] and also can be caused by the use of industrial sewage sludges high in zinc, and can sometimes be cured by liming, though this, in turn, may induce manganese deficiency.

MANGANESE

Manganese deficiency typically occurs on calcareous or newly limed peats, particularly if the water table is high, though it can also occur on some neutral sandy soils and light loams. It can be easily induced by over-liming sandy podzolic and garden soils rich in organic matter. It rarely if ever occurs on acid soils. Many crops are susceptible: oats in particular among the cereals, potatoes, peas and to a less extent beans, sugar-beet and related crops, and many fruit crops and tung trees. Oats suffer from grey-speck disease, sugar-beet from a yellows, and peas from marsh spot.

Manganese deficiency occurs in crops growing on soils that contain adequate quantities of manganese for the crop, but in which the manganese is present in a form unavailable to it. Unfortunately the factors controlling the availability of the soil's manganese are not fully understood. Probably only divalent manganese is available to the plant, but this merely puts the question back to the soil factors that control the proportion of manganese present in the divalent form, a question which is discussed on p. 516.

The main factor so far recognised that controls the availability of manganese in the soil is the pH. The more acid the soil the greater is the availability of the manganese,[4] and indeed the first harmful effect

---

[1] See, for example, D. G. Hill-Cottingham and C. P. Lloyd-Jones, *Plant and Soil*, 1957, **8**, 263; 1958, **9**, 189; 1959, **10**, 194.
[2] E. J. Hewitt, *Nature*, 1948, **161**, 489; *Long Ashton Ann. Rep.*, 1948, 66.
[3] T. Wallace and E. J. Hewitt, *J. Pomol.*, 1946, **22**, 153.
[4] See, for example, H. J. Snider, *Soil Sci.*, 1943, **56**, 187.

of too low a soil pH on some crops is the toxic effect of the large amount of manganese the plant takes up[1] (see p. 523). In this respect it differs from the other trace elements, for it is the only one that can accumulate in plant tissues in quantities far higher than are necessary for optimum growth. Hence, one method of reducing manganese deficiency in a soil is to make the soil more acid, as, for example, by the use of sulphur, or under some conditions of large quantities of ammonium sulphate.[2] It is also possible that a second cause of manganese deficiency may be that some soil bacteria, or some bacteria on the plant roots, oxidise the divalent manganese in the root zone of the crop.[3]

Manganese has several functions in the plant. It is a constituent of some respiratory enzymes, probably sometimes in association with iron, and of some enzymes responsible for protein synthesis. A good manganese supply may also sometimes help counteract the effect of poor aeration. Thus under conditions of poor aeration and low manganese, nitrates are a better source of nitrogen than ammonium ions, as the oxygen in the nitrate can act as a hydrogen acceptor in the respiration processes of the cells. But D. I. Arnon[4] showed that increasing the manganese supply to the root under these conditions had a much larger effect in increasing the growth of the plant (which was barley in his experiments) when ammonium rather than nitrate ions were the source of nitrogen. Manganese may also be concerned with the nitrogen metabolism of the plant. Thus S. G. Heintze[5] found that on fields where the levels of the different forms of soil manganese were fairly uniform, plants developed manganese deficiency symptoms most strongly on those parts of the field where the available nitrogen (actually the nitrifiable nitrogen, see p. 518) was highest, and this was not due to any extra growth the higher level of available nitrogen caused. On the other hand, plants suffering from manganese deficiency appear to have a higher concentration of nitrates and of most plant amino acids than normal plants, which suggests that manganese plays some role either in the synthesis of a particular amino acid, or of proteins from amino acids.[6]

The dressings of manganese required to effect control of these deficiency diseases depends on the method of control practised. Manganese deficiency induced by over-liming can often be cured by spraying as little as 1–2 lb. per acre of manganese sulphate, but rates of 5–20 lb. per acre are commoner for sprays; and up to 40–50 lb. per acre for incorporation in peat soils.

[1] M. J. Funchess, *Alabama Agric. Exp. Sta.*, *Bull.* 201, 1918; H. G. M. Jacobson and T. R. Swanbank, *J. Amer. Soc. Agron.*, 1932, **24**, 237; T. Wallace *et al.*, *Nature*, 1945, **156**, 778; J. B. Hale and S. G. Heintze, ibid., 1946, **157**, 554.
[2] D. W. Goodall, *J. Pomol.*, 1943, **20**, 136, for apple trees.
[3] F. C. Gerretsen, *Ann. Bot.*, 1937, **1**, 207.   [4] *Soil Sci.*, 1937, **44**, 91.
[5] *J. Agric. Sci.*, 1946, **36**, 227.   [6] E. J. Hewitt *et al.*, *Nature*, 1949, **163**, 681.

ZINC

Zinc-deficiency diseases are of great importance on many orchard soils in the U.S.A.; citrus, deciduous fruits, pecans and tung plantations all suffer in several areas, and in Florida maize and perhaps other crops in addition. Zinc-deficiency diseases typically show up in climates having bright sunlight, are usually restricted to heavy soils or to sandy soils containing peat, and are most pronounced in slightly acid or neutral soils. Zinc deficiency has not been considered of any economic importance in European crops, because zinc-deficiency symptoms have not been recognised here. But W. A. Roach's observations,[1] already quoted, on the response of many crops on some marshland soils of Kent which show no visible signs of zinc deficiency to additions of zinc, suggests that its importance here may have been under-estimated.

Plants differ markedly in their power of extracting zinc from the soil. On the zinc-deficient soils of Florida native weeds seem to be far better collectors of zinc than planted crops: L. H. Rogers, O. E. Gall and R. M. Barnette[2] found that native weeds growing on fallow land contained on the average 140 p.p.m. of zinc in their dry matter whilst a cover crop of crotalaria only contained 4–11 p.p.m., and they suggested that the best way of preparing the land for maize is to allow these native weeds to cover the land and then plough them in before the maize is sown. In the same way lucerne, which appears to be a strong extractor of zinc, is a valuable cover crop in orchards suffering from zinc deficiency, whenever it can be grown without competing with the trees for water or other nutrients.

The power of a plant to extract zinc from the soil also depends on the extensiveness of its root system. Thus zinc deficiency can occur in citrus trees growing on some heavy soils because the trees cannot form an extensive enough root system to tap a sufficiently large volume of soil from which to extract their zinc. It can be cured in these cases by growing crops that are efficient extractors of zinc and ploughing them in as green manures.

There is some evidence[3] that zinc deficiency can sometimes be caused by the soil micro-organisms competing with the plants for the small quantities of available zinc present.

COPPER

Copper deficiency typically occurs in crops growing on newly reclaimed peats in Europe and the eastern States of the U.S.A., causing the so-called Reclamation Diseases.[4] But it has also been

[1] E. Malling Res. Sta. Ann. Rept., 1945, 29, 83.   [2] Soil Sci., 1939, 47, 237.
[3] W. H. Chandler, Bot. Gaz., 1937, 98, 625.
[4] For an account of these diseases and their cure in Holland, see W. J. Melchers and H. J. Gerritsen, Koper als Onmisbaar Element voor Plant en Dier, Wageningen, 1944.

found on some sandy and gravelly soils in Australia and South Africa.

Copper appears to have two quite separate functions: one directly concerned with plant nutrition and one with the condition of the soil. Its function as a nutrient lies in its being a constituent of some enzymes, such as the oxidation-reduction enzyme polyphenol oxidase.

Its function in neutralising a harmful condition in the soil can be surmised from the fact that the quantity of copper sulphate that must be added to a soil to get maximum crop yield varies a hundred-fold. Thus 250 lb. per acre of copper sulphate are commonly used in the Florida Everglades,[1] about 50 lb. on some European and 10 lb. on some Michigan peats,[2] about 25 lb. on some calcareous sandy soils in South Australia[3] that apparently contain ample copper but in an unavailable form, and lowest of all, $2\frac{1}{2}$ lb. per acre is the recommended dressing, and 10 lb. is harmful, on some sandy soils in Western Australia.[4] W. S. Smith[5] suggested that the role of copper in the copper-deficient peats was to precipitate or inactivate certain toxins present in the peat, which he believed he had isolated.

In soils where the role of copper appears to be mainly as a nutrient, i.e. where low dressings only are required, it is possible that there is an interaction between the need for zinc and for copper, in the sense that crops may respond to zinc if copper is also given, but not if it is withheld.[6] Also, in these same conditions it is possible that copper responses are larger in hot, dry summers than in cool, moist ones.[7]

MOLYBDENUM

Molybdenum is another element now known to be needed for the growth of some plants in the field, but it differs from the other elements so far mentioned in that plants can probably be grown perfectly satisfactorily without it, provided their nitrogen supply is present as ammonium ions. Plants grown without a molybdenum supply in the presence of nitrates accumulate nitrates in their tissues and the molybdenum is apparently essential for the nitrate-reducing enzyme.[8] Again leguminous plants are unable to fix nitrogen in the absence of an adequate molybdenum supply, and in fact every nitrogen-fixing organism so far recognised requires molybdenum for this process.

[1] O. C. Bryan, *J. Amer. Soc. Agron.*, 1929, **21**, 923.
[2] R. E. Lucas, *Proc. Soil Sci. Soc. Amer.*, 1946, **10**, 269.
[3] D. S. Riceman and C. M. Donald, *J. Dept. Agric. S. Aust.*, 1939, **42**, 959.
[4] A. S. Wild and L. J. H. Teakle, *J. Dept. Agric. W. Aust.*, 1942, **19**, ser. 2, 71, **242**.
[5] *Diss.*, Wageningen, 1927.
[6] For Michigan peat soils, see R. E. Lucas, *Proc. Soil Sci. Soc. Amer.*, 1946, **10**, 269.
[7] Again for Michigan peats, see P. M. Harmer, *Proc. Soil Sci. Soc. Amer.*, 1946, **10**, 284. He also gives a list of the responsiveness of different crops to copper shortage.
[8] See, for example, E. G. Mulder, *Plant and Soil*, 1948, **1**, 94; E. J. Hewitt *et al.*, *Nature*, 1949, **163**, 681.

Molybdenum deficiency in the field was first recognised in Australia,[1] New Zealand and Tasmania,[2] and the crops first proved to need molybdenum were the clovers. Leguminous plants could only be grown on some of these acid sandy soils if they were given a dressing of between $\frac{1}{2}$ and 2 lb. per acre of either ammonium or sodium molybdate; and cases have been reported of clovers responding to similar dressings of molybdenum in Europe.[3]

Molybdenum deficiency has also been recognised in the field on non-leguminous crops such as cauliflowers, where it gives a deformity known as "whiptail",[4] and it has also been produced in a number of other crops, such as tomatoes[5] and lettuce[6] by growing them in water or sand cultures, but none of the laboratory examples so far found are inconsistent with the assumption that the sole function of the molybdenum is concerned with nitrate utilisation in the plant.

BORON

Boron would appear to be essential for all plants in greater or less degree. A shortage of boron typically affects the meristem or actively dividing tissues, so that characteristic symptoms of boron deficiency are death of the growing points of shoot and root, failure of flower buds to develop, disintegration of the vascular tissue and breaking down and blackening of the softer tissues. In the field, deficiency is shown in various ways, as in the heart rot of sugar-beet, "raan" of swedes, cracked stem in celery and browning in cauliflower. Boron deficiency does not necessarily indicate an actual shortage of boron in the soil; it may be present yet unavailable to the plant. It can be induced by over-liming, and it also shows up more strongly in dry than in wet seasons. The condition can be remedied by the addition of 10–12 lb. per acre of borax to the soil, heavier dressings usually being harmful unless the soil has been over-limed. It cannot usually be rectified by spraying a soluble borate on to the plant.

The primary role of boron appears to be concerned both with the uptake of calcium by the roots and with its efficient use in the plant, and sometimes the one and sometimes the other process first limits growth at low boron concentrations.[7] This was first demonstrated by W. E. Brenchley and K. Warington[8] for broad beans (*Vicia faba*), and has been confirmed for a number of other crops. It also appears to

[1] A. J. Anderson, *J. Aust. Inst. Agric. Sci.*, 1942, **8**, 73.
[2] E. F. Fricke, *Tasm. J. Agric.*, 1943, **14**, 69; 1944, **15**, 65; 1945, **16**, 1.
[3] H. Bortels, *Arch. Mikrobiol.*, 1937, **8**, 13; K. A. Dmitriev, *Khim. Sotsial. Zemled.*, 1938. No. 10, 80.
[4] W. Plant, *J. Hort. Sci.*, 1951, **26**, 109.
[5] D. I. Arnon and P. R. Stout, *Plant Physiol.*, 1939, **14**, 599.
[6] K. Warington, *Ann. Appl. Biol.*, 1946, **33**, 249.
[7] For a symposium on this, see *Soil Sci.*, 1944, **57**.
[8] *Ann. Bot.*, 1927, **41**, 167; 1934, **48**, 743.

have a secondary role in broad beans, in which plant it was first recognised as an essential nutrient by Warington,[1] for an adequate boron supply is essential for the vascular system in the root to throw off branches to supply the nodule bacteria with carbohydrate,[2] so preventing them from becoming parasitic.

The importance of boron for plant development is sufficiently well recognised to make it a usual practice in some places to incorporate a small amount of borax with the fertilisers for sugar-beet, tobacco, turnips and doubtless other crops also. J. J. Lehr[3] has outlined the boron relations in plants and soil in a thesis drawing special attention to its importance for brassica crops, tomato and maize, and has also indicated the possible lowering of the boron status of many soils owing to the increasing difficulty of obtaining organic fertilisers, the greater purity of many of the inorganic fertilisers, and the frequent substitution of sulphate of ammonia for Chilean nitrate, which has a high boron content.

The supply of available boron can be readily washed out of soils, hence boron deficiency is typically found on highly leached soils. On the other hand, marine sediments are usually well supplied with it. Boron, like most other minor elements, should be supplied to the soil in small frequent dressings, to minimise any risk of the toxic effects of too high a concentration.

Trace Elements in Animal Nutrition

Animals have not quite the same trace-element needs as plants.[4] Thus all animals require iodine, though iodine-deficiency diseases have rarely been reported among livestock. They need iron, manganese, copper and zinc, as do plants, but do not seem to require boron. Cattle and sheep, however, need cobalt, an element not apparently required by plants. Normally, if pastures cannot adequately supply the trace element needs of the grazing animals, these can be met either by giving the animals licks or drenches containing the missing trace element, or by mixing these in with the main fertilisers, usually with the super-phosphate given to the pastures.

The difference between the trace-element requirements of plants and animals can be seen in the effects of different hill grazings on the thriftiness of the sheep they carry. Thus, it is probable that sheep do better on some of the heather grazings than on the improved leys because the heather herbage is richer in trace elements.[5] The substitution

---

[1] *Ann. Bot.*, 1923, **37**, 629.
[2] W. E. Brenchley and H. G. Thornton, *Proc. Roy. Soc.*, 1925, **98** B, 373.
[3] Thesis. *De Betekenis van borium voor de plant*, Utrecht, 1940.
[4] For a review, see F. C. Russell, *Imp. Bur. Anim. Nutr., Tech. Comm.* 15, 144.
[5] B. Thomas *et al.*, *Emp. J. Expt. Agric.*, 1945, **13**, 93.

of improved leys for the unimproved heather may require either the sheep or the land being given additional amounts of the more important trace elements, if any benefit is to be reaped from the increased amount of herbage produced.

The two main trace-element deficiency diseases in animals are due to copper and cobalt. Copper deficiency can occur in cattle grazing on copper-deficient pastures; but it can also occur on pastures apparently adequately supplied with copper for reasons which are not fully known, although in part the copper in these forages appears to be unavailable to the animal, and in part to be induced by a high sulphate or molybdenum content.[1] Thus teartness in pastures appears to be a molybdenum-induced copper deficiency, for the pastures giving this trouble have a herbage abnormally high in molybdenum. These troubles are ameliorated by feeding the animals extra copper.

Cobalt is needed by ruminants in much larger quantities than by non-ruminants, probably to help with the fermentation of food in the rumen, for the cobalt must be given by the mouth or as a pellet in the rumen—it is no use injecting it into their bodies. Many poor pastures all over the world are now known to have too low a cobalt content for sheep or cattle to thrive on them. In Great Britain these are mainly found on some hill pastures, and the sheep suffer from a disease known as pine. Dressings of $\frac{1}{2}$ to 2 lb. per acre of a cobalt salt are applied to the pastures and the effect lasts about three years. In New Zealand, where the soils are very deficient in phosphate also, it is usually applied mixed with superphosphate.

Animals can suffer from other deficiency diseases besides those due to trace elements. Thus, in parts of South Africa the herbage has such a low content of phosphate that the animals grazing on it suffer from acute phosphate starvation (see p. 462). Again, sheep need a fairly high content of available sulphur in their herbage to produce wool, as wool contains a high proportion of cystine, a sulphur-containing amino acid. The spring flush of good pastures on soils low in available sulphur can give a fodder too low in sulphur for the sheep, with a consequence that the quality of the wool falls—the wool becomes brittle and breaks easily.

Pasture plants can, however, contain sufficiently high concentrations of some elements in their tissues to be definitely harmful to animals feeding on them. The best known example is probably selenium in the United States. Prairie and range plants growing on seleniferous soils are not affected by the selenium, and some species can accumulate very large amounts; but animals feeding on these prairies may suffer severe selenium poisoning. Similarly, pasture grasses and clovers on

[1] See, for example, C. F. Mills, *J. Sci. Food Agric.*, 1957, **8**, S 88.

some of the heavy Lower Lias clays of southern England may accumulate concentrations of molybdenum[1] that can seriously harm calves and young cattle grazing them. These are the teart pastures already mentioned in the paragraph dealing with copper-deficiency diseases.

The relation between the minerals composing the soil and the health of livestock grazing on the pasture or range can thus be very close. Thus the cobalt content of a rock tends to follow the magnesium content —their ions are of a similar size, hence hill grazings on granitic rocks, low in magnesium, tend to induce pine in sheep, whilst those on rocks well supplied with serpentine will be healthy.[2] Again, since some plants are much better extractors of these elements than others, the botanical composition of the herbage,[3] and because of this the way the grazing is managed, can affect the health of the stock markedly.

[1] W. S. Ferguson, A. H. Lewis and S. J. Watson, *J. Agric. Sci.*, 1943, **33**, 44.
[2] For examples, see E. B. Kidson, *J. Soc. Chem. Indust.*, 1938, **57**, 95; R. L. Mitchell, *Proc. Nutr. Soc.*, 1944, **1**, 183.
[3] For examples of the power of plants to concentrate rare earths, see W. O. Robinson, *Soil Sci.*, 1943, **56**, 1.

CHAPTER IV

QUANTITATIVE STUDIES ON PLANT GROWTH

ATTEMPTS HAVE BEEN made in the past to find mathematical expressions for the relationship between the quantity or concentration of plant nutrients present and the growth of the crop, and in particular its yield. Two types of solution of this problem are possible:

1. A hypothesis is set up which seems to fit the facts; it is expressed by an equation and this is then applied to the experimental data.

2. The experimental data are studied by statistical methods and an empirical equation or regression formula is fitted thereto, with no assumption or hypothesis as to the underlying causes.

Owing to the complexity of the problem—plant growth is dependent on so many factors—no general solution can be expected by either method. The first procedure has, in fact, been far more widely followed, and has been of more practical utility than the second.

A number of different hypotheses have been put forward on the relationship between the amount of plant nutrient or other factors affecting plant growth and the growth or yield of the plant. One of the earliest was due to Liebig, who expressed it as the Law of the Minimum: the amount of plant growth is regulated by the factor present in minimum amount and rises or falls according as this is increased or decreased in amount. The relation between plant growth and the amount of the limiting nutrient present in the soil can, therefore, be represented as a curve such as is shown in Fig. 3: growth

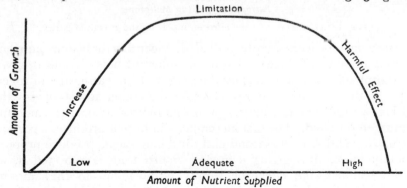

FIG. 3. General relation between any particular nutrient or growth factor and the amount of growth made by the plant.

increases with additions of the limiting factor until it ceases to be
limiting, then plant growth becomes independent of this factor as it
increases still more until a point is reached when it is becoming toxic
and causes plant growth to decrease. This law unfortunately has only
a very limited validity, for if several factors are low, but none too low,
increasing any one will increase the yield, as will be shown in the
section on the interaction of nutrients.

The Relation between Growth and Nutrient Supply as found by Experiment

The first good experimental investigation was made by Hellriegel in
the eighties of the last century. Barley was grown in pots of sand, all

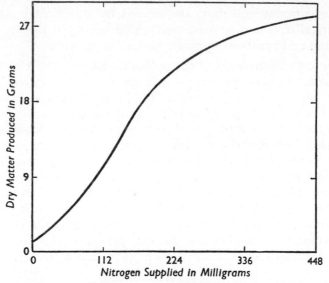

FIG. 4. Effect of increasing the nitrogen supply on the growth of barley.

necessary factors were amply provided, excepting only one nutrient
salt, the amount of which varied in the different pots. Table 13 gives
an example of his results: it shows the effect of increasing the nitrogen
supply on the total dry matter produced and on other aspects of growth,
and Fig. 4 shows the dry matter produced plotted against the amount
of nitrogen supplied. The first increment of nitrogen produces a certain
increase in yield, but the second and third increments produce propor-
tionately more, thus giving a greater return than is expected if, as
Liebig assumed, the effect be simply proportional to the amount
present. The fourth and fifth increments, however, produce less effect.
The curve, therefore, resembles an S and is described as sigmoid; this

is a common shape for curves showing total growth made after the lapse of a definite period of time, though perhaps less common for curves relating to environmental factors.

TABLE 13

Effect of Increasing the Nitrogen Supply on the Growth of Barley in Sand Cultures: H. Hellriegel and H. Wilfarth[1]

Nitrogen given as calcium nitrate

Mgm. of nitrogen supplied . .	—	56	112	168	280	420
Dry matter in crop, gm. . .	0·74	4·86	10·80	17·53	21·29	28·73
Increased yield for each extra 56 mgm. nitrogen . . .	—	4·12	5·94	6·73	1·88	2·97
Grain, per cent of dry matter in crop	11·9	37·9	38·0	42·6	38·6	43·4
Weight of one grain, mgm. .	19	30	33	32	21	30

Field experiments can lead to similar results if the factor under consideration is at a sufficiently low level. The effect of increasing dressings of sulphate of ammonia on the yield of wheat on the permanent wheat field at Rothamsted is given in Table 14, both for the

TABLE 14

Response of Wheat to Sulphate of Ammonia Broadbalk Field[2]

	Grain yield				Straw yield			
Nitrogen supplied annually in manure, lb. per acre . .	0	43	86	129	0	43	86	129
Period, 1852–71 Yield in cwt. per acre . .	9·5	14·9	19·9	21·7	14·9	24·5	35·4	41·3
Increase for each 43 lb. of nitrogen	—	5·4	5·0	1·8	—	9·6	10·9	5·9
Period, 1902–21 Yield in cwt. per acre . .	7·0	11·1	16·2	19·2	10·5	19·0	30·6	39·5
Increase for each 43 lb. of nitrogen	—	4·1	5·1	3·0	—	8·5	11·6	8·9

twenty-year periods, 1852–71 and 1902–21. In both cases the second dose of nitrogen gives the largest response in the straw, and the same is true for the grain response in the latter period, but in the first twenty years, before the fertility of the unmanured had fallen very much, the response to the first dressing was rather larger than to the second.

[1] *Ztschr. Rübenzucker-Ind.*, Beilageheft, 1888.
[2] E. J. Russell and D. J. Watson, *Imp. Bur. Soil Sci., Tech. Comm.* 40, 1940. The plot receiving no nitrogen has received none since 1839 at the latest.

Thus the sigmoid curve does not always occur in field experiments, but perhaps only when the factor considered is at a very low level.

The Assumed Relation between Growth and Nutrient Supply

The smoothness of the curves found by experiment suggests that they can be expressed by a mathematical equation. E. A. Mitscherlich was among the first to do this, and his equation is certainly the best known and most widely used. He assumed that a plant or crop should produce a certain maximum yield if all conditions were ideal, but in so far as any essential factor is deficient there is a corresponding shortage in the yield. Further, he assumed that the increase of crop produced by unit increment of the lacking factor is proportional to the decrement from the maximum, or expressed mathematically:

$$\frac{dy}{dx} = (A - y)C,$$

where y is the yield obtained when x is the amount of the factor present, A is the maximum yield obtainable if the factor was present in excess, this being calculated from the equation, and C is a constant. On integration, and assuming that $y = 0$ when $x = 0$,

$$y = A\left(1 - e^{-Cx}\right).$$

This curve is not sigmoid in shape, but everywhere concave to the axis representing the nutrient supply. Mitscherlich's experiments were made with plants grown in sand cultures supplied with excess of all nutrients excepting the one under investigation. Table 15 shows the results

TABLE 15

Yield of Oats with Different Dressings of Phosphates. Mitscherlich[1]

P_2O_5 in manure	Dry matter produced	Crop calculated from formula	Difference	Difference expressed in terms of probable error.[2]
Grams	Grams	Grams	Grams	
0·00	9·8 ± 0·50	9·80	—	—
0·05	19·3 ± 0·52	18·91	− 0·39	− 0·8
0·10	27·2 ± 2·00	26·64	− 0·56	− 0·3
0·20	41·0 ± 0·85	38·63	− 2·37	− 2·8
0·30	43·9 ± 1·12	47·12	+ 3·22	+ 2·9
0·50	54·9 ± 3·66	57·39	+ 2·49	+ 0·7
2·00	61·0 ± 2·24	67·64	+ 6·64	+ 3·0

[1] *Landw. Jahrb.*, 1909, **38**, 537.
[2] If this figure is less than 3, the agreement is considered satisfactory.

obtained with oats and monocalcium phosphate. Mitscherlich claims to show by experiment that the proportionality factor C (called "Wirkungswert", or "faktor" in Mitscherlich's papers) is a constant for each fertiliser, independent of the crop, the soil or other conditions. If this were so an experimenter knowing its value could, from a single field trial, predict the yields obtainable from any given quantities of the fertiliser, a result of great practical value. Further, it would be possible to estimate by direct pot experiment the amount of available plant food in a soil, one of the most difficult of all soil problems.

Mitscherlich has, indeed, used his formula for this purpose,[1] and in his very interesting book[2] he applies the expression in a variety of ways. Some work of E. M. Crowther and F. Yates[3] furnishes a later example of its use. By its aid they could put together in convenient tables all the results of fertiliser experiments that have been made on the various crops in Great Britain; and from these they formulated a suitable national war-time fertiliser policy for the country.

Mitscherlich's work was extraordinarily stimulating and caused a veritable flood of controversy when it was first developed. His equation has been of great practical value though it is certainly not exact. Thus, the "Wirkungswert" for a particular nutrient is not a constant but depends somewhat on the other conditions of growth.[4] Further, the response curve is often sigmoid, fertiliser in excess decreases the crop yield, and the calculated maximum yield of the crop is sometimes far in excess of anything that can be obtained.

Other workers[5] have tried to improve on Mitscherlich's equation, and have had some success. But the interest in more exact equations has died down because the response of a crop to a fertiliser depends on many factors, such as the level of other nutrients present[6] and on the environmental conditions, so that no simple exact quantitative relation between the supply of a fertiliser and the crop response can exist.

The Interaction of Nutrients

The Law of the Minimum, namely, that the amount of plant growth is regulated by the factor present in minimum amount, and rises or falls according as this is increased or decreased in amount, implies that

[1] *Landw. Jahrb.*, 1923, **58**, 601.

[2] *Bodenkunde für Land- und Forstwirte*, Berlin, 1913, and subsequent editions.

[3] *Emp. J. Expt. Agric.*, 1941, **9**, 77. For another example, see O. W. Willcox, *Soil Sci.*, 1955, **79**, 467; 1956, **81**, 57; **82**, 287.

[4] See, for example, E. R. Bullen and W. J. Lessels, *J. Agric. Sci.*, 1957, **49**, 319.

[5] See, for example, B. Baule, *Landw. Jahrb.*, 1918, **51**, 363; 1920, **54**, 493; K. A. Bondorff, *Nord. JordbrForsk.*, 1923, **5**, 136; *Kgl. Vet. Landbohöjsk. Aarsskr.*, 1924, 293; E. A. Mitscherlich, *Ztschr. Pflanz. Düng.*, 1928, A **12**, 373; B. Balmukand, *J. Agric. Sci.*, 1928, **18**, 602.

[6] For a review of the work of plant physiologists on this subject, see F. G. Gregory, *Ann. Rev. Biochem.*, 1937, **6**, 557.

if two factors are limiting, or nearly limiting growth, adding only one of them will have little effect on growth, whilst adding both together will have a very considerable effect. Two such factors are said to have a large positive interaction in such circumstances, for the response of the crop to both together is larger than the sum of the responses to each separately. If the crop response to the two factors together equalled the sum of its responses to each separately, we would say the two factors showed no interaction, or worked entirely independently of each other; and if the response to the two factors together was less than the sum of the responses to each factor separately, they are said to have a negative interaction with each other.

Two examples can serve as illustrations of such joint effects. The first is taken from a series of fertiliser experiments made at Rothamsted between 1938 and 1945, in which the response of potatoes to farmyard manure, sulphate of ammonia, muriate of potash and superphosphate is determined in all possible combinations of these fertilisers. Table 16 shows some of these responses for the three years 1939, 1943 and 1945, in which the crop only gave a low yield in the absence of fertiliser and manure.

This table shows that in the absence of farmyard manure, potatoes give a bigger response to nitrogen if the potassium supply is adequate than if it is short, and, similarly, a bigger response to potassium if the nitrogen supply is adequate. Thus, in the example given there is a positive interaction between these two fertilisers: nitrogen in the absence of potassium increases the yield by 0·4 ton, potassium in the absence of nitrogen increases the yield by 2·5 tons, and if given together the yield is increased by 4·3 tons, which is 1·4 tons larger than the sum of the nitrogen alone and potassium alone responses (0·4+2·5=2·9 tons). On the other hand, provided adequate potassium was given, nitrogen gave an increase of between 1·8 and 1·9 tons per acre whether farmyard manure was given or not, whilst farmyard manure gave an increase of between 3·0 and 3·1 tons per acre whether nitrogen was given or not. These two materials thus act independently of each other, so that there is no interaction between them.[1] Potassium and farmyard manure provide an example of a negative interaction: in the presence of adequate nitrogen, potassium alone increases the yield by 3·9 tons per acre, and farmyard manure alone by 6·7 tons per acre, but the two together only increased it by 7·0 tons. Thus the response to potassium in the presence of the farmyard manure was only 0·3 ton, and the negative interaction between the two is 3·6 tons; in fact, in these experiments farmyard manure supplies all the potassium needed by the potatoes.

[1] For other examples of this, see E. M. Crowther and F. Yates, *Emp. J. Expt. Agric.*, 1941, **9**, 77; A. W. Oldershaw and H. V. Garner, *J. Roy. Agric. Soc.*, 1944, **105**, 98. For a possible explanation of this effect, see D. A. Boyd, *J. Agric. Sci.*, 1959, **52**, 384.

TABLE 16

Response of Potatoes to Nitrogen and Potassium[1]

Yield of potatoes in tons per acre

Fertiliser	No N No K	N, No K	No N, K	N, K
No farmyard manure . . .	4·0	4·4	6·5	8·3
With farmyard manure . . .	9·3	11·1	9·5	11·5
Response to farmyard manure . .	5·3	6·7	3·0	3·2

	Response to nitrogen		Response to potassium		N K Inter- action
	K absent	K present	N absent	N present	
No farmyard manure .	0·4	1·8	2·5	3·9	1·4
With farmyard manure.	1·8	1·9	0·2	0·3	0·1

	In presence of adequate potassium			
Response to	FYM alone 3·0	N alone 1·8	FYM+N 4·9	Interaction 0·1

	In presence of adequate nitrogen			
Response to . . .	FYM alone 6·7	K alone 3·9	FYM+K 7·0	Interaction −3·6

The second example illustrates the relationship between the water supply and the responsiveness of the crop to fertiliser, and in particular to nitrogen. C. von Seelhorst[2] at Göttingen made some pot experiments to establish this point over sixty years ago. The results of his experiment are given in Table 17, and they show that the oat crop could only respond to large dressings of nitrogen if the water supply was adequate.

This effect can be illustrated from some field experiments made by F. G. Gregory, F. Crowther and A. R. Lambert[3] in the Sudan. Table 18 shows that cotton can only make efficient use of a large supply of irrigation water if well manured with nitrogen, or, alternatively, that

[1] Dressings given:

	1939	1943 and 1945	
FYM	15	Mean of 8 and 16	tons per acre.
N	0·8	0·6	cwt. N per acre given as sulphate of ammonia.
K	1·33	0·83	cwt. K per acre given as muriate of potash.

[2] J. Landw., 1898, 46, 52.
[3] J. Agric. Sci., 1932, 22, 617. See also F. Crowther, Roy. Agric. Soc. Egypt, Tech. Bull. 24, 1936.

it can only make good use of a high nitrogen supply if there is an adequate supply of irrigation water available.

TABLE 17

Influence of Water Supply on the Effectiveness of Manures on the Growth of Oats

Dry weight of oat crop in grams per pot

Manuring	Nitrogen series			Increased crop for	
	KP	KP, N	KP, 2N	First increment of nitrogen	Second increment of nitrogen
I. Moist soil . . .	67·5	68·5	68·5	1·0	0·0
II. Moister soil . . .	83·6	93·4	94·0	9·8	0·6
III. Wettest soil . .	99·5	119·5	135·0	20·0	15·5

K=0·83 gm. of K as K_2CO_3 per pot; P=0·44 gm. of P as $Ca(H_2PO_4)_2$ per pot; N=5 gm. of N as $NaNO_3$ per pot.

Note.—The moist soil contained 14·35 per cent of water (41·6 per cent of saturation), the moister soil 15·41 per cent at the beginning, increasing to 18·43 (51·7 per cent of saturation) as the experiment proceeded, and the wettest soil 16·44 per cent at the beginning, increasing to 22·59 (63·7 per cent of saturation).

TABLE 18

Influence of Water and Nitrogen Supply on the Growth of Cotton

Yield of seed cotton in kantars per feddan[1]

Amount of sulphate of ammonia added	Rate of watering		
	Light	Medium	Heavy
None	1·38	1·54	1·58
300 lb. per acre	1·98	2·45	2·80
600 lb. per acre	2·28	3·04	3·79

There is a further aspect of the Law of the Minimum that may be extremely important when one is rectifying deficiencies. If crop growth is being severely limited by a few factors, and if, as is usual for most crops, one is interested in the yield of a part of the crop only, such as the grain for example, it will often happen that the maximum yield of this part of the crop is obtained by allowing the individual plants a large amount of space, so the root system of each plant can tap as large a volume of soil as possible. If one now rectifies the limiting deficiencies,

[1] 1 kantar per feddan=300 lb. per acre.

it may also be necessary to increase the number of plants per acre to get the maximum possible increase in yield from this amelioration, for the individual plants will now need less volume of soil from which to get their nutrients. Further, it may also be necessary to change the variety of the crop grown, for it often happens that the variety best adapted to poor conditions has not the potentiality to make really good use of a liberal supply of nutrients, whilst varieties that can make very good growth in optimum conditions may be relatively less satisfactory when growing in poor conditions.[1] Table 19, taken from some work of B. A. Krantz[2] on the manuring of maize in North Carolina, illustrates the need for increasing the number of plants per acre if one is to get the maximum benefit from a high level of nitrogen manuring. Incidentally, this closer spacing has the desirable consequence that it helps to suppress weed growth which otherwise becomes troublesome when generous fertiliser dressings are used with wide spacing.

TABLE 19

The Influence of the Number of Maize Plants per acre on their Response to a Nitrogen Fertiliser

Yield of grain in bushels per acre

Number of Plants per acre	Pounds of Nitrogen per acre			
	20	70	120	170
4,000	39	52	59	57
7,000	39	58	67	65
10,000	41	65	69	72
13,000	36	59	73	73

Least significant difference 8·3 bushels per acre.
Plant numbers obtained by using spacings of 37·4 in., 21·4 in., 15·0 in. and 11·5 in. in rows 42 in. apart.

An important group of interactions between nutrients concerns those between the different cations in the soil and in the plant tissue. It has already been stated (see p. 28) that the leaves of plants tend to have a fairly constant total cation concentration in their dry matter, dependent mainly on the type of plant and to a much less extent on the soil and manuring. One important function of these cations is that of osmotic pressure and pH regulation, and for this purpose the composition of the cations present is largely irrelevant. But the leaves can only function properly if they contain a certain minimum concentration of the essential cations potassium, magnesium, calcium and the trace elements.

[1] For an example of this effect with sugar-cane, see J. A. Potter, *Trop. Agric. Trin.*, 1947, 24, 94.
[2] *Better Crops with Plant Food*, 1947, No. 26.

Provided these minimal concentrations are exceeded, the relative concentrations of the different ions in the leaf are of little importance.[1]

The relative proportions of the cations in the leaf depend on the relative proportions of their available forms in the soil, a dependence that will be discussed in detail on p. 463. The point of immediate importance is that increasing the relative concentration of any one cation in the soil, as, for example, by adding a potassic fertiliser, will increase its concentration in the leaf, and in consequence decrease that of the other cations. If the plant is growing in a soil rather short of available magnesium, so that the magnesium concentration in the leaf is approaching the minimum required for healthy growth, then adding a potassium fertiliser may cause the magnesium concentration to fall below the minimum, so inducing a magnesium deficiency in the crop, which can be very severe if the crop growth is appreciably increased by the potassic fertiliser.[2] This phenomenon is sometimes called an ionic antagonism, and in this particular example one would say that the potassium was antagonistic to the magnesium. These potassium-induced magnesium deficiencies can often be seen on fruit trees and market-garden and glasshouse crops growing on soils low in exchangeable magnesium, for all these crops commonly receive generous dressings of potassic fertilisers. In the same way salt added to a sugar-beet crop may induce magnesium deficiency in the crop.[3] It is important to realise that this is no reason for not using a potassic fertiliser or salt, if the crop responds to either, but it is a very good reason for using in addition a magnesium fertiliser, such as a dolomitic limestone if the soil is rather acid, or otherwise magnesium sulphate.

Large dressings of lime may also induce magnesium or potassium deficiencies in the crop if the soil is low in either. These effects for potassium are, however, most noticeable for some crops on calcareous soils. Thus C. A. Bower and W. H. Pierre[4] found that maize and some of the sorghums, for example, need a fairly high level of potassium in their leaves compared with calcium and magnesium, so usually respond to potassic fertilisers even if the level of available potassium in the soil is fairly high. On the other hand, sweet clover and buckwheat need a much higher level of calcium compared with potassium in their leaves, so are much less responsive to potassic fertilisers on these soils, whilst flax, oats and soybeans came intermediate between these two groups.

[1] For a review and discussion of this, see F. J. Richards, *Ann. Rev. Biochem.*, 1944, **13**, 611. For an example with lucerne, see A. S. Hunter, S. J. Toth and F. E. Bear, *Soil Sci.*, 1943, **55**, 61.
[2] For an example with potatoes, see T. Walsh and T. F. O'Donohoe, *J. Agric. Sci.*, 1945, **35**, 254.
[3] J. B. Hale, M. A. Watson and R. Hull, *Ann. Appl. Biol.*, 1946, **33**, 13.
[4] *J. Amer. Soc. Agron.*, 1944, **36**, 608.

A further example is furnished by the manuring of lucerne on soils rather low in calcium. If one manures lucerne generously with a potassic fertiliser, it will take up potassium in preference to calcium, so the potassium content of the leaves will rise and their calcium content fall:[1] a tendency which may be undesirable for feeding purposes as a calcium-rich fodder is preferable to a potassium-rich one. Hence lucerne growing on a non-calcareous soil rather low in exchangeable calcium should be given small and frequent dressings of the potassic fertiliser rather than a single large one.

[1] For an example of this, see F. E. Bear and S. J. Toth, *Soil Sci.*, 1948, **65**, 69.

CHAPTER V

THE COMPOSITION OF THE SOIL

SOILS PREDOMINANTLY CONTAIN particles initially derived from the disintegration or decomposition of primary igneous rocks. But these particles may have been produced at an earlier geological period, moved by wind, water or ice over considerable distances, and been through one or more cycles of deposition and erosion. The processes that affect or alter these particles will be discussed in subsequent chapters, but one of the most fundamental is brought about by the plants that grow in the soil, for when the plants die they add to the soil energy-containing organic substances which they synthesised during their lifetime, and which serve as a food supply for a vast population of micro-organisms and even animals, which can in consequence inhabit the soil.

The soil mass is permeated with channels between the individual particles composing it, which are filled with water or air. The water, however, contains not only dissolved gases, but also some of the salts present.

Soils may, therefore, consist of four parts:

1. Mineral matter derived from the rocks, but more or less altered by decomposition or by the decomposition of the products of decomposition of other particles.

2. Calcium carbonate and phosphate and some resistant organic compounds derived from plants or organisms present at an earlier period.

3. Residues of plants and micro-organisms recently added to the soil.

4. The soil water, which is a solution of the various soluble and partially soluble salts present in the soil. Under temperate humid conditions this solution is dilute, but under some arid conditions, particularly in areas with poor drainage, it may become very concentrated. During dry periods such soils may contain appreciable quantities of soluble salts as crystals.

The soil has so far been pictured as consisting of a mass of particles, and this will be the aspect adopted in the rest of this chapter. But it must be realised that there is another aspect, of greater fundamental importance from the standpoint adopted in this book, namely, that of the soil as the medium for plant growth, and therefore as a medium for root development. From this aspect, the soil is a network of channels, filled with air and water and bounded by solid surfaces; and its fundamental properties depend on the geometry of this interconnected network, called the pore space, and on the behaviour of water in the pore space, on the properties of the bounding surfaces, and on the mechanisms which supply plant nutrients both to the water in these channels and also to the solid surfaces.

Suitable and fairly simple techniques have been devised, by W. Kubiena[1] in particular, for examining the soil directly under a microscope, which allows one to see something of its texture, that is, of the kind of particles and organic matter present, and something of its structure, that is, how these particles are distributed throughout the soil mass. Thus one can make a rough estimate of the amount of plant material in the soil and its degree of decomposition, the shape of the larger mineral particles and how they are arranged in the soil, and to some extent how the finer particles are distributed; and in particular one can recognise the two principal types of microstructure in a soil, that in which the sand grains are comparatively clean and the finer particles are present in diffuse clusters between them, and that in which the sand grains have the finer particles cemented on to their surface.

The mineral matter itself can be divided into two parts—particles possessing a definite crystal structure, and inorganic material that cannot be so described. The latter is composed of ill-defined precipitates of hydrated oxides of iron, aluminium, manganese and possibly silicon also; the former consist of crystals derived from the original rock, which tend to be the larger particles, and crystals formed from the products of weathering, which are usually the smaller particles. For these reasons mere chemical composition of the soil in bulk rarely gives information of much value: one wants to separate out the composition of the ill-defined deposits from the mineral grains and, as will be shown later, of the finer from the coarser mineral particles.

The Size Distribution of Soil Particles

Mere inspection of soil shows that it is composed of particles of different sizes and very irregular shapes possessing a greater or less tendency to stick together and form larger aggregates. These can be put into three groups, though the separation is not sharp or exact; clods and crumbs which are large and can be broken down by gentle mechanical means; granules, which are smaller, but in which the particles are more tenaciously held, so that some gentle chemical treatment is

[1] *Micropedology*, Ames, Iowa, 1938, *ForschDienst. Sonderh.*, 1942, **16**, 91, for technique, and *Soil Res.*, 1935, **4**, 380, for results. See also G. A. Bourbeau and K. C. Berger, *Proc. Soil Sci. Soc. Amer.*, 1948, **12**, 409.

necessary to separate them; and concretions in which the fine material is bound still more firmly by a cement containing inorganic colloids. The power of forming clods and crumbs resides partly in the organic matter and partly in the mineral particles of smallest size, of which a relatively small percentage suffices.

The process of separating a soil into its component particles, and then estimating the proportion of particles in the various size ranges is usually referred to as Mechanical Analysis, and the methods for doing this are now fairly standardised.[1] The first step is to crush the clods carefully so as much of the soil as possible will go through a 2 mm. sieve, leaving only stones on the sieves. This operation introduces an arbitrary element into the results for those soils which contain rather soft, porous concretionary material, for the harder one crushes the soil the more the concretions are broken down into finer particles. Examples of such materials are firstly chalk, weathered limestone and even sometimes weathered granite, and secondly the presence of inorganic cements weakly binding soil particles together, such as hydrated iron oxides or calcium carbonate. The basic trouble here is that no definite meaning can be given to the phrase "the individual soil particles", but the harder these concretions, the more each can be treated as a separate particle.

The second stage is the dispersion of the crumbs passing the 2 mm. sieve into their constituent particles. This can sometimes be done by violent mechanical agitation in water, but it more generally involves chemical treatment of the soil. Most standard methods oxidise the organic matter by boiling with hydrogen peroxide, or treating with sodium hypobromite,[2] remove calcium carbonate by leaching with hydrochloric acid, and then disperse the soil by shaking in a dilute solution of ammonia or sodium hydroxide. However, innumerable variations in detail have been in use from time to time. As with crushing the soil through a sieve, so again here the methods introduce arbitrary elements into the analytical results, for the greater the amount of organic matter or calcium carbonate that the soil contains, the greater is the proportion of soil material that is being discarded from the analysis, and the greater is the amount of insoluble material from the calcium carbonate and organic matter left behind in the soil.

The next problem in mechanical analysis is to find methods for specifying the size distribution of the soil particles. Since they have

---

[1] For the method in use in Great Britain see G. W. Robinson, *Imp. Bur. Soil Sci.*, *Tech. Comm.* 26, 1933; in America see V. J. Kilmer and L. T. Alexander, *Soil Sci.*, 1949, **68**, 15. For discussions on the whole methodology see *Symposium on Particle Size Analysis*, Supplement to *Trans. Inst. Chem. Eng.*, 1947, and *The Physics of Particle Size Analysis*, Supplement 3, *Brit. J. Appl. Phys.*, 1954.

[2] See E. Troell, *J. Agric. Sci.*, 1931, **21**, 476, and S. J. Bourget and C. B. Tanner, *Canad. J. Agric. Sci.*, 1953, **33**, 579.

irregular shapes, their size cannot be described adequately by any one single measurement, though both their mass and their volume are theoretically definable, except possibly for the smallest particles which absorb a certain amount of any gas or liquid which comes in contact with their surfaces. There are, however, no methods for determining either the mass or volume distribution of the particles, so less direct size properties must be used. In practice the property of the larger particles that is selected to specify their size is the ability to pass, or be retained by, standard sieves, and the property of the smaller particles their velocity of sedimentation in a vertical column of water at a standard temperature, usually 20° C. But since it is difficult to think of particle sizes in terms of their settling velocities, these are usually converted into the diameter of a sphere of density 2·6 that would have this settling velocity, making use of Stokes' equation

$$v = \frac{g\ (\sigma - \rho)}{18\ \eta}\ d^2$$

where v is the settling velocity in cm. per sec., g is the acceleration due to gravity (about 980 cm. per sec²), σ is the density of the settling particle and ρ of the water ($\sigma - \rho$ is taken as 1·6), and η is the viscosity of water (about 0·010 at 20° C) and d is the diameter of the sphere, commonly called the equivalent diameter of the soil particle. The fact that many particles have a density different from 2·6 is no more disturbing to the use of this "equivalent diameter" than the fact that they are not spherical.

The particle sizes are classified into a few conventional groups whose limits, on a few of the scales that have been used, are given in Table 20. On the present International or Atterberg scale, a soil is divided into gravel, which is retained on the 2 mm. sieve, and fine earth which passes; and this in turn is separated into coarse sand, fine sand, silt and clay, the upper size limit for each of the first three functions being ten times the lower. On the present American system, the sands are divided into five classes, the lower limit being 0·05 instead of 0·02 mm. but the same upper limit for clay is used, so American silt is from 50 to 2 μ[1] instead of from 20 to 2 μ. For many purposes the American definitions of silt and sands are being found preferable to the International ones. The upper limit of 2 μ for the clay particles was probably chosen for practical convenience—particles of this size settle 10 cm. in 8 hours— but it has reasonable justification because the properties of silt differ markedly from clay, and two microns represents the approximate upper limit of clay properties. But the coarser clay particles, from 2 μ down to 0·5 or 0·2 μ, have the clay properties only weakly developed and

[1] 1 μ=micron or 10^{-3} mm.

TABLE 20

Names and Sizes of Fractions obtained by Mechanical Analysis of Soils in Different Countries

Older British (replaced 1928)		International (based on Atterberg)[1]		American (Bureau of Soils)[2]		British Civil Engineers[3]	
Name of Fraction	Limits of Diameter of Particles mm.	Name of Fraction	Limits of Diameter of Particles mm.	Name of Fraction	Limits of Diameter of Particles mm.	Name of Fraction	Limits of Diameter of Particles mm.
Fine gravel .	3–1	Gravel (Kies)	above 2	Very coarse sand .	2–1	Coarse sand	2–0·6
Coarse sand	1–0·2	Coarse sand	2·0–0·2	Coarse sand	1–0·5	Medium sand .	0·6–0·2
				Medium sand .	0·5–0·25		
Fine sand .	0·2–0·04	Fine sand . (Mo.)	0·2–0·02	Fine sand .	0·25–0·10	Fine sand .	0·2–0·06
				Very fine sand .	0·10–0·05		
Silt . .	0·04–0·01	Silt . (Schluff, Staub Limon)	0·02–0·002	Silt . .	0·05–0·002	Coarse silt .	0·06– 0·02
						Medium silt	0·02– 0·006
						Fine silt	0·006–0·002
Clay .	below 0·002[4]	Clay . . (Ton, Schlamm, Argile)	below 0·002	Clay . .	below 0·002	Clay . .	below 0·002

typically contain many silt-like particles, so it would probably be desirable to subdivide the clay somewhere between 0·5 and 0·2 μ. Unfortunately there is no international agreement on the definition of clay, and the Dutch workers often use 16 μ for the upper limit, and others 5 μ, and it is not always stated what definition is being used.

The coarse sand, on the International method, and all the sand fractions on the American method, are separated from the finer particles on standard sieves; and the finer particles are separated by sedimentation in water, either by measuring the density of the suspension at a given depth by a hydrometer[5] or by taking samples of the suspension with a pipette from a standard depth after standing for definite periods.[6] This pipette technique can be refined so very shallow sampling depths can be used, which allows a ready functionation of the clay, certainly to 0·5 and perhaps to 0·2 μ.[7] Table 21 gives examples of results obtained

[1] *Int. Mitt. Bodenk.*, 1912, **2**, 312. The international method is described in *Imp. Bureau Soil Sci., Tech. Comm.* 26, 1933.

[2] *Soil Survey Manual*, U.S. Dept. Agric. Handb. 18, 1951, and V. J. Kilmer and L. T. Alexander, *Soil Sci.*, 1949, **68**, 15.

[3] *Soil Mechanics for Road Engineers*, D.S.I.R. Road Research Lab., 1952.

[4] Probably smaller: the calculated value for the upper limit is 0·0014 mm.

[5] G. J. Bouyoucos, *Soil Sci.*, 1927, **23**, 343; 1928, **25**, 365; 1932, **33**, 21; R. G. Downes, *Aust. J. Counc. Sci. Indust. Res.*, 1944, **17**, 197; I. A. Black, *J. Soil Sci.*, 1951, **2**, 118; P. R. Day, *Soil Sci.*, 1950, **70**, 362, and 1953, **75**, 181.

[6] For a discussion on the accuracy of this method see M. Köhn, *Landw. Jahrb.*, 1928, **67**, 485.

[7] A. N. and B. R. Puri, *J. Agric. Sci.*, 1941, **31**, 171; E. W. Russell, *J. Agric. Sci.*, 1943, **33**, 147.

by these methods, where the size of the clay particles is expressed in terms of the negative logarithm of the observed settling velocity in cm. per sec. ($pv = -\log_{10} v$), as well as of the conventional equivalent diameter.

TABLE 21

An Extended Mechanical Analysis of some Clay Soils

	Sand	Silt	Clay	per cent of the clay present in the fraction		
				pv 3·5–4·5 d 1·9–0·6 μ	4·5–5·5 0·6–0·19 μ	<5·5 >0·19 μ
Sudan Gezira . .	16·6	14·1	54·9	9·6	9·1	81·2
Malayan Rubber Soils—						
Clay type . .	10·1	5·0	81·0	6·5	62·1	31·4
Silt type . . .	10·2	27·0	62·0	30·3	44·8	24·8
English Soils—						
Oxford Clay . .	15·6	31·3	47·7	16·7	17·4	66·0
Weald Clay . .	18·3	33·5	48·3	13·5	37·9	48·6
Hereford fruit .	23·7	38·5	31·2	32·0	23·1	44·9

The distribution of particles finer than about 0·2 μ cannot be made by sedimentation under gravity, because such particles diffuse slowly from the part of the suspension where they are concentrated to that part where they are more dilute, due to their Brownian motion. They are therefore diffusing against the direction of settling, and this blurs the sharpness of the separation between different particle sizes. But this complication becomes less important as the gravitational field is increased, so sedimentation in a centrifugal field must be used for finer fractionation.[1]

Fuller information about the size distribution of soil particles would be given by continuous distribution curves instead of a discrete number of fractions, and methods for obtaining such curves have been devised, but unfortunately most methods contain inherent errors and there is no satisfactory method available for obtaining such curves.[2] But for agricultural purposes accurate mechanical analyses have not proved of great value, nor does there seem to be any demand for continuous distribution curves, so little attention has been given to this problem in recent years.

[1] For methods, see C. E. Marshall, *Proc. Roy. Soc.*, 1930, **126** A, 427, and *Proc. Soil Sci. Amer.*, 1939, **4**, 100; and C. Brown, *J. Phys. Chem.*, 1944, **48**, 246.

[2] For a discussion of the older work see B. A. Keen, *Physical Properties of Soils*, London, 1931; and for the more modern, two symposia arranged by the Institute of Chemical Engineers in 1947 and the Institute of Physics in 1954.

Soil Texture

This phrase unfortunately is given different definitions by different people, no less than three different concepts being muddled up in it. Soil texture should be reserved for describing the size distribution of particles in the soil, and such phrases as fine-textured and coarse-textured soils are allowable with this definition. But texture has often been confused with the consistency properties of the soil, which will be discussed on pp. 132–4, and in this sense the terms light and heavy are often used. These words had nothing to do with the density of the soil but with the power required to plough the soil, and it was measured by the number of horses that had to be yoked to the plough. Thus light land would be described as one-horse and heavy land as four-horse land. This property is therefore a measure of the cohesion between the soil particles, and although this is very dependant on the particle size distribution in the soil, it is also dependant on the kind of particles present. The third use of soil texture, in place of soil structure, which

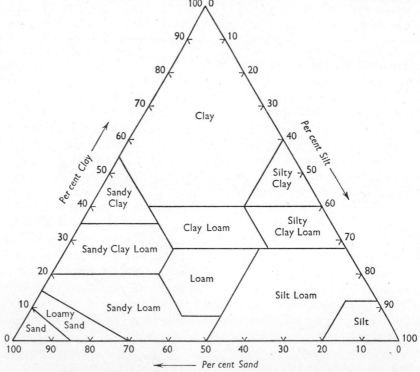

Fig. 5. The composition of the textural classes of soils used by the United States Soil Survey. (Sand 2–0·05 mm., silt 0·05–0·002 mm., clay below 0·002 mm.)

is to be discussed in Chapter XXIII, has no justification whatever.

Soils are grouped into a definite number of textural classes, such as sands, silts, loams and clays, the name of the textural class being that of the mechanical analysis fraction, or textural fraction as it is usually called, whose properties dominate the soil properties, except that loams are soils in which no one fraction dominates. As an example of such a classification Fig. 5 gives the one in use by the United States Soil Survey.[1] An experienced field surveyor can grade soils into these classes simply by feeling the soil when wet between his fingers. For clarity of language it is most desirable that these words be used correctly, and that a mixed phrase such as heavy loam be not used synonymously with clay loam for example; for a heavy loam should mean a loam soil of heavy consistency. If this distinction is borne in mind, much of the confusion that exists on whether one should use mechanical analysis or the "feel" of the soil for textural descriptions will disappear, because two different properties are being measured.

The Mineralogical Composition of the Soil Particles

SAND AND SILT FRACTIONS

These particles can be divided into two main groups: crystalline mineral particles derived from primary rock and rock fragments; and micro-crystalline aggregates or amorphous deposits composed, for example, of calcium carbonate, ferric or aluminium hydroxides, or silica, which have been formed either from products of weathering or from residues of plant and animal life. There may also be present some crystals such as calcite, and possibly quartz, formed in the soil itself, perhaps crystals of some other minerals formed during the weathering process, and perhaps non-crystalline or poorly crystalline residues of the weathering of rock minerals, such as vermiculite.

The principal minerals found in the silt and sand fraction of the soil[2] are:

1. Quartz.
2. Felspars.
   (a) Microcline and orthoclase[3] $KAlSi_3O_8$, which are potash felspars. Both are resistant to weathering, microcline being the more resistant.
   (b) Plagioclase, a series of mixed crystals having albite or soda felspar $NaAlSi_3O_8$ and anorthite or calcium felspar

[1] *U.S. Dept. Agric. Handb.*, 18, 1951.
[2] For details, see for example H. B. Milner, *Sedimentary Petrography*, 3rd ed., London, 1936; A. N. Winchell, *Elements of Optical Mineralogy*, 5th ed., New York, 1937.
[3] The following formulae are given only to show the type of constitution. The composition of actual specimens may differ considerably from the type formula.

$CaAl_2Si_2O_8$ as end members. The sodium-rich members are about as resistant to weathering as orthoclase, whilst the calcium-rich members weather more easily.

3. Micas.

   (a) Containing no divalent metals: muscovite, a potassium aluminium silicate, $H_2KAl_3(SiO_4)_3$, which is fairly stable.

   (b) Containing divalent metals: biotite, a potassium magnesium iron aluminium silicate not very resistant to decomposition. No true micas containing calcium are known, and soda mica is very rare.

   (c) Glauconite: a potassium mica, relatively low in aluminium but high in ferric iron and containing some magnesium and ferrous iron.[1]

4. The Ferromagnesian Minerals, which are low in aluminium and are divided into the pyroxenes $(Mg, Fe)SiO_3$, the amphiboles $(Mg\ Fe)_7(Si_4O_{11})_2(OH)_2$ and the olivines $(Mg\ Fe)_2SiO_4$, where $(Mg\ Fe)$ refers to one ion only. Magnesium and ferrous iron are completely interchangeable in these minerals, and in general there is a certain amount of replacement of either by calcium; whilst in the amphiboles and particularly in hornblende, sodium, potassium, calcium and aluminium may all be replacing part of the magnesium or iron, and aluminium may replace part of the silicon. These minerals are usually not very resistant to decomposition.

5. Various minerals, such as zircon, garnet, apatite (see p. 476), ilmenite $FeTiO_3$, the iron oxides haematite Fe_2O_3, and magnetite Fe_3O_4, and the hydrated oxide limonite $FeO(OH).xH_2O$.

Igneous or primary rocks are composed of these minerals, and Table 22 gives a rough classification of the principal rocks and their mineral constitution.

6. Certain clay minerals which may be present in large particles, such as vermiculites and chlorites, occur in the sand fractions of some soils derived from certain basic igneous rocks. Kaolins are also often present in the silt fraction of soils, particularly if derived from granites. These clay minerals may be cemented by hydrous iron or aluminium oxides or dehydrated iron oxides.[2]

Quartz is by far the commonest mineral in most soils, and also the most resistant to decomposition. In soils derived from sedimentary deposits it often makes up 90 to 95 per cent of all the sand and silt

[1] S. B. Hendricks and C. S. Ross, *Amer. Mineral.*, 1941, **26**, 683.
[2] J. S. Hosking, M. E. Neilson and A. R. Carthew (*Aust. J. Agric. Res.*, 1957, **8**, 45) give examples of these, and see also a series of papers by D. M. McAleese and co-workers, *J. Soil Sci.*, 1957, **8**, 135; 1958, **9**, 66, 81, 289.

particles.[1] Soils directly derived from primary rock contain much less, the actual quantity depending on the quartz content of the rock itself and the amount of weathering it has been subjected to. J. Hendrick and G. Newlands[2] have, for example, found some Aberdeenshire soils derived from a basic igneous olivine-gabbro which are practically quartz-free, and the other soils in their paper illustrate the rapid rise in quartz content to over 70 per cent if the soil has been derived from rock which has already been subjected to weathering. Table 23, which is taken from some results of R. P. Humbert and C. E. Marshall,[3] illustrates this effect by giving the distribution of quartz and felspar in the sand and silt fraction down the profile of a soil derived from granite.

TABLE 22

The Mineral Constitution of the Principal Igneous Rocks

Size of mineral crystals			Constitution					
Coarse	Medium	Fine	Quartz	Alkali felspars	Plagio-clases	Micas	Pyroxenes Amphi-boles	Olivines
Granite	Quartz porphyry } Felsite	Rhyolite	×	×	+	+	O	—
Syenite	Microsyenite	Trachyte	O	×	O	+	O	—
Diorite	Microdiorite	Andesite	O	+	×	+	×	—
Gabbro	Dolerite (diabase)	Basalt	—	—	×	—	×	+
Peridotite } Serpentine }		Picrite-basalt	—	—	O	—	+	×

× plentiful   + less plentiful   O rare   — absent

TABLE 23

Distribution of Quartz and Felspar in the Sand and Silt Fraction of a Soil derived from Granite

Depth in inches . .	0–4	4–10	10–18	18–24	Rotten Rock	Un-weathered Rock
Quartz in fraction (%) .	50	45	30	25	25	32
Felspar in fraction (%) .	28	30	27	36	65	50

[1] This is in marked contrast with the content in the average parent rock material, which according to F. W. Clarke is:

	per cent
Felspars	60
Amphiboles and Pyroxene	17
Quartz	12
Micas	4
Other minerals	7
	100

(analyses of 700 igneous rocks)

He further estimates that the lithosphere is composed of 95 per cent igneous rocks and 5 per cent sediments down to a depth of half a mile (*U.S. Geol. Surv. Bull.* 770, 1924).

[2] *J. Agric. Sci.*, 1923, **13**, 151.   [3] *Missouri Agric. Expt. Sta., Res. Bull.* 359, 1943.

THE CLAY FRACTION

The clay fraction is typically differentiated mineralogically from the silt fraction by being composed predominantly of minerals which are formed as products of weathering and which are not found in un-weathered rocks. These minerals rarely ever occur in particles larger than 2 μ, and are usually present as particles smaller than this. They are much more resistant to weathering in the soil than are rock minerals ground to a comparable particle size, and they comprise the particles that carry the physical and chemical properties characteristic of clays.

The coarser clay fractions, particularly those larger than 0·5 μ in diameter, may contain appreciable proportions of quartz and some-times of mica, but the fractions finer than 0·1 μ are almost entirely clay minerals or other products of weathering, such as hydrated ferric, aluminium, titanium, manganese and silicon oxides.

The great difficulties in making a mineralogical analysis of clay particles are that X-ray photographs cannot be taken of single crystals as they are too small. The advances in our knowledge of the con-stitution of clays, and in methods available for distinguishing between various clays in a mixture have come about through developing ways of forming oriented flakes of clay particles, and treating these with various reagents, such as glycol, whose molecules will take up standard positions between the individual crystals of some clays.[1] Other types of method are also available. These minerals are all hydrated and lose their water at different temperatures, hence they can to some extent be differentiated by their dehydration curves. The energy change in-volved as this water is lost, and other changes which occur in the clay mineral, are most marked in certain critical temperature ranges, which are characteristic for different minerals. Again, some clay mineral particles have characteristic shapes: they may be flat with sharp edges, or have blurred edges, or be rod-shaped, and these can be determined by photographing the particles in the electron microscope.

The result of all this work has been to show that for many soils the clay particles do not all belong to one definite and clearly defined class; they appear either to be a mixture of particles belonging to different mineralogical groups, or even for each particle itself to be a mixture of groups. The main minerals present are kaolinites, illites and hydrous micas, montmorillonites and vermiculites; but because the soil clay particles are usually poorly crystallised, much work has been done on the simpler type minerals, which are only found in the pure state in

---

[1] For an account of these and other methods for recognising and distinguishing between the different clay minerals see *X-ray Identification and Crystal Structures of Clay Minerals*, ed. by G. W. Brindley, London, 1951, and *Differential Thermal Analysis of Clay Minerals*, ed. by R. C. Mackenzie, London, 1955.

certain very restricted localities. For this reason the composition and properties of these type minerals will be discussed in the next chapter.

OTHER INORGANIC COMPONENTS OF SOILS

The soil contains other material beside the definite mineral particles. The main additional component is organic matter, which will be considered later. But there is also present other inorganic material of very indefinite composition. If one examines the sand grains of many soils under a microscope, their surfaces are seen to be coated with an opaque layer, or to have opaque spots on their surface, and these will often persist after all organic matter has been oxidised. This surface matter can be dissolved in suitable acids, and it is found to contain oxides of aluminium, iron and silicon, which may be hydrated.

The difficulty in determining the amount of these non-clay mineral constituents, which are often amorphous, is in finding a reagent which dissolves these without at the same time attacking the clay particles, for no reagent is yet available which will disperse them from the soil. The methods that have had most success involve either reducing the ferric oxides to ferrous ions, or forming iron and aluminium chelate compounds with oxalates, or combining the two using reducing agents in the presence of tartrates or citrates. Initially hydrogen sulphide was used as the reducing agent,[1] but now either nascent hydrogen produced by the action of oxalic acid on magnesium ribbon[2] or sodium hydrosulphide or dithionate ($Na_2S_2O_4$) are used.[3] O. Tamm[4] first introduced oxalates for removing iron—he found a sodium or ammonium oxalate and oxalic acid mixture of pH 3·25 seemed satisfactory, and R. K. Schofield[5] showed the efficiency of this method could be improved if the extraction was made in sunlight. All these methods are liable to decompose some of the iron silicates, for some of the micro-crystalline iron concretions seem to be more resistant than iron silicates to these solvents.

The form in which aluminium and ferric hydrated oxides occur in soils is not always known. Aluminium can occur as the hydroxide $Al(OH)_3$, either as an amorphous precipitate or as micro-crystals of gibbsite, and it also occurs as micro-crystals of diaspore and boehmite $AlO(OH)$. Iron does not occur as the hydroxide $Fe(OH)_3$, the

[1] E. Truog and M. Drosdoff, *J. Amer. Soc. Agron.*, 1935, **27**, 312, and *Soil Sci.*, 1935, **39**, 463.
[2] C. D. Jeffries, *Proc. Soil Sci. Soc. Amer.*, 1945, **11**, 211, and C. H. Williams, *Aust. J. Agric. Res.*, 1950, **1**, 156.
[3] B. C. Deb, *J. Soil Sci.*, 1950, **1**, 212; R. C. Mackenzie, *J. Soil Sci.*, 1954, **5**, 167, and with B. D. Mitchell, *Soil Sci.*, 1954, **77**, 173; N. H. Aguilera and M. L. Jackson, *Proc. Soil Sci. Soc. Amer.*, 1953, **17**, 359.
[4] *Medd. Skogsförsöksanst.*, 1922, **19**, 385, and 1934, **27**, 1.
[5] *J. Soil Sci.*, 1949, **1**, 1.

hydrated forms usually correspond approximately to $FeO(OH)$ and may be present as amorphous limonite and cold precipitated ferric hydroxide, or as micro-crystals of goethite and lepidocrocite, which correspond in crystal structure to diaspore and boehmite respectively. But iron also occurs as the unhydrated oxides Fe_2O_3, known as haematite and maghemite respectively if micro-crystalline, and also as magnetite Fe_3O_4, but this almost certainly is a rock mineral only. The maghemite is the constituent which gives soils their magnetic susceptibility and seems to be formed only in the humus horizons of some soils.[1] The aluminium hydrated oxides are white, the ferric coloured: goethite varies in colour from yellow through brown to red, possibly depending on its state of sub-division, lepidocrocite is usually orange, haematite red and maghemite light brown; and it is likely that it is these compounds, together with organic matter, that give soils their characteristic colours, for when they are removed all soils are white to grey in colour. Maghemite is probably derived from lepidocrocite by dehydration, and lepidocrocite may be the characteristic hydrated oxide formed from the oxidation of ferrous iron in the presence of organic matter,[2] and if this is so, the presence of lepidocrocite or maghemite in a soil is sufficient to prove that at one time ferrous iron and organic matter were present together.

Hydrated aluminium oxide can also form solid solutions in hydrated silica gels, and these are sometimes known as allophane. This is typically the first weathering product of some types of volcanic ash or pumice, and its presence in a soil is good evidence for the presence of ash in the soil. Allophane is naturally an indefinite material, and its properties depend on the intimacy with which the two hydrated oxides are intermixed.[3] In immature soils allophane can have a very high moisture content, possibly because of the original ash being very porous, but it shrinks and dries out irreversibly. As the soil ages allophane becomes more crystalline and eventually becomes the crystalline clay mineral kaolin.[4]

Silica can also occur in amorphous forms, both as a consequence of weathering and as a product of vegetation. Under some conditions, which do not seem to have been investigated in detail, silica can be deposited between soil particles to give a "silica" pan (see p. 591) as happens in some sandstones, in which silica binds the sand particles together. Also all plants contain some silica, which is returned to the

[1] S. Henin and E. Le Borgne, *Ann. Agron.*, 1955, **5**, 11.

[2] H. W. van der Marel, *J. Sediment. Petrol.* 1951, **21**, 12, S. Henin and E. Le Borgne, *Proc. 5th Int. Congr. Soil Sci.*, Leopoldville, 1954, **2**, 13.

[3] See, for example, M. Fieldes, *N.Z. J. Sci. Tech.*, 1956, B **37**, 336, and K. S. Birrell and M. Fieldes, *J. Soil Sci.*, 1952, **3**, 156.

[4] T. Tamura and M. L. Jackson (*Science*, 1953, **117**, 381) suggest details of how this process takes place.

soil as the plant dies. Grasses in particular contain appreciable amounts, often in the form of particles of opal which can be clearly seen using a low power microscope, and these particles can be found in grassland soils,[1] and probably also in tropical grassland and savannah soils subjected to regular firing.

It is likely that the hydrated iron oxides are often present as mixtures with silica, for whenever an iron solvent is used to remove iron, silica is set free also. Kubiena[2], using his thin-section technique, has shown that iron oxides can exist in two forms in the soil: they may be de-flocculated or peptised sols dispersed in silica gels, in which case the solid solution is translucent and has a pale yellow colour, or they may be dense flocculated aggregates which are opaque.

[1] F. Smithson, *J. Soil Sci.*, 1958, **9**, 148.
[2] See his book, *The Soils of Europe*, London 1953, for coloured illustrations showing this.

CHAPTER VI

THE CONSTITUTION OF CLAY MINERALS

THE CLAY MINERALS occurring in the soil are built out of sheets, or layers, of oxygen ions, and so belong to the class of layer-lattice minerals.[1] Three types of layer lattices have been recognised in clay minerals, namely, the kaolin, the micaceous and the chlorite. An amphibole type of chain lattice also occurs in the clay minerals sepiolite and palygorskite or attapulgite.

All clay minerals are built out of two definite building units, namely, four oxygens at the corners of a tetrahedron usually with a silicon ion in the centre, and six oxygens or hydroxyls at the corners of an octahedron, typically with an aluminium or magnesium at the centre. The silicon is thus in 4-coordination, and the aluminium and magnesium in 6-coordination.

The silicon-oxygen tetrahedra in the layer-lattice are bound together by three of the oxygens of each tetrahedron being linked to a second silicon atom. Each tetrahedron is thus linked to three others in such a way that three out of the four oxygens in each tetrahedron lie in a plane in hexagonal packing as shown in Plate III. This sheet has the unit composition $2(Si + O + \frac{3}{2}O) = Si_2O_5^{--}$, hence carries one negative charge per silicon ion, for each silicon ion is attached to one oxygen ion out of the plane and to three shared ions in the plane. The octahedral units are linked together as in the minerals gibbsite $Al(OH)_3$ and brucite $Mg(OH)_2$ by forming two layers of hydroxyl ions in closest packing. Between these two layers are the octahedral holes, each of which contains a magnesium ion in brucite, but only two-thirds contain an aluminium in gibbsite, as shown in Plate III. This double sheet is thus electrically neutral for each mineral. Further, it can be seen that in brucite every hydroxyl touches three magnesium ions, whilst in gibbsite, owing to the empty holes, each hydroxyl usually only touches two aluminium.

Clay minerals of the kaolin group consist of sheets each built out of a silicon-oxygen layer in open hexagonal packing and a gibbsite layer fused with it so that the tetrahedral oxygens lying out of the main plane form part of one layer of the gibbsite structure. Thus minerals of this type consist of three layers: a layer of oxygens in open hexagonal

[1] For reviews of this subject with many photographs of the structure of clay crystals, see *X-ray Identification and Crystal Structure of Clay Minerals*, ed. G. W. Brindley, London, 1951, and R. E. Grim, *Clay Mineralogy*, New York, 1953.

packing, a layer of oxygens and hydroxyls in close packing, and a layer of hydroxyls in close packing. But the open hexagonal layer can only lie on the close-packed layer if the oxygens are smaller than the hydroxyls, and in the ideal case, as shown in the unit cell in Plate III, in the ratio of $\sqrt{3}$ to 2. The structural formula for this unit cell of kaolin is therefore $6O(4Si)4O + 2OH(4Al)6OH$, the Si and Al being put in brackets to show they occur in the spaces between the oxygen or hydroxyl ions. The composition of the unit cell is $Si_4 Al_4 O_{10} (OH)_8$ and the sheet is unsymmetrical, electrically neutral, and 7·2 Å.[1] thick.

Clay minerals of the micaceous type consist of a gibbsite or brucite layer fused with two silicon-oxygen layers, one on either side, as is shown in Plate III. A unit sheet of these minerals therefore consists of four oxygen layers, the first being the one in hexagonal packing, then two in close packing, in which two-thirds of the ions in each layer are oxygen and one-third hydroxyl ions, and finally another silicon-oxygen layer. The unit cell has the structural formula

$$6O(4Si)4O + 2OH (4Al \text{ or } 6Mg) 4O + 2OH (4Si) 6O$$

and the composition $Si_8(Al_4 \text{ or } Mg_6)O_{20}(OH)_4$. This sheet is symmetrical, electrically neutral, and 9·3 Å. thick; and the type minerals having these structures are the micas pyrophyllite (with aluminium) and talc (with magnesium). The former, having two ions per three octahedral holes are often known as dioctahedral micas: the latter, with all three holes filled, as trioctahedral.

Clay minerals of the chlorite type are composed of alternate sheets of brucite and talc.

The Structure of the Kaolin Clay Minerals

Two factors are needed to describe the way the sheets are piled one on top of the other. One is the distance between similar layers in adjacent sheets—the basal spacing of the structure; and the other is the relative positions of the oxygen atoms in corresponding layers of adjacent sheets, for, given the basal spacing, one can still displace or rotate one sheet relative to its neighbour. In the kaolin mineral kaolinite, adjacent sheets take up fixed positions, so that the crystal has three-dimensional symmetry, although the symmetry in the plane perpendicular to the basal spacing is low. In these minerals adjacent sheets are held together by hydrogen bonds; for if a hydroxyl layer of one sheet lies close enough, and in the right relative position to the hexagonal oxygen layer of its neighbour, hydrogen bonds will develop between the hydroxyl and the contiguous oxygen ions, allowing

[1] Å. (Angstrom unit) $= 10^{-8}$ cm.

crystals to be built up in the form of hexagonal plates, which may be as large as 1 μ in size if the mineral is well crystallised, as shown in Plate III.

There are two other kaolin clay minerals found in the soil which differ from kaolinite by not having the regularity of packing of the sheets that kaolinite has. The one with the most disordered packing is halloysite, which contains a mono-molecular water layer between adjacent sheets, there being four water molecules per unit cell, and these molecules form hydrogen bonds with the oxygens of one sheet and with the hydroxyls of the other. The particles of halloysite are usually not flat but tubular, having an outer diameter between 400 and 2000 Å. and a wall thickness of about 200 Å.[1] The cause of this curvature may be that the gibbsite hydroxyls by themselves have a closer packing than is forced on them by the silicon-oxygen layer, for a unit cell of gibbsite has a side of 8·62 Å., but in kaolinite its cell is 8·93 Å. so the hydroxyl layer of a kaolin may tend to contract. This buckling presumably does not happen in kaolinite because of the hydrogen bonds between the gibbsite and the adjacent silicon-oxygen layer, whilst with halloysite the hydrogen bonding is through mobile water molecules.

The other kaolin mineral is sometimes known as the "fireclay" mineral and differs from kaolinite in having a less well-ordered stacking of the sheets, and in having particles with a much less definite shape, whose edges appear blurred and diffuse in electron microscope photographs. It also contains some water, whereas kaolinite does not, and it may consist of halloysite sheets interleaved between sheets of kaolinite.[2]

Isomorphous Replacement

The structure of clay mineral sheets is dominated by the packing of the oxygen and hydroxyls ions in their layers, for the metallic cations merely fit in the spaces between them. Now the radius of the largest sphere that can just fit in the tetrahedral hole between four spheres of radius r is 0·225 r. The radius of an oxygen ion depends on its packing, but when in 4-coordination is 1·29 Å., so the radius of a cation which can just fit into such a hole would be 0·29 Å. A silicon ion is in fact slightly larger than this, so some asymmetry must be introduced into this simple picture.

The radius of the largest sphere that can fit into an octahedral hole, when the six spheres are just touching is 0·412 r, or taking the radius of these oxygens as 1·40 Å., it is 0·61 Å. Table 24 gives estimated values of the ionic radii of a number of cations when in 6-coordination, and

[1] T. F. Bates, F. A. Hildebrand and A. Swineford, *Amer. Mineral.*, 1950, **35**, 463.
[2] For an account of these, see L. Bramao, J. G. Cady, *et al.*, *Soil Sci.*, 1952, **73**, 273.

it is seen that only the aluminium ions will fit into them, all the other ions given in the table being too large. Hence if all the octahedral ions are magnesium, as in talc, these two close-packed layers of oxygens and hydroxyls will not quite touch.

TABLE 24

The Radii in Å. of Certain Ions in 6-coordination[1]

4+		3+		2+		1+	
V	0·63	Al	0·51	Mg	0·66	Li	0·68
Ti	0·68	Cr	0·63	Ni	0·69	Cu	0·96
		Co	0·63	Cu	0·72	Na	0·97
		Fe	0·64	Co	0·73	K	1·33
		Mn	0·66	Fe	0·74	NH₄	1·48
				Mn	0·80		
				Ca	0·99		

The chemical composition of actual kaolin soil clay minerals agrees very closely with the theoretical composition of kaolinite, except that soil kaolins may have a rather higher water content. But the chemical composition of micaceous clays differs appreciably from that of pyrophyllite and talc. They contain too little silicon, usually too much aluminium for the dioctahedral, and too little magnesium for the trioctahedral. In addition they contain other cations, the dioctahedral contain some magnesium, the trioctahedral some aluminium, and both contain ferric and possibly ferrous iron and small amounts of zinc, manganese, chromium and other metals. The reason for this is that some of the silicon ions in the tetrahedral holes are replaced by aluminium, and the other cations can substitute for aluminium and magnesium in the octahedral holes. This replacement of one ion by another of comparable size is called isomorphous replacement,[2] because it hardly alters the size or shape of the lattice. But since the replacement is usually of a larger size for a smaller cation, it distorts the lattice to some extent so replacement is usually strictly limited. Thus in clays rarely as much as 15 per cent of the silicon is replaced by aluminium, and under 5 per cent is common in the montmorillonites; although in the true micas, which are formed at high temperatures 25 per cent are replaced, and in the chlorites up to 50 per cent

[1] Taken from L. H. Ahrens, *Geochem. Cosmochem. Acta*, 1952, **2**, 155.

[2] Isomorphous replacement occurs when the crystal lattice is being formed. It cannot occur afterwards because the ion cannot get out of the hole. It is thus quite distinct from cation exchange where the ions are outside the surface of the lattice. It is interesting to note that silicon never replaces aluminium in 6-coordination, presumably because if the ion in the space is too small the lattice again loses stability.

may be replaced. In the octahedral holes again, except for the substitution of ferric iron for aluminium which can occur to any extent, either only a small proportion of the aluminium or magnesium ions are replaced, or nearly all are replaced by another cation.[1] For reasons not yet explained, isomorphous replacement does not occur to any appreciable extent amongst the kaolin clay minerals, although the fireclay mineral may contain a little ferric iron, and aluminium may substitute to a small extent for silicon.

Isomorphous replacement typically leads to the lattice acquiring a negative electrical charge, for every silicon which is replaced by an aluminium, or every aluminium replaced by a magnesium or other divalent cation causes a unit negative charge due to the charges on the oxygen ions not being fully neutralised. However, clay minerals do not acquire as high a negative charge as would be expected from the extent of isomorphous replacement, presumably because such highly charged lattices are unstable, so some of the charge is neutralised internally by up to 2·22 of every three octahedral holes being filled with cations in the dioctahedral clays, and when aluminium and iron replace some of the magnesiums in the trioctahedral by up to 0·12 out of every three holes being left empty.[2]

The Structure of the Micaceous Clays

A mica such as muscovite is built up of 4-layered sheets in which one silicon in four is replaced by an aluminium ion, so the unit cell carries two negative charges which are neutralised by potassium ions. These potassium ions sit in the holes in the oxygen sheets in such a way that adjacent sheets are regularly stacked one on the other with the corresponding holes lying over each other, thus every potassium ion is in a hole which is surrounded by twelve oxygens, six in each sheet. Such a mineral has a much higher crystal symmetry than have normal clay particles, except that in some glacial tills, many of the clay particles are simply finely ground mica particles. Potassium is the only ion which is found in this position in well-crystallined micas, presumably because it is the only common simple ion whose size is such that it can just fit into this hole formed by these twelve oxygen ions.

The clay minerals based on the mica structure differ from micas in two important respects. First of all the negative charge on the surface is lower, and often much lower than on the micas, being equivalent to

[1] For a review of this subject, see C. S. Ross and S. B. Hendricks, *U.S. Geol. Surv., Prof. Paper* 205B, 1945, and *Proc. Soil Sci. Soc. Amer.*, 1942, **6**, 58, and J. W. Earley, B. B. Osthaus and I. H. Milne, *Amer. Mineral.*, 1953, **38**, 707. These papers give examples of analyses of clay minerals to illustrate the range of replacements found.
[2] R. E. Grim, *Clay Mineralogy*, New York, 1953.

about two-thirds of a unit or less per unit cell instead of two units. Secondly the micaceous clay minerals contain more water of constitution than do the micas, possibly in part because the hydrion H_3O^+ has almost the same size as the potassium ion and replaces potassium in 12-coordination with oxygen. The less hydrated clay minerals are often called illites and the more hydrated hydrous micas, but the names are usually used loosely and often synonymously.

These micaceous-type clay minerals show the property of potassium fixation, which is of great interest in the potassium-supplying power of soils to plants and so is discussed in more detail on p. 512. In actual micaceous clays a part at least of the cations neutralising the negative charge are not potassium, and in soils are usually calcium or aluminium; and if these clays are dispersed in water these cations can be readily replaced by others simply by adding a soluble salt of the other to the water. This is the phenomenon of cation exchange, which will be discussed further in Chapter VII, whilst the potassium ions in the micaceous part of the structure usually are not so accessible, so do not take part in these exchanges. But if some of the calcium is replaced by potassium in actual micaceous clays it will often be found that some of this potassium ceases to be readily exchangeable, and this conversion of potassium from readily to very slowly exchangeable or non-exchangeable form is helped by drying the clay. To a lesser extent ammonium ions, which have a similar size to potassium, also show the same behaviour, and the hydrion does also. There is probably a considerable variation in the extent to which the hydrous micas in the soil show this property, and in particular it is possible that one of the soil clay minerals, called degraded illite by R. Brown[1] and ammersooite by H. W. van der Marel[2] shows it very strongly.

Another group of mica-like clay minerals form the montmorillonite group. In these the negative charges on the clay minerals are neutralised by ions other than potassium or hydrions, and there are no strong bonding forces holding the sheets together. Thus if the clay is strongly dried, so the neutralising cations have been dehydrated, and is then wetted, water molecules can enter between the sheets to hydrate the cations, and if other cations are introduced into the outside solution, they can diffuse between the sheets and replace those originally there. These clays are therefore characterised by having no fixed spacing between the sheets, for the spacing depends on the cations present and on their hydration. In the extreme case of cations which can dissociate relatively easily from the charged surface when the electrolyte concentration in the solution is low, such as sodium ions, the net force between sheets is one of electrical repulsion and the individual sheets

---

[1] *Nature*, 1954, **173**, 644.   [2] *Soil Sci.*, 1954, **78**, 163.

will separate from each. When such a clay deflocculates, the individual particles will be only one sheet thick, and the properties of such suspensions will be discussed further on p. 130. The nomenclature of this group of clay minerals again is not standardised, though amongst the dioctahedral members of this group beidellite is often used for the aluminium-rich, montmorillonite for the magnesium-rich, and nontronite for the iron-rich members.

The distinction between beidellite and montmorillonite is not often made largely because there have been no simple methods for distinguishing between them unless that proposed by R. Greene-Kelly[1] is found acceptable. He found that lithium-saturated montmorillonites, heated to 200° C. collapsed and lost much of their exchange capacity, and that lithium-saturated beidellites did not show this behaviour.

Vermiculite, a mineral which can occur as large crystals, is similar to micas except that it has a higher surface density of charge. It is a trioctahedral mineral with magnesium in most of the octahedral holes instead of aluminium in only two-thirds, and the positive charges between the sheets are neutralised by magnesium ions in 6-coordination with water molecules which take up definite positions with respect to the oxygens of the clay, so the sheets are held together partially by the negative charges on the magnesium ions and partially by hydrogen bonding between the water molecules and the oxygens on the outside layer of the sheet.[2] Chlorite, another mineral which can occur in visible crystals and probably differs from vermiculite in that the interlayer magnesium ions are in 6-coordination with hydroxyls instead of with water molecules, and since this brucite sheet is unchanged, the 4-layer sheet must have a low charge density.

There are also clay minerals in soils which give an X-ray diagram similar to that expected from a dioctahedral vermiculite, but these are more probably montmorillonite particles held together by an adsorbed layer of basic aluminium ions, such as could be produced during weathering under acid conditions, rather than true vermiculites.[3]

Interstratified Clay Minerals and Actual Soil Clay Minerals

The best-established example of an interstratified clay mineral is chlorite, in which brucite sheets are interleaved with talc, to which a vermiculite sheet is closely related; and like talc and vermiculite, chlorites can occur in crystals much larger than clay size. Chlorite

---

[1] *J. Soil Sci.*, 1953, **4**, 233.
[2] A. M. Mathieson and G. F. Walker, *Amer. Mineral.*, 1954, **39**, 231.
[3] See, for example, G. Brown, *J. Soil Sci.*, 1954, **5**, 155; C. I. Rich and S. S. Obenshain, *Proc. Soil Sci. Soc. Amer.*, 1955, **19**, 334; T. Tamura, *J. Soil Sci.*, 1958, **9**, 141, and B. W. Avery, I. Stephen *et al.*, *J. Soil Sci.*, 1959, **10**, 177.

sheets often carry little net charge, as much of the charge due to isomorphous replacement in the talc sheet is neutralised by some isomorphous replacement of aluminium for magnesium in the brucite. In some chlorites the brucite layer is mainly replaced by a gibbsite one, and the chlorites differ from the vermiculites in that the double oxygen layer is a double water layer in the vermiculites and a double hydroxyl layer in the chlorites.

In soil clays interstratification probably occurs under some conditions, and in particular some mica minerals which have become expanded may have a sheet of some other mineral formed between their sheets, giving a randomly interstratified mineral. The fireclay kaolin mineral may also have some halloysite sheets interstratified. The composition of the clay fraction of a soil can therefore be difficult to determine, and this is due not only to the amount of interstratification but also because many of the sheets appear to be poorly crystallised, possibly because of distortions introduced by the isomorphous replacement which has taken place. Thus many of the earlier identifications of clay minerals in soils are not entirely satisfactory, as the complexity of the clay mineral assemblage in some soils was not then realised.

The Charge on the Clay Lattice

Very few accurate determinations have been made of the permanent negative charge on soil clay minerals, for reasons which will be discussed in the following chapter. Kaolinite never seems to carry much charge; it is usually between 3 and 4 milli-equivalents per 100 gm., and can certainly be as high as 7·4,[1] due to a small amount of replacement of silicon by aluminium; and halloysite when found as a pure clay mineral also has a low value. Samples of kaolin and halloysite soil clay minerals often have a higher value, figures of 10–15 milli-equivalents being common and up to 50 being reported. Unfortunately some of these high figures may be due in part to contamination with much more highly charged micaceous and montmorillonitic clays, and it still is not certain how high a permanent negative charge a soil kaolinite or halloysite can have.

The total negative charge on micaceous clays is usually considerably greater than on kaolinites. Illites run from 10 to 40, montmorillonites from 60 to 150, vermiculites from 100 to 150 and chlorites 10 to 40 milli-equivalents per 100 gm. The chain lattice clay minerals of the attapulgite type run from 20 to 30.[2] It is interesting to translate these figures into negative charges per unit cell. Taking montmorillonite as an example,

[1] R. H. S. Robertson, G. W. Brindley and R. C. Mackenzie, *Amer. Mineral.*, 1954, **39**, 118.
[2] R. E. Grim, *Clay Mineralogy*, New York, 1953.

and using a molecular weight of 720, a surface area of 46·1 sq. Å. on each face, and a negative charge of 100 milli-equivalents per 100 gm., there is 0·72 unit charge per unit cell, or a charge density of one negative charge per 130 sq. Å. This calculation is naturally very approximate as isomorphous replacement affects the molecular weight and area of the unit cell. Further, 80 milli-equivalents is probably a more common charge, giving a surface area of 160 Å. per unit charge. This area is large enough to allow large organic cations to neutralise this charge and still to form only a mono-ionic layer on the surface.

Clay particles can carry an electric charge for a second reason, and this is because of the conditions at the broken edges of the crystal sheets. On the edge of a micaceous sheet, the open packed hexagonal oxygens can only touch one instead of two silicon ions, so only one of their negative charges has been neutralised and the other is neutralised by a hydrogen ion in acid conditions, giving a weak silicic acid-like group ≡Si—OH, but this hydrogen ion dissociates in alkaline conditions. This can be seen in the buffer curve of a montmorillonite given in Fig. 9 on p. 95, where the charge on the particle is due solely to its permanent negative charge up to pH 6–7, and it then increases by about 60 milli-equivalents per 100 gm. up to pH 11–12. A rough calculation shows that this is of the order to be expected, for a typical montmorillonite particle is one sheet thick and can be considered to be a circular disc about 200 Å. diameter. There will be a hydroxyl attached to a silicon at about every 5 Å. around the periphery, so such a particle would contain 340 unit cells and 125 broken bond hydroxyls, which is equivalent to 50 milli-equivalents per 100 gm. of clay. Naturally the larger the clay crystal, and most micaceous clay particles are larger, the smaller is the increase in negative charge with increasing pH.

Kaolinite particles also show this effect, though it is probable that the ratio of the pH dependent charge to the permanent negative charge is much higher for the kaolin than the micaceous clay minerals. A. Mehlich and his co-workers[1] in fact estimate the proportion of these two groups of clay minerals in a soil by assuming that all the permanent negative charge on the clay colloids is due to micaceous clays and all the pH dependent charge to the kaolinitic, and although this assumption cannot be strictly valid, yet the results based on it are reasonably accurate.

Kaolinite particles can also acquire a positive charge in acid conditions. R. K. Schofield and H. R. Samson[2] have shown that the conditions on the broken edge of a kaolinite particle under very acid and very alkaline conditions can be represented as follows:

[1] See, for example, N. T. Coleman, S. B. Weed and R. J. McCracken, *Proc. Soil Sci. Soc. Amer.*, 1959, **23**, 146.
[2] *Faraday Soc. Disc.* 18, 1954, 135.

acid conditions   alkaline conditions

This requires that the surface of each unit cell on the broken edge, which has an area of 33 sq. Å., should acquire a positive charge of one unit in acid and a negative charge of two units in alkaline conditions. These positive charges are neutralised either by simple anions, or sometimes in part by very small clay particles, such as montmorillonite particles, sticking to the broken edge. It is also possible that humus particles and large anions such as the polyacrylate anions in some soil conditioners can be held on the edges of these particles. These long chain anions probably act as soil conditioners by virtue of their ability to hold clay particles together edge-to-edge in a random stacking, to give an open porous aggregate that is relatively stable.[1]

[1] See, for example, R. A. Ruehrwein and D. W. Ward, *Soil Sci.*, 1952, **73**, 485.

CHAPTER VII

THE CATION- AND ANION-HOLDING POWERS OF SOILS

SOILS HAVE BEEN known to hold cations since 1850, when H. S. Thompson, a Yorkshire gentleman, discovered first of all that soils had the power to absorb ammonia, and secondly, the more surprising fact, that if a dilute ammonium sulphate solution is percolated through a soil, it is calcium sulphate and not ammonium sulphate which first washes out.[1] He communicated these findings to J. T. Way, Chemist to the Royal Agricultural Society of England, who confirmed these facts, and further showed that potassium salts behave in the same way as ammonium.[2] He called the phenomenon base exchange, because it involves the quantitative exchange of one base or, as we would now say, one cation for another, and concluded that soils must contain insoluble calcium salts which could be converted to insoluble salts of alkalis, and that these salts were connected with the clay in the soil. This conclusion had almost been reached twenty years earlier by an American, Edmund Ruffin of Virginia,[3] who showed that sour soils contain insoluble acids and the function of calcareous manures was to neutralise these acids.

The methods used for investigating these insoluble soil acids have been taken over from the methods developed by physical chemists for estimating the strength of weak soluble acids, as, for example, acetic. The principal method employed is to determine the buffer curve of the acid soil, which is done by making a suspension of the soil and measuring its change of pH as increasing quantities of an alkali are added; for the soil is a buffer, that is, it reduces the rise in pH that would occur if the alkali was added to a volume of water equal to that of the soil suspension. Fig. 6 gives an example of the buffer curve of a weak polybasic acid, and Fig. 7 of an acid soil. In mineral loam and clay soils, the clay fraction is the principal buffer present, though in surface soils, particularly if sandy, the humic part of the organic matter present may make an appreciable contribution. Fig. 8 gives a buffer curve of a soil clay, determined under four conditions, and it shows that the buffer curve depends on the base being used and the salt concentration in the suspension. Because these curves bear some resemblance to those of

[1] J. Roy. Agric. Soc., 1850, 11, 68.
[2] J. Roy. Agric. Soc., 1850, 11, 313; 1852, 13, 123.
[3] An Essay on Calcareous Manures, Petersburg, Va., 1832.

weak acids, soil chemists at one time tried to interpret them in terms of a weak polybasic acid, but interest in this disappeared as the true nature of clay minerals was discovered.

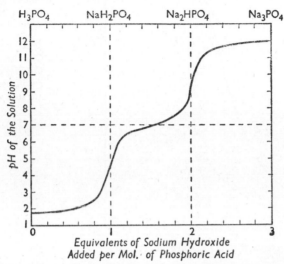

FIG. 6. Titration curve of phosphoric acid with sodium hydroxide.

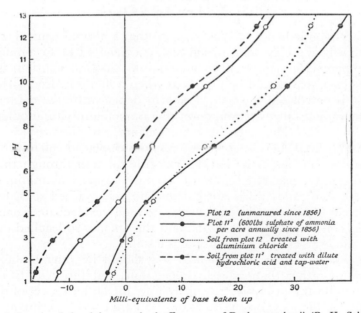

FIG. 7. Influence of aluminium on the buffer curve of Rothamsted soil (R. K. Schofield).

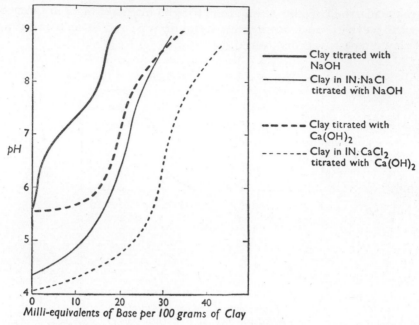

Clay titrated with NaOH

Clay in IN.NaCl titrated with NaOH

Clay titrated with Ca(OH)$_2$

Clay in IN.CaCl$_2$ titrated with Ca(OH)$_2$

Milli-equivalents of Base per 100 grams of Clay

Fig. 8. Titration curve of a clay separated from a Bengal soil, showing the effect of the base used and the salt concentration.[1]

Clay Acid or Acid Clay?

A direct consequence of Way's theory that a normal neutral soil is a calcium salt of a clay acid, which can be converted to an ammonium salt by percolating through an ammonium chloride solution, is that the free clay acid should be produced when a dilute hydrochloric acid solution is percolated through. One can demonstrate the existence of the ammonium salt by washing out the ammonium with another salt, say barium chloride, and show the barium has displaced as much ammonium from the soil as the ammonium displaced calcium. However, if one percolates the barium chloride solution through the acid washed soil, the leachate is found to contain far more aluminium than hydrogen ions; and this is not confined to acid washed soils, for if a neutral salt is percolated through any acid soil the leachate is acid, but its main constituent is aluminium, and the amount so leached out has been called the exchange acidity of the soil.

This result implies that an acid soil should be thought of as an aluminium rather than as a hydrogen soil, and the validity of this picture is illustrated in Fig. 7, which shows the buffer curves of the soil from two of the plots on the Rothamsted Park grass experiment. This

[1] Taken from J. N. Mukherjee and R. P. Mitra, *Indian J. Agric. Sci.*, 1942, **12**, 433.

field is old permanent meadow, and Plot 12 has been unmanured since 1856 and is moderately acid, and Plot 11 has had a complete fertiliser including 600 lb. per acre of sulphate of ammonia annually since then, so is extremely acid. R. K. Schofield has, however, shown that if the mildly acid soil is leached with aluminium chloride, its buffer curve corresponds very closely with that of Plot 11.

One of the most direct methods for studying the origin of the electric charges and the amount of hydrogen and other ions held by an acid clay is by obtaining its heat evolution curve as alkali is added to the

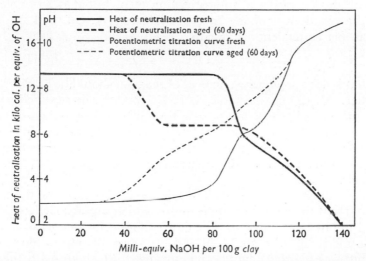

FIG. 9. The heat of neutralisation and the buffer curve of a freshly prepared and an aged acid montmorillonite.

acid clay suspension. Fig. 9[1] shows such curves for an acid montmorillonite freshly prepared by leaching through a hydrogen-saturated cation exchange resin, and for the same suspension after it had stood for 60 days.

The heat evolution curve for the freshly prepared acid montmorillonite shows that for the first 80 milli-equivalents of alkali added, the heat evolved is 13·5 k. cal. per equivalent, and this is due to the reaction

$$H^+ + OH^- \rightarrow HOH$$

and the same figure is obtained if a hydrogen-saturated exchange resin is titrated with an alkali. Thus this freshly prepared acid montmorillonite contains about 80 milli-equivalents of hydrogen ions neutralising its permanent negative charge. The heat evolved then starts dropping until it falls to zero when 140 milli-equivalents of base have been added; and this curve presumably represents the heat of neutralisation of the

[1] W. H. Slabaugh, *J. Amer. Chem. Soc.*, 1952, **74**, 4462.

hydrogen ions dissociating from hydroxyls on the broken edges of the crystal sheets.

The heat evolution curve for the aged acid montmorillonite correspondingly shows that it contained about 45 milli-equivalents of hydrogen ions and about 50 milli-equivalents of something else evolving about 9 k. cal. per equivalent, whilst the aged electrodialysed clay had about 15 milli-equivalents of hydrogen ions and about 60 milli-equivalents of something else evolving about 5 k. cal. per equivalent. Unfortunately not enough work has been done on this phenomenon to allow of any unequivocal interpretation of it, but it is probable that both the reactions evolving in the one case 9 k. cal. and the other 5 k. cal. per equivalent are due to a reaction something like

$$\text{Clay}-\text{Al} + 3\ \text{M}^+ + 3\ \text{OH}^- \longrightarrow \text{Clay}-\text{M} + \text{Al(OH)}_3$$

though it is not known why one heat of reaction should be nearly double the other. M. E. Harward and N. T. Coleman,[1] who repeated parts of this work found the heat of reaction of an aluminium-saturated exchange resin, an electrodialysed montmorillonite and an aluminium-saturated montmorillonite was between 5·5 and 6·5 k. cal. per equivalent, which is intermediate between the two figures obtained by Slabaugh.

Fig. 9 also shows the potentiometric titration curves for the freshly prepared and the aged montmorillonite, which unfortunately were not carried out in a salt solution. The figure shows that the pH of the true H-montmorillonite did not begin to rise appreciably until almost all the exchangeable hydrogen had been neutralised. At about pH 6 the edge hydrogens begin to dissociate, and their neutralisation is complete at about pH 11, as judged by the heat evolution curve. This completion is not shown by the potentiometric curve because the clay begins to decompose at these high pHs. If the titration had been done in N.KCl[2] it is probable that the dissociation would have been complete at about pH 9·5–10, and it is possible that this curve fits a Henderson type dissociation curve with a pK 8·3.[3]

On the other hand the buffer curve for the aged clay shows a fairly steady rise of pH, once the exchangeable hydrogen has been neutralised, and it is not possible from the curve to say at what point the exchangeable aluminium ions have been precipitated or the edge hydrogen ions begin to dissociate. It is, however, often possible to show a distinct break in the curve if the titration had been done in a salt solution, such as N.KCl. This slow rise of pH as the aluminium ions are being

[1] *Soil Sci.*, 1954, **78**, 181.
[2] M. E. Harward and N. T. Coleman, *Soil Sci.*, 1954, **78**, 181 give curves done in N.KCl and in water.
[3] A. M. Rommer and D. Carroll, *Nature*, 1960, **185**, 595.

precipitated, which goes on up to pH 5–7, depending on the concentration of the salt solution, is due to some of the aluminium ions being bound very strongly to the clay surface, so it can in fact hold an appreciable proportion of exchangeable aluminium, possibly partly by the formation of the basic aluminium ion $(AlOH)^{2+}$,[1] when in equilibrium with a solution only containing a very low concentration of these ions.

The conclusion from this work is that if a montmorillonite is treated with a strong H-resin, or with a strong acid, such as N.HCl, a true H-montmorillonite is produced, which if allowed to stand in water, slowly goes over to a mixed aluminium and hydrogen montmorillonite; although the clay will remain a hydrogen clay if it was dispersed in a more weakly dissociating solvent than water, such as methyl alcohol.[2] On the other hand, as Harward and Coleman showed, if the acid clay is prepared by washing with a dilute acid, such as 0·1N.HCl, the mixed hydrogen-aluminium clay is produced initially. The reasons why the hydrogen clay is not stable, and the detailed mechanism of decomposition of the clay to release aluminium ions to help neutralise the charge on the lattice, are not known.

The proportion of hydrogen to aluminium on an acid clay can be determined most simply in the laboratory by a conductometric titration, for this curve is almost a series of straight lines, the first change of slope occurring when all the hydrogen ions neutralising the permanent negative charge have been neutralised, the second when the exchangeable aluminium ions have been precipitated, and the third when all the edge hydrogen ions have been neutralised.[3] But the proportion can be determined by direct chemical analysis, for if an acid clay is leached with a slightly acidified barium chloride or silver nitrate solution, the barium or silver will displace relatively easily both the exchangeable hydrogen and aluminium ions, and the amount of barium or silver held by the clay after leaching can be very easily determined.

There is an important consequence of an acid clay usually being mainly an aluminium clay. If a clay is alternatively leached with a dilute acid and a neutral salt, it will suffer repeated decomposition, for the neutral salt removes the aluminium ions which have to come out of the clay lattice to neutralise the charge on the acid clay. The silica, which is released in this decomposition, usually washes out during the acid leaching.

So far most of the discussion has been on the buffer curves of the clay fraction of a soil, and whilst in most agricultural soils nearly all the buffering of the mineral particles resides in the clay fraction, there are some soils in which a considerable proportion resides in the silt and

---

[1] R. K. Schofield and A. W. Taylor, *J. Chem. Soc.*, 1954, 4445 give the pK for its formation.
[2] R. P. Mitra and H. Singh, *Naturw.*, 1959, **46**, 319.
[3] See, for example, T. M. Lai, M. M. Mortland and A. Timmick, *Soil Sci.*, 1957, **83**, 359.

sand fractions. These are usually soils derived from basic igneous rocks, which are not strongly weathered, and which contain vermiculites or chlorites in these fractions.[1] Amorphous hydrous oxide precipitates in soils may also possess appreciable buffering capacity in neutral or alkaline conditions, and it is probable that allophane shows this most strongly, and that hydrous alumina shows this more strongly than hydrous ferric or titanium oxides.[2] The soluble silica which is always present when a soil is shaken up with water will also contribute to the buffering, but this is normally a very minor contribution.

Cation Exchange Capacity of a Soil

So long as soils were considered as simple acids, there was a definite amount of base that needed to be added to that soil if the acidity was to be neutralised. The early soil chemists thus thought of a soil as possessing a definite base holding, or base exchange capacity; and when it held that amount of base the soil was said to be saturated, whilst if it held less it was unsaturated with bases. But this simple picture is now known not to apply to soils, yet these concepts of base exchange capacity and base saturation have proved so useful in practice that they are still widely used.

The base exchange capacity, or as it is now usually called the cation exchange capacity, is an arbitrary concept arbitrarily defined. The most common definitions are based on determining the amount of simple ions, such as sodium, ammonium, calcium or barium, a soil can hold when the salt solution, usually buffered at about pH 7, is leached through the soil, though some workers have used a higher pH. A. Mehlich,[3] for example, has used pH 8·1 which can be easily obtained using tri-ethanolamine as a buffer. On the whole, all these four cations give about the same exchange capacity, which does not depend very much on the exact technique used, but the variation is far too great for it to be possible to talk about the cation exchange capacity of a soil at pH 7, for example, without at the same time specifying the method by which it has been measured.

One of the reasons that the phrase base exchange capacity rather than cation exchange capacity has remained in use for so long is that this exchange capacity at say pH 7 is approximately independent of the cation used for these simple bases. But if the buffer curve of a clay is determined using say nickel as the cation instead of sodium, the clay

[1] For an example of a soil from basalt in N. Ireland, see D. M. McAleese *et al.*, *J. Soil Sci.*, 1957, **8**, 135; 1959, **9**, 66, 81, 289.
[2] K. S. Birrell and M. Gradwell, *J. Soil Sci.*, 1956, **7**, 130; M. Fieldes, L. D. Swindale, and J. P. Richardson, *Soil Sci.*, 1952, **74**, 197; and W. P. Kelley and J. B. Page, *Proc. Soil Sci. Soc. Amer.*, 1943, **7**, 175.
[3] *Proc. Soil Sci. Soc. Amer.*, 1939, **3**, 162, and *Soil Sci.*, 1948, **66**, 429.

will begin to take up very much more nickel than sodium when the pH begins to approach that at which the hydroxide will precipitate. This behaviour is not due, or at least not solely due, to the formation of a basic ion, for it is shown by calcium and barium, which do not form basic salts, as by magnesium, manganese, nickel and zinc, which do.[1] There is also some evidence that clays will take up larger amounts of copper and zinc than of other metallic cations when the pH is well below that at which the hydroxide could be precipitated, but if this is so, no satisfactory explanation of this effect has been given.[2]

The Anion-holding Power of Soils

Clay minerals can take up anions from acid solutions since, as explained on p. 91, their broken edges acquire a positive charge due to the absorption of hydrogen ions in excess of what is needed to neutralise the charge on the oxygen and hydroxyl ions on these surface edges. This effect is relatively much more noticeable with kaolinitic than with other types of clay. Soils can acquire positive charges in acid solutions for an additional reason, for they may contain precipitated films of hydrated iron and aluminium oxides which display this property. Table 25 shows this effect for a Rothamsted subsoil from which as much of the exchangeable aluminium as possible has been carefully and thoroughly removed.[3] The table shows that these positively charged spots may not be an integral part of the clay particles, for they are apparently removed by treating the soil thoroughly with Tamm's acid oxalate solution in sunlight—a treatment which removes these hydrated precipitates without attacking the clay particles—but their removal may be more apparent than real, for it could be due to the oxalate anions being held tightly on them.

These positive charges need not necessarily be neutralised by simple anions if they are very close to negatively charged spots, for if the electrolyte concentration is not too high, the double layers around the positive and negative spots will interpenetrate with a consequent decrease in the cation concentration in the interpenetrating layers. Hence such a system can only show its maximum absorption for anions when the electrolyte concentration is sufficiently high to compress the double layers so much that there is no interpenetration. R. K. Schofield[3] has, however, found that in many soils these spots are so close together that still more powerful methods are necessary to separate these double layers, showing that they must be extremely close together. Fig. 10,

[1] C. A. Bower and E. Truog, *Proc. Soil Sci. Soc. Amer.*, 1940, **5**, 86.
[2] L. E. DeMumbrum and M. L. Jackson, *Proc. Soil Sci. Soc. Amer.*, 1956, **20**, 334, and *Soil Sci.*, 1956, **81**, 353.
[3] R. K. Schofield, *J. Soil Sci.*, 1949, **1**, 1.

TABLE 25

Uptake of Ammonium and Chloride by a Rothamsted Subsoil from an N/5 Ammonium Chloride Solution at different pHs

Uptake in milli-equivalents per 100 grams of oven-dry soil

pH	Chloride adsorbed	Positive charge	Excess of NH_4 over Cl adsorbed	Negative charge
2·05	1·5	2·0	19·5	21·5
2·3	1·3	1·8	21·3	23·1
2·6	1·2	1·7	21·7	23·4
3·1	1·2	1·7	21·6	23·3
3·3	1·1	1·6	21·7	23·3
3·8	0·6	1·1	22·3	23·4
5·5	0·0	0·5	24·0	24·5
6·2	—0·4	0·1	25·7	25·8
7·15	—0·6	—0·1	27·0	26·9
7·4	—0·5	0·0	28·2	28·2

Samples treated with Acid Ammonium Oxalate

Uptake in milli-equivalents per 100 grams of untreated oven-dry soil

pH	Chloride adsorbed	Positive charge	Excess of NH_4 over Cl adsorbed	Negative charge
2·5	—0·3	0·2	23·2	23·4
3·65	—0·5	0·0	23·5	23·5
4·15	—0·6	—0·1	23·3	23·2
7·5	—0·4	0·1	26·8	26·9

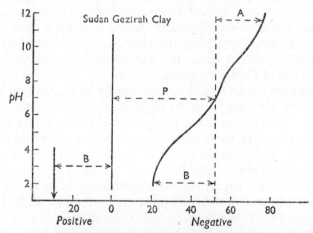

Charge in Milli-equivalents per 100 grams of Soil.

FIG. 10. The titration curve of a heavy alluvial clay soil.
P is the permanent negative charge on the clay.
A is the additional negative charge developed at high *p*H.
B is the positive charge developed at low *p*H.
The arrow shows the maximum uptake of chloride from alcoholic HCl.

taken from Schofield's paper, shows the buffer curve for a Gezirah clay soil when as much of the exchangeable aluminium as possible had been washed out, so it should have given a curve similar to montmorillonite below pH 6–7. Schofield showed that the curve below pH 7 was primarily due to the effect of pH on the number of positive charges, for he measured the total positive charges on the soil by measuring the absorption of chloride from alcoholic hydrochloric acid, which suppressed the double layer altogether. The figure shows that the buffering below pH 7 is almost exactly equal to the positive charges determined in this way, thus demonstrating that this buffer curve is really the curve for the disappearance of positive charges as the pH rises rather than the appearance of negative charges.

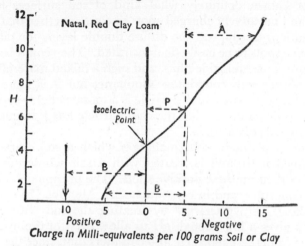

Fig. 11. The titration curve of a tropical red loam.
P is the permanent negative charge on the soil particles.
A is the additional negative charge developed at high pH.
B is the positive charge developed at low pH.
The arrow shows the maximum uptake of chloride from alcoholic HCl.

It is interesting that there are some soils in which the positive charges in acid conditions can be larger than the permanent negative charge, and such a soil then acquires a net positive in a sufficiently acid medium. Fig. 11, also from Schofield's paper, gives an example of the buffer curve of such a soil, which is a soil from Natal, and shows that it is positively charged below pH 4 and negatively charged above. Such a soil is said to be amphoteric and to possess an iso-electric point, which occurs at about pH 4 for this soil in the conditions under which this buffer curve was obtained. Amphoteric soils, such as this one, however, appear to be very rare in nature, and the conditions under which they are formed are not known.

A consequence of a soil having positive and negative spots very close together, so the double layers around them interpenetrate when the salt solution around them is very dilute, is that if conditions are made suitable for anion absorption to take place, for example by making the solution acid or increasing the salt concentration, both the anion and the cation of the salt are absorbed on the neighbouring positive and negative spots, so the soil will absorb a neutral salt under these conditions.[1] If the soil is now leached with water, the salt will either be held against leaching if the anion is strongly absorbed, or will only be washed out slowly; and this salt retention, measured under standard conditions of leaching, can be used to demonstrate the presence of such positive charges on the soil particles.[2]

It is not known definitely what kind of soil surfaces have their positively and negatively charged spots so close together that one must take precautions to suppress the diffuse double layers for the presence of the positive spots to be easily demonstrated. They could be produced on mixed humus-sesquioxide films, and such a mixed material probably occurs in surface soils containing allophane, but it is more probably either that the surface of a clay particle is a mosaic of clay surface and a sesquioxide precipitate, or that the clay particle has a sesquioxide film absorbed on its broken edge.

The number of these positive charges which a soil carries can also be determined if the soil is treated with a salt whose anion is very strongly absorbed on these positive spots. The phosphate anion nearly fulfils this condition, and in consequence A. Mehlich[3] has proposed to measure these positive charges by treating the soil with phosphoric acid, which gives a low enough pH to allow most of the hydroxyl ions to dissociate from these spots. He also considers that, since the phosphate is held very strongly on these spots, the increase in the cation exchange capacity of the soil brought about by this treatment measures the number of such positive spots on the sesquioxide films.

Anion exchange differs from cation exchange in that most soils possess a permanent negative charge, hence show reasonably quantitative cation exchange over a wide pH range, but they do not possess a permanent positive charge, so anion exchange phenomena are very pH dependent. But in acid conditions anion exchange can be quantitative, and the tightness with which the anions are held depends very strongly on the anion.[4] Thus chlorides and nitrates are only weakly held by soils, and can be removed completely by reducing the electrolyte

1 See, for example, A. S. Ayres and H. H. Hagihara, *Soil Sci.*, 1953, **75**, 1, and E. J. Kamprath, W. L. Nelson and J. W. Fitts, *Proc. Soil Sci. Soc. Amer.*, 1956, **20**, 463.
2 W. A. Berg and G. W. Thomas, *Proc. Soil Sci. Soc. Amer.*, 1959, **23**, 348.
3 *J. Ass. Off. Agric. Chem.*, 1953, **36**, 445.
4 See, for example, A. Demolon and E. Bastisse, *Ann. Agron.*, 1934, **4**, 53.

concentration around the particles, so the double layer due to a negative charge on a particle interpenetrates and replaces that due to a positive charge. Other anions, such as phosphate and some polyvalent anions, are held closer to the positive charges, so that the double layer due to the negative charges cannot expel them. Hence, these anions cannot be washed out by distilled water, but need to be displaced by other anions.

The exchange and retention of phosphate anions in particular have been investigated because of their agricultural importance. They can probably be adsorbed and tightly held as monovalent $H_2PO_4^-$ ions. They can be removed by other strongly adsorbed anions such as divalent arsenate, silicate, citrate, oxalate, hydroxyl and fluoride; but possibly only the arsenate and silicate give typical exchange reactions.[1] Thus the citrate and oxalate ions may displace the phosphate more by dissolving the iron-rich material responsible for the positively charged spots than by anionic exchange, and a high concentration of hydroxyl ions normally causes some decomposition of the whole complex. The effect of fluoride is also uncertain, as more fluoride is adsorbed than phosphate displaced.

The pH of a Soil

The *p*H of an aqueous solution is defined as the negative logarithm of the hydrogen-ion activity in the solution, which is the same as the hydrogen-ion concentration if the solution is very dilute, but which is increasingly smaller than this concentration as the salt content of the solution increases. This concept appears to be quite definite so long as one is dealing with volumes large compared with molecular dimensions, for the individual molecules and ions composing the solution are uniformly dispersed throughout it within the limits set by variations due to molecular and ionic thermal movements. These volumes may, however, have to be very large, in terms of molecular dimensions, at the end of the *p*H range of importance in soils. Thus a solution at *p*H 7 will, on the average, contain one hydrogen ion in a cube of side 0·25 μ —just about the minimum-sized volume visible fairly clearly in a microscope fitted with a 1/12 in. objective. But the *p*H of a soil dispersed in water is not a simple concept like this; for the soil particles, which carry ions attached to them, are very large compared to molecular dimensions, and the ions are, therefore, not uniformly distributed throughout the solution. The concept of the *p*H of a soil, or rather a soil suspension, can therefore only be discussed in relation to the properties of the ionic atmosphere around the soil particles.

[1] L. A. Dean and E. J. Rubins, *Soil Sci.*, 1947, 63, 377; L. T. Kurtz, E. E. De Turk and R. H. Bray, ibid., 1946, 61, 111.

Consider a negatively charged soil particle dispersed in water. The negative charge is neutralised by cations, but these cations do not necessarily sit firmly on the negative charges: a proportion dissociate into the dispersion medium. Thus as one goes from the surface of the soil particle outwards, the concentration of cations gradually decreases until it becomes very small. This diffuse layer of cations is known as the diffuse double layer—a double layer because there is a negative charge on the clay surface which is balanced by this diffuse cloud of positive charges; and the thickness of this layer is measured by the distance one must go from the surface until the cation concentration becomes inappreciable (see p. 126). But soils are never bathed in pure water; there are always some salts dissolved in it. One effect of these salts is that their cations and anions intermingle with the exchangeable cations in the double layer and make it less diffuse or more compact: in fact they reduce the difference in cationic concentration between the neighbourhood of the clay surface and the bulk of the solution. The more concentrated the salt and the higher the valency of its ions, the thinner the double layer and the more nearly is the cation concentration just outside the clay surface the same as in the solution away from the clay surface; and this holds for every species of cation in the double layer.

This effect of salts is directly relevant to the limitations inherent in the concept of the pH of a soil. The hydrogen-ion concentration in the solution surrounding the soil particles is less than, or the pH of the solution is higher than, that close to the soil particles themselves, due to the hydrogen-ion concentration gradient in the double layer. And as the double layer is made more compact by adding an electrolyte to the soil water system, so the hydrogen-ion concentration gradient across the double layer is reduced, and the pH in the solution falls, to become more nearly equal to that close to the surface of the soil particle. The pH of the solution is thus greater than the pH at the particle surface, and if a soil suspension is allowed to settle through a solution, the pH of the solution is higher than that of the sediment; and as the salt concentration increases, so do the differences decrease.

The apparent pH of a soil, as determined electrometrically on a paste or suspension of the soil made up with water, depends not only on the salt concentration in the solution, but also on the amount of water added to make the suspension, as is shown in Table 26 for three Arizona soils.[1] This shows that the higher the ratio of water to soil, the higher is the apparent pH of the soil; and this effect is more noticeable in soils not containing salts or gypsum,[2] and is a consequence both of a diluter

[1] W. T. McGeorge, *J. Amer. Soc. Agron.*, 1937, **29**, 841. For further examples, see M. R. Huberty and A. R. C. Haas, *Soil Sci.*, 1940, **49**, 455, and 1941, **51**, 17, and L. E. Davis, *Soil Sci.*, 1943, **56**, 405.   [2] R. F. Reitemeier, *Soil Sci.*, 1946, **61**, 195.

suspension and more diffuse double layers. Again if one samples the same soil at different times of the year, or under fallow as contrasted to under crop, the apparent pH is usually higher in cool moist weather, or in winter than in warm dry weather, or in summer; and it is usually higher under crop in summer than under fallow;[1] although these variations are usually smaller than the variations from site to site in the same field.[2]

TABLE 26

v *The Effect of Soil-Water Ratio on the Soil's pH*

Calcareous alkaline soils from Arizona

Volume of water added per 100 gm. dry soil	pH of soil suspension or paste		
	Soil 1	Soil 2	Soil 3
10 c.cm.	7·45	9·10	7·95
25 c.cm.	7·60	9·40	8·00
100 c.cm.	7·70	9·85	8·20
1,000 c.cm.	8·15	9·90	9·20

This dependence of soil pH on salt concentration and on the soil-water ratio used, due to their effects on the diffuseness of the double layer around the soil particles, can be reduced by making all the measurements under conditions when the double layer is reasonably compact, that is, by making them when the soil is dispersed in a standard salt solution. R. K. Schofield and A. W. Taylor[3] have proposed the use of a 0·01 M. calcium chloride solution for temperate soils, on the grounds that it approximates to the calcium concentration in the soil solution (see p. 464), it causes little cation exchange, it compresses the double layers reasonably, and it does not give appreciable junction potentials with the calomel electrode. The pH of a soil measured in this solution is more constant and is much less dependent on the soil-solution ratio, and it presumably is closer to the pH of the solution around the plant roots, than is the pH measured in a water suspension; and it is typically lower by between 0·5 to 0·9 units, the difference tending to be greater in near neutral than in very acid soils.

The pH of a soil is influenced by two other factors besides the pH rise from the surface of the soil particles to the soil solution in bulk. In the

[1] See, for example, L. D. Bowen, *Soil Sci.*, 1927, **23**, 399; A. M. Smith and I. M. Robertson, *J. Agric. Sci.*, 1931, **21**, 822; M. Raupach, *Aust. J. Agric. Sci.*, 1951, **2**, 73, and Y. Kanchiro, Y. Matsusaka and G. D. Sherman, *Hawaii Agric. Exp. Sta., Tech. Bull.* 14, 1951.

[2] See, for example, G. M. Robertson and K. Simpson, *E. Scot. Coll. Agric. (Edinburgh), Tech. Bull.* 8, 1954, and M. Raupach, *Aust. J. Agric. Res.*, 1951, **2**, 83.

[3] *J. Soil Sci.*, 1955, **6**, 137, and *Proc. Soil Sci. Soc. Amer.*, 1955, **19**, 164. See also R. C. Turner and W. E. Nichol, *Canad. J. Soil Sci.*, 1958, **38**, 63.

first place, soils may contain substances capable of changing their degree of oxidation and reduction, with consequent fall or rise in pH. Thus waterlogged soils are commonly nearly neutral and have some sulphides present. If such a soil is drained the sulphides become oxidised to sulphates and the pH may fall from 7 to 4 or below. And if a sample of such a waterlogged soil is taken, and allowed to air-dry slowly before its pH is determined, the pH may fall strongly, whilst if the soil is left waterlogged its pH will rise slowly.[1] Again if a well-aerated soil containing nitrates or sulphates becomes waterlogged, the nitrates may be reduced to nitrogen gas and the sulphates to sulphides, each process raising the pH of the soil.

The pH of a soil is also influenced by the carbon dioxide concentration in the soil air. The higher this concentration the lower the pH, and the pH of a neutral or calcareous soil is very sensitive to small changes in the carbon dioxide concentration when the concentration itself is low, that is, when it is not very different from the atmospheric value of 0·03 per cent.

Table 27 illustrates the magnitude of this effect for some neutral non-calcareous soils.[2] In calcareous salt-free soils its magnitude can

TABLE 27

Effect of Carbon Dioxide Concentration on the pH of neutral soils

Pressure of CO_2 atmospheres	pH measured in water			pH measured in 10^{-3}M. $CaCl_2$		
	0·0004	0·001	0·05	0·0004	0·001	0·05
Soil 1	7·01	6·92	6·53	6·46	6·37	6·22
„ 2	7·42	7·20	6·70	6·77	6·75	6·38
„ 3	8·09	7·44	6·98	7·52	7·05	6·69

be calculated approximately from the solubility of calcium carbonate and carbon dioxide in water and the dissociation constants of carbonic acid, because in such soils the pH is basically determined by that of the system: calcium carbonate—calcium bicarbonate—carbon dioxide—water which is given by the equation

$$2pH = K + pCa + pCO_2$$

where pCO_2 is the negative logarithm of the partial pressure of carbon dioxide, in atmospheres, in equilibrium with the solution, pCa the

[1] For examples of this effect, see M. Romanoff, *J. Res. Natl. Bur. Stand.*, 1945, **34**, 227, and *Gas*, 1945, **26**, 49.
[2] W. E. Nichol and R. C. Turner, *Canad. J. Soil Sci.*, 1957, **37**, 96. For further examples, see R. S. Whitney and R. Gardner, *Soil Sci.*, 1943, **55**, 127, and **56**, 63.

negative logarithm of the activity of the calcium ions, and K is a constant whose value lies between 10 and 10·5, depending on the value used for the solubility constant of calcium carbonate. The reduction of pH is therefore approximately proportional to the logarithm of the partial pressure of carbon dioxide, a result which has been confirmed experimentally. Table 28 gives the pH of a clay—calcium carbonate—carbon dioxide—water system, and the concentration of calcium in the soil solution.

TABLE 28

The pH and Calcium Ion Concentration of a Calcium Carbonate and a Calcareous Clay Suspension in Equilibrium with Carbon Dioxide at Varying Pressures

Carbon Dioxide Pressure in atm.	pH of Calcium carbonate suspension	pH of Clay suspension	Calcium held by the clay milli-equiv. per 100 gm.	Calcium ion conc. in solution in milli-equiv.
0·00033	8·42	8·57	71·3	0·53
0·001	8·00	8·30	68·0	0·75
0·003	7·77	7·95	62·4	1·14
0·01	7·33	7·62	52·2	1·70
0·03	7·00	7·30	37·9	2·52
0·1	6·65	6·95	—	3·84

The pH of the suspension depends somewhat on the presence of the clay, for F. Simmons,[1] from whose work this part of the table has been derived, found that the pH was about 0·3 units lower in the absence than in the presence of the clay. The last column of the table gives the solubility of calcite in water in the absence of clay, and is calculated from some results of G. L. Frear and J. Johnston.[2] Hence the two sets of figures are not quite comparable, but they give the orders of magnitude of the effects observed. Further, if the soil contains a soluble calcium salt dissolved in the soil solution, this will lower the pH still further, as is shown in the second part of Table 27.

The calculations which have been made in the foregoing paragraphs are based on the assumption that the calcium carbonate in the soil is present as calcite. But S. R. Olsen and F. S. Watanabe,[3] by comparing observed with calculated values of pH, have shown that in some soils at least part of the calcium carbonate is in a form more soluble than calcite, so for a given carbon dioxide concentration, the pH is higher than expected: and this can be particularly noticeable in clay soils in

[1] *J. Amer. Soc. Agron.*, 1939, **31**, 638.   [2] *J. Amer. Chem. Soc.*, 1929, **51**, 2082.
[3] *Soil Sci.*, 1959, **88**, 123.

which much of the carbonate is present in the clay fraction. Crops growing on such soils are liable to show iron chlorosis,[1] possibly because of the higher HCO_3^- ion concentration around their roots.

One consequence of the soil being a fairly well buffered system is that if a fresh sample of soil is shaken up quickly in say a 0·01 M. solution of calcium chloride and its pH measured almost immediately, it will correspond reasonably to the pH of that soil in equilibrium with the mean carbon dioxide concentration which has recently persisted in that soil.

The pH of a calcareous soil containing few exchangeable sodium or magnesium ions thus cannot exceed about 8·5 when in equilibrium with the atmosphere, but if the CO_2 concentration rises to 0·1 per cent, a low figure for most soils, the pH has already dropped to 8, and if it rises to 1 per cent, a common figure for pastures, the pH is under 7·5. Now, as will be shown later (p. 533), many plants suffer from phosphate and minor element deficiencies if the pH rises much above 8, and hence they can only thrive on calcareous soils if they can maintain an adequate concentration of carbon dioxide around their roots. This is more easily achieved in soils of low porosity, such as clays than in soils of high porosity, such as well-drained sands, and in soils rich in organic matter than in poor, and in soils under pasture than under arable.

Recently it has been realised that a calcareous soil can have a pH greater than 8·5 because if water, initially in equilibrium with the carbon dioxide in the atmosphere, percolates through a calcareous soil in which no carbon dioxide is being produced, the solution loses some bicarbonate or carbonate ions to calcium ions on its way down, and its equilibrium concentration of calcium ions is about $1·4 \times 10^{-4}$ M., the solution is effectively in equilibrium with a carbon dioxide partial pressure of 10^{-6} atmosphere and the pH is about 9·9.[2] R. C. Turner and his co-workers have in fact measured pH's between 9·7 and 8·8 for the equilibrium solution of different soils in the laboratory. It is still too early to be certain of the significance of this result in practice, but presumably the pH in the subsoil of a calcareous soil, low in organic matter and carrying a rather indifferent crop, may be much higher than has been assumed in the past, and this could be of importance if a crop not well adapted to a calcareous soil is growing on the land.

Soils normally only have a pH over 8·5 if they contain enough exchangeable sodium for sodium carbonate to be present in the soil solution. These soils are known as alkali soils and are discussed on p. 598, but Whitney and Gardner showed that even if their pH is above 9·5, when measured in equilibrium with the atmosphere, it may be below 8 when in equilibrium with air containing 1 per cent of CO_2. Hence, in

[1] P. H. Yaalon, *Plant and Soil*, 1957, 8, 275.
[2] R. C. Turner, *Soil Sci.*, 1958, 86, 32, and with W. E. Nichol and K. E. Miles, *Canad. J. Soil Sci.*, 1958, 38, 94.

calcareous and alkali soils the effective pH for as far as the plant roots are concerned can be considerably lower than the pH determined by shaking up in water because of the greater concentration of carbon dioxide the roots can maintain in their immediate neighbourhood, and this effect can be still further increased due to the electrolyte concentration in the solution.

Soils do not normally have pH's below about 4·0 to 4·5 unless they contain free acids such as sulphuric; and this limit is set by the behaviour of the complex hydrated aluminium ions in the soil solution. For, as already explained, soils containing appreciable amounts of replaceable hydrogen appear to be unstable and decompose to release sufficient aluminium to neutralise the greater proportion of the net negative charge on the mineral soil particles. Thus in Assam, India, some acid tea soils have received very large dressings of sulphate of ammonia over the years, yet their pH has not been much affected because it is about 4·5.[1]

So far it has been assumed that the pH of a soil is something that can be measured accurately, but in fact this assumption is not always true. In particular the usual potentiometric methods for measuring pH are only valid if the liquid junction potential at the calomel or other reference electrode is zero, an assumption that cannot be proved, and is certainly untrue if the reference electrode is put into a rather dry soil. This is in fact the reason one measures the soil pH in suspension because there is no certain means of telling at what moisture content the assumption breaks down. Further, the activity coefficient of a single ion cannot, strictly speaking, be measured, but only the product of two ions of opposite charge, for example, the product of hydrogen and the chloride activity, or their ratio if of the same charge, for example, the ratio of the hydrogen to the square root of the calcium, as it is divalent.[2]

This discussion has therefore brought out the following points concerning the pH of a soil:

1. The correct interpretation of the measured pH of a soil may be very difficult.

2. There is no such thing as the pH of a soil-water system when dispersed in pure water, because the pH rises across the diffuse electrical double layers.

3. The pH of a soil as usually measured depends on the salt concentration in the soil solution and the CO_2 concentration in the soil air, which are constantly changing.

4. Typically the pH of a soil in the field varies appreciably over the field, even when all the samples are taken the same day.

[1] N. G. Gokhale and N. G. Bhattacharyya, *Emp. J. Exp. Agric.*, 1958, **26**, 309.
[2] For a discussion on the subject of pH scales and similar topics, see R. G. Bates, *Electrometric pH Determinations*, New York, 1954, and J. Small, *Modern Aspects of pH*, London, 1954.

These conclusions mean that the pH of a soil can have no precise significance in Soil Science, a conclusion which is amply justified by experience, as will be discussed in Chapter XXIX. They also mean that very rarely can one make any use of a really accurate measurement of the pH of a field soil, even if one measures it in a suitable salt solution, and it is probable that little information of value would be lost if one only measured the pH of field samples to the nearest 0·2 of a unit.

The Lime or Calcium Hydroxide Potential in a Soil

The fundamental objection to measuring the acidity of a soil in the field by its pH is that, strictly speaking, its pH cannot be exactly measured, and in fact has no precise meaning. The reason for this is that the activity of a single ion need not be constant throughout a solution containing charged colloid particles. There are, however, ionic activity products and ratios which are constant throughout the suspension, and which are therefore characteristics of that suspension. Thus the product of a suitable activity function of an anion and a cation present in the solution is a constant, so also is the ratio of the suitable activity functions of two anions or two cations. The activity function involved is the activity itself if the ion is monovalent, the square root of the activity if divalent, and the cube foot if trivalent. Thus if the solution contains hydrogen and chloride ions, then pH$+p$Cl, which is in fact the activity of hydrochloric acid, is constant, and if it contains calcium and hydroxyl ions, then $\frac{1}{2}p$Ca$+p$(OH) is constant, and it is the activity of calcium hydroxide in the solution.

R. K. Schofield and A. W. Taylor[1] have suggested that it would be theoretically preferable, and probably preferable from the practical point of view also, to specify the acidity of a soil by its calcium hydroxide potential rather than by its pH. This has the added advantage that it is a much more constant property of the soil than its pH, as it does not depend on the moisture content or on the concentration of dissolved neutral salts, at least if they are only in dilute solution. Thus if some typical Rothamsted soils were shaken up in calcium chloride solutions whose concentration varied from 1 to 30×10^{-3} M., the calcium hydroxide potential of the soil was constant to within 0·02 unit; and provided the solution did not exceed 10^{-2} M., it could be calculated from pH$-\frac{1}{2}p$Ca, where the pH is as measured electrometrically and the calcium ion activity is calculated from the usual Debye-Hückel formula, for

$$\tfrac{1}{2}p\text{Ca} + p(\text{OH}) = 14\cdot2 - (p\text{H} - \tfrac{1}{2}p\text{Ca}).$$

They further showed that if one shook the soil up in a 0·01 M. calcium chloride solution, the soil had little effect on the calcium ion concentra-

[1] *J. Soil Sci.*, 1955, **6**, 137, and *Proc. Soil Sci. Soc. Amer.*, 1955, **19**, 164.

tion, so one could calculate what they called the lime potential, namely, $pH - \frac{1}{2}pCa$, to within 0·02 unit by replacing $\frac{1}{2}pCa$ by its value at 0·01 M., namely, 1·14. This constancy of the lime potential to 0·02 unit implies that the pH of the soil measured under these conditions has the generally accepted meaning to within this limit, so that the soil conditions which ensure a constant lime potential also ensure that the pH of the soil has an interpretable significance to this accuracy. They further showed one could determine the alumina potential of an acid soil, $\frac{1}{3}pAl + p(OH)$, in the same way, provided the concentration of aluminium ions was less than 2×10^{-3} M.[1]

The Relative Attractions of Clay for Different Cations

The negative charges on clay particles can be neutralised by any cation except hydrogen, and hence these charges must be accessible to very large cations. This is true for the charges between the layers of montmorillonite, for these can be neutralised by complex amines,[2] and proteins[3]—ions so large that the layers may be forced apart as far as 48 Å.; and the charge density on a montmorillonite surface is low enough, about one negative charge per 140 sq. Å.,[4] to take the largest cations so far used. This accessibility of the charged spots is a characteristic of clay minerals for neither natural zeolites nor artificial permutits show it; and it has the further consequence that, on the whole, cation exchange in clays takes place very quickly.

Clays hold different ions, however, with different intensities. If a clay saturated with calcium ions, for example, is shaken up with a dilute salt solution of different metals, but all of constant normality, it is found that some cations are more powerful displacers of calcium from the clay surface than others. Thus, lithium and sodium ions are poorer displacers of another cation from a clay than potassium or ammonium ions, and these than rubidium or caesium; magnesium and calcium, which are about equally strong and of about the same strength as rubidium, are poorer displacers than strontium or barium; and the hydrogen ions from a strong acid, or polyvalent ions such as trivalent aluminium and lanthanum and tetravalent thorium are still stronger displacers. Table 29, taken from some of K. K. Gedroiz's[5] classic papers on the subject, illustrates this phenomenon, and a further and

[1] See also W. L. Lindsay, M. Peech, and J. S. Clark, *Proc. Soil Sci. Soc. Amer.*, 1959, **23**, 266, for methods of measuring this.

[2] J. E. Gieseking, *Soil Sci.*, 1939, **47**, 1; S. B. Hendricks, *J. Phys. Chem.*, 1941, **45**, 65; see also C. R. Smith, *J. Amer. Chem. Soc.*, 1934, **56**, 1561.

[3] L. E. Ensminger and J. E. Gieseking, *Soil Sci.*, 1939, **48**, 467; 1941, **51**, 125.

[4] S. B. Hendricks, *J. Phys. Chem.*, 1940, **45**, 65.

[5] *J. Expt. Agron.* (Russia), 1918, **19**, 269; 1919, **20**, 31. Manuscript translations by S. A. Waksman and published by U.S. Dept. Agric., and summarised by H. J. Page in *Trans. Int. Soc. Soil Sci.*, Comm. 2, 1926, A, 208.

more detailed example can be found in the work of J. E. Gieseking and H. Jenny.[1]

This result can be stated in the converse way; that if samples of clay each saturated with a different cation are put in a standard salt solution,

TABLE 29

Replacing Power of Different Cations

Milli-equivalents of Mg, Ca or Ba, displaced per 100 gm. of soil by certain cations added as chlorides

Chernozem	Mg	Ca	Ba
Conc. of chloride . . .	0·1 N	0·01 N	0·1 N
Chloride added:			
Li	—	1·4	7·6
Na	13·9	1·8	9·1
K	20·4	5·0	13·5
Rb	—	5·7	15·5
NH₄	20·4	5·7	12·9
Mg	—	5·3	15·4
Ca	35·2	—	20·4

exchangeable sodium ions come out of the clay easier than exchangeable potassium or ammonium, and exchangeable magnesium comes out a little easier than exchangeable calcium, which in turn comes out more easily than strontium or barium. On the whole, exchangeable potassium comes out easier than exchangeable magnesium,[2] and exchangeable barium easier than exchangeable lanthanum or thorium.

The relative tightness of binding for more complex ions has not been worked out in detail, but in general large or complex cations tend to be bound more tightly than small or simple ones. Thus diamines are more tightly held than the corresponding simple amines, and the tetra-substituted ammonium ion is still more strongly held; and large cations such as methylene blue and brucine are so strongly held that it is very difficult to displace them, except with other equally large cations.[3] As a consequence of this very tight binding, clay particles dispersed in an acid medium can be made positively charged by adding just sufficient of one of these large cations to neutralise the negative charges on the clay surface, for these cations do not dissociate at all from the surface. But the clay particles can absorb more milli-equivalents of some large organic cations than corresponds to their negative charge—mont-morillonites, for example, will absorb about double—probably because

[1] Soil Sci., 1936, 42, 273. See also P. Schachtschabel, Koll. Beih., 1940, 51, 199
[2] See also R. H. Bray, J. Amer. Chem. Soc., 1942, 64, 954.
[3] J. E. Gieseking, Soil Sci., 1939, 47, 1.

these cations form an orientated monolayer almost covering the clay surface through hydrogen bonding.[1]

The behaviour of the simple cations is not quite so regular as suggested above, for the difference between the monovalent, or alkali, cations and the divalent, or alkaline earth cations, depends on their concentration in solution. The more dilute the solution containing the cations the more powerful are the alkaline earths relative to the alkali cations as displacers of exchangeable cations; and as the ionic concentration in the solution increases, so do the replacing powers of the alkali metals relative to the alkaline earths (see p. 115).

S. Mattson[2] also claims that the inverse of this is true on the clay surface: clay particles having a high base-exchange capacity, hold calcium relative to sodium or potassium more tightly than clay particles having a low base-exchange capacity. Thus, if a montmorillonite and a kaolin were each put in a solution of potassium and calcium chlorides, the kaolin would take up relatively more potassium in comparison with calcium than would the montmorillonite. Alternatively, plants growing in a montmorillonite soil having a given ratio of exchangeable potassium to calcium will have a higher ratio of potassium to calcium than similar plants growing in a kaolinitic soil having the same ratio of exchangeable potassium to calcium.[3] Further, as a clay becomes more unsaturated, that is, more acid, so it becomes more kaolinite-like in this respect. Thus, as the acidity of a soil rises, so it tends to hold potassium ions relatively more strongly than calcium, or to put it another way, during leaching, which causes increasing soil acidity, calcium tends to go more quickly than potassium.[4]

Potassium ions can show a complication in cation exchange phenomena not shown by most other simple metallic cations, for these ions can move from being in an easily exchangeable to a difficultly exchangeable or fixed form in some clays, and in particular in degraded illites (see p. 87). Thus if a soil containing a degraded illite clay, and to a lesser extent a soil containing an illitic clay which is rather low in exchangeable potassium, is left in contact with a potassium salt for a long time, and particularly if it is repeatedly wetted and dried, it will have absorbed some potassium that cannot readily be displaced by another cation; and the ability of different cations to replace this potassium is quite different from their ability to replace normal exchangeable cations. Thus a sodium salt leaching through a soil containing fixed

[1] R. E. Grim, W. H. Allaway et al., J. Amer. Ceram. Soc., 1947, 30, 137; J. W. Jordan, Min. Mag., 1949, 28, 598; H. Mukherjee, J. Ind. Soc. Soil Sci., 1954, 2, 99.

[2] LantbrHögsk. Ann., 1945, 12, 119; with K. G. Larsson, ibid., 1945, 12, 222; Soil Sci., 1946, 61, 313. For further examples, see A. Mehlich, Soil Sci., 1946, 62, 393; with W. E. Colwell, Proc. Soil Sci. Soc. Amer., 1944, 8, 179; C. E. Marshall, Soil Sci., 1948, 65, 57.

[3] S. Mattson, LantbrHögsk. Ann., 1948, 15, 308.

[4] A. C. Schuffeln and H. A. Middelburg, Netherl. J. Agric. Sci., 1953, 1, 97.

potassium will remove more potassium than the corresponding calcium salt,[1] and both reactions are genuinely exchange reactions, that is, the amount of sodium or calcium removed from the solution equals the amount of potassium coming out.

This behaviour of potassium cannot yet be explained in detail, though it is due to the potassium ions being able to fit almost exactly in the hexagonal holes in the surface oxygen sheets of the clay particle. What is not known for certain is if the holes into which the potassium ions can enter are around the broken edges of the clay particle, or if they are on the flat surfaces; and in the latter case if two clay particles must be reasonably close together and parallel to each other, so the potassiums build up a loose mica-like structure. The only other ion which has been proved to show on similar behaviour is the ammonium ion, which has a radius similar to potassium, and the other ion one might expect to show it is the hydrion $(H_3O)^+$, which also has a similar radius.

Clays hold many cations fairly tightly so that if a sodium-saturated clay is shaken up with a sparingly soluble salt, for example, barium sulphate, an appreciable amount of barium will be taken up by the clay and a corresponding amount of sodium sulphate be found in solution.[2] Correspondingly, if an acid clay is shaken up with a weatherable mineral such as a felspar, for example, some of the metallic ions which were in the felspar will be found on the clay.[3]

The Quantitative Laws of Cation Exchange

Many attempts have been made to develop theoretical laws governing the distribution of cations between the solution and the absorbing complex in the soil. The task is complicated because under many conditions no true equilibrium appears to be reached between the soil and the solution, and the apparent equilibrium may not be reversible, for the ratio of the exchangeable cations on the soil may not depend solely on the ratio of their concentrations or activities in the solution. Many workers have tried to apply the Law of Mass Action to the exchange, but one component—the soil particles—cannot be treated as simple ions of definite valency, so arbitrary assumptions must be made about the behaviour of the cations on the clay surface. The problem falls into two distinct parts: the effect of changing the concentration of the cations in the solution already in equilibrium with the soil in such a way that the equilibrium is not changed; and the effect of changes in the concentration of cations in the solution which cause a change in the equilibrium.

[1] H. D. Mervin and M. Peech, *Proc. Soil Sci. Soc. Amer.*, 1950, **15**, 125.
[2] For an example, see R. Bradfield, *J. Phys. Chem.*, 1932, **36**, 34.
[3] E. R. Graham, *Soil Sci.*, 1940, **49**, 277; 1941, **52**, 291.

The first problem has been solved for most soils under a wide range of conditions, and it can be expressed in the so-called ratio law which R. K. Schofield has enunciated as follows: "When cations in a dilute solution are in equilibrium with a larger number of exchangeable cations, a change in the concentration of the solution will not disturb the equilibrium if the concentrations, or more strictly the activities, of all monovalent ions are changed in one ratio, those of all divalent in the square, and those of all trivalent in the cube, of that ratio."

Schofield verified this law, using a number of Rothamsted soils, by finding a solution containing potassium, magnesium and calcium chlorides of a total chloride concentration of 0·01 N which passed through a column of the soil unchanged. He then showed that another solution containing half the concentration of potassium would only pass through unchanged if the calcium and magnesium concentrations were reduced fourfold, and confirmed that the pII of this solution was 0·3 units higher than that of the first solution, because the hydrogen-ion concentration in the second solution is also halved. Further, using a very acid surface soil, the solution had to contain both aluminium and hydrogen ions if it was to pass through the soil unaltered, and if in a new solution the concentration of the potassium was halved, that of the hydrogen had to be halved and of the aluminium reduced eightfold if it was to pass through unaltered. These results express in a quantitative form, and for a particular set of experimental conditions, the relation between the pH of a soil and the concentration of salts in the soil solution which has already been discussed on p. 104.[1]

This ratio law is probably only strictly valid if the relative concentration of cations close to the fixed negative charges on the clay surfaces is high relative to that in the external solution; and the greater this relative difference in concentration, the more exactly would one expect the ratio law to hold. The great experimental difficulty in testing the validity of this law, however, lies in the great difficulty in determining the activities of salts in anything more than very dilute solutions. But the law quite definitely fails for some soils if the hydrion $(H_3O)^+$ is being considered, because its concentration can alter due to proton transfers at both positively and negatively charged spots on the soil surfaces, which are themselves dependent on the pH of the solution. The Natal soil, whose buffer curve is given in Fig. 11, is an example of such a soil.

The problem of finding a comparable law for the effect of other changes of cation concentration in the solution on the ratio of the exchangeable cations is complicated experimentally by the uncertainty

[1] R. K. Schofield and A. W. Taylor (*J. Soil Sci.*, 1955, **6**, 137, and *Proc. Soil Sci. Soc. Amer.*, 1955, **19**, 164) have given some examples of this.

of deciding when equilibrium is reached and by ionic exchange reactions appearing to be only partially reversible. As an example of a fully reversible reaction, consider a soil and solution containing only two types of cations. The exchange reaction is then said to be reversible if the relative concentration of these two cations on the clay, when equilibrium is reached, depends only on their relative concentration in the solution, no matter what their relative abundance on the clay was at the start of the experiment. This assumption of reversibility—or of independence of past history—may be reasonably valid if both the ions have the same valency, that is, if they are both monovalent, but it may not hold so commonly if the cations have different valencies,[1] although this may only be a consequence of the use of inadequate techniques.

The ionic exchange equation relating the concentrations of the cations in the solution with their relative abundance on the exchange complex is probably known in the special case of all the cations involved having the same valency, provided care is taken to prevent any side reactions being important. Under these conditions the experimental results are approximately in accord with the statement that the ratios of the amounts of cations on the exchange complex are directly proportional to their relative activities in the solution, though the factor of proportionality depends on the clay mineral. Hence merely adding water to a dilute salt solution only containing cations of the same valency and in equilibrium with a soil has little affect on the exchange, in accord with the ratio law.

No comparable generally valid statement can yet be made for the general case of the cations having different valencies. In accord with the ratio law if a salt solution containing cations of different valencies is in equilibrium with a soil, adding water to the system affects the equilibrium by some of the higher valency cations being taken up from the solution and cations of the lower valency being released into the solution. Thus the statement that monovalent cations in solution become stronger extractors of exchangeable cations relative to the divalent as their absolute concentration in the solution increases is merely a direct consequence of the ratio law.

Under some conditions when the equilibrium is reversible, the ratio of exchangeable cations on the clay is proportional to the ratio of the activity of the monovalent, the square root of the activity of the divalent and the cube root of the activity of the trivalent. Thus G. H. Bolt[2] verified this for an illitic clay, using sodium and calcium as the two ions;

[1] C. Krishnamoorthy and A. D. Desai (*Soil Sci.*, 1955, **80**, 325) consider this may be due to the very long time taken for this system to come into equilibrium with the solution unless the clay is very well dispersed.
[2] *Soil Sci.*, 1955, **79**, 267.

but C. Krishnamoorthy and R. Overstreet[1] considered that in general the cation activity ratio in the solution is proportional to a more complex function of the relative amounts of exchangeable cations on the clay, which depends on the type of clay, since clays differ in the relative tightness with which they hold the common cations. This has the consequence that the function is extremely complicated for a soil containing several clay minerals.

An aspect of cation exchange that is now receiving more attention is measuring the exchange produced by adding a very small quantity of an acid or salt to the soil and comparing this with that produced by using a more concentrated solution of the same acid or salt. Thus L. Wiklander and E. Nilsson[2] repeatedly treated sodium-calcium soil with a dilute hydrochloric acid solution until 40 per cent of the exchangeable sodium had been displaced, and they compared the amount of calcium displaced by this treatment with that displaced by a stronger solution of hydrochloric acid which displaced 40 per cent of the exchangeable sodium in the first treatment. They showed that the single treatment with the stronger acid displaced about eight times as much calcium as the repeated treatments with the diluter acid; and in general it is found that this repeated treatment replaces a higher proportion of the less tightly bound cations and a lower proportion of the more tightly bound than does the single treatment, even if the cations have the same valency, as for example sodium and potassium.

This process of exchange produced by very dilute solutions is operative during the leaching of non-saline soils in the field, and it probably operates when plants are taking up nutrients from the soil solution. For this reason R. H. Bray[3] has tried to measure the relative availability of the exchangeable cations in a soil to plants by assuming that it corresponded to the relative amounts displaced when the soil was shaken up in a 0.002 N hydrochloric acid solution. This method has been investigated by a number of workers, particularly in the United States, and it certainly gives results in reasonable accord with field practice. Thus if two soils, one containing mainly a kaolinitic clay and the other a montmorillonitic, have the same ratio of exchangeable potassium to calcium, treatment with dilute acid will remove a higher proportion of calcium from the kaolinitic soil than from the montmorillonitic, in accord with field experience.[4]

It is, however, probably theoretically preferable to estimate the relative availabilities of the cations in the soil by determining their

[1] *Soil Sci.*, 1950, **69**, 41. For more recent equations, see C. A. Bower, *Soil Sci.*, 1959, **88**, 32, and J. V. Lagerwerff and G. H. Bolt, *Soil Sci.*, 1959, **87**, 217.
[2] *Acta Agric. Scand.*, 1952, **2**, 197, and see also, with K. Vahtras, *Soil Sci.*, 1957, **84**, 269.
[3] *J. Amer. Chem. Soc.*, 1942, **64**, 954, and with S. W. Melsted, *Soil Sci.*, 1947, **63**, 209.
[4] For an example, see A. Mehlich, *Soil Sci.*, 1946, **62**, 393, and with F. M. Milam, *Soil Sci.*, 1954, **77**, 227.

relative potentials in the soil solution. In the same way as one can determine the lime potential of a soil by determining $pH - \frac{1}{2} pCa$, so one can determine the potassium potential relative to the calcium by determining $pK - \frac{1}{2} pCa$, or what is often easier $pK - \frac{1}{2} p(Ca + Mg)$; for this is a measure of the partial molal free energy of exchange of these two cations in the soil.[1] A. W. Taylor[2] determined this quantity for a number of nearly neutral Rothamsted soils and found its value varied from 2·6 for a soil low in potassium to 1·6 for a soil well supplied, figures which come within the range of values suggested by Woodruff. The relative potential was reasonably independent of the concentration of potassium and calcium ions in the solution, although as the calcium in concentration was increased, rather more potassium was found in the solution than expected; but this may have been due to the soils containing degraded illite, which can fix large amounts of potassium fairly lightly, and some of these ions may be displaced by calcium as the calcium ion concentration increases.[3]

The Effect of Fertilisers on the Exchangeable Cations held by Soils

Fertilisers are salts farmers add to the soil in order to increase the supply of nutrients to the crops. But these salts contain anions and cations which may interact with the exchangeable cations held by the soil, and so alter some of the soil's properties. The principal types of fertilisers that may have such effects are:

(1) ammonium salts and organic nitrogen compounds that decompose to liberate ammonia;
(2) sodium nitrate;
(3) phosphatic fertilisers, in particular superphosphate;
(4) the potassic fertilisers.

AMMONIUM SULPHATE

The first effect of adding this to a soil is for an exchange reaction to take place, in which the ammonium ions enter the exchange complex and an equivalent amount of other base, usually calcium, is displaced. This displaced calcium then washes out of the soil in association with the sulphate anions introduced in the fertiliser.

The ammonia is then nitrified and the nitrate ions produced are neutralised once again by calcium. In so far as the nitrate is taken up by the plant the calcium ions are free to re-enter the exchange

[1] See, for example, C. M. Woodruff, *Proc. Soil Sci. Soc. Amer.*, 1955, **19**, 36, 98 and 167.
[2] *Proc. Soil Sci. Soc. Amer.*, 1958, **22**, 511.
[3] W. E. Chambers, *J. Agric. Sci.*, 1953, **43**, 473.

complex, but in so far as the nitrate is leached out of the soil, an equivalent amount of calcium is leached out with it.

Hence, the effect of adding an equivalent of ammonium sulphate to the soil is for an equivalent of calcium to be lost with the sulphate, and for another equivalent of calcium to neutralise the nitrate formed, only part of which is leached out of the soil. If all the nitrate is leached out, 150 lb. of calcium carbonate would be needed to make good the loss of calcium through the addition of 100 lb. of ammonium sulphate,[1] and if none of the nitrate is lost, 75 lb. of calcium carbonate would be needed. In normal farming practice the loss of calcium carbonate comes in between these two limits: the various estimates of its loss for each 100 lb. of ammonium sulphate added being between 110 and 120 lb., and these limits apply both to temperate[2] and tropical soils,[3] provided the soil is reasonably provided with exchangeable calcium.

So long as the soil contains a reserve of calcium carbonate the loss falls on this substance and not on the exchangeable calcium. At the end of eighty years, the amounts of exchangeable bases contained in the Broadbalk plots, treated every year with 200 lb. per acre of sulphate of ammonia but which still contain some free calcium carbonate, are given in Table 30.

In absence of calcium carbonate, however, the replaceable calcium

TABLE 30

Exchangeable Bases in Broadbalk Soils[4]

Milli-equivalents per 100 grams of dry soil

	No manure	Sulphate of ammonia only	Super, and sulphates of potash, magnesia and soda		
			Alone	+ Sulphate of ammonia	+ Nitrate of soda
	Plot 3	Plot 10	Plot 5	Plot 7	Plot 16
Calcium . : : .	13·57	13·60	11·96	14·61	14·39
Magnesium : : .	0·75	0·70	0·95	0·90	1·25
Potassium . • • .	0·42	0·30	1·08	1·12	0·95

[1] For lysimeter determinations of this value, see M. F. Morgan *et al.*, *Soil Sci.*, 1942, **54**, 127; J. A. Bizzell, *Cornell Agric. Expt. Sta.*, *Mem.* 252, 1943.
[2] See, for example, W. H. Pierre, *J. Amer. Soc. Agron.*, 1928, **20**, 270, and E. M. Crowther in *Fifty Years of Field Experiments at Woburn*, by E. J. Russell and J. A. Voelcker (1936), p. 334.
[3] F. Leutenegger, *East Afr. Agric. J.*, 1956, **22**, 81.
[4] H. J. Page and W. Williams, *Trans. Faraday Soc.*, 1925, **20**, 573.

is removed from the soil. At Woburn the effect of adding sulphate of ammonia at the rate of 200 lb. per acre for thirty years, and 100 lb. per acre for a further twenty years is shown, on the barley plots, by the following figures.[1]

TABLE 31

Amounts of Exchangeable Calcium, Expressed as Milli-equivalents, per 100 grams of Dry Soil

No manure	Sulphate of ammonia only	Nitrate of soda only	Super, and sulphate of potash		
			Alone	+ Sulphate of ammonia	+ Nitrate of soda
3·76 pH 5·4	0·89 pH 4·5	5·15 pH 5·8	5·00 pH 6·0	1·39 pH 4·8	5·36 pH 5·8

As soon as the exchangeable calcium has fallen below a certain level the soil becomes acid and contains exchangeable aluminium ions and even soluble aluminium sulphate. Under these conditions the loss of calcium from the soil, per 100 lb. of ammonium sulphate added, drops. Thus in some Assam tea gardens, which have received repeated dressings of ammonium sulphate and which are on very acid soils to begin with, each 100 lb. of ammonium sulphate only removes calcium equivalent to 25 to 35 lb. of calcium carbonate.[2] With the exception of tea gardens, and other perennial crops requiring acid soils, the acidity due to the repeated use of ammonium sulphate must be made good by the regular adequate application of a liming material to the soil.

SUPERPHOSPHATE OF LIME

Of all the fertilisers, this has been used in the largest quantity by farmers, particularly in the past. It is made by adding sulphuric acid to ground rock phosphate, and contains 60 per cent of calcium sulphate, as gypsum, and 25 to 30 per cent of the water-soluble mono-calcium phosphate. When this is added to a soil it becomes converted to an insoluble phosphate, which sometimes contains more calcium but need not if it reacts with aluminium ions (see pp. 477, 485). It normally reacts with exchangeable calcium ions in neutral and calcareous soils, to give a dicalcium phosphate or a hydroxy-apatite (see p. 485) and in some acid soils it reacts with aluminium or perhaps ferric ions, whilst in others it will form hydroxy-apatite. If it reacts with calcium, it will

[1] E. M. Crowther, *J. Agric. Sci.*, 1925, **15**, 222; and with J. K. Basu, ibid., 1931, **21**, 689.
[2] N. G. Gokhale and N. G. Bhattacharyya, *Emp. J. Exp. Agric.*, 1958, **26**, 309.

reduce the amount of exchangeable calcium ions somewhat, which will be of no importance in calcareous soils, whilst if it reacts with aluminium or ferric ions it will not affect the level of exchangeable calcium.

There is very little experimental work on the effect of long repeated applications on the pH of a soil. On the slightly acid plots at Rothamsted and Woburn, no effect has been noted, yet there are persistent reports of soils being made acid by the use of either single or triple super-phosphates. The conditions under which additions of superphosphate to a soil affects its pH and exchangeable calcium status still needs further critical experimental examination. One condition under which this happens is on some Australian soils with low calcium reserves and of very low phosphate status. The organic carbon content of these soils under pasture is controlled by the amount of phosphate available for incorporation in the humus. If these soils are manured with super-phosphate, more phosphate becomes available for conversion into organic phosphates, the organic carbon content of the soil rises and so does the number of carboxylic groups the organic matter contains. This depresses the percentage saturation of the soil with calcium ions and in consequence its pH. Thus C. M. Donald and C. H. Williams[1] found that for some subterranean clover pastures in New South Wales, each hundredweight per acre of superphosphate increased the humus content by about one ton, which would have needed about 100 lb. of calcium to bring its pH up to 7, yet the superphosphate only contained about 25 lb. As a consequence the pH of the soil fell by 0·056 units for every hundredweight of superphosphate added.

SODIUM NITRATE

As this soluble salt washes through the soil some of the sodium will be expected to exchange with some of the calcium. Further, as the nitrate is taken up by the plant, so again sodium ions will be left behind in the soil, which may also exchange with the calcium. There is, therefore, a possibility that repeated dressings of sodium nitrate to a soil may slowly increase the proportion of sodium ions in the exchange complex until they influence appreciably the properties of the clay.

A. D. Hall[2] long ago studied this action on the Rothamsted soil, and came to the conclusion that forty or more annual dressings of 5 cwt. per acre of nitrate of soda had spoilt the tilth on some plots on Barnfield. However, a further forty annual applications at this rate on these plots have not had any additional effect, and it is probable that the effects he observed were due to soil variability. Thus, on Broadbalk long-continued application of nitrate of soda at this rate

[1] *Aust. J. Agric. Res.*, 1954, **5**, 664; 1957, **8**, 179.   [2] *Trans. Chem. Soc.*, 1904, **85**, 964.

has had no measurable effect whatever on the tilth. Unfortunately no determinations of the exchangeable sodium content of these soils have been made. Further, fifty annual applications of $2\frac{1}{4}$ cwt. per acre to wheat and barley on the light soil at Woburn did not appear to affect the tilth, except possibly occasionally in wet winters. These results are in accord with a finding of M. Salomon and J. B. Smith[1] in Rhode Island that 53 annual dressings of nitrate of soda, at the rate of nearly 3 cwt. per acre, put up the exchangeable sodium from 0·16 to 0·22 milli-equivalents per 100 grams of soil, on a soil having a base exchange capacity of 11 milli-equivalents. An increase as small as this obviously can have no effect on the soil properties.

On the other hand, there is ample evidence that if dressings of this order are applied to a fallow soil for a period of years, the sodium nitrate will very seriously affect the tilth by breaking down the crumbs and so causing all the coarser pores to become clogged with fine material.[2] This naturally reduces both the rate at which water can percolate into the soil and the air-space in the wet soil when drained. There is also evidence that annual dressings of 5 cwt. per acre applied to rubber plantations[3] and citrus orchards[4] harm the soil structure, but in both cases the harvested material sold off the plantation is low in mineral matter. There is also a strong tradition among many English market gardeners that it harms the tilth, though evidence for this belief is very hard to come by, but it may be because a heavy dressing can harm the tilth temporarily if it is concentrated in a thin layer of soil. This same result holds for the effect of adding agricultural salt (sodium chloride) to the soil in preparation for sugar-beet.

POTASSIUM SULPHATE

This increases the amount of replaceable potassium, apparently at the cost of the calcium and magnesium. Some other action takes place, for a further quantity is retained by the soil in an insoluble but not exchangeable form (see p. 113).

Both at Rothamsted and at Woburn sulphate of potash is without effect on the reaction of the surface soil, though it increases the acidity of the subsoils on the acid plots,[5] possibly through the washing down by rain of the acid liberated by cationic exchange. The effect on the

[1] Proc. Soil Sci. Soc. Amer., 1948, 12, 298.
[2] See, for example, H. Burgevin and S. Hénin, Ann. Agron., 1939, 9, 771; M. Fireman, O. C. Magistad and L. V. Wilcox, J. Amer. Soc. Agrom., 1945, 37, 888.
[3] H. J. Hardon, Meded. Alg. Proefsta. Landbouw. (Java), 1939, No. 35.
[4] D. G. Aldrich, E. R. Parker and H. D. Chapman, Soil Sci., 1945, 59, 299. Arguments from their results are complicated because they found equivalent quantities of ammonium sulphate almost as harmful, though calcium nitrate, sodium nitrate and gypsum or ammonium sulphate and lime were without harmful effect.
[5] E. M. Crowther, J. Agric. Sci., 1925, 15, 222; and with J. K. Basu, ibid., 1931, 21, 689.

exchangeable cations is shown in Table 32, taken from Page and Williams'[1] analyses of the Broadbalk soil.

TABLE 32

Exchangeable Bases in Broadbalk Soil

Milli-equivalents per 100 grams of dry soil

	Unmanured	Sulphate of ammonia and super	Sulphate of ammonia, super, and sulphate of potash	Sulphate of ammonia, super and sulphate of soda
Calcium . .	13·57	15·32	14·89	16·29
Magnesium .	0·75	0·70	0·50	0·70
Potassium . .	0·42	0·32	0·89	0·32

SODIUM SULPHATE

On the Broadbalk wheat field, sodium sulphate acts rather differently from potassium sulphate. It causes no diminution in the amount of replaceable calcium or potassium, but, on the contrary, an increase in the calcium. Apparently, therefore, the sodium has not replaced calcium or potassium, yet something has certainly happened, for more potassium is taken up by the crop. The Broadbalk wheat receiving sodium, but no potassium sulphate, contains more potassium than wheat on the adjoining plot receiving no sodium sulphate (Table 33).

MAGNESIUM SULPHATE

This has the same effect. From Table 33 it appears that in the twenty-year period, 1852–71, the sodium sulphate had enabled the plant to take up an additional 212 lb. of K, whilst the magnesium sulphate has furnished it with an extra 266 lb. over and above what the crop on Plot 11 obtained. The calcium sulphate present in the superphosphate, on the other hand, has had no appreciable effect.

No proven explanation can be given for this difference between calcium sulphate on the one hand and magnesium and sodium sulphate on the other, but the probable cause lies in the low solubility of the calcium sulphate compared with that of the other two. A crystal of magnesium sulphate in the soil will be close to a number of clay particles, and as this crystal dissolves in the soil water, it will temporarily give a high concentration of magnesium ions in the soil solution in its immediate neighbourhood, which will cause a pronounced displacement of exchangeable potassium ions into the solution which in turn

---

[1] *Trans. Faraday Soc.,* 1925, **20**, 573.

TABLE 33

Effect of Calcium, Sodium and Magnesium Sulphates in Increasing the Supply of Potassium and Wheat in Broadbalk[1]

All plots receive 200 lb. per acre of sulphate of ammonia annually

Plot	Nitrogen only	Superphosphates			
		alone	with sodium	with magnesium	with potassium
	10	11	12	14	13
K in straw per cent					
1852–61	0·79	0·68	0·87	0·97	1·07
1862–71	0·64	0·61	0·76	0·79	1·10
1902–21	0·57	0·42	0·52	0·61	1·13
Weight of K removed in crop,[2] in lb./acre/year					
1852–61	22·7	25·7	37·7	41·4	44·1
1862–71	19·2	21·6	31·4	32·4	45·9
1902–21	13·4	12·3	18·6	19·2	40·2
Exchangeable K in soil in milli-equiv. per 100 gm. in 1923[3]					
0–18 in.	0·32	0·32	0·32	0·36	0·89

will exchange, mainly with calcium ions, on neighbouring clay particles. Thus, in the neighbourhood of each crystal of magnesium and sodium sulphate, there will be a thin shell of clay particles having a higher proportion of exchangeable potassium ions than the bulk of the soil, and presumably the wheat roots obtain a proportion of their potassium from these spots before the slow processes of equilibration of this concentration of exchangeable potassium has proceeded very far. Calcium sulphate crystals cannot, on the other hand, give this high concentration of calcium ions, and so cannot show this effect.

[1] I am indebted to R. G. Warren for this Table. Most of the data for 1852–71 are given by J. B. Lawes and J. H. Gilbert, *Trans. Chem. Soc.*, 1884, **45**, 305, and some of the data for 1902–21 by W. E. Chambers, *J. Agric. Sci.*, 1953, **43**, 473.
[2] About one-quarter is in the grain and the rest in the straw.
[3] H. J. Page and W. Williams, *Trans. Faraday Soc.*, 1925, **20**, 573.

CHAPTER VIII

THE BEHAVIOUR OF SOILS AND CLAYS IN WATER

A CLAY PARTICLE, surrounded with water, affects the properties of the water in its immediate neighbourhood; and one of the most important properties affected is the total energy of the system, for when a dry clay is wetted energy is released. This reduction in the total energy can be demonstrated in many ways. When a dry clay is immersed in water, the energy released appears as heat and the heat evolved per gm. of dry soil or clay is called its heat of wetting. When a clay holds a small amount of water, it holds it so tightly that the vapour pressure of the water is very much reduced; and the curve relating the moisture content of the clay to the vapour pressure of water in the atmosphere with which it is in equilibrium may give some information on the way in which the water is held. When the density of a dry clay is determined in water and in a non-polar hydrocarbon, e.g. carbon tetrachloride, it is found that the clay has apparently a higher density in the water than in the hydrocarbon, due to the water molecules being orientated and held in the neighbourhood of the clay surface, so occupying a smaller volume than free water molecules.

It is very important to realise that soils and clays can effect the properties of water in two ways. If the clay is immersed in water its effect on the water is due solely to the properties of its surface. But if the clay or soil only contains a small quantity of water between its particles, so that there are interfaces between the liquid water and the atmosphere, these interfaces will be strongly curved and will directly affect the free energy of the liquid water. These effects are known as capillary phenomena, and are due to the geometry of the system and not to the properties of the solid particles. They are of fundamental importance when the movement of water in the soil is being considered, and will therefore be discussed in Chapter XIX.

A clay particle immersed in water affects the water molecules largely through the exchangeable ions on or near its surface. If the water is either free from electrolytes, or only contains very low concentrations, a proportion of the exchangeable ions dissociate from the soil surface and move into the water, but the majority do not move very far away from the surface. They form what is known as a diffuse double layer: a double layer because the clay surface carries a net negative charge and the water a net positive charge, and diffuse because the net positive charge is distributed throughout a volume instead of over a surface. The properties of these double layers and the effect of other salts on the distribution of the dissociated cations in the neighbourhood of the soil surface can be calculated approximately in certain simple cases by the methods first introduced by G. Gouy and extended by P. Debye and E. Hückel.

Four properties only of this double layer need be stressed in this section. Firstly, its thickness, that is, the mean distance the ions dissociate away from the surface, decreases as the electrolyte concentration in the water increases; and at equal equivalent concentrations of electrolyte divalent cations decrease the thickness of the double layer more strongly than monovalent, and trivalent more strongly than divalent. As a corollary to this, if clay particles are suspended in water containing very little electrolyte, the double layer is thicker if the exchangeable ions are sodium and potassium than if they are calcium or magnesium, and it is probably thicker for sodium than for potassium.

Secondly, the existence of this diffuse double layer causes an electrical potential difference between the surface of the clay particle and the bulk of the solution; that is, work must be done to transfer a cation from the surface of the particle to the bulk of the solution. Hence, this double layer hinders the free interchange of cations between these two regions. A consequence of this effect has already been mentioned on p. 104. Hydrogen ions cannot have the same activity throughout these regions, and in fact the thicker the double layer the smaller will be the contribution of the hydrogen ions that can dissociate from the clay surface to the hydrogen-ion concentration in the bulk of the solution. The more the diffuse double layer is compressed on to the clay surface the more freely will the hydrogen ions be able to move from the clay surface into the solution, and the lower will be its apparent pH. Also, since at a given concentration calcium ions compress the double layer more strongly than potassium, a soil will have a lower pH in a dilute calcium chloride solution than in a potassium chloride solution of the same normality. This result is not confined to hydrogen ions. If, say, a sodium clay is dispersed in pure water, adding a dilute electrolyte to the solution will increase the proportion of sodium ions that dissociate from the clay surface through reducing the potential difference across the double layer.

Thirdly, the proportion of the exchangeable cations that dissociate to form the double layer. The most direct way of estimating this proportion should be by measuring the activities of the cations around the clay particles, using suitable membrane electrodes in the same way as the hydrogen-ion concentration around the clay particle is measured with, say, a glass electrode, but the membrane electrode techniques have not yet been developed for this to be done reliably as they are not yet sufficiently specific for any one of the simple cations. But C. E. Marshall,[1] who has developed these electrodes, considers he can show at corresponding contents of exchangeable cations that only about one-tenth as many calcium as sodium ions are dissociated from a montmorillonite clay, and between one-quarter and one-half that of sodium from a kaolinite, and only about one to three sodium ions per thousand adsorbed are dissociated.

Fourthly, the concentration of the added anions in the diffuse double layer is lower than in the bulk of the solution. Hence, if a dilute solution of sodium chloride is added to a dry clay, and if no chloride is taken up by the clay, the concentration of chloride in the solution will rise, because the chloride will be partially expelled from that part

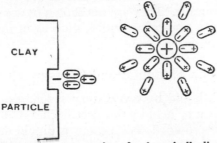

CLAY

PARTICLE

FIG. 12. Diagrammatic representation of a clay micelle dispersed in water.

which is near the clay surfaces from which exchangeable cations dissociate. This phenomenon is sometimes called negative adsorption; and part of the water forming the diffuse double layer is sometimes called bound or unfree water; and because of this phenomenon some workers, such as S. Mattson in particular,[2] have treated the system clay-electrolyte-water as a Donnan membrane equilibrium system. This exclusion of anions from part of the water in the system also creates great difficulties when one is trying to measure the adsorption of anions from dilute solutions by soils, particularly monovalent anions such as chlorides and nitrates which are only taken up in small quantities; for one does not know experimentally from what effective volume of water the anion is expelled.

The exchangeable ions affect the water through the positive charges they carry influencing the orientation of the water molecules in their neighbourhood, for though the water molecule is electrically neutral, it has an excess of positive charge at one end and of negative charge at the other, so behaves like an electric dipole. Fig. 12 illustrates this effect

[1] *Soil Sci.*, 1948, **65**, 57.   [2] See, for example, *Soil Sci.*, 1946, **61**, 313.

diagrammatically. The free negative charges on the clay surface, and the dipole formed by a negative charge on the clay neutralised by an undissociated cation, equally affect the orientation and freedom of movement of the water molecules in their immediate neighbourhood.

This effect of the cation in reducing the freedom of movement of the water molecules is greater the greater the charge on the cation, and the smaller its size, that is, the greater its surface charge density. Thus magnesium ions have a greater effect than calcium, and calcium than potassium. Hence, magnesium clays have a greater heat of wetting,[1] a greater adsorption of water vapour at low relative humidities,[2] and a greater apparent density in water compared with that in an inert liquid[3] than calcium clays and these than sodium clays and those than potassium clays. These ionic effects are not confined to the system clay-water, but are also shown, usually to a smaller extent, with clay and any other liquid whose molecules possess dipole moments, such as the alcohols, for example. They are not shown by systems in which the clay is dispersed in a non-polar liquid, such as in most hydrocarbons or carbon tetrachloride.

Absorption of Liquids and Gases by Dry Clays

Dry clays absorb liquid by two distinct mechanisms. Firstly, molecules of the liquid can be held by the electric charges of the clay and the exchangeable ions, provided they possess a dipole moment or have a dipole moment induced in them by the charges. E. W. Russell[3] has made a fairly extensive investigation of these absorption phenomena and found that simple electrical considerations are quite adequate to explain them. Secondly, liquids can be held in the pores between the clay particles, and any liquid can be held in such a way. R. K. Schofield[4] showed that there is no reason to doubt that the ordinary laws of capillary condensation hold approximately even if the pores are only about ten times larger than the diameter of the liquid molecules.

The adsorption of liquids on the surface of dry clays normally involves the system swelling if the particles were previously in closest packing, though the additional volume occupied is usually considerably less than the volume of liquid adsorbed, for much of the adsorbed liquid occupies the pore space between the particles. A good quantitative analysis of the factors causing a dry clay to swell when wetted with water has not been made, but normally the swelling is greater the higher the cation exchange capacity of the clay, as one would expect;

[1] W. W. Pate, *Soil Sci.*, 1925, 20, 329; L. D. Baver, *J. Amer. Soc. Agron.*, 1928, 20, 921; M. S. Anderson, *J. Agric. Res.*, 1929, 38, 565; H. Janert, *J. Agric. Sci.*, 1934, 24, 136.
[2] M. D. Thomas, *Soil Sci.*, 1928, 25, 485; H. Kuron, *Koll. Chem. Beih.*, 1932, 36, 178.
[3] E. W. Russell, *Phil. Trans.*, 1934, 233 A, 361.
[4] *Trans. 1st Comm. Int. Soc. Soil Sci.*, Bangor, 1938, A 38.

and for a given clay the sodium saturated usually swells more than the calcium saturated and the acid washed, and these swell more than the potassium saturated.[1] The swelling is less in a salt solution than in water, and the more concentrated the solution, the less the swelling. If the liquid merely fills the spore space without being specifically adsorbed on the surface, as, for example, if a non-polar hydrocarbon vapour condenses on a dry clay whose particles are in closest packing, the condensation will involve no change in the volume of the clay system.

The converse process of dispersing a clay in a liquid and then removing the liquid by allowing it to evaporate, causes the volume of the clay-liquid system to be reduced by the volume of the liquid removed until a time comes when further removal of liquid allows air to enter the spaces between the clay particles. If the liquid is not specifically adsorbed by the clay surface, further removal of liquid will only cause a small reduction in volume of the system as the particles will be nearly in closest packing, so further drying cannot bring them much closer together. But if the liquid is specifically adsorbed, as is water, for example, then the thickness of the adsorbed films round the particles will become thinner and the whole system continue to shrink.

Dry clays will also absorb gases, and here we know very much less about the phenomenon and nothing about the mechanism of the absorption. At temperatures of liquid nitrogen ($-183°$ C.), P. H. Emmett, S. Brunauer and K. S. Lowe[2] considered they could calculate from the nitrogen absorption curve the point at which a monomolecular film of nitrogen was formed on the clay surface; and using this method, concluded that the particles in the clay fraction of two soils (Cecil and Barnes) had a surface area of about 40 and 70 sq. m. per gm.

Dry clays absorb permanent gases at room temperatures, and the amount they absorb is in proportion to the gas pressure, and increases as the critical temperature increases. The absorption is very small for helium, neon and hydrogen, larger for oxygen, nitrogen, air and argon,[3] and much larger for carbon dioxide.[4] It is possible that calcium and magnesium clays absorb gases more strongly than potassium clays, which in turn are stronger absorbers than sodium. These absorbed gases are readily displaced by water vapour or water, and, in fact, this displacement of absorbed air is an important mechanism in the observed break-up of dry soil clods when they are wetted.[5]

[1] L. D. Baver and H. Winterkorn, Soil Sci., 1934, 38, 291; 1935, 40, 403.
[2] Soil Sci., 1938, 45, 57; R. A. Nelson and S. B. Hendricks, ibid., 1943, 56, 285.
[3] Unpublished observations of E. W. Russell and G. H. Cashen.
[4] H. Wiessmann and W. Neumann, Ztschr. Pflanz. Düng., 1935, 40, 49; Trans. 3rd Int. Congr. Soil Sci. (Oxford), 1935, 1, 51; M. W. Tschapek, Pedology, 1938, No. 1, 25.
[5] For examples of this effect, see E. W. Russell and R. V. Tamhane, J. Agric. Sci., 1940, 30, 210.

These effects are illustrated in Fig. 13, which shows the changes in volume of a wet soil cylinder as it is first dried and then re-wetted.[1] The higher volume for a given moisture content on re-wetting is due to the adsorbed air that has been displaced and entrapped in the pores.

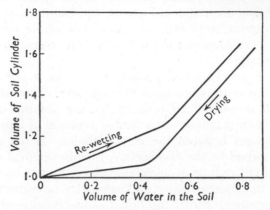

FIG. 13. The effect of drying and wetting a cylinder of moulded soil on its volume.

Deflocculation and Flocculation of Clay Suspensions

If a small amount of sodium clay is shaken up in distilled water it will usually disperse into individual particles, which will repel one another if they come sufficiently closely together; and when the clay particles sediment out, the sediment is compact and difficult to redisperse. This suspension is said to be deflocculated. The cause of the repulsion is due to the interaction of the two diffuse double layers, and of the compact sediment is that the particles are in close packing as they are uniformly distributed throughout the sediment. If now sufficient electrolyte is added, the particles will cease to repel one another when they come close together, but instead will stick to each other, forming loose aggregates or flocs. The suspension is now said to be flocculated. The mechanism of floc formation is not understood, but it only takes place when the diffuse double layer is thin, and since the flocs are very loose the particles can presumably only join up in chains, thus enclosing a large volume of solution. These flocs settle into loose sediments, in which the particles are not uniformly distributed, and hence which can be very easily redispersed.

The phenomenon of deflocculation in clay suspensions is shown most strongly by clays whose exchangeable ions are predominantly sodium, or probably also lithium. It is less strongly displayed by potassium or magnesium, and still less by calcium or acid clays. The minimum

[1] W. B. Haines, *J. Agric. Sci.*, 1923, **13**, 296.

concentration of cations needed to cause flocculation is highest for sodium and lithium clays, lower for potassium, ammonium and magnesium clays, lower still for calcium and aluminium clays, and very much lower for clays containing multivalent or complex cations.[1]

The transitions between deflocculation and flocculation presents phenomena which are not well understood, though they are probably of very great practical importance. If the clay suspension is very dilute, with only a few parts of clay per ten thousand parts of water, the transitional phenomenon is that at electrolyte concentrations inadequate to cause complete flocculation, a portion of the particles stick together in very small and apparently fairly compact flocs and settle through a cloudy suspension. When the clay concentration rises to several parts per thousand of water, this phenomenon of fine flocs settling through a cloudy suspension is still the first to be seen. But as more electrolyte is added a new phenomenon is found. The clay suspension sets into a very weak gel, from which water separates out, allowing the whole to settle uniformly. The clay suspension has a sharp upper boundary and leaves a clear, supernatant liquid. On standing, this gel may break up into flocs, or it may develop pipes through which the liquid, which has become surplus through the contraction, can escape.[2] As the electrolyte concentration becomes still higher, this stage either lasts a very short time before it breaks up into flocs, or flocs form straight away.[3]

This property of forming weak elastic gels, that break up readily in a fluid suspension when shaken, is known as thixotropy.[4] It is displayed most strongly by clays such as bentonites when they hold a large amount of exchangeable sodium ions, and much more weakly by kaolinitic clays, which can only hold small amounts of exchangeable sodium. The cause of this behaviour is not known, but since it takes a definite time for the clay to set as a gel after shaking, the clay particles presumably must take up preferred orientations with respect to their neighbours.[5]

The evidence available is concordant with the picture that the clay particles form a fairly open network, with the particles edge to edge, though there may be some overlap at the edges. Thus R. K. Schofield and C. Dakshinamurti[6] found that the electrical conductivity of a

[1] For a discussion and references to experiments on these topics, see G. Wiegner, *J. Soc. Chem. Indust.*, 1931, **50**, 65 T, and E. W. Russell, *J. Agric. Sci.*, 1932, **22**, 165. See also H. Jenny and R. F. Reitemeier, *J. Phys. Chem.*, 1935, **39**, 593, for later experiments.

[2] See R. K. Schofield and B. A. Keen, *Nature*, 1929, **123**, 492, for a photograph of this.

[3] For a more detailed description of these phenomena, see J. L. Russell, *Proc. Roy. Soc.*, 1936, **154** A, 550.

[4] This phenomenon is discussed in text-books of colloid chemistry, but for a good account, see H. Freundlich, *Thixotropy*, Paris, 1935.

[5] For a review, see E. A. Hauser, *Chem. Rev.*, 1945, **37**, 287. See also *J. Phys. Chem.*, 1939, **43**, 1015.   [6] *Faraday Soc., Disc.* 3, 56.

deflocculated 1 per cent bentonite solution in $N/40$ potassium bromide was 3 per cent greater than the salt solution, but for the thixotropic gel in $N/10$ potassium bromide, it was 16 per cent less.

Deflocculation and Flocculation in Clay Pastes and Clods: Soil Consistency

Flocculation and deflocculation phenomena in concentrated clay pastes are primarily concerned with their rheological properties, i.e. those concerned with the mechanics of their flow and deformation. At a given clay concentration, a deflocculated clay is more fluid than a flocculated, and correspondingly a flocculated is more rigid than a deflocculated, but this rigidity itself is only strongly shown if the paste is subject to weak stress; i.e. it possesses a property analogous to its thixotropic properties in dilute suspensions.

Deflocculated pastes dry to hard, uniform and usually large clods possessing very few cracks, whilst flocculated pastes dry to smaller, more crumbly clods, usually full of cracks. This effect can be seen in Plate V, which shows the effect of drying a deflocculated and a flocculated paste of a sodium clay. Thus, both the uniformity of distribution of particles throughout the system that is characteristic of the deflocculated system, and the non-uniform spatial distribution characteristic of the flocculated system, persist in the dried state. Crumb formation is thus seen to be a characteristic of a flocculated, and hard clod formation of a deflocculated, clay; and the greater the concentration of salts present in the wet clay paste, the weaker, more friable and more porous will be the clods formed when the paste is dried.

Clods formed by drying a deflocculated clay paste differ in another fundamental respect from those formed from a flocculated paste: on wetting, the former typically redisperse into a paste; whereas the latter may swell in the water, but they retain their shape, and do not redisperse. Clods showing the former behaviour are called water-unstable, and the latter water-stable. Soils containing much exchangeable sodium but no free salts give typical hard large clods when dry, which break down again into a liquid mud when wet, whereas salt-free calcium soils give smaller clods which retain their shape on wetting. Potassium and magnesium soils come intermediate: soils rich in high cation-exchange capacity clays saturated with either of these cations give clods showing considerable water instability; whereas acid soils behave almost exactly like calcium ones.

Water instability of clods is confined to those produced from drying a deflocculated paste. Thus, if sufficient sodium chloride or sulphate is added to a sodium clay paste so that it becomes flocculated, the clods formed by drying this paste become water-stable; and sodium clay clods themselves are stable if wetted with a dilute sodium chloride solution. These properties are of great importance in many irrigated soils which contain much exchangeable sodium. So long as fairly salty irrigation water is used the surface tilth remains good, but the soils cannot stand prolonged rain, because rain-water does not contain enough salts to keep the clay particles flocculated. These harmful effects of deflocculated sodium soils can often be aggravated by adding small quantities of sodium carbonate (alkali), which by raising the pH raises the exchangeable sodium content of the soil, causing it to become deflocculated.

The cause of water instability or water stability of crumbs is the same as the cause of deflocculation and flocculation. For a water-unstable crumb deflocculates when shaken up in water because there are repulsive forces between the particles, so the added water can penetrate indefinitely between the clay particles.[1] This not only causes the crumb to swell indefinitely but also to lose its shear strength so that it loses its shape also. A water-stable crumb does not break up indefinitely when shaken gently in water, because such a dry crumb has the property that the clay particles attract each other, and when wetted some water may penetrate between the particles, so the crumb swells to a strictly limited extent, but not enough water can penetrate to allow a separation sufficiently large for the repulsive forces to come into play; hence the wet crumb does not lose its shear strength or its shape. One can get a continuous transition between the typical deflocculated sodium clay and the flocculated calcium clay behaviour by suitably choosing the exchangeable ions and the concentration of a suitable salt in the water.

Flocculation and deflocculation therefore affect the swelling of soils when wetted, and this has the consequence that if a dilute salt solution is percolated through a series of soils containing an increasing proportion of exchangeable sodium ions relative to calcium, the permeability of the soil will drop more rapidly with time the higher the content of exchangeable sodium, and that just before the soil becomes impermeable the solution will become turbid due to fine soil particles dispersing in it. These are factors of great importance in the irrigation and management of saline and alkali soils, and are discussed in detail in Chapter XXXIV.

Flocculation and deflocculation of clay pastes affect other properties besides water stability and permeability. Deflocculated clay pastes are sticky, and mouldable into any desired shape at relatively low moisture

[1] See, for example, K. Norrish, *Faraday Soc.*, *Disc.* 18, 1954, 120, and B. P. Warkentin, G. H. Bolt and R. D. Miller, *Proc. Soil Sci. Soc. Amer.*, 1957, **21**, 495.

contents; flocculated pastes are less sticky, and cease to be mouldable at relatively high moisture contents—they become crumbly or friable at lower moisture contents. This complex factor of lack of stickiness together with crumbliness probably is that recognised in the field as mellowness: a mellow tilth takes cultivation implements at higher moisture contents than a raw tilth, and dries to a crumbly friable soil rather than to hard clods.

Adding calcium carbonate to a heavy clay soil may increase the mellowness of its tilth and reduces the size of clods into which the soil dries, presumably through it causing the clay to become more flocculated. It is, however, not due to it converting an acid clay into a calcium clay, for both these clays behave almost identically in the absence of added electrolyte.

CHAPTER IX

THE PHYSIOLOGY OF THE MICROBIAL POPULATION

The Microbial Population of the Soil

SOILS DIFFER FROM a heap of inert rock particles in many ways, but one of the more important is that they have a population of micro-organisms living in them which derives its energy by oxidising organic residues left behind by the plants growing on the soil or by the animals feeding on these plants. In the final analysis the plants growing on the soil subsist on the products of microbial activity, for the micro-organisms are continually oxidising the dead plant remains and leaving behind, in a form available to the plant, the nitrogenous and mineral compounds needed by the plants for their growth. On this concept a fertile soil is one which contains either an adequate supply of plant food in an available form or a microbial population which is releasing nutrients fast enough to maintain rapid plant growth; whilst an infertile soil is one in which this does not happen, as, for example, if the micro-organisms are removing and locking up available plant nutrients from the soil.

The soil micro-organisms can be classified into major divisions, such as the bacteria, actinomycetes, fungi and algae—the microflora, and the protozoa, worms and arthropods—the microfauna and fauna. But these divisions are not always clear-cut: there are flagellates, such as *Euglena*, that can be classed either with the algae or protozoa, but even more important, there are groups of soil organisms such as the *Myxomycetes* and the *Acrasiae*, which seem to bridge the gap between the microflora and the microfauna and cannot be clearly assigned to either of these groups. For this reason some biologists have introduced the word "protista" to cover all micro-organisms. Protista are not considered plants or animals, but they contain many simple forms of life, some of which have given rise to plants, some to animals, and some to forms that are not clearly either, as, for example, the fungi.

The classification of the soil micro-organisms into orders and genera also presents very difficult problems. The traditional fundamental criteria on which such classification depends are based on an examination of the sexual reproductive organs; but many groups of soil organisms have either never possessed the power of sexual reproduction, as in the bacteria, actinomycetes and blue-green algae, or have effectively lost it, as in many of the soil fungi; so that, for these groups, the generally accepted criteria are not available.

The bacteria form an outstanding example of the difficulties of classification, because not enough is yet known about them for there to be adequate criteria available to separate them into groups.[1] Their shapes are too similar for most of them to be classified by this means, and it seems unlikely that they will be found to possess sufficiently numerous surface characteristics, even when examined with the electron microscope (see Plate VI) for any detailed morphological classification to be possible. Their early classification was developed by pathologists, who were impressed by their specificity, in, for example, their being the cause of an identifiable disease; but the outstanding characteristic of the common soil bacteria is their adaptability rather than their specificity.

The methods of studying what the micro-organisms do in the soil are again very inadequately developed. There are still no satisfactory ways of following what the smaller micro-organisms do, though there are a variety of methods giving partial pictures of their activities. The method of examining a natural soil directly with a microscope, using incident light illumination, has been developed by W. L. Kubiena,[2] and though of considerable value for the study of the larger organisms, e.g. fungi and nematodes, it is still limited by great technical difficulties in the study of bacteria and other organisms that have almost transparent bodies.

J. Rossi and S. Riccardo[3] and N. Cholodny[4] independently devised a method for the direct examination of the soil organisms. Microscope slides or cover slips are buried in the soil for a few days, and carefully dug up, the main lumps of soil removed and the micro-organisms on the slide fixed and stained. Such preparations often give an excellent idea of the methods of growth and of the morphology of the different types of micro-organisms, and one can sometimes even see that one organism has been feeding on another. But the results obtained by this method must be carefully interpreted. In the first place some organisms will grow better on a continuous solid surface than in between the soil particles, hence will develop more strongly on these slides than in the soil. In the second, it has been customary to examine these slides after the organisms have been killed, fixed and stained, so that only their gross morphology, i.e. whether they are cocci, rods, fine hyphae, etc., could be noted, and only rarely were fruiting bodies found.

[1] For a discussion of this problem, see C. B. van Niel, *Cold Spring Harbor Symp.*, 1946, **11**, 285.   [2] *Micropedology*, Ames, 1938.
[3] *Nuovi Ann. dell' Agricolt.*, 1927, **7**, 92, 457. For a summary of Rossi's work in English, see *Soil Sci.*, 1936, **41**, 53.   [4] *Arch. Mikrobiol.*, 1930, **1**, 620.

Techniques such as phase contrast microscopy have, however, now been developed which allow direct examination of the living organisms to be made.

Cholodny[1] has introduced two other methods for observing the behaviour of micro-organisms in the soil. In the first, some moist natural soil is carefully sifted into a glass cell, about 1 mm. deep, with a circular space about 4 mm. in diameter left in the middle, and the cell is then covered with a cover slip. After an interval of time, fungal hyphae may be seen growing out from the soil into this space, and later it is sometimes also possible to see films of bacteria spreading around its periphery. In the second method[2] some fine soil particles are put on a microscope slide, covered with a cover glass, and a drop of water allowed to spread between the two. This is incubated for several days and then examined. Fungi and actinomycetes are seen to be dominant if the soil is only slightly damp, whilst if it is moister films of bacteria, either cocci or short rods, can be seen to spread out radially from the soil particles. These bacteria usually appear to be surrounded by gummy capsules.

More recently C. Rouschel and S. Strugger[3] and E. Burrichter[4] have developed techniques which allow one to see bacteria and other organisms in a fluorescence microscope and P. C. T. Jones and J. E. Mollison[5] and Y. T. Tchan and J. S. Bunt[6] used dyes that stained living but not dead organisms. Rouschel and Strugger found that the dye, acridine orange, when absorbed by living (or recently dead) organisms fluoresces green, but when absorbed by dead cells or organic matter fluoresces red to red-brown. Jones and Mollison found that living (or recently dead) organisms would absorb aniline blue and hold it against a solvent which would remove it from organic matter and dead cells. Bacteria, actinomycetes and living fungal mycelium all stain an intense blue colour by this technique, and can be clearly distinguished from any soil or organic particles they may be on, and some of their photographs are reproduced in Plate VII.

Another group of methods for studying the soil organisms is based on the pure culture plating technique. The soil is shaken up with water and a sample of the soil suspension is diluted, mixed with a suitable culture medium and poured on a plate of nutrient agar. Organisms from the individual colonies can then be picked out and their metabolism and behaviour studied in isolation. This method picks out from among the common soil organisms those that can be brought into suspension by this technique and which will grow on the particular nutrient

[1] *Arch. Mikrobiol.*, 1934, **5**, 148.   [2] *Arch. Mikrobiol.*, 1936, **7**, 286.
[3] *Naturwiss.*, 1943, **31**, 300; *Canad. J. Res.*, 1948, **26** C, 188. See also A. Stöckli, *Schweiz. landw. Mh.*, 1959 no. 4/5, 162.   [4] *Ztschr. PflErnähr*, 1953, **63**, 154.
[5] *J. Gen. Microbiol.*, 1948, **2**, 54.   [6] *Nature*, 1954, **174**, 656.

medium used; it can also be used to pick out less common organisms that possess any easily recognisable characteristic; but it suffers from the defect that usually only a small proportion of the soil micro-organisms appear to develop on these plates (see p. 146), and hence one cannot conclude that the organisms so isolated are a representative sample of the microbial population. Further, it only gives limited information about the reactions the various bacteria actually carry out in the soil, for bacteria can grow on organic substances in pure culture which they would be unable to use in the very competitive environment of the soil.

A third method, developed by Beijerinck and Winogradsky, and of great value in isolating organisms having an "unusual" metabolism, is to alter the soil conditions so they are especially favourable to organisms capable of this metabolism, but unfavourable to other types. Thus Winogradsky was able to encourage bacteria which could derive their energy from the oxidation of ammonia or nitrite by supplying the soil with ammonia or nitrite as the sole source of energy.

These various methods thus supplement each other. The methods of direct observation show something of what the micro-organisms look like in the soil, and often where they live, but only rarely do they show what they are doing; whilst the pure culture methods usually give some indication of what the micro-organisms can do, but not what they look like, or where they are, in the soil.

The Nutrition of the Microflora: Autotrophic and Heterotrophic Organisms

Organisms need food for two distinct purposes: to supply energy for their necessary vital processes and to build up their body tissues. Some of the microflora can use entirely different sources of food for these two purposes, whereas for others and for most animals the same food serves both purposes equally. The microflora use three different methods for obtaining energy: most algae and a few kinds of bacteria can use sunlight direct, some bacteria can use part of the energy set free when certain inorganic compounds are oxidised, e.g. hydrogen or sulphides, whilst most of the microflora can use part of the energy set free when sugars and other organic compounds are degraded or oxidised.

The microflora are classified into autotrophs, which are capable of using the carbon of carbon dioxide as the sole source of carbon for their body tissues, and heterotrophs, which are not so capable. Most autotrophs can utilise more complex forms of carbon, though the nitrifying bacteria and some thiobacilli probably cannot, and many heterotrophs need carbon dioxide as well as complex sources of carbon. On this definition, there is a sharp distinction between heterotrophs and autotrophs, for the autotrophs must be supplied with an external source of energy for the conversion of carbon dioxide into body protoplasm, whilst the heterotrophs can use sugars and other simple organic substances as a source both of energy and of protoplasm. There are also two other important distinctions between these two types of nutrition. In the first place it takes much more energy to convert carbon dioxide than sugars into protoplasmic substances. In the second more energy is released per mole of oxygen used when sugar is oxidised than when inorganic substances are oxidised, as the following examples show:

$$C_6H_{12}O_6 + 6O_2 \rightarrow 6CO_2 + 6H_2O + 686 \text{ Cals.}[1]$$
$$NH_4^+ + 3O_2 \rightarrow NO_2^- + 2H_2O + 158 \text{ Cals.}$$
$$2NO_2^- + O_2 \rightarrow 2NO_3^- + 43 \text{ Cals.}$$
$$2H_2S + O_2 \rightarrow S + 2H_2O + 65 \text{ Cals.}$$
$$S + 2O_2 \rightarrow SO_4^- + 142 \text{ Cals.}$$
$$4FeCO_3 + O_2 + 6H_2O \rightarrow 4Fe(OH)_3 + 4CO_2 + 81 \text{ Cals.}$$

Green plants, most algae and some bacteria are capable of autotrophic growth, whilst most bacteria, and possibly all actinomycetes and fungi, can only grow heterotrophically.

Autotrophic organisms are the primary producers of organic matter; and though the higher green plants are usually the most important suppliers of energy-rich material to the soil, some of the autotrophic micro-organisms may contribute appreciably. Autotrophic organisms fall into two groups: the photosynthetic group, which contain chlorophyll of one kind or another and are capable of using the energy of sunlight to reduce carbon dioxide to sugars, and the chemosynthetic group, which have to carry out ancillary inorganic oxidations to obtain this energy.

Photosynthetic organisms are probably of little importance in the soil and are mainly confined to the algae, though under some conditions a few photosynthetic bacteria may be found. Algae can be important on or just below the soil surface. But the predominant photosynthetic organisms are green plants.

Chemosynthetic autotrophic organisms probably only exist among the bacteria: the soil forms can derive their energy from a considerable range of oxidations, such as that of hydrogen to water, hydrogen sulphide to sulphur, thiosulphates and thionates, thence to sulphates, ammonia to nitrites and nitrites to nitrates, ferrous iron to ferric iron, and possibly divalent manganese to a more complex ion. Some can

---

[1] 1 Cal. = 1 kg. calorie = 1000 calories.

obtain their energy by carrying out intermolecular rearrangements such as

$$6KNO_3 + 5S + 2CaCO_3 \rightarrow 3K_2SO_4 + 2CaSO_4 + 2CO_2$$
$$+ 3N_2 + 634 \text{ Cals.},$$

which can be performed by the fairly common soil bacteria *Thiobacillus denitrificans*.[1]

Autotrophic organisms can obtain their nitrogen supply from ammonium or nitrate salts, and these are usually the preferred sources; some, perhaps the majority, have difficulty in using most amino acids. A few autotrophic organisms can use or fix atmospheric nitrogen as their primary source, for example, all photosynthetic bacteria growing under suitable anaerobic conditions and some blue-green algae under aerobic conditions.

Heterotrophic organisms are usually classified according to the complexity of their essential nutritional requirements. Most members of the microflora can use simple sugars as their main source of body fuel, but they vary in the types of sugar they can make use of. The majority can use glucose (dextrose) as their primary source, and produce, sometimes only if necessary, enzymes capable of converting a wide range of carbohydrates into this sugar.

Heterotrophic organisms have a wide variety of demands in their food supply. The unspecialised members can obtain all the carbon for their body tissues from simple sugars or fatty acids and their nitrogen from inorganic nitrogen compounds, or, for some bacteria, from gaseous nitrogen. These processes are possible because the organisms can synthesise all the enzymes needed for their life and growth. Other members need more complex food supplies and one can consider that this is due to the organism losing its power to synthesise one or more of these enzymes. The first enzymes that usually cease to be synthesised, as the organism becomes more exacting in its food requirements, fall into two groups: those needed for producing from simple nitrogen sources the whole range of amino acids required for building up the body proteins, and those needed for the organism's respiratory processes. If any of the first group are missing, the organism must be supplied with the essential amino acids, and if any of the second, with the prosthetic groups of the respiratory enzymes which it has lost the power of synthesising. The latter, which are usually members of the vitamin B complex, are only needed in very small quantities, as with vitamins for the human being. In contrast, the amino acids must be supplied in considerably greater quantity if the organism is to reproduce rapidly. Carbon dioxide is also an essential growth factor for many heterotrophic

[1] R. E. Buchanan and E. I. Fulmer, *Physiology and Biochemistry of Bacteria*, vol. 1, 433, London, 1928.

bacteria and fungi. Werkman and Wood[1] have been able to follow a little of the chemistry of this carbon dioxide need by using radioactive carbon, and have obtained evidence that it is needed to convert pyruvic acid—a product of sugar fermentation—into oxalacetic acid, which plays an important role as a hydrogen carrier in the respiratory oxidation of sugars.

This loss of power of synthesising critical substances is scattered over many groups of the microflora in such an erratic way that it has no systematic significance. On the whole, the exactingness of the organism is a reflection of its usual food supply: the more specialised the supply, as, for example, in a well-adapted parasite, the more likely the organism is to have lost the power of synthesising some of the enzymes produced by related organisms utilising a less specialised food supply. It has always been assumed in the past that autotrophic organisms, that is, organisms deriving the carbon of their protoplasm from carbon dioxide, could synthesise all the enzymes and amino acids needed for their growth. This assumption is now known to be false for some of the photosynthetic sulphur bacteria, as some need one or more constituents of the B vitamin complex.[2] Hence there may also be other members of the autotrophic bacteria, in the sense defined above, that need some of the growth-promoting substances—a possibility that has not yet been properly investigated.

All micro-organisms need minerals as well as sources of carbon and nitrogen, though the relative amount needed varies widely with different types. As with plants, potassium and phosphate are needed in considerable quantities, sodium, magnesium, calcium, iron and sulphur often in relatively high quantities, manganese, copper, zinc, boron and cobalt usually in small quantities by most organisms, whilst molybdenum or vanadium are probably necessary if the organisms are either using nitrate or atmospheric nitrogen as their source of energy.[3] Micro-organisms, however, differ very considerably amongst themselves in their requirements of these elements. The function of most of these metals is to form part of the prosthetic group of an enzyme; thus, iron and copper are needed for various porphyrins taking part in hydrogen transfer during respiration. Azotobacter forms a good example of an organism needing a trace metal only when certain enzymes are required; it can only fix atmospheric nitrogen when supplied with traces of molybdenum or vanadium, but it can grow perfectly well in the absence of this metal if an available supply of ammonium ions is present.

[1] For a review of this work, see C. H. Werkman and H. G. Wood, *Adv. Enzymol.*, 1942, **2**, 135; and H. A. Krebs, *Ann. Rev. Biochem.*, 1943, **12**, 529.
[2] S. H. Hutner, *J. Bact.*, 1946, **52**, 213.
[3] For a review of the nutrition of fungi, see R. A. Steinberg, *Bot. Rev.*, 1939, **5**, 327.

The Respiration of the Microflora: Aerobic and Anaerobic Organisms

All organisms must respire to live, but they have developed different methods of respiration. Some—the obligate aerobes—must have access to free oxygen, whilst others either do not need such access—the facultative anaerobes—or else can respire only in the absence of free oxygen—the obligate anaerobes. Most soil members of the fungi and actinomycetes require conditions of good aeration, and few, if any, members outside the yeasts have been recognised as anaerobes. The soil bacteria, on the other hand, include groups having all degrees of tolerance to progressive oxygen deficiencies, ranging from strict obligate anerobes through numerous groups relatively insensitive to the oxygen supply to strict obligate aerobes. Little quantitative work has been done on the range of oxygen tensions of the various soil bacterial or even fungal groups, so that one cannot yet classify the bacteria at all accurately by the range of oxygen tensions they can tolerate.

Respiration can be defined as the process of carrying out a chemical reaction which liberates energy with the transfer of part of the energy so liberated into energy available for the vital needs of the organism. The typical sources of energy in the heterotrophic cell are sugars, mainly or perhaps only glucose, and the process of respiration normally consists in breaking down the sugar molecule into simpler ones having smaller total heats of formation. The mechanism of this breakdown can be most simply pictured as transfers of hydrogen atoms from the sugar to a hydrogen acceptor coupled with the residues taking up either water, or the hydroxyl groups from water, when necessary. Thus, the complete oxidation of glucose to carbon dioxide and water involves the tacking on of at least six hydroxyl groups to the six carbon atoms and the removal of at least twenty-four hydrogen atoms, twelve from the sugar itself and twelve from the six water molecules dissociated in the process, and these reactions are brought about by a battery of respiratory enzymes coupled with their appropriate prosthetic groups or co-enzymes that function as hydrogen carriers. Some of these prosthetic groups or co-enzymes contain a member of the vitamin B complex in their constitution, some are metal porphyrins, such as cytochrome, and some are simple 4-carbon dicarboxylic acids, such as oxalacetic.

Oxygen is the final hydrogen acceptor in aerobic respiration, and combined oxygen can play this role under anaerobic conditions. Thus, many bacteria can reduce nitrates to nitrogen gas or ammonia during respiration, a process involving the transfer of nine hydrogen atoms from the sugar for each molecule of nitrate so reduced to ammonia,

whilst other bacteria can reduce sulphates to sulphides, a process involving the transfer of eight hydrogen atoms per molecule of sulphate
reduced. Even the oxygen of carbon dioxide can be so utilised, and
again eight hydrogen atoms are transferred for each molecule reduced
to methane, and this is probably the principal source of the methane
produced in anaerobic decompositions.

Oxygen sources are not necessary for anaerobic respiration. The
simplest type, in which one molecule of sugar is split up into two of
lactic acid,

$$C_6H_{12}O_6 \rightarrow 2C_3H_6O_3$$

a reaction brought about by a number of bacteria, involves no transfer
of hydrogen at all. But, in general, when an external oxygen supply
is not available, respiration proceeds by part of the products of respiration acting as hydrogen acceptors and the remainder as hydrogen
donors. The extreme case of this is the typical end-product of the
anaerobic fermentation of carbohydrates by a mixed bacterial flora
which produces only methane and carbon dioxide,

$$C_6H_{12}O_6 \rightarrow 3CO_2 + 3CH_4.$$

Here the carbon of the methane has accepted the maximum number
of hydrogen atoms a carbon atom can accept, and the carbons of the
CO_2 have donated the maximum number. This process need not go
to completion, thus alcohol yeast converts glucose into alcohol and
carbon dioxide

$$C_6H_{12}O_6 \rightarrow 2C_2H_5OH + 2CO_2$$

and here only two instead of three of the carbon atoms have lost all
their hydrogen.

The outstanding difference between the anaerobic and aerobic
fermentation of sugar lies in the energy liberated. Oxidising glucose
to carbon dioxide and water liberates about 690 Cals. per mol. of sugar
oxidised; but converting glucose to lactic acid liberates about 18 Cals.,
or to alcohol and carbon dioxide about 30 Cals., or to methane and
carbon dioxide about 50 Cals. per mol. of sugar decomposed. Thus
anaerobic organisms need to decompose far more organic material to
derive a given amount of energy than do aerobic organisms; alternatively, given additions of organic matter will furnish far greater
opportunity for increase of microbial activity in aerobic than in
anaerobic conditions.

The By-products of Microbial Metabolism: Microbial Excretions

Micro-organisms, like larger organisms, take in food and excrete
by-products, which are either products of respiration or components

in the food supply that cannot be assimilated. Autotrophic non-photosynthetic organisms must naturally always be excreting the oxidised product of the substrate from which they have derived their energy, whilst heterotrophic organisms must always be excreting carbon dioxide.

Many micro-organisms can multiply in a well-aerated carbohydrate solution and excrete little else except carbon dioxide if the solution contains adequate quantities of ammonia or nitrate. If the conditions are altered—for example, if the nitrogen supply or the degree of aeration is greatly reduced—these same organisms will begin to excrete a variety of energy-rich compounds instead of the fully oxidised carbon dioxide. Thus, if growth under aerobic conditions is being limited by a reduction in the nitrogen supply, the micro-organisms may keep up their carbohydrate intake but make less efficient use of it. They will then excrete suitable quantities of partially oxidised carbohydrate of relatively high energy content to carry away the energy they have not needed to use.

The excreted products of respiration by heterotrophic organisms growing under limiting conditions consists of two distinct types of compounds: complex carbohydrate gums typically produced by many groups of bacteria under aerobic conditions, and a variety of simple soluble compounds, such as the aliphatic acids from butyric to formic or the derived aldehydes, ketones or alcohols, the simple dibasic acids succinic and oxalic, and the simple hydroxy-acids such as citric, tartaric and lactic—though citric, tartaric and oxalic acids are mainly excreted by certain groups of fungi, such as the Aspergilli.

Micro-organisms usually excrete the nitrogen of originally combined nitrogen which is surplus to their requirements as ammonia under aerobic conditions, though some of the larger may excrete urea or uric acid. But if the aeration is reduced, or anaerobic conditions set in, complex and usually foul-smelling amines are produced along with ammonia, such as the aliphatic amines cadaverine and putrescine and the aromatics indole and skatole.

Micro-organisms may also excrete usually small quantities of substances that cause the medium in which they are growing to become "stale", that is, the organism will no longer grow in the medium although there is an adequate food supply present. Some of the compounds so excreted have powerful antibiotic activity such as penicillin excreted under suitable conditions by the fungus *Penicillium notatum*, and these excreted products can affect the microbial population in the immediate neighbourhood of the organisms excreting them.

CHAPTER X

THE ORGANISMS COMPOSING THE POPULATION

Bacteria

HISTORICALLY, BACTERIA HAVE been far the most important group of soil organisms; they were the first to be studied intensively, and for long were regarded as the only organisms important in normal conditions. Laboratories and departments were set up for their study in most agricultural research institutions, and for many years they received more attention than all the other soil organisms put together, although they had not been shown to play such a predominant role in the vital processes of the soil as was implied by this one-sided development.

THE NUMBER OF BACTERIA IN THE SOIL

Bacteria cannot usually be seen in a natural soil when it is examined under a microscope, but techniques have been developed, based on the use of dyes that either stain living bacteria in the soil, but not the soil colloids or organic matter,[1] or stain the living bacteria so they have a different colour from the organic matter when examined in a fluorescent microscope (see p. 137). These techniques have shown that the bacteria mainly live on the surface of the soil and humus particles, and that they hold on to these surfaces very tightly.

Techniques for counting bacterial and similar cells in the soil have been developed (p. 137), of which the first to be used extensively was that of H. G. Thornton and P. H. H. Gray.[2] One difficulty of their technique is that the dye they used, erythrosin, stains moribund as well as newly dead bacteria the same colour as active ones, and it also stains actinomycete spores, which look very similar to bacteria, the same colour as the bacteria. Dyes are now available which distinguish more sharply between living and dead bacteria, but these methods still tend to overestimate the number of active bacterial cells in the soil. The number of organisms counted by these techniques will be referred to in this book as the total cell count in the soil.

The method that has normally been used to count the number of bacteria in the soil is the so-called "plating" technique and is much more indirect. A known weight of soil is shaken up with water and some of this suspension, after dilution, is added to a nutrient agar solution

H. J. Conn, *New York State Agric. Expt. Sta., Tech. Bull.* 64, 1918. S. Winogradsky, *Ann. Inst. Pasteur*, 1925, **39**, 299. [2] *Proc. Roy. Soc.*, 1934, **115** B, 522.

and poured on to petri dishes or plates. After incubation the number of bacterial colonies developed on the plate is counted, and so the number present per gm. of soil can be calculated. But the number so calculated can only be considered the number present in the soil if:

(1) each colony on the plate developed from one and only one bacterium;

(2) all the bacteria in the soil sample are brought into suspension;

(3) all the bacteria in the suspension can grow on the nutrient medium used.

None of these conditions, in fact, holds; some bacteria regularly seem to consist of colonies held together by gummy substances, and so are counted as one organism instead of many; some particles of soil and organic matter hold on to bacteria so tightly that dispersion of the bacteria from the substrate is not complete; some bacteria cannot grow in close proximity to others;[1] and no nutrient medium has yet been discovered on which all soil bacteria will develop. Hence, the plating method will under-estimate the number of soil bacteria.

The direct and the plating method thus over- and under-estimate the number of bacteria in the soil, but the difference between the numbers is surprisingly large, as is shown in Table 34,[2] which refers to some arable plots cropped every year with mangolds (Barnfield) and to some grass plots from which one or two hay crops are taken annually.

The direct method is seen to give over a hundred times as many bacteria on the arable and a thousand times as many on the grass plots as the plating method. All other workers who have used the direct methods of counting have obtained numbers of the order of 10^9 bacteria per gm. of soil[3] whilst their plate counts are usually about a hundred times smaller, although F. A. Skinner, P. C. T. Jones and J. E. Mollison[4] taking all precautions to get as high a plate count as possible, found that the total cell count on the Broadbalk plots were only about fifteen times higher than the plate, the mean values of the two being 5146×10^6 and 337×10^6 per gm. soil. The weight of other evidence, such as the rate of respiration of the soil bacteria (p. 219), and the number of bacteria needed to maintain the protozoal population feeding on them give results more in conformity with the higher numbers obtained by the direct count.

---

[1] For a discussion of the effect of this factor on the number of bacteria counted, see a series of papers by N. James and M. L. Sutherland, *Canad. J. Res.*, 1940-3, **18** C–**21** C.

[2] Unpublished data of H. G. Thornton and P. H. H. Gray.

[3] Thus G. Strugger, *Canad. J. Res.*, 1948, **26** C, 188, using his fluorescent microscope technique found between 1 and 8.6×10^9 per gm. soil.

[4] *J. Gen. Microbiol.*, 1952, **6**, 261. For a comparison with the Muguga (Kenya) soils see J. Meiklejohn, *J. Soil Sci.*, 1957, **8**, 240, who found the ratio varied from 4 to 80.

The reasons why the plate count gives numbers of bacteria so much too low have not been analysed out in detail, with the consequence that there is no logical justification for concluding that the bacteria isolated from the soil on nutrient media are representative of the soil bacteria as a whole. It is, in fact, commonly assumed that they are, and that the cause of the discrepancy lies more in the other factors already mentioned than in the inability of a substantial majority of the bacteria to grow on any of the less selective media used, but this possibility cannot yet be ruled out.

TABLE 34

Bacterial Numbers in Rothamsted Field Soils

Manuring	pH	Numbers per gm.		Ratio: total count to plate count
		Total cell count (direct method)	Plate count	
Barnfield				
Plot *(Arable, Mangolds)*				
1-O Farmyard manure .	7·6	3,733,000,000	28,860,000	129
4-A Complete minerals + ammonium sulphate	7·2	1,766,000,000	15,100,000	117
8-O No manure . .	8·0	1,005,000,000	7,550,000	133
Park Grass				
13 Farmyard manure .	4·6	2,395,000,000	2,250,000	1064
11-I Complete minerals + ammonium sulphate	3·8	2,403,000,000	1,350,000	1780
12 No manure . .	5·6	3,041,000,000	7,500,000	405

The figures given in Table 34 can be used to estimate the weight of the bacteria in an acre of soil. The typical soil bacteria are very small. Their mean volume is not known, but is probably between 0·5–0·2 μ^3 or 0·5–0·2 10^{-12} c.cm.,[1] so if there are three thousand million bacteria per gm. of soil, they will weigh between 1·5 and 0·6 mgm. per gm. of soil or, assuming they average this number throughout the top 6 inches of soil and the top 6 inches of soil weighs about 1,000 tons per acre, the bacteria will weigh between 1·5 and 0·6 tons per acre live weight or say between 650 and 250 lb. dry weight. This soil would probably contain about 3 per cent of organic matter by dry weight, so that there would be about 30 tons of dry organic matter per acre of soil, of which the bacteria would only constitute less than 1 per cent. The assumed volume of a soil bacteria may have been under-estimated, so it is

[1] See, for example, I. V. Tiurin, *Pedology*, 1946, 11.

possible that the bacteria may constitute somewhat more than this 1 per cent of organic matter.

THE TYPES OF SOIL BACTERIA

The prime difficulty in the classification of the soil bacteria can now be appreciated. The only certain way the bacteria can be classified is by their behaviour on different nutrient media, but it is possible that the majority of the types of bacteria present in the soil have never yet been grown on any medium. And in all the discussions of bacterial classification which involve platings this limitation must be remembered.

The soil bacteria can be classified by their nutritional requirements. The division between autotrophs and heterotrophs has already been mentioned (p. 138). The heterotrophs can be classified according to the complexity of their nutritional requirements, as has been attempted by Lochhead and his co-workers.[1] They isolate soil bacteria on as non-selective a medium as possible, and then test the proportion that can grow on media of increasing simplicity. Thus they have suggested seven groups as follows:

1. Those growing in a simple glucose-nitrate medium containing mineral salts.
2. Those that can only grow when ten amino acids are added to this medium.
3. Those that can only grow when cysteine and seven growth factors (aneurin, biotin, etc.) are added.
4. Those needing both the amino acids and the growth factors.
5. Those needing yeast extract.
6. Those needing soil extract.
7. Those needing both yeast and soil extract.

They found that fertile soils contain a greater proportion of bacteria with complex requirements, i.e. belonging to groups 5, 6 and 7, than infertile; that the soil extract from a fertile soil has a greater growth promoting power than from an infertile; and that the bacteria in the immediate vicinity of plant roots fall more into groups 2, 3 and 4, than into the more complex groups.[2] H. Katznelson and F. E. Chase[3] found that adding generous dressings of farmyard manure to a soil increased the proportion of bacteria having complex growth requirements at the expense of those having very simple ones, and V. Garcia, working with soils from some of the Rothamsted plots, confirmed this result and found that soils which had large dressings of fertilisers had the same distribution of bacterial types as the unmanured.

[1] A. G. Lochhead and F. E. Chase, *Soil Sci.*, 1943, **55**, 185.
[2] P. M. West and A. G. Lochhead, *Canad. J. Res.*, 1940, **18** C, 129. See also H. Katznelson and L. T. Richardson, ibid., 1943, **21** C, 249.   [3] *Soil Sci.*, 1944, **58**, 473.

This classification can, however, be criticised on two grounds. First, as the various growth factors in yeast and soil extract are recognised, some may be simple substances that should be included in the simpler media. Thus A. G. Lochhead and R. H. Thexton[1] subsequently showed that vitamin B_{12} is an important constituent in some soil extract media, and there is no fundamental reason why this should not have been included in the growth factor mixture used for groups 3 and 4. Secondly, it can be criticised on the grounds that it measures properties connected with the environment of the soil, rather than with the inherent properties of the bacterial population, for some bacteria which appear to have complex growth requirements can be trained to produce the enzymes necessary to make for themselves some at least of these requirements.

The morphological classification of soil bacteria is also difficult, as some groups can have several forms. A usual classification for the soil bacteria has been into six groups:

1. Small cocci, usually about $0.5\ \mu$ in diameter.
2. Short straight rods, about $0.5\ \mu$ in diameter and $1-3\ \mu$ long; the shorter often being called coccoid rods.
3. Short curved rods—the Vibrios.
4. Long rods.
5. Rods sometimes showing branching.
6. Thin flexible rods, with very thin cell walls, usually under $0.5\ \mu$ in diameter and $2-10\ \mu$ long.

There also appear to be some very small bacteria in the soil, existing as cocci or coccoid rods with diameters down to $0.15\ \mu$, but some of these may be stages in the life of larger bacteria.[2] Groups 4 and 5 are usually Gram-positive bacteria, and are at the present time assigned to the Proactinomycetes, now called Nocardia and classified with the actinomycetes, and to the Corynebacteria and Mycobacteria, which are groups of organisms now considered to be intermediate between true bacteria and actinomycetes;[3] group 6 are Gram-negative and include the soil Cytophaga and Sporocytophaga groups and any other Myxobacteria present. This classification is of only limited value, unless its limitations are clearly recognised, for many organisms classified in groups 4, 5 and 6 also exist as cocci and small rods; and many will, in fact, take this form when growing in conditions of limited food supply such as exist in normal soils. Under these conditions they will be indistinguishable visually from members of groups 1 and 2, with the

[1] *Nature*, 1951, **167**, 1034.
[2] See P. P. Laidlaw and W. J. Elford, *Proc. Roy. Soc.*, 1936, **120** B, 292, for a possible example of small soil bacteria in sewage.
[3] Bergey's *Manual of Determinative Bacteriology*, 5th ed., Baltimore, 1948.

consequence that many of the short and coccoid rods seen in the soil either on Cholodny slides or by direct microscopic observation will appear as members of groups 4, 5 and 6 when grown on plates. Further, many of the long rods will only show branching if grown under special culture conditions, so that no one medium can pick out all the bacteria having this property.

There is no necessary correlation between these two methods of classification; thus bacteria existing as short rods may be found in all the nutrition groups. This is an example of the general statement already made for the microflora that the loss of power to synthesise essential growth substances has little correlation with systematic classification.

Direct observation of the bacterial flora in soils shows up the overwhelming predominance of short and coccoid rods in most soils, though cocci, which may principally be actinomycete spores, predominate in a few. Clumps of cocci or coccoid rods can sometimes be seen embedded in slime and some of the organisms are surrounded by gummy capsules. Large rods are relatively rare and occur either in chains or singly. Large cocci sometimes occur, commonly in groups of two, three or four together in a colony. Plate VII shows typical bacterial colonies of these kinds.

The plating technique, particularly if a nutrient-poor non-selective medium is used, picks out, as Conn showed several years ago, many small slow-growing short rods. C. B. Taylor and A. G. Lochhead,[1] for example, found about 90 per cent of all the bacteria picked out were short rods, which Lochhead[2] and L. E. Topping[3] consider to belong mainly to the Corynebacteria, Mycobacteria and Nocardia, though H. J. Conn and I. Dimmick[4] consider that the first two differ too much from the pathogens of these names and suggest they be put in a new genus *Arthrobacter*. Conn considers there is a second main group of these bacteria related to legume nodule bacteria,[5] and he suggests these be put into a second new genus *Agrobacter*.[6] This would include the common soil species that has been called *Achromobacter radiobacter* as well as *Phytomonas tumifaciens*, a common soil bacteria that can produce crown galls on the roots of some plants. Many of the common strains are characterised by great variability of morphology, depending on the nutrient medium in which they are growing; by their ability to grow on a very wide range of nutrients, although many need traces of

[1] *Canad. J. Res.*, 1938, **16** C, 162.
[2] *Proc. 3rd Int. Cong. Microbiol.*, New York, 1939, 686.
[3] *Zbl. Bakt.* II, 1937, **97**, 289; 1938, **98**, 193.
[4] *J. Bact.*, 1947, **54**, 291. H. L. Jensen (*Ann. Rev. Microbiol.* 1952, **6**, 77) gives reasons why he does not accept this.
[5] *Bact. Rev.*, 1948, **12**, 257.   [6] *J. Bact.*, 1942, **44**, 353.

yeast or soil extract for growth; and by low metabolic activity, that is, they develop best when they are growing slowly in media only containing low concentrations of nutrients. Under these conditions H. J. Conn and M. A. Darrow[1] showed that they are extremely efficient users of sugars, utilising about 50 to 60 per cent for CO_2 production, 25 to 30 per cent for building into their body tissue, and excreting only about 15 per cent, and also that they build into their protoplasm about 70 to 80 per cent of the nitrogen they consume.

S. Winogradsky,[2] using his direct microscopic method of observing the soil bacteria, suggested the name autochthonous, that is, indigenous, for this common microflora of short and coccoid rods. He considered that this population characterises soils containing no easily fermentable material, and he pictured it feeding on the soil humus. Conn and Lochhead have developed this idea by showing that many members of this population are characterised by low biochemical activity, some having very complex nutritional requirements, and others great adaptability.

Winogradsky contrasted this autochthonous population with the dormant zymogenous group that springs into prominence whenever fermentable material is added to the soil, but which sinks down again as soon as it is exhausted. He pictured this population as composed of long rods and spore-formers. The existence of this separate population is, however, doubtful. Taylor and Lochhead[3] found that the addition of 15 tons per acre of farmyard manure did not change the types of bacteria in the soil, but only increased their number, and Cutler and Crump[4] found that Plot 2 on Broadbalk Field at Rothamsted, which has had a dressing of 14 tons of farmyard manure per acre most years since 1843, carried the same dominant bacterial species as Plot 3, which has been unmanured all this time. Cutler and Crump, in their very detailed studies, were able to show, however, that different fields carried different predominant populations; thus, Broadbalk Field, which carries a wheat crop nearly every year, has a different population from Barnfield, which carries mangolds annually, suggesting that the crop has a greater influence than the manure on the population.

There are also bacteria in the soil that feed on some of the common species of soil bacteria. They do this by excreting a substance that dissolves, or lyses, the bacterial membrane that encloses the living protoplasm, and then absorbing the liquid cell contents.[5] These bacteria belong to the Myxobacteria, or slime bacteria. They were originally

[1] *Soil Sci.*, 1935, **39**, 95.
[2] *C.R.*, 1924, **178**, 1236.
[3] *Canad. J. Res.*, 1938, **16** C, 162.
[4] Private communication from Miss L. M. Crump.
[5] See, for example, J. M. Beebe, *Iowa St. Coll., J. Sci.*, 1941, **15**, 307,3 19; and A. E. Oxford and B. N. Singh, *Nature*, 1946, **158**, 745.

considered to feed on animal dungs, as that was the only food on which
they could be made to grow and form the characteristic fruiting bodies
by which they are recognised, but it is now known that their food is either
living or dead bacterial cells and possibly other micro-organisms.

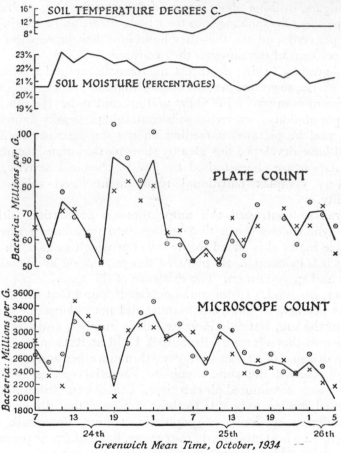

FIG. 14. Total cell and plate counts of bacteria from two-hourly samples of fallow garden
plot soil.
Note.—In the curves shown here, the dots and crosses represent numbers found in duplicate
samples; all curves show mean values.

Although many species are known, soils only seem to contain very few.
Thus, B. N. Singh[1] only found three species commonly present and a
fourth more rarely. He found them in all the British arable soils and in
about two-thirds of the pasture soils he examined, and in the single
soil in which he tried to count them there were between 2,000 and
80,000 per gm.

[1] J. Gen. Microbiol., 1947, I, I.

These higher predaceous bacteria are not the only members of the Myxobacteria present in the soil, as many of the cellulose and chitin[1] decomposers, such as the *Sporocytophagas* and the *Cytophagas*, belong to this group,[2] but it has not yet been conclusively shown that they can ever form the characteristic fruiting bodies of the predaceous species.

THE FLUCTUATIONS IN THE NUMBER OF SOIL BACTERIA

The numbers of bacteria in the soil are never stationary. D. W. Cutler, L. M. Crump and H. Sandon,[3] as long ago as 1920–1, showed the numbers counted by their plating technique fluctuated from day to day during the course of the year, and C. B. Taylor[4] showed these fluctuations occurred from hour to hour, whether they were counted by Thornton and Gray's total cell count method, or were counted on mannite or soil extract plates. He found that the fluctuations in numbers determined by these three methods were uncorrelated, as is shown in Fig. 14,[5] where the plate count was made on soil extract agar, suggesting that the fluctuation in total numbers is made up of a series of fluctuations occurring independently in different groups of bacteria.

The causes of these variations are not known, though presumably they are related in part to the protozoal activity in the soil. Further, Taylor has shown that these variations occur even if the soils are kept at a constant temperature and moisture content.

Bacteriophages[6]

Some groups of bacteria can be attacked by bacteriophages, which appear to be bodies similar to plant and animal viruses. Their typical form of attack is to cause a sudden lysis, or dissolving, of the outer bacterial membrane, which allows the contents of the bacterial cell to diffuse into the liquid medium. In this property, bacteriophages resemble the bacteriocidal substances excreted by other micro-organisms. Where the phages differ from these substances is that they multiply in the living cell before lysis, and in fact the only way they can be multiplied is by growing them on susceptible strains of bacteria. It has also been claimed that some phages can grow in bacteria without lysing them, that is, they appear to be well-adjusted parasites.

Phages have been recognised attacking species of bacteria belonging to all the main widely distributed groups, and also some species of

---

[1] For a review of this subject, see R. Y. Stanier, *Bact. Rev.*, 1942, **6**, 143.
[2] R. Y. Stanier, *J. Bact.*, 1947, **53**, 297.   [3] *Phil. Trans.*, 1922, **211** B, 317.
[4] *Proc. Roy. Soc.*, 1936, **119** B, 269.
[5] Taken from H. G. Thornton and C. B. Taylor, *Trans. 3rd Int. Cong. Soil Sci.*, Oxford, 1935, **I**, 175.
[6] For a review, see M. Delbrück, *Adv. Enzymol.*, 1942, **2**, 1, from which the substance of this account is taken.

actinomycetes, but it is still doubtful whether any have been found attacking fungi. The phages of greatest practical interest from the point of view of crop growth are those attacking the nodule bacteria, but very little is yet known about their distribution in nature, nor even how often they are of any importance in causing "clover sickness" or a reduction in the nitrogen-fixing ability or number of nodule bacteria in soil (see p. 342).

Actinomycetes

These organisms form a transition between the bacteria and the fungi, and on the bacterial side there is a series of organisms ranging in form from true bacteria, through the Mycobacteria and the Nocardia to true actinomycetes, the soil forms of which are now classified in the genera Streptomyces and Micromonospora;[1] and it is probable that there is this same continuity between actinomycetes and simple filamentous fungi. Further, in the soil some actinomycete filaments look like fungal mycelia and some of their spores like bacteria, though their spores typically differ from bacterial by having a waxy surface that does not readily wet. Thus, when a soil suspension is being made, many of them will float on the surface of the suspension, thus preventing any accurate count of their numbers by the usual dilution techniques.

Actinomycetes form very fine, often much-branched, hyphae when growing, and these hyphae may break up into spores, either by the tip of the hypha producing one or two spores or else by a length of hypha, often a length of hypha twisted into a coil, breaking up into a line of spores. In the soil these characteristic hyphal coils are only produced if they have free access to air, so that they are typically produced in the surface pores of a moist soil which are shaded from the direct sun.[2] The actinomycetes in the soil may also be responsible for the characteristic smell of newly ploughed land, for when they are sporing in pure cultures, they give off odours that vary from earthy to musty.

The soil actinomycetes are nutritionally a very adaptable group; they are probably without exception heterotrophic, and can use a wide range of carbon and nitrogen compounds, such as celluloses, hemicelluloses, proteins and possibly lignin.[3] They do not seem to need any growth-promoting substances. Only a few actinomycetes are parasitic on plants and then usually on their roots.

The activity of actinomycetes in a soil cannot yet be determined.

[1] S. A. Waksman and A. T. Henrici, *J. Bact.*, 1943, **46**, 337; and D. Erikson, *Ann. Rev. Microboil.*, 1949, **3**, 23.
[2] D. Erikson, *J. Gen. Microbiol.*, 1947, **1**, 45.
[3] S. A. Waksman, *Antonie van Leeuwenh.*, 1947, **12**, 49.

Direct methods of observation, such as those of Jones and Mollison, should be able to be used to give estimates of the length of actinomycete hyphae in soils, in so far as they can be distinguished from fungal hyphae. H. L. Jensen[1] has, however, made estimates of their relative activities in different soils by assuming it is proportional to the density of their hyphae on Cholodny slides buried in the soil. Actinomycetes, however, often develop extensively on plates used to count the number of bacteria in the soil, but these probably usually develop from spores. As already mentioned, since actinomycete spores are waxy and difficult to wet, the plating technique usually seriously under-estimates the number present in the soil.

Soil actinomycetes are typically aerobic organisms and, like the fungi, are commoner in dry than wet soils. They are also commoner in warm than cool soils; thus Jensen found that they can be the dominant members of the microflora at temperatures around 28° C. if the water supply is restricted, and many of them can thrive in the aerated parts of a compost heap even when the temperature reaches 60° to 65°C. They also appear to be very active under pastures, and may be the dominant micro-organisms in the surface layers of grassland in this country if the soil is not too acid.

Fungi

The fungi form the third of the three great groups of the soil microflora, and whether they, the actinomycetes or the bacteria predominate in a soil depends on local conditions. Soil fungi in most normal arable soils are too small to be seen either with the naked eye or with a magnifying glass, although they can often be seen growing on the surface of dead leaves and other plant debris. Fungal filaments can sometimes be seen in arable soils using Kubiena's microscope technique, and they often appear on Cholodny slides buried in the soil. Jones and Mollison were also able to see fungal mycelia in normal arable soils, using their direct staining technique, but considered that much of the mycelium was either dead or inactive. They found more pieces of mycelium than spores, though there may be more spores than active pieces of mycelium. Jones has also observed that as fungal mycelium grows, the active dark staining part of the fungus keeps in the vicinity of the growing points and leaves light staining and presumably fairly empty pieces of mycelium behind. Fungi are certainly predominant in some raw humus or mor soils,[2] where some are usually visible to the naked eye, and they may constitute an important part of

[1] *Proc. Linn. Soc. N.S.W.*, 1943, **68**, 67.
[2] L. G. Romell, *Cornell (N.Y.) Agric. Expt. Sta., Mem.* 170, 1935.

the zymogenous microflora[1] of normal agricultural soils, but the extent of their contribution to the autochthonous flora of these soils is still debatable.

The soil fungi mainly belong to the group that form filaments or mycelia, with the exception of some organisms belonging to the Myxomycetes or slime fungi, and a few yeast-like organisms. They belong to the Phycomycetes, which have branched unseptate mycelia, and to either the Moniliaceae, a group of Fungi Imperfecti, or, where the perfect form is known, to a related group in the Ascomycetes, which have branched septate mycelia. Basidiomycetes certainly occur in some soils, particularly forest and grassland soils, though whether they are present in appreciable numbers in old arable soils is uncertain. The soil Phycomycetes mainly belong to the Saprolegniales, to the genus *Pythium* and to the Mucoraceae, including the genera *Mucor*, *Rhizopus* and *Zygorrhynchus*. The soil Moniliaceae belong mainly to the genera *Trichoderma*, *Aspergillus*, *Penicillium*, *Cephalosporium* and *Fusarium*.[2] The soil Basidiomycetes belong to the Hymenomycetes, or mushroom-like, and the Gasteromycetes, or puffball-like fungi; and are of most importance in forest soils, where they include many species which can attack lignin strongly, and others which form mycorrhiza on tree roots (see p. 232). Basidiomycetes are also responsible for the "fairy rings" of old pasture, and naturally include the field mushroom *Psalliota campestris* often found growing in pastures. In addition there are fungi which can catch and feed on nematodes, mainly belonging to the Hyphomycetes, of which the species *Arthrobotrys oligospora* appears to be the most common,[3] and others which feed on amoebae, mainly belonging to the Phycomycetes and put in the family Zoopagaceae, though some of the former feed on amoeba and other protozoa and some of the latter on nematodes.[4]

There are still, however, considerable difficulties in isolating, identifying and counting soil fungi, partly because they can be present either as spores or bits of mycelium and the former can usually be isolated and grown on artificial media more easily. Many bits of mycelium can be seen in soils, and with suitable techniques some can be isolated from the bulk of the soil micro-organisms and transferred to culture media,[5]

[1] W. Kubiena and C. E. Renn, *Zbl. Bakt.* II, 1935, **91**, 267, and H. L. Jensen, *Proc. Linn. Soc., N.S.W.*, 1934, **59**, 200.
[2] For a description of typical soil fungi, see J. C. Gilman and E. V. Abbott, *Iowa St. Coll. J. Sci.*, 1927, **1**, 225, J. C. Gilman, *A Manual of Soil Fungi*, Ames, 1945, and A. Niethammer, *Die Mikroskopischen Bodenpilze*, The Hague, 1937.
[3] C. L. Duddington, *Nature*, 1954, **173**, 500. He finds the second most common is an unidentifiable mycelium, which presumably does not belong to either of Drechsler's two groups.
[4] C. Drechsler, *Biol. Rev.*, 1941, **16**, 265, and for a list of common English species, see C. L. Duddington, *Nature*, 1954, **173**, 500.
[5] J. H. Warcup, *Nature*, 1955, **175**, 953.

and some can be made to grow out of soil crumbs on to agar plates from which again they can be transferred on to culture media.[1] It is unlikely that all pieces of mycelium can be isolated from soils in this way, as some are confined to pieces of decaying plant or animal remains, and some either will not grow on the culture media used or will not form fruiting bodies so cannot be identified. But these techniques have shown that a number of fungi are more common inhabitants of the soil than had previously been supposed, and in particular species of *Rhizoctonia* and some Basidiomycetes appear to be much more widespread.[2]

There are not yet any reliable methods available for estimating quantitatively the activity of the soil fungi as measured, for example, by their contribution to the oxygen uptake by the soil, or the carbon dioxide production in it; though qualitative observations indicate that it is greatest shortly after fresh organic matter has been incorporated. The older work on fungal numbers and activity was based on counting fungal colonies on plates, in the same way that bacterial numbers are counted. By making conditions in the plates unsuitable for bacteria, by making the medium acid for example, and by preventing any of the fungi from growing quickly, by adding rose bengal and streptomycin for example,[3] it is possible to get a considerable proportion of the spores or pieces of mycelium to grow; and the numbers counted vary from a few thousands to over a million per gram of soil.

The soil fungi are probably all heterotrophic, but the species present have a wide range of food requirements, ranging from those which can utilise simple carbohydrates, alcohols and organic acids, and nitrates or ammonia as their source of nitrogen, through those which can use celluloses and lignins, and those which require either growth factors, such as members of the B group of vitamins, to those which can only grow in competition with the general soil population as parasites of living plant roots and parasites and predators of living soil animals. Nearly all soil fungi need to be supplied with either inorganic nitrogen salts or organic nitrogen compounds, though some yeasts, a *Saccharomyces* and a *Rhodotorula*, which are mainly sub-soil inhabitants, can fix atmospheric nitrogen.[4]

The saprophytic fungi can be very efficient converters of food into microbial tissues; some can synthesise 30 to 50 per cent of the carbon

---

[1] J. H. Warcup, *Ann. Bot.*, 1951, **15**, 305; *Trans. Brit. Mycol. Soc.*, 1957, **40**, 237; 1959, **42**, 45; and R. H. Thornton, *Research*, 1952, **5**, 190. See C. G. C. Chesters and R. H. Thornton, *Trans. Brit. Mycol. Soc.*, 1956, **39**, for a discussion on the various methods available.

[2] C. G. C. Chesters, *Trans. Brit. Mycol. Soc.*, 1949, **32**, 197. J. H. Warcup, *Nature*, 1955, **175**, 953; *Ann. Bot.*, 1951, **15**, 305; R. H. Thornton, *Nature*, 1956, **177**, 230, and with J. D. Cowie and D. C. McDonald, *Nature*, 1956, **177**, 231.

[3] J. P. Martin, *Soil Sci.*, 1950, **69**, 215.

[4] G. Metcalfe and S. Chayen, *Nature*, 1954, **174**, 841, and E. R. Roberts and T. G. G. Wilson, ibid., 842.

in the food into their cell substance,[1] which is higher than the corresponding figure for most bacteria when growing in the presence of an abundant food supply, though possibly not so much higher than for the autochthonous flora (see p. 151). This high efficiency of conversion has the corollary that rapidly growing fungi make very high demands on the available nitrogen of the soil, much of which is subsequently only slowly released in a form available to plants. Some of these fungi synthesise humic-like substances or their precursors, and they may contribute appreciably to the humic matter in the soil.

The filamentous fungi generally need aerobic conditions to flourish, though they do not need aerobic conditions all along their filaments: they are capable of sending filaments into poorly aerated pockets of soil, but only if much of the filaments are growing in well-aerated conditions, and only these well-aerated parts ever produce spores. Species differ amongst themselves, however, in their tolerance to poor aeration. Thus P. Burges and E. Fenton[2] found that *Penicillium nigricans*, a fungus usually restricted to the upper 5 cm. of the surface soil, is less tolerant of a high CO_2 concentration than *Zygorrhynchus vuillemini*, a species which is usually more abundant below 10 cm. But typically fungi are more common near the surface of the soil than lower down, and H. L. Jensen,[3] in Denmark, found them more common on light well-aerated soils than in heavier, as shown in Table 35. They can tolerate a wide pH range, though typically they flourish under acid conditions such as occur in heaths and forests,[4] probably because few bacteria are really active in such acid soils.

S. D. Garrett[5] has developed an ecological classification of the soil fungi based on the principal food supply they use in the highly competitive environment of the soil. The true saprophytes range from the "sugar" fungi, which can only use relatively simple and easily decomposable organic matter, but not cellulose or lignins, through the cellulose decomposers to the lignin decomposers. There are two other important groups in the soil: the specialised root-inhabiting fungi, which will be discussed further in Chapter XIII, and the fungi which are predaceous either on other fungi[6] or on other members of the soil population, including the soil fauna.

The sugar fungi are typically Phycomycetes, and since there are a very large number of different organisms in the soil which can use the same simple organic compounds for food, they must be adapted to

---

[1] S. A. Waksman, *Principles of Soil Microbiology*, 2nd ed., London, 1931, p. 244.
[2] *Trans. Brit. Mycol. Soc.*, 1953, **36**, 104.
[3] *Soil Sci.*, 1931, **31**, 123.
[4] H. L. Jensen, *J. Agric. Sci.*, 1931, **21**, 38; J. H. Warcup, *Trans. Brit. Mycol. Soc.*, 1951, **34**, 376, and S. L. Jansson and F. E. Clark, *Proc. Soil Sci. Soc. Amer.*, 1952, **16**, 330.
[5] *New Phytol.*, 1951, **50**, 149.
[6] For a review, see J. E. de Vay, *Ann. Rev. Microbiol.*, 1956, **10**, 115.

exploit these food supplies ahead of their competitors. Their primary source of food is injured, moribund or recently dead plant tissues. They are widely distributed through the soil typically as spores though sometimes as pieces of sterile (but viable) mycelium; the spores germinate immediately a suitable food source comes near, and the hyphae or mycelia grow very rapidly, so dominating the population there before other organisms have begun to multiply. In addition many of them produce antibiotics, and the growth of their hyphae is often only prevented by a relatively high antibiotic concentration.

TABLE 35

Effect of $CaCO_3$ on Numbers of Fungi, Actinomycetes and Bacteria in Soils as found by Plating Methods

Number per gram of soil

	Heath soil				Sand soil				Light loam			
	pH	Fungi, thousands	Bacteria+Actino-mycetes, millions	Actinomycetes, per cent	pH	Fungi, thousands	Bacteria+Actino-mycetes, millions	Actinomycetes, per cent	pH	Fungi, thousands	Bacteria+Actino-mycetes, millions	Actinomycetes, per cent
Untreated soil .	3·7	610	0·84	0	4·7	341	5	61	5·8	127	8	36
CaCO₃ added .	7·5	393	398	21	7·6	365	23	35	7·6	120	17	20

The cellulose decomposing fungi, which mainly belong to the Ascomycetes, Fungi Imperfecti and Basidiomycetes, come intermediate between the sugar and the lignin fungi in their rate of growth. Many of them are widely distributed throughout the soil as spores, and many of them, like many of the sugar fungi, can be made copious producers of antibiotics. It is also possible that a number of them are relatively tolerant of antibiotics, in that a higher concentration is needed to reduce their growth rates than for the other groups of fungi.

The lignin fungi are species of the higher Basidiomycetes and are characterised by very slow growth rates. Slow growing is not an ecological disadvantage for them because there is little competition for their food supplies as no other organisms are known to decompose lignins in lignin-rich material. They decompose lignins more easily if there is a reasonably high cellulose content associated with the lignins which is not too readily accessible to other micro-organisms. Once established the fungus seeks new sources of food by sending out thick mycelial strands or rhizomorphs into the soil, apparently to allow the point on the strand at which it begins its attack on another piece of lignified material, usually the apex, to be relatively well supplied with food; for the fungus appears to expend considerable energy in initiating the decomposition of such material. Garrett himself illustrates this by the crude analogy that one cannot start a coke fire with paper and matches only. This behaviour is also shown by the higher Basidiomycetes which are specialised root-inhabiting parasitic fungi of tree roots, for their rhizomorphs also can usually only gain entry to a root if they arise from a root which is already heavily attacked (see p. 230). The typical field conditions in which these fungi are dominant are the surface litter of forest soils and the mat in old turf soils. In these sites the decomposition of litter is sufficiently slow for there to be time for it to be reasonably uniformly distributed throughout the soil surface layer, and mycelial migration from one food source to another can take place over short distances. Typically these Basidiomycetes do not produce antibiotics;[1] nor can their mycelia grow in regions where other fungi, such as *Trichoderma viride*, are producing them (see p. 231).

Algae

The soil algae are microscopic chlorophyll-containing organisms, and belong mainly to the Cyanophyceae (Myxophyceae) or blue-green, the Xanthophyceae or yellow-green, the Bacillariaceae or diatoms and the Chlorophyceae or green algae. The soil forms typically comprise smaller and simpler species than the aquatic forms, and consist either of species which only occur as small organisms or of dwarfed forms of species that can occur as large organisms.[2] The morphology of the soil forms is also simple: they occur either as simple unicellular organisms or simple filaments or colonies. Many of the soil algae have their cell walls covered with a thick layer of a gummy substance; whilst the cell walls of most diatoms are partially silicified.

The soil algae are found not only on the surface and just under the surface, where sunlight or diffused light may be able to penetrate, but also several inches below the surface where no light can penetrate. The surface and immediate sub-surface forms presumably function as green plants, converting the carbon dioxide of the air into their protoplasm and taking up nitrates or ammonia from the soil. What activity those in the dark can display is still undecided. The earlier workers, such as B. M. Bristol Roach,[3] considered that the algae grew heterotrophically below the soil surface, and she found on arable land that

[1] P. W. Brian, *Bot. Rev.*, 1951, **17**, 357, gives examples of some which do and J. H. Warcup, *Ann. Bot.*, 1951, **15**, 305, of some which probably do.
[2] See J. W. G. Lund, *New Phytol.*, 1945, **44**, 196, and 1946, **45**, 56, for a recent discussion on the validity and interpretation of this generalisation for the diatoms; he gives the references to the earlier work on which it was based.   [3] *J. Agric. Sci.*, 1927, **17**, 563.

there were often more algae at a depth of 4 inches than at the surface. The common soil algae can certainly grow in the dark on a medium containing sugars, but it is very doubtful how far the algae could compete with the bacteria or fungi for such readily assimilable compounds which are nearly always in extremely short supply. J. L. Stokes[1] showed in some laboratory experiments that adding such substances as sugars, lucerne meal, straw or manure to a soil, and incubating in the dark, increased the numbers of bacteria very considerably, but had little effect on the numbers of algae. Y. T. Tchan and J. A. Whitehouse,[2] using fluorescent-microscopy technique, found that algae only appeared to multiply in the top few millimetres of the soil surface under natural conditions, and those cells found lower down were probably washed down from the surface, or as suggested by F. E. Fritsch several years earlier, carried down by the soil fauna or by tillage operations.

The relative importance of the different groups of algae in different soils has not yet been worked out. It seems to be generally true that in temperate soils green algae and diatoms are probably about equally common and the blue-green less common, though the relative differences between the blue-green and the rest may be larger in infertile than in fertile soils.[3] In many tropical soils, however, the blue-green appear to be the dominant algal group.

Algae develop most readily in damp soils exposed to the sun, hence usually have their maximum development in spring and autumn when the soil is damp, the sun not too hot and other vegetation rather dying down. They develop most freely on fertile soils well supplied with bases, available phosphates and nitrates, and tend to be sparse on light, infertile, acid soils.[4] Bristol Roach at Rothamsted found that generous dressings of farmyard manure increased their number compared with unmanured soil, though Stokes in New Jersey found that farmyard manure had a depressing effect on algal numbers. The explanation of the difference between the two centres may be due to the much greater degree of nitrogen starvation on the Rothamsted than on the New Jersey control soil, so that the algae on the Rothamsted manured soil may only have been responding to the available nitrogen in the manure. Lund[5] has also found that the green algae form the dominant group of algae in acid soils, but as the soils become more neutral the blue-green algae and the diatoms become relatively as important, and on fertile soils the blue-green may be the dominant group.

The numbers of algae occurring in a gram of soil vary widely

[1] *Soil Sci.*, 1940, **49**, 171.   [2] *Proc. Linn. Soc. N.S.W.*, 1953, **78**, 160.
[3] E. W. Fenton, *Trans. Bot. Soc. Edinburgh*, 1943, **33**, 407.
[4] J. W. G. Lund, *New Phytol.*, 1945, **44**, 196, and 1946, **45**, 56.
[5] *New Phytol.*, 1947, **46**, 35.

according to conditions. Both Bristol Roach and Stokes record numbers up to 100,000 or 200,000, though up to 800,000 per gm. have been reported in some Utah[1] and Hungarian[2] soils and up to 3,000,000 in some Danish soils.[3] One can make a rough estimate of the volume of this algal protoplasm as it is a reasonable approximation to take the volume of each alga equal to a sphere of 10 μ radius, and this gives volumes of the order of a few tenths of a cubic millimetre per gram of soil.

The soil algae probably affect plant growth in four ways: they may add some organic matter to the soil, help bind the soil particles on the surface together, improve the aeration of swamp soils and fix atmospheric nitrogen.

The amount, and the significance, of the organic matter algae add to normal soils is not known, but the part played by this organic matter in recolonising burnt or barren land is fundamental. F. E. Fritsch and E. J. Salisbury[4] found slimy green algae as the primary colonisers of burnt-over heathland in England. M. Traub[5] found blue-green algae were the primary colonisers on the barren mineral layer created by the eruption of Krakatoa in 1883; W. E. Booth[6] found them growing actively on bare eroded soil in Oklahoma, and he made the interesting additional observation that this algal film over the surface did not reduce the infiltration capacity of the soil;[7] and N. N. Bolyshev and T. I. Evdokimova[8] found they produced the slippery surface crust or takyr on saline lake-bed soils in central Asia.

Algae may help the aeration of swamp soils by converting the dissolved carbon dioxide in the water to dissolved oxygen. U. Brizi[9] observed that *brusone* disease of marsh rice, which he attributed to inadequate aeration, did not appear if algae developed plentifully on the surface of the marsh (see also p. 263). Again H. B. Engle and J. E. McMurtrey[10] have shown that adding green algae to water cultures in which tobacco is growing improves the aeration of the solution if the culture is kept in the light, resulting not only in an improved growth of the tobacco plants, but also in an increased immunity of their roots to fungal infections.

Some of the blue-green algae of the family Nostococcaceae, including

[1] T. L. Martin, *Proc. 3rd Int. Cong. Microbiol.*, New York, 1940, 697.
[2] D. Fehér, *Arch. Mikrobiol.* 1936, 7, 439.
[3] J. B. Petersen, *Dansk. bot. Archiv.*, 1935, 8, Nr. 9.   [4] *New Phytol.*, 1915, 14, 116.
[5] *Ann. Jard. Bot. Buitenzorg*, 1888, 7, 221. This has since been somewhat qualified by C. A. Barker, *The Problem of Krakatoa as seen by a Botanist*, The Hague, 1930.
[6] *Ecology*, 1941, 22, 38.   [7] *Pedology*, 1944, Nos. 7–8, 345.
[8] This observation has been confirmed for the algal crust on desert soils in Arizona by J. E. Fletcher and W. P. Martin, *Ecology*, 1948, 29, 95.
[9] *Ann. Inst. Agrar.*, Milan, 1906, 6, 59; 1908, 7, 107; see also the work of W. H. Harrison and P. A. S. Aiyer, which is described on p. 263.
[10] *J. Agric. Res.*, 1940, 60, 487.

members of the genera *Nostoc, Anabaena, Aulosira* and *Cylindrospermum* as well as a few belonging to the families Rivulariaceae, Stigonemataceae and Scytonemataceae[1] have been shown to possess the power of fixing nitrogen from the atmosphere,[2] and thus have simpler food requirements than any other organisms, since they can obtain both their carbon and nitrogen from the air. This power of nitrogen fixation is not dependent on light, for these algae can fix nitrogen readily in the dark if supplied with sugar, but it is lost if the algae are supplied with nitrates, ammonia or asparagine. They need, however, small quantities of molybdenum,[3] and there seems little reason to doubt that the enzyme system responsible is similar to that of Azotobacter. Allison and Singh found the optimum pH for fixation was on the alkaline side of neutrality, from about pH 7 to 8·5, and fixation probably occurred in the range pH 6–9.

These nitrogen-fixing blue-green algae are probably of great importance in rice culture. It has always been rather difficult to understand how many tropical rice soils can carry rice crops almost indefinitely without showing signs of nitrogen starvation. Singh found the algal film that developed on paddy rice soils in the United Provinces and in Bihar in India was composed of blue-green algae, all of which were active nitrogen fixers. He found that his species of *Anabaena*, which came from Indian rice-fields, could excrete over 40 per cent of the nitrogen fixed as soluble organic compounds, and although these compounds may not be immediately assimilable by the rice,[4] they are probably rapidly rendered so. A. Watanabe[5] has shown that species of *Tolypothrix* which were very active nitrogen fixers, appreciably improved the yields of rice, by implication, though not quite by direct proof, through increasing the nitrogen supply to the plant. Nitrogen-fixing blue-green algae are often the dominant organisms in the algal crusts which form on desert soils and these crusts may be high in nitrogen.[6] There is no evidence yet that algae play any significant role in enriching the soils of the temperate regions with nitrogen, although species belonging to genera containing nitrogen-fixing forms are fairly widespread.

One can summarise our present-day knowledge of the importance

[1] A. Watanabe, S. Nishigaki and C. Konishi, *Nature*, 1951, **168**, 748, and A. E. Williams and R. H. Burris, *Am. J. Bot.*, 1952, **39**, 340.
[2] K. Drewes, *Zbl. Bakt.* II, 1928, **76**, 88; F. E. Allison, S. R. Hoover and H. J. Morris, *Bot. Gaz.*, 1937, **98**, 433; P. K. De, *Proc. Roy. Soc.*, 1939, **127** B, 121; G. E. Fogg, *J. Expt. Biol.*, 1942, **19**, 78; and R. N. Singh, *Indian J. Agric. Sci.*, 1942, **12**, 743.
[3] H. Bortels, *Arch. Mikrobiol.*, 1940, **11**, 155.
[4] Engle and McMurtrey found that tobacco plants in water culture could not use any nitrogen that may have been excreted by a nitrogen-fixing strain of *Nostoc* growing in the solution.
[5] A. Watanabe, S. Nishigaki and C. Konishi, *Nature*, 1951, **168**, 748.
[6] J. E. Fletcher and W. P. Martin, *Ecology*, 1948, **29**, 95.

of algae in the economy of the soil by saying that they have been shown to be of great importance in colonising bare soil or soil devoid of organic matter, but that only the blue-green algae have proved important agriculturally, and then only in hot climates. It is possible that they are of prime importance in the cultivation of rice, which is grown under water-logged conditions, by supplying the rice roots with free oxygen and by fixing atmospheric nitrogen which they can use either directly or indirectly; and, since rice forms the staple diet of nearly half the human race, this role is, on a world agricultural basis, by no means negligible.

Protozoa

E. J. Russell and H. B. Hutchinson[1] were the first to suggest that protozoa played an active part in the microbial life of the soil, for they assumed that their activity could explain some of the consequences of partially sterilising a soil. Since then protozoa have been found in soils all over the world, and H. Sandon[2] has given detailed lists and descriptions of the various species known up to 1927.

Protozoa are minute animals, and the soil forms consist mainly of rhizopods and flagellates, though a few ciliates can usually be found. The rhizopods include the amoebae, of which *Naegleria gruberi* and *Hartmanella hyalina* are typical representatives, and the testaceous rhizopods, which are similar organisms, but which have a hard shell covering parts of their body, of which *Difflugia* and *Euglypha* are common soil genera. The soil amoebae vary enormously in size, the common small ones, such as are shown in Plate VII, being from 10 to 40 μ, but they go up to giant forms several tenths of a millimetre in size. The flagellates have one or more flagellae to help them move, and are usually small organisms 5 to 20 μ in length. The commonest soil forms are species of *Cercomonas*, *Oicomonas* and *Heteromita*. The ciliates, which have many short cilia covering the whole or part of their bodies, are most commonly represented by *Colpoda cucullus* and *C. steinii*, and are usually 20 to 80 μ in length.

The soil protozoa are typically small organisms, considerably smaller than the normal protozoal fauna of stagnant water for example, but whereas the water forms have a large volume of space in which they can move, the soil forms are restricted to moving in the soil pores, and then only in those containing some water, for they cannot move in dry soil. Furthermore, they can only be active when living in a water film. The majority form cysts during their life-cycle, and in this state they

[1] *J. Agric. Sci.*, 1909, **3**, 111, and 1913, **5**, 152.
[2] *The Composition and Distribution of the Protozoan Fauna of the Soil*, Edinburgh, 1927.

can withstand desiccation, though whether desiccation itself can encourage encystment has not been definitely established. Others can apparently go into a state of suspended animation when the soil dries out, reviving immediately it becomes damp again.[1] Encystment is a definite phase in the life-cycle of some soil amoebae, so that the number of active amoebae of these species present in the soil depends on the rate of encystment and of hatching. Further, the rate of hatching seems to be dependent on the type of bacteria growing in the neighbourhood of the cysts, presumably because hatching is stimulated by products of excretion specific to these groups of bacteria.[2]

Protozoa, or protozoa-like organisms, can feed in three ways: some possess chlorophyll and are autotrophic, but these are confined to a few genera of flagellates such as *Euglena*; some, again mainly flagellates, can feed saprophytically, absorbing nutrients from solution in pure cultures, but what proportion of these do this in the highly competitive environment of the soil is not known; most can feed, and normally only feed, by capturing and digesting solid particles such as bacteria.

Bacteria form the staple food supply of the protozoal population, though small algae, yeasts, flagellates and amoebae are also ingested. But not all bacteria can serve as food. Amoebae, for example, will eat some species of bacteria voraciously, other species only if there is no more acceptable source of bacteria available, and other species not at all.[3] Singh has found that these inedible species include practically all the bacteria producing red, green, blue or fluorescent pigments so far tested, and some of these seem to excrete substances that are definitely toxic to the amoebae. Thus, the protozoa must exert a strong selective influence on the composition of the bacterial population.

The effect of protozoa used to be considered entirely harmful to bacterial life, it being thought that the protozoa reduced the beneficent action of the bacteria in maintaining soil fertility, but it has now been established that some bacteria, in pure culture, work more efficiently in the presence than in the absence of predaceous protozoa. For example, D. W. Cutler and D. V. Bal[4] showed that Azotobacter fixed more nitrogen when mixed with the ciliate *Colpidium colpoda*, and Table 36, taken from D. W. Cutler and L. M. Crump's book,[5] shows the influence of amoebae on the rate of oxidation of sugars by bacteria. The bacterial efficiency is here defined as the weight of carbon dioxide produced in millionths of a gram by 1,000 million bacteria per

[1] J. M. Watson, *Nature*, 1943, **152**, 694.
[2] I am indebted to Miss L. M. Crump for these unpublished observations of hers.
[3] P. Frosch, *Zbl. Bakt.* I, 1897, **21**, 926; R. Oehler, *Arch. Protistenk.*, 1916, **37**, 175; L. B. Severtzova, *Zbl. Bakt.* II, 1928, **73**, 162; and B. N. Singh, *Ann. Appl. Biol.*, 1941, **28**, 52, 65; 1942, **29**, 18; and *Brit. J. Expt. Path.*, 1945, **26**, 316.
[4] *Ann. Appl. Biol.*, 1926, **18**, 516.
[5] *Problems in Soil Microbiology*, London, 1935.

twenty-four hours, when the bacteria and amoebae are growing in an aerated solution.

Protozoa cannot yet be counted directly in the soil. The older methods for determining their numbers were based on letting them feed on an uncontrolled bacterial population, and the numbers so

TABLE 36

Average Efficiencies per 1,000 million Bacteria at Different Bacterial Densities in the Presence and Absence of Amoebae

Density of bacteria in millions per cubic centimetre of solution	Weight of CO_2 produced in 10^{-6} gm. per 1,000 million bacteria in 24 hours	
	Bacteria + amoebae	Bacteria alone
0–100	73·2	—
100–200	15·6	9·3
200–300	13·4	7·9
300–400	10·6	8·3
400–500	10·1	3·7
500–600	6·2	3·5

determined varied rapidly from day to day, from a few hundred to as many hundred thousand, and the proportion encysted from 0 to 100 per cent, within twenty-four hours.[1] But it is possible that these large fluctuations are spurious and are due to an unsatisfactory counting technique, for B. N. Singh introduced an improved method, based on counting the protozoa on a controlled population of an edible bacteria, and found very much smaller fluctuations.

These short-period fluctuations in protozoal numbers make it difficult to study the effects of external conditions on the protozoal fauna, as only factors having a very large effect on numbers are sufficient to override them. The effect of season can, however, be demonstrated, for at Rothamsted protozoal numbers are higher in spring and autumn than in summer or winter. On the other hand, protozoal numbers do not seem to be very sensitive to changes in the moisture content, aeration or pH of the soil, nor even to the organic matter content of the soil, although the bacterial numbers are. Thus, on the permanent mangold field (Barnfield) at Rothamsted, B. N. Singh found that a plot which had received no manure for nearly ninety years contained between 400 and 11,000 active amoebae on nine different sampling dates from April 1945 to August 1946; a plot which had received many annual dressings of 14 tons of farmyard manure

[1] See, for example, D. W. Cutler, L. M. Crump and H. Sandon, *Phil. Trans.*, 1922, 211 B, 317.

contained between 6,000 and 45,000 on these same sampling dates; and a plot that had received for many years a heavy dressing of fertiliser without any farmyard manure contained between 9,000 and 31,000. The organic carbon in the two soils receiving no farmyard manure was about 0·8 per cent, whilst in the farmyard manure plot it was about 2·5 per cent, and the bacterial numbers, which were determined by total cell count on only two of these occasions, were between 5,000 and 8,000 million on the farmyard manure and between 2,000 and 3,000 million on the other two. A similar example from Broadbalk Field at Rothamsted is given in Table 45 on p. 203.

There must presumably be a relation between the numbers of protozoa and of bacteria present in the soil since certain species of bacteria are the principal source of food for the protozoa, but this subject has received little attention recently, and the results of the older work are unreliable as the techniques used for counting were inadequate. Hence no reliable estimates can yet be made of the numbers of bacteria that are consumed daily by the protozoal population.

Amoeboid and Flagellate Stages of Other Organisms

A number of organisms which look like flagellates and amoebae may not be protozoa at all, but a stage in the life-cycle of organisms belonging to other groups. Using modern techniques, K. B. Raper has described in some detail certain species of Acrasieae,[1] which have an amoeboid stage termed Myxamoebae. During this stage these organisms live in the soil as amoebae feeding on bacteria, and reproduce by simple fission, but at some stage in their life-history they congregate together, forming characteristic structures that produce spores, which grow into amoebae when conditions for growth become favourable again. B. N. Singh[2] has shown that British soils only contain two species of these organisms, both belonging to the genus *Dictyostelium*, and he isolated these two from thirty-three out of the thirty-eight arable soils, but only from three out of the twenty-nine pasture soils he examined.

In the same way organisms which are flagellates during part of their life-cycle may belong to the algae or fungi. In particular, there are species of soil myxomycetes, or slime fungi, that exist as flagellates during part of their life-cycle, feed on bacteria and divide by simple fission; but at another stage pairs of flagellates will fuse and grow into a large multinucleate plasmodium, or mass of naked protoplasm, behaving as a large amoeba and continuing to feed on bacteria, yeast,

---

[1] See, for example, *Amer. J. Bot.*, 1940, **27**, 436, for pictures of these organisms.
[2] *J. Gen. Microbiol.*, 1947, **1**, 11, 361.

fungal mycelium and small protozoa. Under certain conditions, not yet known, it breaks up into spores which in due course become flagellates again.

There are also large, amoeboid-like organisms in the soil that feed on bacteria and small protozoa and are multinucleate like myxomycete plasmodia, but that do not appear to give rise to flagellates. T. Goodey[1] isolated two species of such multinucleate organisms, which he put in the genus *Leptomyxa*, and B. N. Singh[2] has recently shown that one of these species is widespread in British soils. He isolated it from all the arable soils he examined, where it numbered about 1,000 per gram of soil, but he only found it present in about one-third of the pasture soils.

[1] *Arch. Protistenk.*, 1914, **35**, 80.   [2] *J. Gen. Microbiol.*, 1948, **2**, 8, 89.

CHAPTER XI

THE SOIL FAUNA OTHER THAN PROTOZOA

THE INVERTEBRATE FAUNA of the soil has only recently been studied in any detail,[1] and the reason for its relative neglect compared with microbial studies has been partly the difficulty of quantitatively isolating the animals from the soil mass, and partly the very great problems of their systematic classification when they are separated out. Again until recently very little was known about the actual food of many members of this population, and even now our knowledge is very incomplete largely due to lack of interest in the subject by research workers, but again partly to lack of any adequate techniques for studying what they are feeding on in the soil. But recently several workers have developed techniques for fixing and sectioning the soil without disturbing its structure,[2] which allows one to see where the smaller members of the population are, which in turn gives a more complete picture of the activity of this population than we have had before.

The size of the soil invertebrate population depends both on the food supply and also on the physical condition of the soil. The soil invertebrates need a fairly well aerated soil for active growth: they cannot thrive in water-logged soils nor in wet soils that have been puddled by the trampling of cattle. However, if the soil is fairly open, such as the surface of a forest or old pasture soil, and the soil becomes temporarily water-logged by heavy rain or flooding from above, enough air bubbles are likely to be entrapped in the soil pores for the smaller animals to survive for considerable periods of time. This entrapping of air bubbles does not take place to anything like the same extent if the water table rises to the soil surface, and this has a far more serious consequence for the more aerobic members of the population. The population is, on the whole, more tolerant of dry conditions, so a large proportion of the animals tend to concentrate in the top 1–2 inches of the soil surface, and in many soils only a few groups, such as the earthworms, are common in the next 2–3 inches.

The food supply determines the size of the population in normal soils, and it consists primarily of dead plant tissue, but it also includes

[1] For an excellent account of our knowledge on this subject up to 1955, see *Soil Zoology*, London, 1955, and in particular the papers by W. Kühnelt, pp. 3 and 29, and D. K. McE. Kevan, pp. 23 and 452.
[2] See, for example, N. Haarlov and T. Weis-Fogh, *Oikos*, 1953, **4**, 44, and *Soil Zoology*, 1955, p. 429.

living plants and the soil microflora. This combination of need for good aeration and a very superficial food supply has two important consequences. First, it is very difficult to define what is meant by the soil animals, for many of them are living in the litter as well as in the soil. Second, if the litter is distributed unevenly on the soil, as for example in a tussocky pasture or meadow, many of these animals will also be very unevenly distributed over the soil surface. In such a pasture there are a number of quite different environments in and above the soil, each with its characteristic population, so it is misleading to lump them all together as if they were a uniform population. It has been found, in all the investigations in which the effect has been looked for, that in fact the animals of a given species are not distributed uniformly or at random throughout the soil but always show a tendency to congregate in some places and be rare in others.[1]

The food supply of the invertebrate population is not restricted to dead or living plant material, although this is the most important. In addition there is a population feeding on the excreta of the primary population and another that is feeding on the population itself. Animals feeding on dead plant tissues or their associated microflora are commonly called saprophagous, on living plants phytophagous, on animal excreta coprophagous, and on other animals predaceous. The higher and the larger members of the community may use all these methods of obtaining their food, though, generally speaking, only specialised genera are predaceous on the larger invertebrates.

The foresters have studied the sources of food more intensively than other workers. They have shown that one bit of primary organic matter often passes through the gut of several different groups of animals before being degraded to resistant humus. Thus A. P. Jacot[2] showed that the process of decomposition of leaf litter or dead plant roots could be as follows: first, the more resistant material is softened by fungi, then it is eaten by saprophagous animals, particularly mites, which continue the decomposition of the plant material, possibly with the aid of a microbial population in their gut; and finally the undigested material is excreted and forms the food supply for a whole chain of other animals until it is converted to resistant humus-like material. In fact, if soils poor in earthworms are examined under the microscope[3] a great part of the "humus" present is recognisable as the excreta of soil invertebrates. It is also possible that animals are important producers of humus in cool well-aerated dung-heaps, for they can occur in very large

[1] See, for example, G. Salt and F. S. J. Hollick, *J. Exp. Biol.*, 1946, **23**, 1, for wireworms, and *J. Animal Ecol.*, 1948, **17**, 139, for animals in pasture soils.
[2] *Ecology*, 1936, **17**, 359.
[3] W. L. Kubiena, *Bodenk. PflErnähr.*, 1942, **29**, 108. See also P. E. Müller, *Studien über die natürlichen Humusformen*, Berlin, 1887.

numbers under these conditions[1] and must be responsible for an appreciable fraction of the decomposition taking place.

The digestion of this organic matter naturally involves the gradual oxidation of its carbon into carbon dioxide and its nitrogen into simpler forms, thus resulting in a decreasing carbon-nitrogen ratio. Thus, L. Meyer[2] found that earthworms feeding on rye-straw composted with basalt meal reduced its C/N ratio from 23 to 11 during a period of two years whilst the soil micro-organisms alone only reduced it to about 18 during the same period. Very little is yet known about the types of material in the plant debris that are available to the different species of the saprophagous fauna. But it appears probable, for example, that some woodlice and millepedes can only digest the sugars, starches and accessible proteins in the plant tissues; some termites, snails and earthworms can digest part of the celluloses and hemicelluloses contained in the plant tissues, and some nematodes and mites can live symbiotically with, or predaceously on, the cellulose-decomposing bacteria attacking the tissues.[3] It is also possible in many forest and pasture soils that fungal mycelium forms the transition compounds between plant and animal tissue, for the majority of the soil fauna appears to have no power of digesting the celluloses, hemicelluloses or lignins in the dead plant tissues: this is attacked by fungi and converted into their protoplasm, and it is their mycelia that forms the principal food supply of a large proportion of the mites and springtails, as is shown by a study of the contents of their gut.[4]

The soil fauna can for many purposes be divided into two groups: the meso- or meio-fauna which are too small when mature to affect the pore size in the soil, and so are without mechanical influence on it, and the macrofauna, which increase the size of the pores in which they move. The former group includes the rotifers and nematodes, which live in the soil water films, and the micro-arthropods—the mites, springtails and other small insects—which live in the air spaces.

The larger soil fauna have three very important effects in the soil: they assist the aeration and drainage of the soil through the channels and burrows they leave behind them as they move through the soil in search of food; they macerate and grind up the plant litter they eat, excreting it in a form more readily available to the attack of the soil micro-organisms; and they distribute this macerated plant debris together with some of the microflora throughout the volume of soil in which they are working. The saprophytic soil fauna can have two other effects on the soil. In the first place their excreta compose the typical

[1] H. Franz, *Bodenk. PflErnähr.*, 1943, **32**, 336.
[2] *Bodenk. PflErnähr.*, 1942, **29**, 119.
[3] H. Franz, *ForschDienst.*, 1942, **13**, 320.
[4] K. H. Forsslund, *Medd. Skogsförsöksanst.*, 1945, **34**, 1.

humus form in the soil (see p. 567), a fact emphasised by W. L. Kubiena[1] as a result of his direct microscopic observations on the forms of humus actually present in undisturbed surface soils. The gut of these animals is therefore an important site for humus formation, and this is particularly true for many species of earthworm which ingest soil along with their food and excrete mull humus in the form of wormcasts. In the second place, many of the larger saprophytic animals attack freshly dead plant tissues, and if for any reason the supply of suitable food is reduced, they will start attacking the corresponding plant tissue before it is dead, thus sometimes becoming a serious pest to farmers and gardeners. This typically happens on the farm when the rate of supply of organic matter to the soil is suddenly reduced, as, for example, when a long ley or an old pasture is ploughed out.

The effect of the soil fauna in moving soil is sometimes very considerable. Earthworms, ants, termites and moles may all put appreciable amounts of sub-surface or subsoil on the soil surface, and in the semi-arid steppes there are a number of other mammals that burrow into the soil, down to 10 feet at times, bringing up soil from this depth and leaving it as mounds on the surface. These burrows often get filled with surface soil giving the typical channels of black soil, or *crotovinas* to use the Russian word, in the light-coloured parent material in these areas, as is illustrated in Plate XXX. On poorly drained soils other burrowing animals, such as crayfish, can be active. Thus J. Thorp[2] has described how these animals will make burrows down from the surface to the water table, if it is within the top 10 feet; and he found them active on many soils having a pronounced clay pan. Thus these animals are not only bringing subsoil up to the surface but also burrowing through a clay pan and so assisting in the mass movement of water.

The soil fauna can be of indirect importance in agriculture through some of them being alternative hosts to certain animal parasites, and this particularly concerns the fauna of pastures, for the grazing animal can easily pick up infected soil invertebrates with its fodder. Thus, the liver fluke and some of the lungworms of sheep must pass a part of their life-cycle in certain gasteropods (slugs and snails); so that good drainage of pastures, by reducing the gasteropod population, reduces the incidence of these diseases. Again, some sheep and horse tapeworms have, as alternative hosts, species of orebatid mites which are common in old matted pasture but which do not flourish in young leys. But it is not always possible or desirable to control the alternative host; thus some lungworms of pigs have certain common species of earthworms as alternative hosts, and it is both difficult, and probably

[1] See, for example, his book *The Soils of Europe*, Madrid and London, 1953.
[2] *Sci. Mon.*, 1949, **68**, 180. He gives field descriptions of the soil-moving effects of many of these animals with estimates of the weight of soil they move.

also undesirable, to try to reduce the incidence of this disease by eliminating the earthworm host.

The invertebrates that have been most frequently recognised in soils include amongst the mesofauna nematodes, acarine mites and collembola, pauropoda, symphyla, thysanura and protura; and amongst the macrofauna enchytraeid worms and earthworms, millepedes and centipedes, many insects mainly dipterous flies and beetles, and a few crustacea and gasteropods. Photographs of some typical members of the fauna of English soils are given in Plates VIII and IX.

TABLE 37

The Size Distribution of Wireworms (Agriotes spp.) in two Cambridge Pastures[1]

Length of wireworm in millimetres	Per cent by numbers in the size class	
	Field I	Field 2
2–6	59	52
6·1–10	26	23
10·1–14	9	12
14·1–24	6	13

The techniques used in the past have missed or greatly underestimated the numbers of rotifers and flatworms (planarians) amongst the mesofauna and the numbers of immature forms of the macrofauna. This results in the age distribution being wrongly determined, for the characteristic of the population is the high proportion of immatures present, as shown in Table 37 for the wireworm population in two Cambridge pastures. The earlier techniques would have missed almost all of the smallest group, which makes up over half the total numbers.

Only a few analyses of the soil invertebrate population have been made[2] and, with few exceptions, the published data only give the numbers of animals found without any reference to their weight. Table 38 gives an example of the average number of different groups found during one year in an old pasture field and in two neighbouring plots on Broadbalk Field at Rothamsted, one of which has received

[1] G. Salt and F. S. J. Hollick, *Ann. Appl. Biol.*, 1944, **31**, 52.
[2] H. M. Morris, *Ann. Appl. Biol.*, 1922, **9**, 282, and 1927, **14**, 442, for Rothamsted fields; M. Thompson, ibid., 1924, **11**, 349, and E. E. Edwards, ibid., 1929, **16**, 299, for some fields around Aberystwyth; and J. Ford, *J. Animal Ecol.*, 1935, **4**, 1951, and G. Salt, F. S. J. Hollick et al., *J. Animal Ecol.*, 1948, **17**, 139 for pastures. For forest soils, see C. H. Bornebusch, *Forstl. Forsoegsv, Danmark*, 1930, **11**, 1; A. P. Jacot, *Ecology*, 1936, **17**, 359; and T. H. Eaton and R. F. Chandler, *Cornell Agric. Exp. Sta.*, Mem. 247, 1942. For tropical soils, see A. H. Strickland, *Trop. Agric. Trin.*, 1944, **21**, 107; and *J. Animal Ecol.*, 1945, **14**, 1; 1947, **16**, 1, and G. Salt, *Bull. Entomol. Res.*, 1952, **43**, 203.

14 tons of farmyard manure almost every year since 1843 and the other none at all during this period. The technique used would certainly have missed a great many of the mesofauna, and their numbers will have been greatly under-estimated, but it should have counted all the larger invertebrates.

TABLE 38

Numbers of Small Animals found in Soil at Rothamsted[1]

Numbers are in millions per acre in the top 9 in. of soil

	Broadbalk (continuous wheat)		Grassland
	Manured	Unmanured	
Insects:			
Springtails (Collembola) . . .	40·6	28·3	54·1
Beetle larvae (Coleoptera) . .	5·9	0·9	2·3
Fly larvae (Diptera) . . .	19·4	3·8	11·1
All others	3·4	0·5	11·0
Myriapods	4·5	1·8	1·8
Arachnids:			
Mites (Acarina)	6·5	1·9	2·9
Spiders (Araneae)	0·17	0·07	1·2
Woodlice (Isopods)	0·04	0·05	—
Slugs and Snails (Gasteropods) . .	0·04	—	0·05
Oligochaetes	2·6	0·6	8·4
Nematodes	1·5	0·2	7·6
Total	84·6	38·2	100·5
Period of observation . . .	Feb. 1936 to Jan. 1937		Apr. 1936 to March 1937

The effect of farmyard manure in the arable field and of organic matter in the pasture is to put up the populations considerably. But these figures refer only to the numbers present, and since some of the animals are almost microscopic and others large, the table gives no indication of the relative importance of these groups in the soil. One can make a rough calculation of the dry weights of the animals on the two Broadbalk plots using some older and less complete data of Morris,[2] which are given in Table 39. This shows that the really numerous animals are so small as to make a negligible contribution to

[1] K. D. Baweja using W. R. S. Ladell's apparatus.
[2] *Ann. Appl. Biol.*, 1922, **9**, 282.

the total dry weight, but that the earthworms and myriapods form nearly 90 per cent by dry weight of the population. But this result is only true if the numbers of the mesofauna have not been grossly underestimated. It would still be reasonably true if the numbers had been

TABLE 39

Approximate Nitrogen Content and Dry Weight in Pounds per Acre of the Small Animals on Broadbalk Field

	Manured			Unmanured		
	No. in thousands per acre	Nitrogen lb. per acre	Dry weight[1] lb. per acre	No. in thousands per acre	Nitrogen lb. per acre	Dry weight[1] lb. per acre
Earthworms . .	1010	10	110	460	5	50
Myriapods . .	1780	4	80	880	2	40
Insects:						
Collembola . .	2390	0·02	0·2	690	0·005	0·05
Wireworms						
(Elateridae larvae)	200	0·5	4	165	0·4	4
Ants . . .	2950	0·7	6	690	0·2	1
All others . .	2370	0·3	3	930	0·1	1
Arachnids[2] . .	970	0·2	2	347	0·05	0·5
Potworms and						
Nematodes . .	3600	0·2	3	790	0·05	0·8
Total about . .		16	210		7–8	100

under-estimated by a factor of ten, but not if by a factor of 100. Unfortunately there is no adequate evidence, using modern techniques, what their correct number is, and the factor of 100 cannot yet be dismissed as much too high. In general, soils have more mites than springtails[3] and the opposite result found at Rothamsted is almost certainly due to inadequate techniques.

Bornebusch[4] discussed the problem of measuring the importance of the different types of animal in the soil, and concluded that the total weights of each animal do not accurately correspond to the quantity of organic matter oxidised by the animals, for he showed that the small soil animals need considerably more oxygen for respiration, which is equivalent to needing that much more food, per unit of body weight than do the larger animals. He separated out several groups of animals from the surface layers of ten different Danish forest soils, and determined

[1] Morris does not give these dry weights; they have been calculated from the nitrogen contents of the different groups and their contribution to the nitrogen per acre.
[2] The figures for nitrogen and dry weight were not determined. Morris assumed the arachnids had the same nitrogen content as an equal number of insects.
[3] P. W. Murphy, *J. Soil Sci.*, 1953, **4**, 155, has collected some data on this.
[4] *Forstl. Forsoegsv. Danmark*, 1930, **11**, 1.

the live weight and oxygen need for each group. Table 40 gives a summary of his results for two typical soils under beech forest, the first a good mull carrying a flourishing ground vegetation, and the other a raw humus or mor almost bare of ground vegetation.

TABLE 40

The Numbers, Weights and Oxygen Consumption of Various Groups of Animals in Danish Forest Soils

	Mull soil under beech pH 6·1–5·8			Raw humus under beech pH 5·6–3·6		
		Per cent contribution to the			Per cent contribution to the	
	Numbers in millions per acre	total weight of the animals present	total oxygen con- sumption of the animals present	Numbers in millions per acre	total weight of the animals present	total oxygen con- sumption of the animals present
Earthworms . .	0·72	75·1	56·2	0·33	22·4	12·2
Enchytraeid worms	2·16	1·5	6·0	3·16	6·5	14·4
Gasteropods .	0·42	7·0	7·3	0·21	13·4	7·5
Millepedes . .	0·72	10·6	15·0	0·16	4·7	3·9
Centipedes . .	0·32	1·8	3·5	0·08	2·1	2·0
Mites and spring- tails . . .	17·85	0·4	4·5	45·5	2·3	16·1
Diptera and Elater- idae larvae	0·99	2·4	3·7	5·28	43·8	35·2
Other insects, iso- pods and spiders	1·91	1·2	3·8	2·63	4·7	8·7
Total number of animals . .	25·0 million per acre			57·2 million per acre		
Total weight of animals . .	630 lb. per acre			214 lb. per acre		
Oxygen used per sq. m. at 13° C.	0·33 litre per day			0·20 litre per day		

Mites and springtails abound in these soils and, on the basis of numbers alone, form almost the whole population, though they make a negligible contribution to its total weight. But their contribution to the total oxygen demand, or to the total quantity of organic matter oxidised away by the population may become appreciable, particularly in the raw humus or mor soils. The table also illustrates the important point that the oxygen demand of the soil fauna, or the rate at which it oxidises the soil organic matter, does not necessarily increase with increases in the total number of animals present.

These results also show, as did Morris's (see Table 39), that where earthworms thrive they form the major portion of the total weight of

Plate V

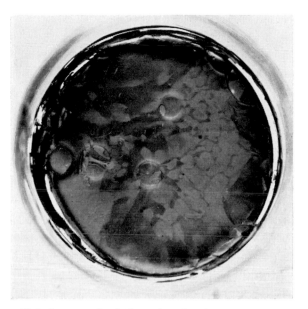

Dried paste of a deflocculated sodium saturated
Lower Lias clay

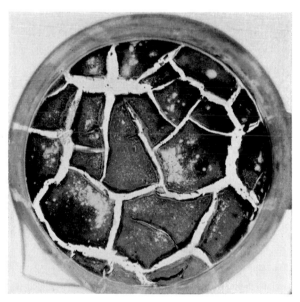

Dried paste of a sodium saturated Lower Lias
clay flocculated with sodium chloride
(p. 132)

Plate VI

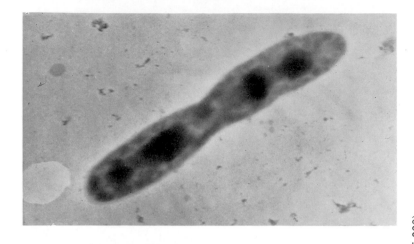

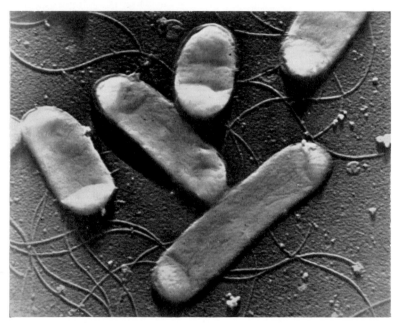

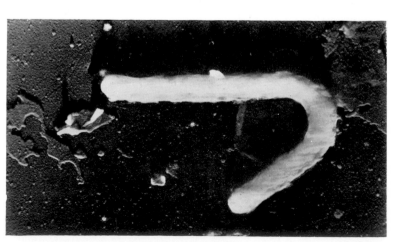

Electron microscope photographs of three types of bacteria (× 25,000)

The first two have been gold shadowed before being photographed. The second shows flagellae of the bacteria

(p. 136)

Plate VII

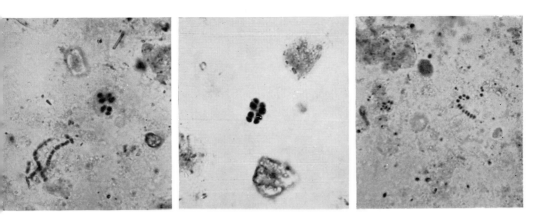

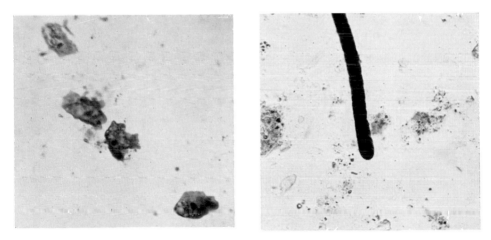

Bacterial colonies (*top*) and amoebae and a fungal hypha (*bottom*) in the soil, as displayed by Jones and Mollison's direct staining technique (x 1,000)

(*p. 137*)

Plate VIII

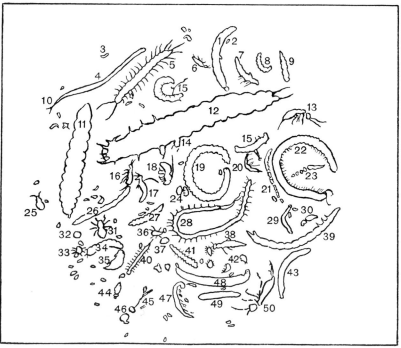

Typical members of the soil fauna (natural size)
(For key, see opposite page)
(p. 173)

Plate IX

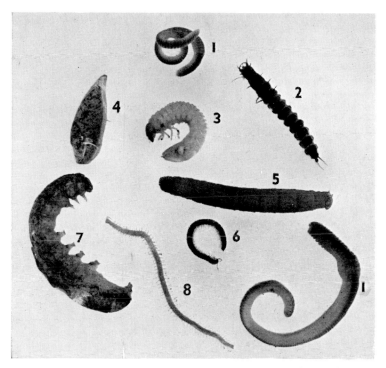

Plate X

Part of the root system of Scots pine (*Pinus sylvestris*), showing differentiation into long roots and short forked mycorrhizas

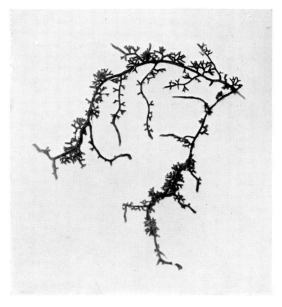

Lower photograph: natural size; upper photograph: x 6
(p. 233)

Plate XI

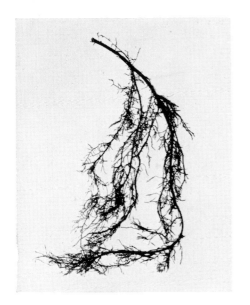

(Half natural size)   (x 7)

Part of the root system of the date palm (*Phoenix dactylifera*). The fine feeding roots are all mycorrhizas

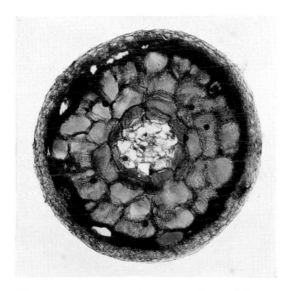

Transverse section of a mycorrhiza of Scots pine, formed by association with *Boletus bovinus* (x 130)

(p. 233)

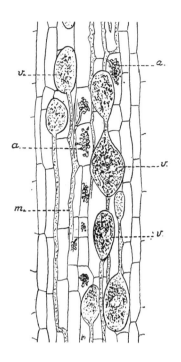

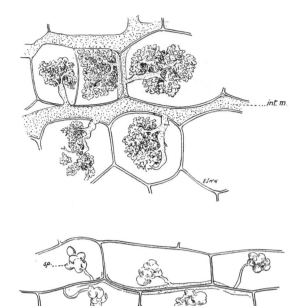

Plate XII

Vesicles in a strawberry
rootlet (× 60)

Arbuscules in strawberry rootlets (× 600)
(*Top*) well developed; (*Bottom*) partially
decomposed

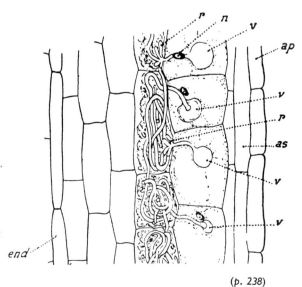

Vesicles and pelotons in
autumn crocus roots
(× 210)

m = mycelium; int. m. = inter
cellular mycelium;
v = vesicles; a = arbuscules;
sp = sporangioles;
end = endodermis;
ap = as = epidermis

(*p.* 238)

the animal population. Thus Bornebusch found that the weight of all animals excluding earthworms varied from 35 to 170 lb. per acre for the ten different soils he studied, but in the two good mull soils of his group the half a million earthworms present weighed about 500 lb. per acre. Further, in two forest sites, on which he only took a few samples, the $1-1\frac{1}{2}$ million per acre weighed 1,500–1,800 lb., which, as he points out, equals the weight of livestock carried per acre on first-class Danish pastures, although the earthworms will only be respiring about one tenth the amount of carbon dioxide that the livestock would.[1] The relation between the numbers of earthworms and their weight is not, however, simple for it depends on the species present. Thus, in Table 40 the average weight of an earthworm in the mull is about 300 mgm.—they were mainly the medium-sized *Allolobophora turgida*, now known as *A. caliginosa*—whilst on the raw humus soil they are mainly the small *Dendrobaena octoedra*, which only weigh about 67 mgm.

One other use can be made of the respiration figures given in Table 40. Bornebusch estimated the annual oxygen consumption of the animal population in the various soils he studied; it was about 90 and 60 gm. per sq. m. per year in the two soils given in the table, and this is approximately the weight of food oxidised by the soil animals, for about 1 gm. of oxygen is needed to oxidise 1 gm. of organic matter to carbon dioxide. He further estimated that the annual leaf fall returns about 400 gm. of organic matter per sq. m. to the soil, so that, ignoring the weight of plant roots being decomposed, about which nothing is known, the animal population is responsible for the oxidation of about 15 to 20 per cent of the plant remains.

An example of a more modern estimate of the numbers of arthropods present in a pasture soil is given in Table 41. This field, which is on a gault clay, has been under grass for at least ten years and been used principally for grazing though it has been cut for hay.[2] In addition to those animals given in the table, the following occurred in numbers less than 1 million per acre: Psocoptera, Lepidoptera and Hymenoptera amongst the insects, and Chelonethida. The table shows that a number of arthropods lived in the subsoil, which was on the whole well supplied with roots and was stained with humus down to 7–8 inches.

The number of soil animals in the surface soil works out at about 1 per c.cm. of soil, rising to a maximum of 3 per c.cm. in the samples with the highest number. The authors consider the modal volume of the population as about 5×10^{-5} c.cm. per individual, so the volume of the mesofauna to the volume of soil is about 1 to 20,000, and if the

[1] K. Mellanby, *Soils and Fert.*, 1960, **23**, 8.
[2] G. Salt, F. S. J. Hollick et al., *J. Animal Ecol.* 1948, **17**, 139. H. Franz, *Bodenkt. PflErnähr.*, 1943, **32**, 336, found similar total numbers in the top 4 in. of Austrian pasture soils.

surface soil contains 5 per cent of air when wet but well drained, they would occupy about 0·1 per cent of the air space. P. W. Murphy has collected the corresponding figures for forest mor, which came out to 2–15 per c.cm. with an animal-to-mor ratio by volume of about 1 to 30,000.

TABLE 41

Numbers of Arthropods collected from surface and subsoil on a Cambridgeshire Pasture, 23 November 1943

(* Numbers of animals so marked are known to be under-estimated)

Numbers in millions per acre

	Surface soil 0–6 in.	Subsoil 6–12 in.
Thysanura	15·0	11·8
*Protura	1·1	4·4
*Collembola	174·7	73·6
Thysanoptera	4·4	0·2
Hemiptera	61·7	10·2
Coleoptera	11·4	6·4
Diptera	2·1	0·6
Total Insects	271·5	107·7
Araneida	0·57	0·0
*Acarina	485·5	180·8
*Pauropoda	0·1	2·4
Symphyla	1·1	14·6
Diplopoda	0·65	0·97
Chilopoda	0·87	1·75
Total Arthropods	760·4	308·4

G. Salt[1] has repeated his determinations of the number of arthropods in soils at a number of sites in East Africa, at elevations from 2,300 to 6,400 feet above sea-level, and under Star grass (*Cynodon plectostachyum*), and Kikuyu grass (*Pennisetum clandestinum*) and under forest. The numbers found were remarkably constant between sites and worked out at about 160 million per acre in the surface 6 inches compared with 760 million in the Cambridge pasture. The number in cultivated soils in East Africa was lower, at about 100 million per acre. The only soil carrying a higher number of arthropods than this was the Kawanda (Uganda) soil under elephant grass (*Pennisetum purpureum*) which had 350 million per acre compared with 106 million on neighbouring bare fallow soils or soils under cassava, and one year under elephant grass was sufficient to give this build-up.[2]

[1] *Bull. Entomol. Res.*, 1952, **43**, 203.   [2] *Bull. Entomol. Res.*, 1955, **46**, 539.

Nematodes

The nematodes or eelworms are non-segmented worms with cylindrical or spindle-shaped bodies, and a large proportion are about 0·5 to 1·5 mm. long and about forty to fifty times as long as they are broad. Soil nematodes fall roughly into three groups:

1. Those living on the soil microflora and possibly on decaying organic matter. They form the most numerous group both in numbers and species.

2. Those predaceous on the soil fauna, including protozoa, other nematodes, tardigrades and oligochaetes. Many of these species can use a wide range of foods, but a few, such as some of the larger dorylaims, seem to be restricted to oligochaetes or other specific groups of animals.

3. Those parasitic on plants and usually fairly specific in their food requirements. They have been more extensively studied than the other soil nematodes.

H. Mikoletzky,[1] H. Franz[2] and C. O. Nielsen[3] have studied the composition of the nematode populations in a variety of soils in Bucovina, Austria and Denmark, and recognised nearly 200 different species; but of these only between 20 and 30 were common. The composition of the population was not found to be very dependent on the soil or on the method of soil management used in this part of Europe. Very little, however, is yet known about the principal sources of food of this free-living population or their effect on the decomposition of the soil organic matter; though Nielsen, both from an examination of the gut contents of nematodes extracted from the soil, and from feeding experiments, concluded that most of them were predaceous, feeding on bacteria, algae, protozoa and, for the larger ones, other nematodes, though a proportion sucked the juices from roots and possibly fungal hyphae also. He found no evidence that any fed on plant debris. The population is not confined to the surface of the soil, but most of it is found in the top 10 cm.

Franz, Nielsen, A. Stöckli[4] and D. Robertson[5] have counted the number of nematodes in soils, and the first two have also classified them into species, and Nielson has also estimated their weight and their oxygen consumption. Both Nielsen and Robertson found that arable soils contain about 1 million per square metre, weighing about 1 gram (9 lb. per acre) whilst Franz, Nielsen and Stöckli found that pastures contained from 2 to 20 million, weighing between 5 and 20 grams per

[1] Arch. Naturgesch., 1921, 87 A, No. 8.
[2] Zool. Jahrb. (Syst), 1942, 75, 365.   [3] Natura Jutlandica, 1949, 2, 1.
[4] Ber. Schweiz. Bot. Ges., 1943, 53 A, 160, and Z. PflErnähr., 1952, 59, 97.
[5] Proc. Roy. Phys. Soc. Edinb., 1926, 21, 83.

square metre (45–180 lb. per acre). Nielsen and Stöckli also give the numbers in a mor soil under spruce and in a mixed woodland, which are similar to those in an arable field. These total weights are therefore small compared with the 100–600 pounds per acre of the remainder of the soil fauna, with the exception of those for some pastures. Nielsen showed, however, that their contribution to the oxygen consumption and carbon dioxide evolution of the soil fauna was considerably larger than the weight figures indicate, since they have a much higher metabolic rate than the general population.

The predaceous nematodes may possibly help to keep the numbers of the plant parasitic nematodes in control, for they can certainly feed on them. Numerous investigators have tried to alter the soil conditions in such a way that these predaceous nematodes would reduce the members of the plant parasites so much that they could not affect the host plant appreciably. So far, however, these attempts have met with little success, possibly because the predaceous nematodes are not specific in their food requirements, but will feed on the saprophytic nematodes and other invertebrates, including young earthworms, as readily as on the parasitic nematodes.

Enchytraeid Worms

These worms have not received much attention in the past. C. O. Nielsen[1] has made a fairly detailed study of their numbers and weights in several Danish soils. They occur principally in the top 5 cm. of the soil but work down to 50 cm., and may number up to 10,000 per sq. metre in arable, 100,000 in mull and 200,000 in heath and coniferous forest soils. He estimated 100,000 per sq. metre had a live weight of about 25 lb. per acre. It is not certain what they feed on, but they consume rotting material and may feed on the bacteria and fungi which it contains. They also appear to control pathogenic eelworm numbers if present in adequate numbers, possibly by feeding on their early larval stages.[2]

Earthworms

The importance of earthworms was first stressed by Charles Darwin in his book *The Formation of Vegetable Mould through the Action of Worms*[3]— one of the classics of soil science—and also by V. Henson.[4] But in spite of this early start, and of their obvious importance in soils, for a long

[1] *Soil Zoology*, London, 1955, p. 202; see also *Oikos*, 1953, **4**, 187, for his methods.
[2] For a short review, see B. G. Chitwood and B. A. Oteifa, *Ann. Rev. Microbiol.*, 1952, **6**, 151, and B. Schaerffenberg, *Z. PflKrank. PflSchutz.*, 1950, **57**, 183.
[3] Published by J. Murray (London) in 1881, and reissued by Faber & Faber in 1945 under the title *Darwin on Humus and the Earthworm*.
[4] *Ztschr. wiss. Zool.*, 1877, **28**, 354; *Landw. Jahrb.*, 1882, **11**, 661.

time little work was done on their ecology. Yet both C. H. Bornebusch,[1] working with Danish forest soils, and H. M. Morris,[2] working with Rothamsted arable soils, found that where earthworms flourished they constituted between 50 and 75 per cent of the total weight of the animals present, although on a further calculation of Bornebusch (see p. 177) their effectiveness in decomposing organic matter was not quite as high as this figure might suggest. Further, foresters such as P. E. Müller[3] and W. Kubiena[4] have remarked on the fact that the only obvious animal excreta in soils containing earthworms is that of the earthworm, whilst on soils not containing earthworms the excreta of a large number of other animals becomes obvious. The conclusion seems to be justified, therefore, that in north-western Europe where earthworms flourish they dominate the whole soil fauna.

From the agricultural point of view earthworms can be classified into two groups: the family Lumbricidae, and the other families belonging to the sub-order of the order Oligochaeta. The earthworms of north-western Europe are all Lumbricids but the native species in India, Africa, the Americas and Australasia are not. However, as the native vegetation is replaced by European or Eurasian species, e.g. the ryegrass/white clover pastures of New Zealand, the European species of earthworms seem to have come along with the plants, and dominate these soils—the native species being unable to live in this entirely new soil habitat.

The general problems of earthworm zoology have been described in a monograph, now rather out of date, by J. Stephenson.[5] Their separation into genera and species presents great taxonomic difficulties, particularly for sexually immature individuals, so many of the earlier workers either did not identify the species they were studying, or worse, gave incorrect identifications. Some species can only reproduce sexually, some parthenogenetically and some can use either mode.[6] They lay their eggs in cocoons, and the young earthworm takes from six to eighteen months to reach maturity, depending on species and food supply.[7] L. Cernosvitos and A. C. Evans[8] have published a key for the identification of the twenty-five British species belonging to eight genera, of which seventeen are widespread. They vary in size from the large *Lumbricus terrestris*, which may have a length exceeding 25 cm. and weighs between 2 and 7 gm. to small species with lengths about 2·5 cm. and weighing about 50 mgm. The factors controlling

[1] *Forstl. Forsoegsv. Danmark*, 1930, **11**, 1. [2] *Ann. Appl. Biol.*, 1922, **9**, 282; 1927, **14**, 442.
[3] *Studien über die natürlichen Humusformen*, Berlin, 1887.
[4] *Bodenk. PflErnähr.*, 1942, **29**, 108.   [5] *The Oligochaeta*, Oxford, 1930.
[6] S. Muldal, *Heredity*, 1952, **6**, 55.
[7] For a discussion of the factors affecting the rate of cocoon production in British soils see A. C. Evans and W. J. McL. Guild, *Ann. Appl. Biol.* 1948, **35**, 471.
[8] *Synopses of the British Fauna*, Linnean Soc. No. 6, 1947.

which species will be dominant and which almost lacking in a soil are
not yet known in any detail. In British pastures one or more of the
larger worms such as *Allolobophora longa* and *nocturna*[1] and *L. terrestris*
are usually dominant, though in leys and in highly productive pastures,
such as some of those in New Zealand, *A. caliginosa* and *L. rubellus* may
be the dominants. In British arable soils *A. caliginosa*, *A. chlorotica* and
Eisenia rosea are usually important, and the first two are often the
dominants in leys of several years' duration which come in arable
rotations. In addition another fairly large worm, *Octolasium cyaneum*,
and the smaller *L. castaneus* and *Dendrobaena rubida* are fairly common in
British pastures and *E. foetida* in farmyard manure heaps.

The habits of life of the different species of earthworms differ appreciably. Some certainly feed on the dead roots of grasses and clovers as
shown for *A. caliginosa* in New Zealand pastures by R. A. S. Waters.[2]
Many feed on surface litter, some coming on to the surface to collect
it and then drag it down into their burrows, and others only pulling
down the litter that is directly over their burrow. Little is known about
their food preferences. In forests elm, ash and birch litter is eaten more
freely than oak and beech, and pine and spruce litter is hardly eaten
at all. Many eat cow dung readily, and it is a common sight to find
colonies of several species underneath each cow pat on pastures. All
British earthworms probably possess the enzyme cellulase in the fore
half of the gut, although there is a very great variation between species
in the amounts present, and many possess chitinase also, so presumably
they can digest cellulose of plant tissue and the chitin of fungi and
perhaps insect cuticle also.[3]

Typically earthworms consume soil along with plant debris, but they
do not always do this. Thus sometimes they will consume large amounts
of mown grass without any soil. Their excreta, in the form of worm
casts, therefore typically contains a high proportion of soil. Most
species excrete this in the body of the soil, often in their burrows, but
some make casts on the soil surface. At Rothamsted only *A. longa* and
nocturna have been proved to make casts regularly on the surface, but
other species such as *L. terrestris* sometimes do.

The shape of the burrow, and its depth, also depends on species.
Some are always making new burrows and live entirely in the surface
layer of the soil, others, particularly the larger ones, have fairly permanent burrows, which may be 5–6 feet deep for *L. terrestris* but is
usually much shallower, and may be 12 inches deep for *A. longa* and
nocturna. The *Allelobophora* species appears to burrow continuously in
the surface layer of the soil, whilst the Lumbricus species may only

---

[1] These two species are classed together as *A. terrestris* by some authors.
[2] *N.Z. J. Sci. Tech.*, 1955, **36** A, 516.   [3] M. V. Tracey, *Nature*, 1951, **167**, 776.

make new burrows in the surface soil when the food supply above their burrow is exhausted.[1]

Earthworms can only thrive in soils under certain specific conditions. They are intolerant of drought and frost;[2] and hence dry sandy soils, and thin soils overlying rock are not usually favourable environments for them.[3] They need a reasonably aerated soil, hence heavy clays or undrained soils are also unfavourable as are pastures whose surface is puddled by overgrazing in wet weather. Thus under given conditions of management they will be most numerous in loams and less numerous in sands, gravels and clays.[4] Many can, however, survive up to a year in water if it is reasonably aerated:[5] and the author has found them alive in late autumn in undrained English clay pastures in burrows already filled with water due to the late autumn rains. Earthworms are much more active in spring and autumn, when the surface soil is moist and warm, than in summer when the surface is usually dry, and in winter when it is too cold. A. Stockli[6] has given an example of the effect of spring rainfall on the weight of earthworm casts produced on a Swiss pasture: 3 tons per acre for the three months April to June one year when the rainfall during this period was $10\frac{1}{2}$ inches, and 10 tons the next when it was $16\frac{1}{2}$ inches.

Most earthworms, including all the larger species, need a continuous supply of calcium, which they convert into calcium carbonate and excrete from special glands in their digestive tract. Earthworms are, therefore, absent on soils low in calcium. They are also absent from acid soils, and in fact if they are put on the surface of a soil that is too acid they are unable to burrow into it and very soon die. It is not known what factor in an acid soil is such an irritant, but it is not pH for J. E. Satchell[7] has shown that sulphuric acid solution must be below pH 3·0 before five common British species of earthworms found it a strong irritant, yet they were unable to live on a Rothamsted soil at pH 4·4 although they behaved perfectly normally if it was at pH 5·0.

These laboratory findings agree on the whole with field observations, for very rarely are soil-burrowing earthworms found in soils below pH 4·5, though small ones may be found living in the mor layer above forest soils whose pH is less than this. This pH is in fact fairly critical, for above it in woodland and pasture soils earthworms account for a high proportion of the weight of the soil fauna and below it for a relatively low proportion, as is shown in Table 38. C. H. Bornebusch

[1] A. C. Evans, *Ann. Mag. Nat. Hist.*, 1947, **14**, 643.
[2] For examples of the effect of frost limiting earthworm numbers, see H. Hopp, *Proc. Soil Sci. Soc. Amer.*, 1948, **12**, 503, 508.
[3] W. Kubiena, *Bodenk. PflErnähr.*, 1942, **29**, 108.
[4] W. J. McL. Guild, *Ann. Appl. Biol.*, 1948, **35**, 181.
[5] B. L. Roots, *J. Exp. Biol.*, 1956, **33**, 29.
[6] *Landw. Jahrb. Schweiz.*, 1928, **42**, 1.   [7] *Soil Zoology*, London, 1955, p. 180.

in fact divided up the earthworms in Danish forest soils into two groups: acid-tolerant litter-dwelling species such as *Bimastus eiseni* and *Dendrobaena octaedra* and *rubida*, which can be found in litter with a *p*H below 4 and are not usually found in soils or litter above *p*H 5, and an acid-intolerant group of soil-burrowing species, which are normally present in soils with a *p*H above 4·5. But Satchell has found in some English Lake District woodlands a third group which are present both in very acid and in neutral soils, two of which are mainly surface or litter dwellers and three, *L. terrestris* and *rubellus* and *Octolasium cyaneum*, which are soil dwellers. It is not known how commonly these last three are found in acid soils for he also found the two that occur at Rothamsted absent or almost absent from pastures below *p*H 4·5 although present in considerable numbers in soils above that *p*H.

The weight of earthworms present in soils can be impressive. Bornebusch's figures for the numbers and weights of earthworms in Danish forest soils has already been referred to (see p. 177), where on two good forest sites he found 1–1½ million per acre weighing 1,500–1,800 lb. A. G. Davis and M. M. Cooper,[1] on productive four-year-old rye-grass/white clover leys on a deep brick earth at Wye, Kent, found about 2½ million per acre weighing nearly 1,500 lb. and P. D. Sears and L. T. Evans[2] and R. A. S. Waters[3] at the Grasslands Station, Palmerston North, New Zealand, found on their most productive pastures numbers up to 3 million per acre and weighing 2,100 lb.; and they noted a close correlation between the productivity of the pasture and the weight of earthworms, and they also noted that the weight of earthworms in their pastures is about equal to the weight of sheep the pasture can carry (see p. 177). Waters gives a figure of 170 lb. of worms present for every 1,000 lb. of dry matter produced, averaged over the year. The New Zealand pastures differ from the English in that the winter at Wye checks growth for more months than it does at Palmerston North.

The weights and numbers for typical British pastures are much lower than these figures, but so is their carrying capacity for sheep or stock. Numbers of the order of half a million per acre, weighing up to 600–1,000 lb. are common, whilst old arable fields may contain from a quarter to half as many but which may only weigh 100 lb., because they are of the smaller species. Ploughing out a pasture does not affect the earthworm population much in the first year, but it may drop rapidly in subsequent years.[4] Heavy dressings of farmyard manure

[1] *J. Brit. Grassland Soc.*, 1953, **8**, 115.
[2] *N.Z. J. Sci. Tech.*, 1953, **31** A, Suppl. 42.
[3] *N.Z. J. Sci. Tech.*, 1955, **36** A, 516. A. Finck, *Z. PflErnähr.*, 1952, **58**, 120, compared numbers and weights on productive German pastures.
[4] See, for example, A. C. Evans and W. J. McL. Guild, *Ann. Appl. Biol.*, 1947, **34**, 307, and 1948, **35**, 485, and W. J. McL. Guild, *J. Animal Ecol.*, 1951, **20**, 88, and 1952, **21**, 169.

applied to arable soils increase the number of earthworms they contain. Thus Plot 2 on Broadbalk Field at Rothamsted, which receives 15 tons per acre annually has about 1 million earthworms per acre, weighing about 440 lb., whilst plots receiving heavy dressings of fertiliser and giving the same average wheat yield have between 200,000 and 500,000 weighing between 50 and 100 lb. In countries with cold winters, earthworm numbers are increased appreciably by keeping the soil surface covered with a mulch of straw, farmyard manure or similar material.[1] Once again it must be emphasised that all the figures for weights and numbers given here are minimum figures, because some at least of the techniques used to collect all the worms from a sample of soil may be inefficient.[2]

Earthworms, where they flourish, as in virgin soils and pastures, are the principal agents in mixing the dead surface litter with the main body of the soil, so making it more accessible to attack by the soil micro-organisms. Peat formation is, in fact, typical of uncultivated land too acid for earthworms; thus at Rothamsted a mat of dead vegetation is accumulating on all the pasture plots whose pH is below 4, apparently solely because there are no earthworms or other animals capable of mixing this debris into the body of the soil.

Earthworms improve the aeration of a soil in two ways. They are very extensive channellers and burrowers, and these channels serve to improve the drainage of the surface soil, to give regions of good aeration and to loosen the whole soil throughout the zone in which they are working. They are most active in the surface layers of the soil, rarely working the soil intensively below 6 to 8 inches, though a few species will make burrows to much greater depths which often serve as passages for plant roots to penetrate into the subsoil. They can also play an important role in irrigated fields, for N. A. Dimo[3] found up to six million channels per acre coming to the soil surface in fields of irrigated lucerne; and these allow the irrigation water to penetrate rapidly through the surface layers of the soil into the subsoil. C. H. Edelman[4] gives an example from Holland of gang mowing a grass orchard on a clay loam giving 2 million large worm channels and many more smaller ones per acre, and A. Finck[5] in Germany found up to 4 million in the subsoil of well-manured arable fields and 1 million common on normal arable.

They also improve the aeration and at the same time the water-holding power of the actual soil crumbs, for the outstanding action of the earthworm is to ingest soil particles along with the organic matter,

[1] H. Hopp, *Proc. Soil Sci. Soc. Amer.*, 1948, **12**, 503, in Maryland, U.S.A., and A. Finck, *Z. PflErnähr.*, 1952, **58**, 120, in Germany.
[2] See, for example, J. A. Svendsen, *Nature*, 1955, **175**, 864.
[3] *Pedology*, 1938, No. 4, 494.
[4] *Trans. 5th Int. Congr. Soil Sci.* (Leopoldville), 1954, **1**, 119.
[5] *Z. PflErnähr.*, 1952, **58**, 120.

grind up the organic matter with the soil particles in its gizzard in the presence of calcium carbonate secreted by some of its digestive glands, and excrete this calcium-saturated intimate mixture of organic matter and soil as a blackish-brown mould or loam. This mould or mull, which in most soils is probably only produced by earthworms, is admirably suited for plant growth, having a very desirable air-water régime. On the lighter soils it has a considerably higher water-holding power than the soil itself, and on the heavier is more mellow and has a very favourable structure.

However, a word of warning must be given here. These remarks only apply to casting species of worms. Thus A. C. Evans[1] found at Rothamsted that the top few inches of pasture soil had a pore space of 67 per cent when these were dominant, but only one of 40 per cent when they were absent, even though the total weight of worms was about the same on the two fields. Further, he also found that where casting species were dominant the surface soil was rather higher in silt and clay, and lower in coarse sand than the subsurface, and this would increase the water-holding power of the surface soil. Again, as will be mentioned on p. 442, A. K. Dutt[2] and R. J. Swaby[3] found that wormcasts only possessed a stable structure if they were produced on pasture soils; they had this property to a much less extent when produced on arable soils and subsoils.[4]

The chemical composition of wormcasts differs from that of the soil mass because the worms feed selectively on the material in the soil, concentrating in the cast most of the nitrogen and mineral constituents present in the organic matter ingested. Thus, the casts are richer in available plant nutrients than the soil, as is shown by some results of H. A. Lunt and H. G. M. Jacobson[5] given in Table 42. This effect is due to the breakdown of the organic matter by the worms or by the microflora in their gut and, for as far as plants growing on the soil are concerned, could equally well be brought by the soil microflora, provided a mechanism was available for mixing up the organic matter with the soil. There is no evidence yet that the passage of inorganic soil particles through the worm's alimentary canal affects the availability of the plant nutrients they contain, nor is there any need to assume the existence of this effect, for, as Lunt and Jacobson point out, the wormcasts are poorer in plant nutrients than the original litter. Nor is there any evidence that the passage of the soil through the earthworm alters the bacterial or fungal flora appreciably.[6]

[1] *Ann. Appl. Biol.*, 1948, **35**, 1.   [2] *J. Amer. Soc. Agron.*, 1948, **40**, 407.
[3] *J. Soil Sci.*, 1950, **1**, 195.   [4] *Z. PflErnähr.*, 1952, **58**, 120.
[5] *Soil Sci.*, 1944, **58**, 367.
[6] G. M. Day, *Soil Sci.*, 1950, **69**, 175. But see a note by J. N. Parle (*Rothamsted Ann. Rept.*, 1958, 70) for a contrary opinion.

There is still much uncertainty whether earthworms directly affect the fertility of soils. As long ago as 1910 E. J. Russell[1] showed that crop growth was improved if dead earthworms were added to the soil, and that their bodies nitrified very quickly, but he could not show that living earthworms affected the growth of the crop. A. C. Evans has

TABLE 42

The Chemical Composition of Wormcasts compared with that of the Whole Soil (Connecticut)

Depth of sample	Arable soil			Forest soil (mean of 4 soils)			
	Cast	0–6 in.	8–16 in.	Cast	Al	A3	B
	In parts per million of soil						
Exchangeable calcium .	2790	1990	481	3940	747	155	171
Exchangeable magnesium	492	162	69	418	140	43	59
Exchangeable potassium .	358	32	27	230	138	32	25
Available phosphorus .	67	9	8	9	7	3	3
Nitrate nitrogen . .	21·9	4·7	1·7	—	—	—	—
Total carbon In per cent .	5·17	3·35	1·11	15·6	5·9	2·1	1·0
Total nitrogen in per cent	0·353	0·246	0·081	0·625	0·327	0·130	0·064
C/N	14·7	13·8	13·8	25·1	18·0	16·3	15·0
pH	7·0	6·4	6·0	5·3	4·6	4·6	4·7
Per cent of base saturation	93	74	55	63	32	18	12

recently reinvestigated this problem and could not show that living worms increased the green weight of crops growing in the soil, though they appeared to increase its dry weight, a result that is difficult to interpret, but one that could be due to the improved physical condition of the soil. An observation of Hopp and Slater[2] is in accord with this conclusion, for they found that either active earthworms (*A. caliginosa*) or an infestation of ants living in tubs of a loam soil planted to a grass-clover mixture, increased the proportion of clover to grass. The direct effect of worm activity on plant growth must still, therefore, be considered unsettled, though the effect, if it exists, cannot be large.[3]

Darwin first drew attention to the great quantity of soil earthworms can move per year; he estimated that the earthworms on some pastures outside his house could form a new layer of soil 7 inches thick in thirty years, or that they brought up annually about 20 tons of soil per acre, enough to form a layer 0·2 inch deep. This figure represents fairly well the amount of earth the casting species of earthworms can put on the soil surface every year. Thus, A. Stöckli found a similar figure in

[1] *J. Agric. Sci.*, 1910, **3**, 246. For additional confirmation, see B. Lindquist, *Svensk. SkogsvFören Tidskr.*, 1941, **39**, 179. H. Hopp and C. S. Slater, *J. Agric. Res.*, 1949, **78**, 325, also confirmed most of these conclusions.

[2] *J. Agric. Res.*, 1949, **78**, 325, and *Soil Sci.*, 1948, **66**, 421.

[3] For a summary of work until 1957, see J. E. Satchell, *Soils and Fert.*, 1958, **21**, 209.

some Swiss, and A. C. Evans in some Rothamsted, pastures. It is not yet possible to estimate from what depth the soil cast on the surface has been derived, but most of it has probably come from the top 4 to 6 inches.

This figure, however, does not represent the total amount of soil that passes through the gut of the earthworms each year, for this has been derived purely from the casting species. No attempt has yet been made to measure this accurately, but A. C. Evans[1] has made a rough estimate by assuming the weight of wormcasts produced by worms is proportional to the weight of the worms. His results for some Rothamsted fields with different cropping histories are given in Table 43, and show that some fields have high earthworm activity although

TABLE 43

Estimated Consumption of Soil by Worms at Rothamsted

Cropping of Field	Number of worms thousands/acre		Weight of worms	Worm casts	Soil excreted below ground	Total soil con- sumption
	A. nocturna and A. longa	Others	lb./acre	tons/acre	tons/acre	tons/acre
Old pasture (1) .	340	430	880	25	12	36
(2) .	140	170	540	11	9	20
Established leys:						
18 years old .	120	130	500	12	10	21
8 years old .	30	330	660	2	21	23
5 years old out of woodland	50	190	650	2	17	19
5 years arable after old pasture .	30	130	120	3	2	5

few casting species are present, so only very few wormcasts are produced. A. nocturna and A. longa are the casting species present, so their numbers are given separately. The table also shows that normal arable soils have a low earthworm activity compared with established leys and pastures.

Earthworms, such as L. terrestris, have a second effect on soil transport, for they also excrete surface soil into their deeper burrows, but the amount of surface soil they transport into the subsoil is probably small.

One can summarise our present knowledge on the importance of earthworms in agriculture as follows. They are of very great importance in undisturbed forest and pasture soils above pH 4·5, for they are the principal agents in mixing dead plant debris on the surface of the soil with the soil itself, and in doing this they help to keep the surface

[1] Ann. Appl. Biol., 1948, 35, 1.

soil loose and well aerated. They may also play an important role in the conversion of plant litter into humus, as their gut may form a favourable environment for the necessary chemical changes to take place, but this has not yet been rigorously proved. Only three British species produce wormcasts on the surface of the soil, all the rest excreting in the soil itself.

Arthropods

MESOFAUNA

The soil-inhabiting acarine mites vary from about 0·1 to 1 mm. in size and are present in very considerable numbers, belonging to a large number of genera and species. Each species has probably fairly specific food requirements, but the mites as a whole feed on a wide range of materials such as decomposing plant remains and fungi, though perhaps many of those appearing to feed on plant remains are in reality feeding on the micro-organisms carrying out the decomposition, and a number are predaceous on other members of the mesofauna. A. P. Jacot[1] has described how they will feed on the inside of a dead root leaving a channel with its outer corky layer. The springtails or collembola are rather larger, 0·5 to 2 mm. in size, and are minute wingless insects. There are probably considerably fewer species in the soil than of mites, and each species may be less specific in their food. They feed on decaying plant tissue and the micro-organisms decomposing it, and on dead insects, and presumably on the remains of other members of the soil fauna. The species present in the soil vary with the depth at which they live, the soil surface inhabitants being pigmented, and have well developed eyes and springing organs, all of which are lacking or poorly developed in the subsoil dwellers.

The mites and springtails have been extensively studied in forest soils, where they concentrate in the F. and H. layers of forest litter. Although they occur there in very large numbers, P. W. Murphy[2] estimates that there are only about 80 per c.cm. of air space in the moist well-drained condition, and N. Haarlov[3] estimates they occupy less than 0·1 per cent of the surface area accessible to them in this condition. They appear to decompose the organic matter very slowly for Murphy found almost as many in a litter layer that had been ploughed under to a depth of 9 inches twenty years previously as in the surface soil of a heathland planted to sitka spruce (*Picea sitchensis*).

LARVAE OF BEETLES AND DIPTEROUS FLIES

The larvae of several beetles and dipterous flies live in the soil and can be important burrowers and channellers in it. They occur in

[1] *Ecology*, 1936, **17**, 359, and *Quart. Rev. Biol.*, 1940, **15**, 28.
[2] *J. Soil Sci.*, 1953, **4**, 155.   [3] *Soil Zoology*, London, 1955, p. 167

considerable numbers in some forest soils, particularly in the mor layer, as can be seen from Table 40, and some grassland soils. They are normally saprophagous, but they will attack either the roots of agricultural crops or the young plant just above ground level. Among the principal agricultural pests on living crops are wireworms, which are the larvae of elaterid beetles, predominantly of the genus *Agriotes*, and leatherjackets, which are the larvae of crane flies (Tipulidae).

ANTS AND TERMITES

Ants and termites have many features in common. They are social insects living in nests, and for many genera these nests are in the soil. Some genera fill the soil with passages and chambers for their brood without making any mound, whilst others make mounds either out of surface or of subsoil without, however, mixing in any humic matter in the way earthworms do. This channelling and burrowing in the soil can have a very appreciable effect on the aeration and ease of drainage of soils, and H. Hopp and C. S. Slater showed that they could be as efficient as earthworms in improving plant growth in this way.[1] They are very active insects and can forage over very considerable distances for their food, so are common in land carrying a sparse vegetation, such as the fringes of deserts. There are genera in each group which harvest green leaves, often of grasses, and bring them back to their nests to be used as a food base on which they cultivate fungi in special gardens or combs on which they feed. Some of the ants also collect the seeds of the grasses at the same time. In semi-arid country, particularly if the grass is scarce due to overgrazing, these insects can remove almost all the remaining grass, complicating the problem of rehabilitating the range enormously, and leaving it exposed to water run-off and soil erosion. J. Thorp[2] has described this harmful effect of ants in the Great Plains area in the centre of the U.S.A., where he finds 10–20 ant hills per acre each surrounded by a circle of bare soil from 6 to 40 feet in diameter, and W. G. H. Coaton[3] describes the corresponding trouble with termites on similar rangeland in Zululand, South Africa.

Ants differ from termites in that they are not confined to equatorial and sub-tropical regions, but are common inhabitants of temperate soils. They can also differ in their feeding habits, for many genera of ants are predaceous, feeding on the mesofauna and smaller or more immature members of the soil macrofauna, including termites, of which they are one of the principal predators. They are not restricted to the soil fauna, but prey on insects feeding on plants and crops. A much quoted example of the control of an insect pest by a species of ant is

[1] *Soil Sci.*, 1948, **66**, 421.
[2] *Sci. Monthly*, 1949, **68**, 180.
[3] *Farming in S. Africa*, 1954, **29**, 243.

that of the Corrid bug *Pseudotherapsis wayi* causing premature nut drop of coconuts in Zanzibar and the coastal area of East Africa, which can be fairly effectively controlled by the ant *Oecophylla longinoda*. Unfortunately this ant is itself preyed upon by three other species[1] which do not feed on this bug, and we have yet to learn how to control the fortunes of battle between warring species of ants.

Ants also differ from termites in that some genera cultivate aphis or coccids in their nests and feed on their exudates. These "milch cows" may either be cultivated on roots of plants, particularly of grasses, or may be tended on the leaves of trees or other plants, and the tending includes protecting the aphis or coccid colonies against attacks by fungi and predators which would otherwise keep them in check.[2] The size of the ant colony may be controlled by the size of the colonies it can tend, and the damage done to crops by these colonies may be greater than any benefit that may accrue to the crop from the incidental reduction of insect numbers brought about by these same ants.

Termites differ from ants in that many genera have developed the use of fungal gardens to a much greater extent, and use wood as the base on which to grow the fungi. They are in consequence the dominant insect in many of the woodland and forest soils of the equatorial and sub-equatorial regions, the ants in these areas being primarily predaceous on them.

Naturally the detailed habits of the different species of ants and termites, even if using the same general method of obtaining their food supply and living in the same kind of nest, differ very considerably. In spite of the importance of these animals in the decomposition of plant residues and in the control of the soil population, little is known about their biology, feeding habits or digestive processes. It is very difficult, for example, to count the number of these insects on an acre of land, or estimate the weight or kind of food they consume per year. Hence in the following account of termite activity in soils, there must be many gaps, and probably a good deal of faulty deductions from observations, which must be borne in mind.

Termites are the dominant animals in many tropical soils, in the sense that they probably consume more organic matter per acre per year than any other group. H. Drummond,[3] who was one of the first commentators on their activity, described them as the topical analogue of the earthworm, a phrase that has often been quoted. The termites can be classified into a number of groups, such as the dry-wood termites,

---

[1] M. J. Way, *Bull. ent. Res.*, 1953, **44**, 669.
[2] M. J. Way, *Bull. ent. Res.*, 1954, **45**, 93 and 113, describes the behaviour of the ant *Oecophylla longinoda* in protecting colonies of the scale insect *Saissetia zanzibarensis* on clove trees.
[3] *Tropical Africa*, London, 1888.

which live in trees and therefore have no effect on the soil, the wood-feeding termites which are probably of more importance in the damage they do to buildings than in their effect on the soil, the fungus-growing termites and the humus-feeding ones.[1] They can also be classified by the mounds they build, some building very large ones, others small ones, and others burrowing in the soil but building none, but having their nests at different depths. In Africa, Siam and Malaya all the large mound builders are fungus growers, but in Australia they are not. In Africa some harvester termites collect green leaves, and carry them into nests 10 feet or more below the soil surface, with the consequence that all the mineral nutrients in the leaves not required by the termites will be left far below the topsoil.

Little is known of the effect of the so-called humus-eating termites on the soil organic matter. They pass humus-rich topsoil through their gut, though whether they break down the humus in the soil or partially decayed plant remains or any fungi and other micro-organisms in the soil is not known. They do not, however, enrich the soil they excrete in humic matter as earthworms do; they are said to impoverish the top-soil, but it is not certain what is meant by this phrase.

Some species of termites have very considerable ability to penetrate through hard pans and possibly into laterite crusts, and termite activity certainly seems to be a factor in causing the particular structure of the vesicular or vermicular laterite crusts so common on the Miocene peneplains of central Africa (see p. 561).[2]

The termites with the most spectacular effect on the soil, the large mound builders, belong to the genus *Macrotermes* in Africa. They are probably confined to "miombo", that is, *Brachystegia-Isoberlinia* woodland which is characterised by having an adequate rainy season and a long dry one, and they cover hundreds of thousands of square miles of equatorial and southern Africa. The mounds can be 40–60 feet in diameter and up to 25 feet high, and their remains may persist long after a change of climate has changed the vegetation. The mounds are not inhabited all the time by the termite which built them, but serve as a shelter for other species of ants and termites, and some of these may inhabit the mound even when the building species is in occupation. These mounds may contain hundreds of tons of earth above soil level, and commonly occur at a spacing of about one per $1\frac{1}{2}$ acres, which gives a measure of the distance around the mound that these termites will forage. The important factor for most of these mound-building termites is an adequate wood supply. Soil pH, soil type and depth, and

[1] See, for example, W. V. Harris, *E. Afr. Agric. J.*, 1949, **14**, 151, and *Soil Zoology*, London, 1956.

[2] H. Erhart (*C.R.*, 1951, **233**, 804, 966; 1953, **237**, 431) has discussed this problem with reference to the laterite crusts in French West Africa.

topographical position are unimportant, except they avoid wet sites though they may build on soil that has impeded drainage so is temporarily water-logged in the rains.

The exact shape and architecture of the mounds depends somewhat on the species present and other local conditions, but no detailed description of these variations has been given. The mound consists of two parts, a compact outer casing and an inner nest. The soil forming the mound is subsoil, which may have come up from as much as 9 feet, though most is derived from depths of 1–3 feet, but the channels from which the subsoil is derived can extend far beyond the mound itself. The mound consists of sand grains, usually about 2 mm. in size, cemented with finer soil particles, below 0·2 mm., which the termite carries in its crop. If the soil is sandy the mound will usually have more clay in it than the surface soil, and this would also happen if the subsoil is heavier than the surface soil. The casing is continually eroding away as it carries no vegetation if the mound is inhabited, though it gets grassed over or protected by trees if it is deserted. There is thus over a period of years a very considerable movement of subsoil to the surface which is liable to be washed down hill in the rains, so giving soil creep. This has the consequence that all particles larger than about 2–4 mm. accumulate in a fairly definite "stone-line" at the bottom of the zone of maximum termite activity, though this is not the only mechanism which gives this characteristic feature of many tropical soils. Little is known about the average rate of transport of subsoil to the surface in these mound areas, but P. H. Nye,[1] working in an area of rather small mounds, estimated it at ½ ton per acre per year. This figure should be compared with Nye's estimate of 20 tons/acre of wormcasts produced during the six months of rain by the worm *Hippopera nigeriae* on a neighbouring area under a bush which shades the ground and has an abundant leaf fall. The soil in the cast is surface soil and is all finer than 0·5 mm. and mostly finer than 0·2 mm.

Inside the casing is the nest, which is full of channels and contains a number of chambers filled with the fungus gardens. The soil is again subsoil but it tends to have a higher *p*H and be more saturated with exchangeable bases than the original subsoil, presumably because at least part of the minerals present in the wood brought in are left behind in the soil when the wood has disappeared.[2] The decomposition of the wood by the fungi is so efficient that this soil is hardly enriched in organic matter. One would expect the soil in the nest to contain more phosphate as well as more bases, but the evidence for this is inconclusive, P. R. Hesse[3] finding no extra phosphate but R. L. Pendleton[4]

[1] *J. Soil Sci.*, 1955, **6**, 73.
[2] This has also been noted by J. B. D. Robinson, *J. Soil Sci.*, 1958, **9**, 58.
[3] *J. Ecol.*, 1955, **43**, 449 (East Africa).   [4] *Thai Sci. Bull.*, 1941, **3**, 29 (Siam).

finding extra in some of the mounds he investigated. The fate of the minerals in the wood that is introduced has not yet been worked out.

This lack of knowledge complicates the interpretation of another feature found in some mounds, which is a layer of concretionary or nodular calcium carbonate at the base of the mound. Hesse only found this in calcareous soils or on land with impeded drainage which collected calcium salts from higher land during the rainy season. But Pendleton, and C. G. Trapnell have found examples of accumulation sometimes on acid soils, where the only reasonable explanation seems to be that the calcium was derived from the wood brought in.

There has been much discussion on the fertility of soils in a termite mound compared with the soil around it, but much of the inconsistencies in the literature seem to be due to the elementary mistake of ignoring the fact that soil fertility is made up of many different factors. If the soil around the mound is acid and low in calcium, and the crop being grown is a calcium-demanding crop, such as sisal, one would expect to find better sisal on the mounds, and even on mounds that have been more or less levelled, than on the soil around; and this effect can be seen quite strikingly on some Tanganyika sisal estates. On the other hand if the soil has a reasonable pH, and the surface soil is fairly well supplied with humus, the mound is likely to carry a poorer crop because since it is derived from the subsoil it will be lower in organic matter and is likely to release less nitrate nitrogen for the crop. Until more critical studies of the soil conditions are made in areas where the crop is better and where it is worse on the mound than on the surrounding soil, the matter must be left in this unsatisfactory position.

Areas where these mound-building Macrotermes are common can be difficult to cultivate, because the mounds themselves are difficult to cultivate, and if knocked down with a bulldozer can be built up again surprisingly quickly. Since these termites are primarily wood eaters, the hope would be they would soon die out, and this is seen in some areas of East Africa, but some of the termites start attacking annual crops instead and can be a very serious trouble. Again it is very difficult to maintain mulches on the surface of the soil in areas where soil-inhabiting termites of any kind are active, as they can be very rapidly harvested by the termites.

Myriapods and Isopods

Both millepedes (Diplopoda) and centipedes (Chilopoda) are present in soils, often in considerable numbers, and recently a number of zoologists have begun to study them in considerable detail.[1] In general

[1] For a general account, see J. G. Blower, *Soil Zoology*, London, 1955, p. 138.

the food of the millepedes is decaying plant litter, and the centipedes are predaceous on the immature forms of the larger soil fauna. Some millepedes at least, and possibly all, are unable to digest cellulose, so must consume a very large volume of litter to extract sufficient sugars and other simple carbohydrates for their requirements, hence can be very important as mechanical comminuters and mixers of litter with soil. Some consume a certain amount of soil, possibly only soil on the litter but do not appear to excrete a mull humus but a mull-like moder in Kubiena's terminology.[1] In both the millepedes and centipedes there are species adapted for burrowing in the soil and species that mainly feed and live above or on the soil surface.

The humidity of the air controls the suitability of the environment for both these groups of animals. Many species have little ability to control water loss from their body in a dry atmosphere, and many cannot control water intake if placed in water. A good forest mull, or the surface layers of forest soils with leaf litter forms a very favourable environment for most species. Hence forest soils that are not too acid, but for some reason are not suitable for high earthworm populations, such as acid sandy soils, usually have a high millepede population.

In agriculture millepedes are found in some pastures, and may occur in considerable numbers in arable soils well supplied with farmyard manure, and these may be so high that they can be a pest for crops such as potatoes.[2]

The wood-lice—isopods—are predominantly saprophagous or phytophagous, but their relative importance in the decay of organic matter and in altering the soil structure is unknown, though their gut may be a favourable environment for the humification of plant residues to take place.[3] They probably often thrive in sites too dry for earthworms. Thus N. A. Dimo[4] has shown that they may be very active channellers and burrowers during the summer in semi-desert soils, that is, during a period when the earthworms are aestivating. He found them burrowing down to 2 to 3 feet and bringing up during the season about 2 tons of soil per acre in a condition of small crumbs with a mellow structure.

Gasteropods

Slugs and snails are the two soil representatives of the Gasteropods, and so far little is known about their distribution or numbers. Most are surface feeders, usually active in damp conditions, hence either burrow into the soil or into a dense, shady spot, such as under stones or leaves

[1] J. G. Blower, *Trans. 6th Int. Congr. Soil Sci.* (Paris), 1956, C 168.
[2] For a discussion of the cause of high numbers, see J. L. Cloudsley-Thompson, *Proc. Zool. Soc.*, 1951, **121**, 253.
[3] H. Franz, *Bodenk. PflErnähr.*, 1943, **32**, 336.   [4] *Pedology*, 1945, No. 2, 115.

or in thick grass tussocks during the day. Some species of snails contain high concentrations of the enzyme cellulase in their gut, so obviously must digest cellulose, but it does not seem to be known if the principal soil-inhabiting slugs have this enzyme or if their food is confined to simple sugars. The forest floor is the well-adapted environment for them, and as B. Lindquist[1] has shown, litter and fungi appear to be their principal sources of food.

In agricultural soils, H. F. Barnes and J. W. Weil[2] have also shown that the food of slugs is usually dying vegetation, such as freshly fallen leaves, fallen and old grass, and so on, and that they mainly attack the actively growing parts of plants only when other food is scarce. They are therefore typically scavengers rendering old plant tissues more usable by the smaller members of the animal population by excreting them in a macerated and partially digested form. Some slugs, such as species of *Testacella*, are predaceous on other slugs, worms and centipedes. Normally, the numbers of slugs on arable land is not very high, though in some areas they may damage potatoes. However, D. C. Thomas[3] has given an example of a wheat-field carrying 600,000 slugs per acre and weighing about 400 lb., which is equivalent to about two sheep, but they are only serious pests in gardens and market gardens.

The Soil-inhabiting Mammals

Animals of the mouse family—mice, voles and shrews—and moles are present in appreciable numbers in some undisturbed soils, such as forest and prairie soils, and to a less extent in some pastures. Though their total weight per acre is only small, probably under 5 lb. in forest soils[4] and up to 10 lb. on open ranges,[5] they can cause a very important loosening of the surface layers of the soil by honeycombing it with their burrows and nests, and many of them also transport an appreciable amount of sub-surface or subsoil and leave it on the soil surface as mounds.[6] Some semi-arid soils can also carry a population of mammals that burrow into the deeper subsoil, and these burrows may be filled in course of time with surface soil rich in humus. Thus, these soils have numerous channels of dark soil running in the lighter humus-poor subsoil as is shown, for example, in Plate VII.

[1] *Kungl. Fysiograp. Sällsk. i Lund Forkandl.*, 1941, **11**, Nr. 16.
[2] *J. Animal Ecol.*, 1944, **13**, 140; 1945, **14**, 71.
[3] *Ann. Appl. Biol.*, 1944, **31**, 163; 1947, **34**, 246.
[4] W. J. Hamilton and D. B. Cook, *J. Forestry*, 1940, **38**, 468.
[5] W. P. Taylor, *Ecology*, 1935, **16**, 127.
[6] For detailed examples, see W. J. Hamilton, *Bull. New York Zool. Soc.*, 1940, **43**, 171, and J. Thorp, *Sci. Mon.*, 1949, **68**, 180.

CHAPTER XII

THE GENERAL ECOLOGY OF THE SOIL POPULATION

THE VARIOUS GROUPS of soil organisms do not live independently of each other, but form an interlocked system more or less in equilibrium with the environment. This is obviously true for the predators, but it is equally true for the saprophytic species, for they are all competing for the available food supply, and each has developed a series of symbiotic and antibiotic relations with its neighbours for increasing its ability to get its share of the available food. Thus the composition of the population in any soil achieves a certain equilibrium which depends on the environment; and for any particular soil farmed on a definite system the equilibrium is fairly stable. The soil, in fact, usually appears to be fairly "well-buffered" biologically. Hence, if any particular soil-inhabiting organism is absent from a soil it cannot usually be made an active component of the soil population merely by inoculating it into the soil;[1] it can only be introduced by altering the environment either through the crops grown on the soil, the energy-containing material added to the soil, or the general environmental conditions of life in the soil itself. This limitation naturally applies with much less force if the organism has a close relationship with any of the crops growing on the soil. D. Parks[2] showed this stability of population applied to some extent even if a foreign fungus was introduced with the food supply. He buried pieces of rotting grass, in which various saprophytic fungi were actively growing, in a soil and found that after a short time the soil fungi had displaced most of the foreign fungi from the rotting grass.

This stability of the population naturally refers to the conditions holding under normal conditions. It may be upset when new sources of energy-material, such as plant debris, composts or farmyard manures are added to the soil, for these additions can cause a rapid, though temporary, rise in certain groups, particularly some of the fungi.

The Distribution of Micro-organisms through the Soil Space

The soil micro-organisms are not uniformly distributed throughout the soil. In spite of their very large numbers, there are relatively large

[1] For an example of an attempt to do this, see S. A. Waksman and H. B. Woodruff, *Soil Sci.*, 1940, **50**, 421. [2] *Trans. Brit. Mycol. Soc.*, 1955, **38**, 130, and 1957, **40**, 283.

volumes of the soil, on the microscopic scale, which appear to be un-
occupied yet available for colonisation. A. Burges,[1] who has stressed the
importance of this fact, suggests that one of the major problems in soil
microbiology is to obtain a proper understanding of the size and extent
of the soil microhabitats. Direct microscopic observation shows that the
fungi tend to congregate round particles of decaying plant and animal
debris, and the bacteria live on these as well as on the surface of
soil particles.[2] P. C. T. Jones and J. E. Mollison,[3] using their direct
staining technique, were able to show that the bacteria are present in
colonies or clumps as is shown in Plate VII, and the proportion of
clumps containing, say, n bacteria in the soil is proportional to x^n/n,
where x is a number smaller than unity and depends on the population.
Thus, the distribution of bacterial colonies and of bacteria in the
colonies found in the soil of the permanent mangold field at Rothamsted
is as follows:

Number of bacteria in the colony	1	2	3	4	5	6	7 and over
Observed proportion of colonies in the population	51	23	8	7	3	2	5
Calculated proportion of colonies in the population	53	20	10	6	4	2	5
Observed proportion of bacteria present in colonies of each size . . .	23	21	11	12	7	6	21

These figures actually refer to the plot receiving 14 tons of farmyard
manure per acre per annum, but the figures are almost identical for
the unmanured plot, and for a plot receiving only fertilisers which has
the same average yield of mangolds as the farmyard manure plot. Thus,
this distribution may be characteristic of a soil and not strikingly
dependent on the manurial treatment.

The Rossi-Cholodny slide technique has been the method most
extensively used for investigating the distribution of the soil micro-
organisms. The technique consists in burying a microscope cover slip
in the soil, leaving it there for a certain time and then digging it up;
and it is based on the assumption that the organisms developing on the
slip are representative of those in the soil. This is only partially true
because water tends to condense on the slide and many of the organisms
which develop on it do so because they can grow in this water film.
Again the aeration conditions around the slide tend to be better than
in the body of the soil and it is difficult to ensure that the pockets of

[1] *Micro-organisms in the Soil*, London, 1958.
[2] C. Rouschel and S. Strugger, *Naturwiss.*, 1943, **31**, 300; *Canad. J. Res.*, 1948, **26** C, 188.
[3] *J. Gen. Microbiol.*, 1948, **2**, 54.

good, medium and poor aeration on the surface of the slip are about the same as in the undisturbed soil.

The results obtained by using this technique are entirely concordant with other knowledge, and will be described for three conditions—in fallow soil, in soil carrying a crop, and in soil to which fermentable organic matter has been added.

In a fallow soil[1] only a sparse population develops on the slips, extensive development only taking place near pieces of organic matter. The bacteria seem to be mainly small organisms in small colonies, which appear to be pure cultures of the organisms and which may be compact or loose and composed of cocci or short rods. A few of the looser colonies often contain rather longer rods, all lying more or less parallel to each other. There are a number of isolated bacteria, commonly short rods, scattered over the slide, long rods are scarce and usually occur near pieces of organic matter, and the larger cells commonly occur in clusters of two to four. Actinomycetes are fairly common, usually occurring as a line of spores, or conidia, each about the size of small coccus or coccoid rod, and hence indistinguishable from them if occurring individually. Fungal mycelium is rare, and this often is attacked by bacteria.

In cropped land the population does not differ in kind but becomes more numerous. Extensive bacterial development occurs around some plant rootlets, the colonies of coccoid or short rods becoming so dense that they cannot be resolved into their constituent organisms under the microscope. Actinomycetes in particular, and fungal mycelium to some extent, share in this general development, though they are not conspicuous in the immediate neighbourhood of the rootlets.

The effect of adding fermentable organic matter can easily be seen. The population becomes much more dense, and typical groups of bacteria develop. Thus, adding sugars can give many Azotobacter-like colonies appearing on the slide, and adding cellulose many typical Cytophaga-like bacteria. This initial bacterial attack is often followed by development of fungi and actinomycetes, which are later attacked by other bacteria.[2] In acid soils, or when some types of organic material resistant to decomposition are added, fungi develop initially, but decomposition is slower than when bacterial development begins. Thus, fungal mycelia can often be seen radiating from pieces of decomposing organic matter, though after a few weeks' decomposition the fungi may be mainly represented by spores.[3] But fungi, being large micro-organisms, can be seen directly in the soil with a suitable microscope and their development followed. W. Kubiena

[1] See, for example, R. L. Starkey, *Soil Sci.*, 1938, **45**, 207.
[2] J. Ziemiecka, *Zbl. Bakt.* II, 1935, **91**, 379.
[3] H. L. Jensen, *Proc. Linn. Soc. N.S.W.*, 1934, **59**, 200.

and C. E. Renn,[1] for example, followed the development of different groups of fungi when various substances were added to the soil and showed that the species developing depended on the air supply, so that the fungal flora was not the same inside as on the surface of the soil crumbs.

W. Kubiena[2] has stressed the control which the size of the soil pores has on the development of the soil fungi; typically their spores and fruiting bodies are smaller, and sometimes much smaller, in the soil where space is restricted than in pure cultures where there is no such restriction. This dwarfing effect of the soil pore-space on the size of organisms affects protozoa and diatoms; thus, both he and M. Koffmann[3] found the largest ciliates present in the soil were only 18 to 22 μ in size, whereas they often attain 60 μ in cultures, and it also controls the size of some of the arthropod population, for W. Kühnelt[4] found that soils with large pores contained larger mites than soils with small pores. This control is naturally not effective for those organisms possessing the power of increasing the pore size, such as the burrowing and channelling invertebrates.

The weight of the different organisms in the soil cannot yet be determined accurately, largely because of the great uncertainty in the weight of the individual organisms. A Rothamsted arable soil containing 3 per cent organic matter, or, say, 60,000 lb. per acre of dry organic matter in the top 6 inches of soil, will contain about 3,000 million bacteria or similar-sized cells and about 30,000 flagellates and 20,000 amoebae. The dry weight of the bacteria was estimated at up to 650 lb. per acre on p. 147, and this will include most of the actinomycetes. The amount of dry matter in the fungal hyphae and spores is not known, but if one assumes that there is about 40 metres of mycelium per gram of soil, as suggested in Table 45, and this has an average diameter of 5 μ, there will be about 1,500 lb. of fungal mycelium per acre, if it is all alive. However, a proportion of this is undoubtedly dead, so the organic matter content of the mycelium will probably be less. But a dry weight of 300 lb. per acre is possible, which is comparable to that of the bacterial. A rough calculation gives the weight of protozoa as about 150 lb. per acre live weight, or 30 lb. per acre dry matter, and Table 39 suggests that the soil fauna, excluding the protozoa and nematodes, have a dry weight of 100 to 200 lb. per acre. Therefore a very rough calculation indicates that the weight of the dry matter in the soil population in an arable soil may be of the order of 1,200 lb. per acre, or something between 1 and 2 per cent of the organic matter.

[1] *Zbl. Bakt.* II, 1935, **91**, 267.
[2] *Micropedology*, Ames, 1938.
[3] *Arch. Mikrobiol.*, 1934, **5**, 246.
[4] Quoted by P. W. Murphy, *J. Soil Sci.*, 1953, **4**, 155.

The Effect of the Energy Supply

The general requirements of the soil organisms are the same as those of plants: energy, nutrients, water, suitable temperatures and the absence of harmful conditions. The great difference between them is the source of energy: green plants derive their energy directly from sunlight, and the soil organisms—apart from the photosynthetic forms—obtain theirs either directly or indirectly from the products of plant metabolism. The size of the soil population is thus controlled by the rate at which energy-containing material synthesised by plants is added to the soil.

The organisms derive their energy in different ways from the added plant tissues; some attack the dead or dying plant tissues, or even the tissues of the living plant, and these form the primary source of energy for the remainder of the population, which is either predaceous on them while alive or else lives on the waste products of their metabolism or on their dead bodies. The number, or the activity, of the micro-organisms is controlled by the amount of energy that can be released by the decomposition of the added organic matter and, no matter how many stages or what organisms are involved in its degradation, only a certain definite amount of energy can be extracted; and this amount cannot exceed the energy set free when the organic matter is completely oxidised.

The energy in the organic matter differs fundamentally from the nutrients in it. Nutrients can be used over and over again by an unending succession of organisms. An atom of nitrogen never loses its value; it might in the course of a single day form part of a fungus, a bacillus which decomposed it, an amoeba which ate the bacillus, and a bacterium which decomposed the dead amoeba; for all these organisms one and the same atom of nitrogen would be a perfectly good nutrient.

But energy cannot be used in this way. It is as indestructible as matter, but once transformed to heat, it cannot be used by micro-organisms or any other living things; whatever energy is dissipated by one organism becomes out of reach of the others. It follows, therefore, that no factor affecting the trophic life in the soil which does not add to the stock of energy material can permanently increase the numbers of all the groups; if one group increases, others necessarily decrease.

The supply of energy and the turnover of nutrients thus become the chief factors determining the kinds and numbers of organisms in the soil. An exact measure of the amount of energy available to micro-organisms in a given weight of soil cannot yet be made, though the amount of energy transformed in a given period can be estimated by determining the total quantities at the beginning and at the end.

Estimates obtained from analytical data for two of the Broadbalk plots are given for illustration only in Table 44.

This great increase in the amount of energy dissipated in the two plots is barely reflected in the numbers of micro-organisms present in

TABLE 44

Annual Energy Changes in Soil: Broadbalk

Approximate estimates only

Millions of kilo-calories per acre per annum

	Farmyard manure added	No manure added
Added in manure	14	Nil
Added in stubble	2	0·3
Total added	16	0·3
Net loss from soil	Nil	0·5–1
Stored in soil	0·5–1	Nil
Dissipated per annum	15	1
Per day: Calories	41,000	2,700
Equivalent to the requirements of . . .	12 men	¾ man
The human food grown provides for . .	2 men	½ man

the soil, for whereas the farmyard manure plot is dissipating fifteen times as much energy each year as the unmanured, or as the neighbouring plots receiving fertilisers only, yet it has scarcely twice as many bacteria or protozoa, and only about the same number of fungi, as these plots, as can be seen in Table 45. Only the protozoa seem to be really dependent on the fertility of the soil, in the sense that their active numbers roughly follow the average wheat yield.

Clearly, the organisms on the farmyard manure plot must be living much more actively than on the other plots, presumably because they pass a smaller proportion of their time in resting stages.

So far as present knowledge goes, the soil organisms are living right up to their income in the matter of nutrients and energy supply. Any increase in the available organic matter capable of supplying energy at once increases the numbers of micro-organisms. Further, it appears to be a fairly general rule that, under natural conditions, the greater the number of soil-inhabiting organisms in a soil, the greater the number of species present, but this generalisation has not yet been adequately tested.

TABLE 45

The Effect of Long-continued Applications of Farmyard Manure and Fertilisers on the Numbers of Micro-organisms in some Broadbalk plots[1]

Numbers per gram of air-dry soil

Mean of six determinations made at monthly intervals from 20-1-48 to 23-6-48

Treatment	Unmanured	Complete fertiliser	Farmyard manure
Plot number	3	7	2
Number of bacteria			
Total cells in thousand millions .	1·6	1·6	2·9
On plates in millions . . .	50	47	67
Number of Fungi			
Pieces of mycelium in millions .	0·85	0·94	1·01
Length of mycelia in metres . .	38	41	47
On plates in millions . . .	0·16	0·26	0·23
Number of Protozoa			
Total in thousands . . .	17	48	72
Active in thousands .	10	10	52

The Activity of the Soil Population

The numbers of micro-organisms in a soil give no direct measure of the activity of the microbial population. The activity of the population is not a concept that can be given a quantitative definition, but for many purposes it can be measured by the amounts of either CO_2 or heat evolved by the population, that is, by the rate at which either the oxidisable carbon compounds or the energy available for organic growth are being dissipated. Neither of these definitions gives a perfect measure of the activity, for there is no necessary connection between the heat or CO_2 evolution of an organism and the amount of growth it makes; nor, in fact, are these two definitions always concordant, for the amount of CO_2 produced per calorie evolved increases as the oxygen tension decreases because energy-rich materials are then being either stored in or lost from the soil.

In general, the CO_2 evolution increases as the number of bacteria increases. D. Fehér[2] found a close correspondence between the bacterial numbers, as determined by the plating technique, and the CO_2

[1] Unpublished observations of P. C. T. Jones, J. E. Mollison, and F. A. Skinner. I am much indebted to these workers for permission to use their data. The data for protozoa have been published by B. N. Singh, *J. Gen. Microbiol.*, 1949, **3**, 204.

[2] *Arch. Mikrobiol.*, 1934, **5**, 421; 1938, **9**, 193.

evolution at different seasons of the year for different soils, and concluded that the activity of the whole population rose and fell with the numbers of bacteria so determined. But H. L. Jensen[1] found the CO_2 evolution was poorly correlated with the bacterial numbers so determined, but was sometimes well correlated with them when determined by the total cell count. The only conditions when the fungi seemed to contribute appreciably to the CO_2 evolution was when there was a vigorous growth of mycelium on buried Cholodny slides, and this occurred for only one or two weeks after fermentable organic matter was added to the soil.

The Relation between Microbiological Activity and Soil Fertility

In the early days it was often noted that fertile soils had higher bacterial numbers, often higher nitrate contents and higher CO_2 evolution than infertile,[2] and many attempts were made to measure soil fertility by some simple procedure based on this result. There certainly can be a connection between bacterial numbers, CO_2 evolution and soil fertility.[3] Thus, H. G. Thornton and P. H. H. Gray[4] found a good correlation between bacterial numbers, determined by the total cell count method, and the yield of barley straw on some plots on Hoosfield, the permanent barley field at Rothamsted, as is shown in Fig. 15. But no general correlation between bacterial numbers and crop yields has been found even at Rothamsted, for Table 45 on p. 203 showed that the total cell counts of bacteria on Broadbalk do not follow yields at all: Plot 3 and Plot 7 have about the same cell count, yet in the last ten years Plot 7 has had an average yield of wheat more than double that on the unmanured. Nor would a close correlation be expected, for the fertility of a soil is a very complex property, and the various factors contributing to it affect the microbiological activity in different ways.

However, the activity of certain groups of organisms can be used to measure the contribution of selected factors to the fertility of a soil. Thus, *Azotobacter*, which is sensitive to calcium and phosphate deficiencies, can be used to determine a deficiency of either of these.[5] Other organisms have also been used for measuring the phosphate

[1] *Proc. Linn. Soc. N.S.W.*, 1936, **61**, 27.

[2] E. J. Russell, *J. Agric. Sci.*, 1905, **1**, 261; with A. Appleyard, ibid., 1915, **7**, 1.

[3] J. R. Neller, *Soil Sci.*, 1920, **10**, 29; S. A. Waksman and R. L. Starkey, *Soil Sci.*, 1924, **17**, 141.

[4] *Proc. Roy. Soc.*, 1934, **115** B, 522.

[5] H. R. Christensen and O. H. Larsen, *Zbl. Bakt.* II, 1911, **29**, 347; *Soil Sci.*, 1923, **15**, 329. Another technique using *Azotobacter* was developed by S. Winogradsky and J. Ziemiecka, *Ann. Inst. Pasteur*, 1928, **42**, 36. For an application of this technique to Rothamsted soils, see J. Ziemiecka, *J. Agric. Sci.*, 1932, **22**, 797.

status of a soil, such as the fungus *Aspergillus niger*[1] and suitable species of *Cunninghamella*;[2] and the use of *Aspergillus niger* has also been suggested for measuring the amount of available copper in the soil.[3]

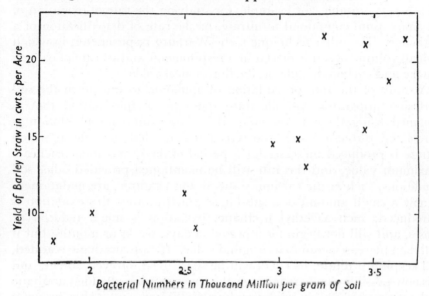

FIG. 15. Relation between bacterial numbers, determined by total cell count and the yield of barley straw on differently manured plots on Hoosfield.

Biochemical Processes brought about by Soil Micro-organisms

It is often important to study biochemical reactions taking place in the soil under conditions when one is not concerned with the actual species of micro-organisms responsible for them. Thus it is of great importance to study the rate at which compounds potentially toxic to the soil population or to plants are decomposed in the soil, and these include many present-day herbicides and insecticides. Again the actual compounds in which many inorganic elements occur is of great importance for plant growth, such as those containing inorganic nitrogen, sulphur, manganese and iron, and these also are closely controlled by the soil micro-organisms.

Two general techniques have been developed to study the ability of the soil population to carry out certain chemical and biochemical reactions, and the detailed chemical or enzyme processes involved. The more powerful of the two, and particularly useful if the substances concerned are water-soluble, is the perfusion technique in which a

[1] A. Niklas, *Ztschr. Pflanz. Düng.*, 1933, A **32**, 50; R. Martin, *Ann. Agron.*, 1943, **13**, 27.
[2] A. Mehlich, E. B. Fred and E. Truog, *Soil Sci.*, 1934, **38**, 445.
[3] J. Smit, *Proc. 3rd Int. Congr. Microbiol.*, New York, 1939, 693.

solution is repeatedly percolated through a column of soil, usually under well-aerated conditions, and the solution is analysed at suitable intervals to study the rate of progress of the relevant chemical reactions. This is very suitable, for example, for studying the rate of oxidation of an ammonium compound to nitrate, or the rate of detoxification of a herbicide. The other technique is the Warburg respirometer, in which a small volume of soil is placed in a respirometer and its rate of oxygen uptake and carbon dioxide production is measured.

A study of the rate of oxidation of ammonia to nitrate in the soil perfusion apparatus will illustrate the type of information that is obtained using these techniques. If a dilute ammonium solution is percolated through a soil, one typically finds that the rate at which nitrate is produced increases for a period of days, and then reaches a maximum value, and this rate will be maintained provided other soil conditions, such as the calcium status in this example, are maintained. If now a small amount of a substance which inhibits this oxidation is introduced, such as ethyl urethane, oxidation is much reduced or ceases, and will not begin for a period of days, weeks or months, but it will then increase again to its original value. If more urethane is added, still keeping it dilute, its effect will be short-lived, or even absent, and it is now possible slowly to increase the concentration of added urethane without the ammonium oxidation being inhibited, and it thus becomes possible to detoxify a relatively high concentration of urethane which if used initially would have inhibited the oxidation of ammonium for a very long time.[1] Instead of urethane, nitrite could have been used to show this last effect, for soils can be conditioned to oxidise concentrations of nitrite which would have been toxic to the bacteria oxidising them if used initially at that concentration.

An experiment such as this brings out three points of importance: there is a certain maximum rate at which a given amount of soil can carry out a chemical change; it takes the soil a period of time to decompose an inhibitor of a biochemical reaction, but later on its addition has little if any effect on the reaction; and soils can be adapted to decompose toxic substances at concentrations which if used initially would entirely prevent the reaction from taking place.

The present interpretation of the first of these results is that the micro-organisms can only occupy a limited number of spots on the surfaces of the soil particles, and once they have multiplied up and occupied these spots, they cease to multiply, except to make good losses due to other organisms grazing on them. The organisms are fairly firmly anchored to these spots, as their cells do not appear in the

[1] J. H. Quastel and P. G. Scholefield, *Appl. Microbiol.*, 1953, **1**, 282, and *Proc. Roy. Soc.*, B, 1955, **143**, 159.

percolating solution, and the spots are fairly specific to the organism. Thus J. H. Quastel and P. G. Scholefield[1] showed that the sites for the ammonium and nitrite oxidising bacteria are different from those oxidising arsenites. Nothing is yet known about why the organisms stick to specific spots, nor on what soil particles these spots are situated, nor how specific they are for different organisms. This phenomenon may only be shown for reactions in which bacteria are the organisms responsible, as these are the only ones which have been investigated.

The interpretation of the second result is that when a new compound is introduced into the soil, it may take weeks or months for a large population of an organism which can decompose it to build up. What is not known is whether these organisms were initially present in the soil in very low numbers as resting cells, so it takes a fairly long time for them to multiply up, or whether a micro-organism already present in the soil undergoes a mutation which enables it to carry out this decomposition. Under some conditions it would seem that the latter is probably correct, because of the very long lag period that is sometimes found. What is known is that the new organisms may be extremely specific for the particular chemical introduced. Thus in the example given above, the soil which will decompose ethyl urethane after an interval of time will not decompose methyl or propyl urethane. The interpretation of the third result is that organisms can be trained to become tolerant of a poison by conditioning them to relatively low concentrations which are not fully toxic, and gradually increasing the concentration. This effect is well known in conditioning bacteria to become tolerant to antibiotics and insects to insecticides.

The Break-down of Toxic Chemicals in the Soil

This property of soils to acquire the ability to decompose compounds not normally present in them, but which may be toxic to the microbial population if used in high enough concentration, has been known for a long time. Thus soils can acquire the ability to oxidise phenol, cresols and hydrocarbons.[2] But interest has recently centred round the ability of the soil to decompose the whole host of new synthetic substances used as herbicides and insecticides. These substances have been selected because of their ability to affect plant or animal life at very great dilutions, and their continued use in agriculture would be extremely dangerous if they persisted in the soil for long periods unchanged. The kind of result found for the decomposition of the urethanes applies equally to the herbicides. Thus a soil which has acquired the ability to

[1] *Soil Sci.*, 1953, **75**, 279.
[2] See, for example, R. Wagner, *Ztschr. Gärungsphysiol.*, 1914, **4**, 289, and P. H. H. Gray and H. G. Thornton, *Zbl. Bakt. Abt.* II, 1928, **73**, 74.

decompose the herbicide 2-4-D (2, 4, dichlorophenoxyacetic acid) will usually decompose MCPA (2, methyl 4, chlorophenoxyacetic acid) but not 2, 4, 5 T (2, 4, 5 trichloro phenoxyacetic acid).[1] Again some of the organisms which decompose DNOC (2, 4 dinitro-ortho-cresol) decompose any nitrophenol in which the nitro group is in the para-position, such as p-nitrophenol, 2, 4 dinitrophenol or 2, 4, 6 trinitrophenol, but they cannot decompose o- or m-nitrophenols or 2, 5- or 2, 6 dinitrophenols.[2]

Some compounds have a constitution that is so resistant to microbial attack that they will last for very long periods in the soil. Thus the herbicide CMU ($Cl.C_6H_4.NH.CO.N(CH_3)_2$) and other substituted ureas are fairly persistent, and the insecticides DDT and BHC (γ-hexachlorobenzene) are very persistent and may remain in appreciable amounts in the soil for four to six years after commercial dressings,[3] and in the case of BHC it may cause a taint in potatoes, tobacco and other crops grown on a soil treated with it for up to this number of years.

In all the examples which have been studied of the decomposition of organic compounds which are toxic to most of the soil organisms when they are added to a soil, the same general conclusion has been reached on the build-up of ability to decompose these active substances. The organisms responsible for the decomposition, in so far as they have been isolated, are bacteria. The substance must initially be present at a low enough concentration not to kill the majority of the soil organisms. It may remain in the soil undecomposed for a period of weeks or months, which is usually shorter in soils having a high than a low microbial activity, for example, in surface soils than in subsoils.[4] The substance then begins to decompose, sometimes to another substance also very difficult to decompose but not necessarily toxic and after a time it too decomposes.[5] Further additions decompose more quickly, and the concentration of the active substance can be slowly increased without affecting the rate of decomposition, until a concentration is reached which would have been definitely toxic to the soil population if it had been added initially.

Processes involving Inorganic Compounds

Soils contain a number of inorganic compounds which can be changed chemically by the micro-organisms without becoming part of the

[1] L. J. Audus, *Plant and Soil*, 1951, **3**, 170.
[2] H. L. Jensen and K. Gundersen, *Nature*, 1955, **175**, 341.
[3] N. Allen, R. L. Walker *et al.*, *U.S.D.A. Tech. Bull.* 1090, 1954; L. W. Jones, *Soil Sci.*, 1952, **73**, 237, and J. E. Dudley, J. B. Landis and W. A. Shands, *U.S.D.A. Farmers Bull.* 2040, 1952.
[4] A. S. Newman, J. R. Thomas and R. L. Walker, *Proc. Soil Sci. Soc. Amer.*, 1952, **16**, 21.
[5] L. J. Audus and K. V. Symonds (*Ann. Appl. Biol.*, 1955, **42**, 174) give an example where the intermediate is phytotoxic.

microbial protoplasm, and these processes typically involve oxidations or reductions. Thus in well-aerated soils, in which all the inorganic substances are in their most stable oxidised state, the principal changes the soil organisms will bring about are the oxidation of inorganic substances which were present in a reduced state in microbial or plant cells. Thus it is under conditions of only moderate aeration, such as occur in most soils, that biochemical changes involving the state of oxidation of inorganic compounds are most noticeable.

As a general rule, soils contain micro-organisms capable of converting all the normal inorganic constituents to that state of oxidation or reduction which would be predicted if they are to be in equilibrium with the oxidation-reduction potential of that soil. Typical reversible oxidation-reduction processes involving inorganic substances in the soil are the system nitrate-nitrite, sulphate-sulphide, manganese dioxide-manganic ions, and ferric-ferrous ions. There are naturally other oxidation and reduction processes going on, such as the oxidation of ammonium to nitrite, the reduction of nitrite to nitrous oxide or nitrogen gas, and the production of hydrogen gas and methane in very poorly aerated soils; and some of the oxidations and reductions may not be straightforward because of the production of organic substances which themselves may bring about a reduction process, and this applies particularly to the ferric-ferrous system.

The organisms responsible for these oxidations and reductions are usually bacteria, and certainly in some examples the species carrying out the oxidation are different from these carrying out the reductions. In general the oxidations are carried out by specialised autotrophs whilst the reductions are brought about by unspecialised heterotrophs. Correspondingly an oxidation may involve several organisms: the oxidation of ammonium to nitrate involves two, and the oxidation of sulphur or even sulphides to sulphates several. The general course of these oxidations and reductions, and the intermediate products and the enzymes involved, are being studied, and it is possible that manganese and thiosulphates will prove to be involved in normal oxidation-reduction cycles operative in many soils [1]

The study of what organisms are in fact responsible for any particular biochemical reduction or oxidation taking place in the soil can be very difficult, particularly if an observation made by S. M. Bromfield[2] on sulphate reduction in soils turns out to be of general relevance. He showed that in some soils which were partially sterilised with carbon tetrachloride the addition of sucrose and ammonium sulphate caused hydrogen sulphide to be produced, even in reasonably well-aerated conditions, due apparently to two species of bacterium which he isolated.

[1] See, for example, J. H. Quastel, *Proc. Roy. Soc.*, B, 1955, **143**, 159, and with H. Gleen, *Appl. Microbiol.*, 1953, **1**, 70.   [2] *J. gen. Microbiol.*, 1953, **8**, 378.

But he also showed that if certain other bacteria and fungi were present, the growth of the sulphate-reducing bacteria was not inhibited but that they ceased to produce hydrogen sulphide. Thus it is possible that some of the biochemical processes carried out by a micro-organism depend on what other micro-organisms are present in its neighbourhood.

Symbiotic and Antibiotic Relations between the Microflora

The various groups of soil organisms do not live independently of each other; they form an interlocked system more or less in equilibrium in a given soil, and most organisms have developed a series of symbiotic relations with their neighbours. It seems to be a characteristic of all micro-organisms that they excrete complex organic compounds when growing actively, usually only in very small amounts, and much of the symbiotic and antibiotic relations take place through the action of these substances on other organisms in their neighbourhood. These relations are, however, rarely very specific, so that there seem to be no examples in the soil in which one organism affects or is dependent upon only one other organism.

There are two types of beneficial interactions which presumably occur in the soil. Two organisms may be living together because one can use the excretion products of the other; and this will probably occur more commonly when the air or nitrogen supply is restricted, for then a greater proportion of the ingested carbon is usually excreted. Again, it is possible that two organisms living together can effect a decomposition neither can do when growing alone, and although there are few if any examples of this in the soil, there are numerous examples of two soil organisms carrying out a decomposition more quickly when growing together than when alone.[1]

Other soil organisms develop antibiotic relations with selected species,[2] which are brought about by their excreting substances into the soil solution that prevent the affected organisms from growing or that kill them by lysis, that is, by dissolving their outer membrane. The fungus *Penicillium notatum* which excretes penicillin is such an organism, but in the soil the fungus *Trichoderma viride* is a much more important example, for it excretes two antibiotics—gliotoxin and viridin—having very powerful effects on the soil population and particularly on plant pathogens living in the soil.

[1] See, for example, A. G. Norman, *Ann. Appl. Biol.*, 1930, **17**, 575, and S. A. Waksman and I. J. Hutchings, *Soil Sci.*, 1937, **43**, 77. For an example when one bacterium is a cellulose decomposer, see L. Enebo, *Nature*, 1949, **163**, 805.

[2] S. A. Waksman, *Soil Sci.*, 1937, **43**, 51, and *Bact. Rev.*, 1941, **5**, 231, has given full historical reviews of the development of these ideas and has described many examples of this antibiosis. See also his book *Microbial Antagonisms and Antibiotic Substances*, 2nd ed., New York, 1947.

The ability to produce antibiotics is not confined to fungi, for it is also strongly developed by many actinomycetes and bacteria. At least half the soil fungi and actinomycetes probably produce such substances,[1] but the proportion of bacteria producing them is probably much smaller. The substances so far recognised usually act only on other members of these three groups, but there are some bacteria, such as *Pseudomonas aeruginosa* and *Ps. pyocyanea*, which produce substances that can kill species of soil protozoa belonging to the amoebae, flagellates and ciliates.[2] These substances appear to have very varied chemical composition and are often named after the organism producing it, as, for example, penicillin, mentioned above. But just because these antibiotics are produced in the soil, it does not follow that their concentration in the soil solution is high enough to have any pronounced effect on the neighbouring micro-organisms, particularly since there are many soil organisms which decompose them in dilute solution. The zone of action of these antibiotics is therefore probably confined to a region very close to the actively excreting organisms, and since these are often confined to pockets containing pieces of decaying organic material which forms a readily available source of energy for fungi, it is likely that concentrations of antibiotics sufficiently high to affect an appreciable volume of soil only occur in such pockets. Many antibiotics are inactive or are rapidly inactivated in neutral soils, but are relatively stable in acid soils, so it is probable that widespread control of micro-organisms will be more common in acid sands, such as acid sandy heaths, than in neutral loams.[3] It is not yet known how far the power of producing these lytic substances goes hand in hand with the power of feeding on the lysed organisms. Some of the fungi and actinomycetes that can be readily grown on simple culture media and that can lyse the cells of suitable bacteria, can obtain at least part of their food requirements from these lysed cells.

The quantities of these antibiotic substances produced, and their influence on the antagonised organism, depend on external conditions such as food supply, aeration and soil reaction, but the details of these dependencies must be worked out for each organism concerned though, in general, production is most rapid when the organism is growing rapidly on a suitable food supply. These antibiotic substances may collect in the subsoil, for A. S. Newman and A. G. Norman[4] found that the microflora of an arable soil below the depth of cultivation responded to additions of fermentable material much more slowly than did those in the surface soil, and this response was not increased by inoculating the subsoil with some surface soil.

[1] R. L. Emerson *et al.*, *J. Bact.*, 1946, **52**, 357.
[2] B. N. Singh, *Nature*, 1942, **149**, 168; *Brit. J. Expt. Path.*, 1945, **26**, 316.
[3] E. G. Jefferys, *J. Gen. Microbiol.*, 1952, **7**, 295.   [4] *Soil Sci.*, 1943, **55**, 377.

Crops may perhaps sometimes suffer from these substances. Thus, R. A. Steinberg[1] has shown that tobacco plants show morphological deformities if grown near some strains of non-pathogenic bacteria in otherwise aseptic conditions, and this was due to soluble organic compounds diffusing from the bacterial cells; and he could reproduce these symptoms by allowing a very low concentration of some organic compounds, such as the amino acid isoleucine, to build up around the roots.[2] Now these symptoms are typical of "frenching" in tobacco, a disease not apparently due either to a nutrient deficiency or to a pathogenic organism. Hence, he suggested that the cause of frenching in the field is due to too high a concentration of diffusible microbial products accumulating in the soil near the tobacco roots.

Bacteria can also be parasitic on soil fungi. Cholodny slides buried in soil repeatedly show portions of fungal mycelia being attacked by bacteria: one end of the mycelium appears free from bacteria, then comes a large concentration of small rods and cocci on what appears to be almost empty mycelium, and behind this the original line of the mycelium can be followed by colonies of bacteria outlining the old wall.[3] The interpretation of this observation is not clear. P. C. T. Jones[4] showed that even if the fungi were growing in the absence of bacteria the main fungal protoplasm appeared to keep in the growing parts of the mycelium, leaving the back parts almost empty, and it may be that the bacteria are simply attacking these nearly empty regions. On the other hand, R. L. Starkey[5] considered that the fungal tissue on which the bacteria were living could not provide enough food for the development of all these bacteria, and assumed they can extract nutrients from the living mycelium before it is killed. Bacteria may, therefore, play an important role in limiting the amount of fungal mycelium in a soil, though their importance cannot yet be assessed as there are so many organisms in the soil that can feed on fungal mycelium; and, in fact, it seems that the life of any long piece of mycelium in the soil must be fairly short. These observations only apply to phycomycete and other fast-growing hyphae and not to the slow-growing rhizomorphs of basidiomycetes.

These interrelations between the various members of the microflora may be of considerable importance in the control of plant pathogens in the soil, for the growth of some pathogenic fungi can be inhibited by some common soil fungi and bacteria. R. Weindling[6] has claimed that the soil fungus *Trichoderma viride* can control the damping-off of

---

[1] *J. Agric. Res.*, 1947, **75**, 199.
[2] *Science*, 1946, **103**, 329; *J. Agric. Res.*, 1947, **75**, 81.
[3] See, for example, D. M. Novogrudsky, *Mikrobiologia*, 1948, **17**, 28.
[4] I am indebted to Mr. Jones for this information.   [5] *Soil Sci.*, 1938, **45**, 207.
[6] *Phytopath.*, 1932, **22**, 837; 1934, **24**, 1153; 1936, **26**, 1068; with H. S. Fawcett, *Hilgardia*, 1936, **10**, 1. He called the fungus *T. lignorum*.

citrus seedlings by a *Rhizoctonia*, and A. Lal[1] that it can control *Ophiobolus graminis*, the fungus causing "take-all" in wheat and barley. J. P. Chadiakov[2] has also claimed that bacteria of the genera *Pseudomonas* and *Achromobacter* can control some *Fusaria*, causing a wilt of flax.

The great practical difficulty is to find means of encouraging these desirable fungi or bacteria to multiply, for they can only control the pathogenic organisms effectively if they are sufficiently active in the soil, that is, if they have an adequate food supply. It cannot usually be done by inoculating the desirable organism into the soil, as it will not be able to compete with the indigenous population for food, nor in general will adding an inoculum of a desirable organism already present help, for again the extra numbers of the organism will not usually be able to find enough food to keep them active. However, C. H. Meredith[3] has reported what appears to be an exception to this rule, for he claimed to have reduced the severity of panama disease in bananas, caused by the fungus *Fusarium oxysporum* var. *cubense* by adding to the soil an inoculum of an actinomycete derived from the soil itself which is antagonistic to this fungus.

The only way desirable organisms can have their activity increased is by altering the soil conditions. This can be done in two ways: either by adding organic matter and increasing the activity of the whole saprophytic population, and this will usually increase the activity of organisms that are antagonistic to specialised plant pathogens; or by altering the soil conditions in such a way that the desirable organisms can obtain a larger share of the available food supply. Thus, the fungus causing root rot in cotton, *Phymatotrichum omnivorum*, can be kept in control in irrigated Arizona fields by adding 10 to 15 tons of manure or other decomposable organic matter annually to the soil well before the cotton is planted.[4] Weindling and Fawcett showed that the *Rhizoctonia* fungus causing damping-off of citrus seedlings could be controlled in the field by *Trichoderma viride* if the soil was made sufficiently acid for the *Trichoderma* and similar fungi to multiply at the expense of the majority of the soil population. And the cotton root rot fungus can be attacked by saprophytic fungi in the roots of the cotton plant after harvest if the cotton plant is then cut below the crown; for this injury allows saprophytic fungi to enter the roots rapidly and destroy the root rot fungus in the process of attacking the root cells themselves.[5] Some further methods of controlling fungi attacking plant roots will be described later on pp. 228 *et. seq.*

---

[1] *Ann. Appl. Biol.*, 1939, **26**, 247.
[2] *Mikrobiologia*, 1935, **4**, 193.   [3] *Phytopath.*, 1946, **36**, 983.
[4] C. J. King, *U.S. Dept. Agric.*, Circ. 425, 1937; for corresponding results in Texas, see R. B. Mitchell *et al.*, *J. Agric. Res.*, 1941, **63**, 535.
[5] F. E. Clark, *U.S. Dept. Agric.*, *Tech. Bull.* 835, 1942.

The problem is in some ways easier when the pathogenic fungus can only live in plant tissue, and is carried over in the soil in infected tissue, for anything that hastens the decomposition of the plant remains in the soil hastens the killing-out of the fungus. However, although the problem is easy in theory, it is difficult to find suitable methods in practice because the infected plant remains are usually resistant to decomposition. As an example, *Ophiobolus graminis*, the cause of take-all in wheat and barley, is carried in the soil in infected straw, and it is not possible to get all the stubble decomposed between harvest-time in August and the beginning of the next growing season in March. But it may be possible to help the soil organisms in their work of destroying the pathogen if its resistance can be weakened in any way. In the particular case of *Ophiobolus*, S. D. Garrett[1] has shown this can be done by depleting the soil of available nitrogen directly after harvest; for the fungus, which is growing in the nitrogen-poor straw, appears to need some soil nitrogen during this period. Hence, any device which does this, such as under-sowing the corn with Italian rye-grass or trefoil (*Medicago lupulina*), for young trefoil takes up soil nitrogen in autumn, will weaken the fungus.[2] When the rye-grass or trefoil is ploughed in in the spring, the readily available nitrogen in the green manure is released as nitrate which the young barley crop takes up. Since the resistance of corn to damage by *Ophiobolus* is increased as the general level of fertility, and of available nitrogen in particular, is increased, trefoil is preferable to Italian rye-grass as the under-sown crop.

Interactions between the Soil Microflora and Fauna

The standard example of the relation between the soil's fauna and microflora is that between the protozoa and bacteria, though B. N. Singh's work has shown that other protozoal-like organisms, such as myxobacteria, *Acrasieae*, giant amoeboid organisms and presumably myxomycetes all feed on bacteria as well. Bacteria, however, vary in their edibility to these different organisms: some bacteria appear to be readily eaten by them all, some by only a few, and a few appear to be inedible to all the organisms tested—these latter mainly being pigmented bacteria which may secrete strong antibiotics. Thus, out of eighty-seven different bacterial species of various origin tested for edibility by five groups of these organisms, a soil amoeba, a myxamoeba, a giant amoeba and two myxobacteria, twelve were eaten by all five groups, twenty-five were eaten by four, seventeen by three,

---

[1] *Ann. Appl. Biol.*, 1944, **31**, 186; 1948, **35**, 435.
[2] For an agricultural example from the English chalk lands, see R. Sylvester, *Agric.*, 1947, **54**, 422, and S. D. Garrett, ibid., 425.

thirteen by two, thirteen by one group only, and seven, confined to coloured bacteria most of which produced a red or a pink pigment, such as *Chromobacterium violaceum* and *Pseudomonas aeroginosa*, were not eaten by any.[1] Thus, the great majority of soil bacteria can be eaten by at least one group of these bacterial feeders known to be present in the soil.[2]

The soil fauna can affect the microflora in several ways: the larger saprophytic soil animals, by being motile, distribute both the decaying organic matter and some of the microbial population throughout the soil layer in which they are working; for they will be ingesting food at one place, mixing it with bacteria in their gut, and excreting it at another. In fact, this process of comminuting and distributing dead plant litter throughout the surface layers of the soil is the predominant action of the larger soil invertebrates on the microbial population.

Animals feeding on decaying organic matter, and particularly those that ingest soil at the same time, also affect the composition of the microbial population, for these animals will always be taking into their gut the micro-organisms attached to the plant residues or soil ingested, and be subjecting them to the action of their digestive juices, though whether they can in fact affect the composition of the microbial population is not known. It is possible that earthworms can depress fungal development in the soil by feeding on fungal mycelia, for it is an interesting fact, of unproven generality, that fungal mycelia only seem to develop abundantly in those soils of the temperate regions where earthworms are scarce, though more experimental work is needed to establish the validity and interpretation of this generalisation.

There appears to be another interaction of importance, this time between the soil invertebrates and the protozoa, for some of the saprophytic invertebrates carry a protozoal population in their gut to help digest some of the more resistant plant products, such as cellulose, which the animal appears to feed on. Thus, the digestive tracts or organs of some soil invertebrates constitute an important environment of the soil protozoa—an environment of presumably great activity.[3]

The Effect of Soil Conditions on the Soil Microflora

The composition of the soil population depends on soil conditions, particularly on the sources of energy available and on the air and water régime, but it does not show striking geographical changes. The same characteristic groups of bacteria, fungi, algae and protozoa are much

[1] F. J. Anscombe and B. N. Singh, *Nature*, 1948, **161**, 140.
[2] For a recent review, see H. G. Thornton and L. M. Crump, *Rothamsted Ann. Rept.*, 1952, 164.
[3] For an account of this, see E. A. Steinhaus, *Insect Microbiology*, Ithaca, N.Y., 1946.

the same in arctic, temperate and tropical soils, the differences between zones being far less marked than are those for the distribution of higher plants and animals. The reasons for this constancy of the soil population are to be sought, partly in the nature of the organisms themselves, partly in the soil as a habitat. It is possible, and indeed probable, that micro-organisms are less susceptible to environmental conditions than are the larger forms; also the biological conditions at a depth of from 2 to 7 or 8 inches below the soil surface are more constant than on the surface itself; the temperature is more even (p. 359), and the atmosphere is almost always humid and nearly saturated: there are no marked differences in degree of humidity such as affect profoundly the distribution of plants.

The numbers of the bacteria in particular and their associated protozoa are constantly varying. The causes of these variations cannot be completely analysed, for in a mixed interrelated population such as occurs in the soil, a change in numbers of a single species will automatically cause the changes in the numbers of other species. These fluctuations make it difficult to trace the effect of external conditions on the behaviour of any group of soil micro-organisms, and this difficulty can only be overcome by devising long series of experiments using proper statistical control to minimise their importance.

Nearly all the work on the effect of soil factors on the numbers of the bacteria, actinomycetes and fungi has been done using the plating technique, so that many of the results given in the next sections are uncertain. It is very desirable that they be checked, using the more direct methods of estimating bacterial numbers and the amount of actinomycete and fungal hyphae present.

SOIL MOISTURE AND SOIL TEMPERATURE

These two factors have quite different influences on two distinct aspects of the soil microflora: their numbers and their activity. The bacterial numbers in a soil appear to increase with increasing moisture content, a result found by every investigator, though it has only been established for numbers based on the plate count. H. L. Jensen,[1] working with a pasture soil in New South Wales, found the numbers of actinomycetes were almost independent of the moisture content, so that the ratio of actinomycetes to bacteria increased as the moisture content decreased, but the number of fungi increased with moisture content; whilst W. G. E. Eggleton,[2] using an English pasture soil, found the actinomycetes increased somewhat with moisture content, though not as much as the bacteria, but the number of fungi was independent of the moisture content. It is, however, probable that these fungal

[1] Proc. Linn. Soc. N.S.W., 1934, 59, 101.   [2] Soil Sci., 1938, 46, 351.

results reflect more the limitations of the technique used than their field behaviour, for H. J. Conn,[1] using the Cholodny slide technique and soils incubated in the laboratory, found that fungal mycelia were prominent in the drier and absent in the wetter conditions—a result in accord with our general knowledge that many soil fungi thrive in fairly dry conditions but demand good aeration for active growth.

The effect of the usual variations of soil temperature on the number of micro-organisms is still undecided. The careful work of Jensen and of Eggleton on pasture soils, and N. James and M. L. Sutherland[2] on a fallow soil in Winnipeg all failed to show any effect of temperature on the numbers of the soil bacteria if the associated moisture effects were eliminated. Eggleton found the number of actinomycetes increased somewhat with temperature, a result not found by Jensen, and neither found any effect of temperature on the number of fungi. On the other hand, D. W. Cutler and L. M. Crump,[3] using a fallow soil at Rothamsted, found the numbers of bacteria tended to decrease with increasing temperature, and D. Fehér and M. Franck,[4] using Hungarian pasture and forest soils, found they increased.

The effect of the season of the year on the number of bacteria, as determined by the plating method, appears to be small for soils that are either fallowed or are under forest or permanent pasture: the linear regression with moisture content accounts for about half the total variability (variance) of the bacterial numbers in Jensen's, Eggleton's, and James and Sutherland's[5] experiments. But the effect of an annual crop on bacterial numbers is considerable. James and Sutherland found the number of bacteria in the wheat soil, reduced to a standard moisture content, was the same as the fallow soil at the end of May, but was nearly double that at the end of September. The effect of season on actinomycetes and fungi has not been so fully investigated. Under pasture conditions Jensen found less of the variability could be removed by the temperature and moisture regression, though Eggleton found about as much of the actinomycete as the bacterial variability could be so accounted for; whilst J. Singh,[6] working on the permanent wheat and mangold plots at Rothamsted, found no apparent seasonal effect on the numbers of fungi or actinomycetes.

The effect of the moisture content of the soil, or the tension of the soil water on its general microbiological activity has not been examined in detail. Fig. 16 shows the result of an old experiment by A. E. Traaen[7]

[1] *New York State Agric. Expt. Sta., Tech. Bull.* 204, 1932.
[2] *Canad. J. Res.*, 1940, 18 C, 435.
[3] *Problems in Soil Microbiology*, London, 1935, p. 14.
[4] *Arch. Mikrobiol.*, 1933, 4, 447; 1937, 8, 249; 1938, 9, 193.
[5] *Canad. J. Res.*, 1943, 21 C, 119.
[6] *Ann. Appl. Biol.*, 1937, 24, 154.
[7] *Zbl. Bakt.* II, 1916, 45, 119.

on the effect of moisture content, and this type of result is probably generally true, namely, that if the soil is too wet activity is restricted through poor aeration, that there is a relatively wide range of moisture contents at which activity is relatively little affected, but once the moisture content falls into the wilting point range the activity drops again, only this time fairly rapidly.

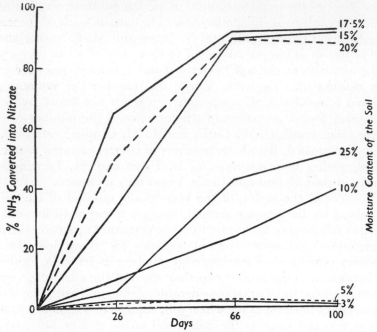

FIG. 16. Effect of moisture content of the soil on the proportion of ammonia, added as ammonium sulphate, oxidised to nitrate.

Variations of temperature cause many changes in the activity of the micro-organisms that are not connected with their number. The activity of all organisms increases with increasing temperature up to a maximum and then decreases when the higher temperatures are injuring the organism. Thus, the net effect of temperature on the activity of the soil organisms is the product of the number of organisms present and their individual activities; and the maximum activity usually occurs when the numbers are falling. The relation between temperature and activity can, however, become very complex when two or more organisms are living together. Thus, E. H. Richards[1] showed that the rate of nitrogen fixation by *Azotobacter*, living in the presence of starch-decomposing organisms of the Aerogenes group and

[1] *J. Agric. Sci.*, 1939, **29**, 302.

feeding on the by-products of the decomposition, had two optimum temperatures, the one at the higher temperature corresponding to low numbers but high activity due both to the temperature directly and also to the more abundant food supply produced at the higher temperature by the Aerogenes bacteria.

H. L. Jensen[1] investigated the effect of temperature on the relation between the CO_2 evolution of a soil and the number of bacteria it contained, and showed that as the temperature rose the CO_2 evolved per 1,000 million bacteria, as determined by the direct cell count, increased from about 16 per cent of their dry weight per day at 15°C. to 30 per cent at 28°C. and to 50 per cent at 37°C., whilst if plate counts were used as the basis there was no clearly marked temperature dependence, and for some soils the CO_2 evolution per day would be over sixty times the dry weight of the organism, which would correspond to higher rates than observed for young cultures of active bacteria growing under optimal conditions. He considered the fungi were inactive under these conditions.

When decomposable organic matter was added to the soil, Jensen found that the fungi, as measured by the abundance of mycelia on the Cholodny slides, came into prominence, and the density of mycelium was correlated with the CO_2 production; in fact, the multiple correlation of this and the total cell count for bacteria with CO_2 production was about 0·8. At low temperatures, 4° to 7°C., the importance of the fungi was small compared with the bacteria, at 14° to 16°C. it was about equal to that of the bacteria, at 28°C. it was considerably larger, and at 37°C. it was equal or less; but in all these cases this was only true for the first week of decomposition, after that the fungal activity fell off rapidly compared with the bacterial.

THE EFFECT OF SOIL REACTION

The effect of soil reaction can be very marked under conditions of extreme acidity, though, as will be discussed later in connection with plants (see p. 523), the effect of the hydrogen-ion concentration may be less important than associated effects such as the lack of calcium or phosphates, or the presence of soluble aluminium and manganese compounds.

One of the most important effects of great acidity is the absence of burrowing animals, such as the earthworms, which mix the surface litter with the soil. Dead and partially decomposed plant material accumulates on the surface as a mat, and the population below the soil surface lives under conditions of very small annual additions of nutrients. It is possible that fungi may be transferring nutrients from the mat to

[1] *Proc. Linn. Soc. N.S.W.*, 1936, **61**, 27.

the soil by sending their mycelia into each region, but the importance of this transfer has not been established.

Acid soils probably carry a larger fungal but a smaller bacterial flora than neutral soils. Acid mor soils, whose pH usually lie below 4, are typically characterised by a profuse development of fungal mycelia, which are far less prominent on less acid mull soils (see p. 568). But if the acidity is not extreme, the evidence is not extensive enough to admit of any rigid generalisations. Thus the bacterial population on Rothamsted pasture soils is not dependent on pH in the range 3·8–5·6 if bacterial numbers are determined by Thornton and Gray's total cell count, though they are depressed at the lower pH if determined by the plate count. Jensen's work, just quoted, suggests that the total cell count gives a more accurate estimate of bacterial numbers, with the consequence that at the present time it is best to assume that the total bacterial population is not very dependent on soil reaction.

The type of bacteria present in the soil depends on the soil reaction. Nitrifiers, i.e. bacteria oxidising ammonia to nitrites and nitrates, are relatively inactive in acid soils, though the pH by itself cannot be the sole cause of this, as it also depends on the vegetation. Thus, C. Olsen[1] found that nitrates were produced down to pH 3·8 in Danish pasture soils, but only to pH 4·5 in forest soils, whilst H. L. Richardson[2] found very little nitrate produced below pH 6 in a Rothamsted pasture. Again, the common species of the aerobic nitrogen-fixing Azotobacter are usually absent in soils with pH below 5·7.

Very little definite information appears to be available on the effect of alkaline reactions on the type of micro-organisms present in the soil, though there is some evidence that nitrifying organisms may be limited by phosphate starvation under very alkaline conditions.

Partial Sterilisation of the Soil

The soil population can be greatly simplified, and undesirable groups of pathogens can be eliminated from the soil by partial sterilisation. This consists either in heating the soil with steam or in adding to it sterilising solutions such as formalin and carbon disulphide, and this treatment increases the fertility of the soil markedly for a time.

Steaming soils is now normal practice in many glasshouse areas. Low-pressure steam is blown through the soil for a short time and this heats the soil sufficiently to kill most of the soil organisms and in particular nearly all those parasitic on plant roots. The soil is then left for a few weeks, often after a good flooding to get the subsoil moist, because if a crop is planted directly after steaming it either grows very badly,

[1] C.R. Lab. Carlsberg, 1923, 15, 1.   [2] J. Agric. Sci., 1938, 28, 73.

or not at all, whilst after a short rest it makes excellent growth. Not all the consequences of this steam treatment are yet understood. In general it causes a rapid rise in ammonium production, which may or may not nitrify after several weeks,[1] probably depending on how soon and how effectively nitrifiers are introduced into the soil. It also causes a rise in the soluble organic matter, and if the soil is rather acid, it may also cause a marked rise in the readily extractable manganese.[2] It is possible, but by no means certain, it is one or all of these three factors which cause the serious depression in plant growth directly after the steaming. The effect on the micro-organisms is that initially it depresses the number of bacteria and protozoa, but these are probably back to their normal numbers before very long.[3] The effect on the fungal population, however, is much more marked, and the range of species and numbers present, may be depressed for 12–18 months, even if fungi are introduced into the soil.[4]

The effect of partial sterilisation with chemicals is somewhat similar, except for the effect on the fungi. Formalin[5] and carbon disulphide[6] in particular kill most of the fungi, but encourages the *Trichoderma viride* group, and shortly after treatment they become the dominant group and remain so for many months.

There is still no agreed explanation of these effects. E. J. Russell and H. B. Hutchinson,[7] who first investigated the phenomenon in 1908, suggested that this process killed the protozoa, so allowing the bacteria to decompose the soil organic matter more vigorously, for it was known that the protozoa fed on the bacteria. Whilst it is quite certain this explanation is not correct, none of the others which have been proposed from time to time have been any more successful in giving a reasonable quantitative explantion of the flush of ammonium production, or incidentally of the humus decomposition, nor of why a heat-sterilised soil is such an unfavourable environment for fungi for such a long time.[8]

These problems of partial sterilisation are gaining in practical importance at the present time with the introduction of relatively cheap sterilising agents, such as calcium chloracetate and the chlorinated

[1] See, for example, J. N. Davies and O. Owen, *J. Sci. Fd. Agric.*, 1951, **2**, 268, and 1953, **4**, 248, and C. D. Oxley and E. A. Gray, *J. Agric. Sci.*, 1952, **42**, 353.
[2] T. W. Walker and R. Thompson, *J. Hort. Sci.*, 1949, **25**, 19, C. K. Fujimoto and G. D. Sherman, *J. Amer. Soc. Agron.*, 1948, **40**, 527, and F. H. Dalton and C. Hurwitz, *Soil Sci.*, 1948, **66**, 233.
[3] B. N. Singh and L. M. Crump, *J. gen. Microbiol.*, 1953, **8**, 421.
[4] N. R. Smith, *Proc. Soil Sci. Soc. Amer.*, 1939, **3**, 188, D. E. Bliss, *Phytopath.*, 1951, **41**, 665, J. H. Warcup, *Trans. Brit. Mycol. Soc.*, 1951, **34**, 519, and J. E. Mollison, ibid., 1953, **36**, 215.
[5] J. H. Warcup, *Trans. Brit. Mycol. Soc.*, 1951, **34**, 519, and 1952, **35**, 248.
[6] D. E. Bliss, *Phytopath.*, 1951, **41**, 665.
[7] *J. Agric. Sci.*, 1909, **3**, 111; 1913, **5**, 152.
[8] See, for example, S. A. Waksman and R. L. Starkey, *Soil Sci.*, 1923, **16**, 137; *Soils and Fert.*, 1948, **11**, 357; and I. Szladits, ibid., 1952, **15**, 299.

hydrocarbons, e.g. D-D, which is a mixture of 1,3-dichloropropene and 1,2-dichloropropane. These chemicals have been found to control root-attacking nematodes in the laboratory and to give very considerable increases of crop when added at the rate of several hundred pounds per acre to eelworm-infested land. But it appears that at least under some conditions the chemicals are not affecting the nematodes in the field,[1] so the crop is not responding to the decreased attack of the nematodes so much as to the general increased fertility brought about by the partial sterilising effect these chemicals have on the soil.

EFFECT OF DRYING A SOIL AND OF HEATING A DRY SOIL

It has been known from time immemorial in India that heating a soil, either by lightly burning it or by burning stubble on it, will increase the yield of the following crop. This practice is known as *rab* and is mentioned in the Vedas,[2] and also by Vergil,[3] who was aware that the benefit of this treatment was very short lived. A similar practice in areas having an intense dry season is to leave the bare soil exposed to the sun, so it gets baked out. This is again practised in India and in Egypt, where it is known as *Sheraqi*.[4] Some investigations on these effects were made in the early 1920's,[5] but only recently have they received the attention they deserve because of their great importance in tropical agriculture.[6]

Drying a soil, or heating it and re-wetting it results in a flush of decomposition of the soil humus, and a flush of ammonium and then of nitrates, provided the soil has been inoculated with a little fresh soil before re-wetting; and this flush lasts for 5 to 10 days. The more intensely the soil is dried, the higher the temperature it is heated to and the longer the soil is kept dry, and the higher the organic matter content of the soil, the larger is the magnitude of the flush. Further, a soil can be dried and wetted a number of times, and on each re-wetting another flush occurs of only slightly less magnitude than the previous one. As a very rough figure, if a soil is dried to 100°C, about 1–2 per cent of the organic matter is decomposed at each flush. The cause of this flush is presumably the same as that found in the partial sterilisation of the soil, but it is not yet possible to say what fraction of the organic

---

[1] See, for example, D. G. O'Brien et al., *J. Helminth.*, 1939, **17**, 41; E. E. Edwards, ibid., 51; D. Price Jones, *Ann. Appl. Biol.*, 1947, **34**, 240.
[2] "Like to a tender plant whose roots are fed,
    On soil o'er which devouring flames have spread".
    Stories of the Buddha's Former Births, trans. H. L. Francis.
[3] Georgics, Bk. 1, 84–93.
[4] See, for example, J. A. Prescott, *J. Agric. Sci.*, 1919, **9**, 216; 1920, **10**, 177.
[5] See, for example, A. F. Gustafson, *Soil Sci.*, 1922, **13**, 173, and A. N. Lebediantzev, *Soil Sci.*, 1924, **18**, 419.
[6] See, for example, H. F. Birch, *Plant and Soil*, 1958, **37**, 9; 1959, **11**, 262; 1960, **12**, 81; and *Trop. Agric. (Trin.)*, 1960, **37**, 3, from whose papers the data in the next paragraph are taken.

matter becomes decomposable, or how the organic matter that was resistant to decomposition becomes converted into a decomposable form. The practical consequences of this effect in the field, particularly in regions having either erratic rainfall or a pronounced wet and dry season, are discussed in more detail on pp. 289 and 304.

Much less critical work has been done on the effect of drying a soil or burning vegetation on the soil on the numbers of micro-organisms in the surface soil. J. Meiklejohn,[1] for instance, working at Muguga, Kenya, examined the effect of burning on the micro-organisms in the top inch of the soil, and found it caused a slight reduction in the number of bacteria, whether determined by direct count or by dilution plates, which persisted for several months; and whilst burning initially caused a reduction in the actinomycete count, after a few weeks the actino-mycete numbers, as determined by the plate count, was higher than on the unburned plots.

[1] *J. Soil Sci.*, 1955, **6**, 111.

CHAPTER XIII

THE ASSOCIATION BETWEEN PLANTS AND MICRO-ORGANISMS

The Rhizosphere Population

THE INFLUENCE OF the plant roots on the soil population in their neighbourhood is considerable, for plant roots, rootlets and root hairs may carry large concentrations of micro-organisms on their surface.[1] Not all the rootlets or root hairs carry these concentrations, and those that carry them are not necessarily uniformly covered with them. The interfacial volume between the plant rootlets and the bulk of the soil, in which this population lives, is often called the Rhizosphere;[2] but this volume has no exact bounds, for some of the rhizosphere population may penetrate the outer surface of the rootlet and some will extend into the neighbouring soil.

The early work on the relations between the microbial population around the plant roots and that in the bulk of the soil was confined to showing that more bacteria could be plated from soil in the immediate neighbourhood of plant roots than from soil well away from the roots. The Rossi-Cholodny slide technique can be made to give a clear picture of the micro-organisms around rootlets,[3] but improved techniques employing either direct observation of the living rootlet *in situ* or improved methods of fixing, staining, cleaning and mounting rootlets show that the Rossi-Cholodny pictures give only a partial picture.

The picture obtained from viewing living plant rootlets in the soil[4] is that there are obvious concentrations of micro-organisms around the rootlets, but that there appear to be few in the body of the soil itself. Large colonies of small bacteria occur in clumps, or even sheaths around the rootlets, and large numbers of motile bacteria may be swimming in the thin water films around them, and actinomycete and fungal hyphae of various types can be seen on the surface or even penetrating their epidermal cells. This concentration of the microflora

[1] For reviews of this subject, see H. Katznelson, A. G. Lochhead and M. I. Timonin, *Bot. Rev.*, 1948, **14**, 543. F. E. Clark, *Adv. Agron.*, 1949, **1**, 242 and R. L. Starkey, *Bact. Rev.*, 1958, **22**, 154.
[2] L. Hiltner, *Arb. deut. landw. Ges.*, 1904, **98**, 59, first used this word.
[3] See N. Hulpoi, *Arch. Mikrobiol.*, 1936, **7**, 579; R. L. Starkey, *Soil Sci.*, 1938, **45**, 207; and M. I. Timonin, *Canad. J. Res.*, 1940, **18** C, 444, for photographs of the kind of information these slides give.
[4] This description is taken from M. B. Linford, *Soil Sci.*, 1942, **53**, 93.

around the plant roots encourages the development of predatory protozoa and nematodes which feed on this population.[1]

The size of this population has mainly been investigated using the plating technique[2] and since this may give numbers for the bacteria in the soil a hundredfold smaller than is obtained by the total cell count, it is possible that the rhizosphere effect might be in part a reflection of this difference between techniques, for as will be shown later, the rhizosphere population tends to grow rather easier on relatively simple media and to have a higher activity, hence to grow more quickly on the relatively concentrated nutrient media used in the usual plating technique.

The significance of this population for plant growth is not fully understood. It probably helps the plant to extract phosphate[3] and possibly other nutrients from difficultly available compounds, though whether this is entirely due to the higher CO_2 concentration the micro-organisms produce around the root hairs has not been established. The population, on the other hand, must obviously derive some benefit from the plant; presumably a proportion at least must draw their energy supply from the plant, partly directly from the living and partly indirectly from the dead or dying tissues, but no estimates are yet available of the proportion of the carbohydrate fixed by the plant that is used by this population.

In spite of these limitations there is little doubt about the correctness of the general conclusions reached by this older work, namely, that the soil in the immediate neighbourhood of the plant roots carries a larger, or possibly only a more active, population than that away from the roots. It is consistent with all qualitative observations so far made, and also with the evidence from the rate of CO_2 production of the soil, which is greater near the root than a little way away from it. In fact R. L. Starkey[4] found that there was a rough correlation between the rate of evolution of CO_2 by roots and the number of bacteria in the rhizosphere, suggesting that the microbial population on the root makes an appreciable contribution to the rate of CO_2 evolution in the immediate neighbourhood of the root surface.

It is still more difficult to assess the relative importance of the rhizosphere population compared with the general soil population when expressed as the proportion of the bacteria present per acre of soil in these two populations. N. A. Krassilnikov[5] has made a rough estimate of uncertain validity and concludes that there is probably about twice

[1] See also H. Katznelson, *Soil Sci.*, 1946, **62**, 343.

[2] R. L. Starkey's work (*Soil Sci.*, 1929, **27**, 319, 355, 433; 1931, **32**, 367) is a good illustration of the type of results obtained by these methods.

[3] F. C. Gerretsen, *Plant and Soil*, 1948, **1**, 51.

[4] *Soil Sci.*, 1931, **32**, 367.   [5] *Mikrobiologia*, 1944, **13**, 144.

the weight of bacteria in the lucerne rhizosphere as in the body of the soil, namely, about 2 tons and 1 ton live weight per acre respectively; whilst the bacterial rhizosphere of a wheat crop growing in relatively infertile soil probably only weighs about 5 lb. per acre and, in consequence, is negligible compared with the rest of the population.

The size of the bacterial rhizosphere population depends on the plant and on its stage of development, but is not very dependent on the fertility of the soil;[1] though since the less fertile soil will often have a lower population, the difference in numbers between the rhizosphere and the soil populations may be higher in the less fertile than the more fertile soils.[2] For a given plant, the population is most numerous when it is making its most vigorous growth.[3] The effect of the type of plant has not been investigated critically, but under comparable conditions clovers, sweet clovers and lucerne probably carry a considerably higher population than arable crops, including beans.

The plant roots will sometimes supply a part of the population with simple amino acids and with growth factors such as aneurin and biotin. A. I. Virtanen[4] showed that pea roots might sometimes excrete the amino acids, aspartic acid and β-alanine; P. M. West[5] showed that the roots of flax and tobacco could excrete growth factors such as aneurin and biotin; and H. Lundegårdh and G. Stenlid[6] found that wheat roots could excrete nucleotides and flavanones. Further, Lochhead and other Canadian workers have shown that the rhizosphere bacterial population differs from that in the soil as a whole by having a lower proportion of bacteria that require complex growth substances, such as yeast and soil extract, and a higher proportion with very simple requirements, although those on some crops, e.g. flax, require some simple growth substances and those on others, e.g. red clover, require amino acids as well.[7] This presumably indicates that these crops excrete such substances, lending support to the hypothesis that leguminous crops excrete amino acids even when their root system is too young for the sloughing off of rootlets or nodules to be expected.

The rhizosphere bacterial population differs from that of the soil in its morphological as well as its nutritional composition. R. L. Starkey[8] showed that a large proportion of the rhizosphere bacteria belong to

[1] F. E. Clark and C. Thom, *Trans. 3rd Comm. Int. Soil Sci.*, New Brunswick, 1939, A, 94.
[2] P. M. West and A. G. Lochhead, *Canad. J. Res.*, 1940, **18** C, 129.
[3] H. Katznelson, *Soil Sci.*, 1946, **62**, 343.
[4] *Cattle Fodder and Human Nutrition*, Cambridge, 1938.
[5] *Nature*, 1939, **144**, 1050.
[6] *Arch. Bot.*, 1944, **31** A, No. 10.
[7] R. H. Wallace and A. G. Lochhead, *Soil Sci.*, 1949, **67**, 63. For earlier work, see A. G. Lochhead, *Canad. J. Res.*, 1940, **18** C, 129; A. A. Hildebrand and P. M. West, ibid., **19** C, 183; H. Katznelson and L. T. Richardson, ibid., 1943, **21** C, 249; A. G. Lochhead and R. H. Thexton, ibid., 1947, **25** C, 20.
[8] *Soil Sci.*, 1929, **27**, 355.

the *Radiobacter*, or in Conn's terminology (see p. 150) the *Agrobacter* group which includes the nodule bacteria for leguminous plants. These are Gram-negative, non-spore formers, which may include some fluorescent types as well, but spore-formers are rare. Lochhead[1] showed that the population has a higher activity, e.g. it contains a higher proportion of forms that are coloured and are motile and that will grow more actively in nutrient media than the soil population as a whole.

Little additional knowledge about the occurrence of specific groups of bacteria in the rhizosphere is available. H. Katznelson[2] found that the population around mangold roots appeared to have a higher proportion of cellulose decomposers and anaerobes, such as *Clostridia*, than the soil as a whole, but that *Azotobacter* showed no concentration in the rhizosphere, a result in accord with much other work.[3] M. I. Timonin[4] found that manganese oxidising bacteria could be so prevalent in the rhizosphere of some varieties of oats that the oats could not take up enough manganese, so suffered from grey speck disease, whilst other varieties of oats, growing under the same conditions, had a smaller population of these bacteria and could take up enough manganese. The numbers of manganese oxidisers in the rhizosphere could be increased and in consequence the severity of the grey speck symptoms, by applying a straw mulch to the soil; and the numbers and the grey speck symptoms could be decreased by adding partial sterilising agents such as chloropicrin, formaldehyde and even calcium cyanamide to the soil.

Russian agronomists have, for a number of years, been adopting the practice of inoculating the seed of many of their crops with what they consider to be rhizosphere bacteria, so as to produce a population which will give the crop the maximum benefit. The bacterial culture usually used consists of strains of *Azotobacter*, although the non-Russian evidence that this is a rhizosphere dweller is weak. R. Cooper,[5] who has reviewed much of the Russian work, and visited many areas where these so-called "bacterial fertilisers" are used, states that this inoculation is considered to increase crop yields by about 10 per cent on between 50 and 70 per cent of the fields to which it is applied, and it is most likely to benefit crops on neutral soils, well supplied with phosphate and water. In addition a strain of *Bacillus megatherium*, which is claimed to increase the availability of soil phosphate to the crop, is sometimes used, either by itself or in conjunction with *Azotobacter*. Cooper comments,

[1] *Canad. J. Res.*, 1940, **18** C, 42.   [2] *Soil Sci.*, 1946, **62**, 343.
[3] See, for example, F. E. Clark, *Soil Sci.*, 1948, **65**, 193.
[4] *Proc. Soil Sci. Soc. Amer.*, 1947, **11**, 284. For earlier work on this, see F. C. Gerretsen, *Ann. Bot.*, 1937, **1**, 207. For a possible example of zinc deficiency in orchards caused by rhizosphere bacteria, see D. R. Hoagland *et al.*, *Proc. Amer. Soc. Hort. Sci.*, 1938, **34**, 210, and P. A. Ark, ibid., 216.   [5] *Soils and Fert.*, 1959, **22**, 327.

however, that few critical field experiments appear to have been made to justify this widespread practice, and that there is in fact no universally accepted theory of why the crops respond to this inoculation; for some workers consider the effect may not be through increasing the nitrogen supply to the plant so much as through the bacteria either producing some growth-promoting substances, or destroying some plant toxins present in the soil close to the roots.

Association of Fungi with Plant Roots

Plants, even apparently healthy plants, carry a considerable fungal population in and around their roots in addition to the bacterial. The hyphae of some of these fungi penetrate the root, entering a few of the epidermal cells and sometimes killing them,[1] but little is known in detail about either the spatial distribution of the hyphae—what proportion of their length lies on the root surface, what is in the soil itself, and the proportion of these hyphae which enter the epidermal root cells—or what are their principal sources of food. But the roots can also be attacked by fungi which, having entered the root, grow extensively within it, and which then need not have any living hyphae left in the soil. This association between the plant root and the fungus growing in it has been much studied by plant pathologists because some of these root-inhabiting fungi cause very serious crop losses, and since the plant roots become infected whilst growing in the soil, this association should also be of great interest to the soil microbiologist, although it has been relatively little studied by him. Our knowledge on this subject has been summarised in an excellent book by S. D. Garrett, *The Biology of Root Infecting Fungi*,[2] and the following account is largely taken from it, for the book is a study of the ecology of fungi living between the soil and the plant roots.

The root-infesting fungi can be divided into three groups: the mycorrhizal, the specialised and the unspecialised root-disease fungi. There are a number of fungi which are transitional between the second and third groups and there are some perhaps between the first and second. The fungi, in general, belong to Garrett's sugar fungi nutritionally (see p. 158), that is, they can only use simple organic compounds for their food supply; but the specialised root inhabitants are ecologically confined to that habitat for normal growth.

The unspecialised or primitive root-disease fungi, such as species of *Pythium*, *Fusarium*, *Verticillium* and *Rhizoctonia* (*Corticium*) *solani*, are normal members of the general saprophytic soil population. They are typically responsible for the "damping off" of seedlings, that is, they can

---

[1] See, for example, P. M. Simmonds and R. J. Ledingham, *Sci. Agric.*, 1937, **18**, 49, and M. D. Glynne, *Trans. Bit. Mycol. Soc.*, 1939, **23**, 210. They studied the fungal flora on wheat roots, in Canada and Rothamsted respectively.   [2] Cambridge, 1956.

only attack juvenile and not mature roots and plant organs. They kill the tissues they attack often by toxic exudates, which include pectin-hydrolysing enzymes; and they are fast growing if there is a suitable food supply present. They can only do serious damage to seedlings if the seedlings are checked in such a way that their tissues remain juvenile, as, for example, if the soil temperature is high enough to allow germination but sufficiently low to give very slow growth.[1] The specialised *Fusarium* and *Verticillium* vascular wilt fungi fall into the same group, for they appear to be long lived in the soil, and can only attack juvenile roots, but once in the root they escape into the vascular system, and initially are confined there by the active resistance of the living cells to infection, though once a cell dies the fungus enters. Plant resistance to these vascular wilts thus occurs entirely in the root system.

The specialised root-inhabiting fungi fall into two fairly distinct groups; the mycorrhizal and the root-rot fungi. They do not grow in the soil, except in so far as they are deriving their food supply from a root, or their resting sclerotia or other organs are germinating near a living root. The mycorrhizal fungi are primarily sugar fungi and probably only attack either juvenile roots or the growing point of laterals, whilst the root-rot fungi have considerable power to decompose cellulose and possibly even lignin, and attack the more mature host cells, and show some degree of symbiosis with them, in that they do not initially kill or seriously disorganise the cells they are attacking. Thus they usually take a consider-able time to kill the plant. They grow on the root surface before they penetrate into the root cells, and for fungi which attack mature tree roots such as *Armillaria mellea*, *Fomes lignosus* and *F. annosus*, their mycelia may run along a root for many feet before they send down branches into root cells themselves. Further, in undisturbed equatorial forests, *A. mellea* grows over the surface of the roots of some species of trees as a weft without penetrating into the roots properly, provided the tree is healthy. Only if the forest tree is weakened, by a very severe drought for example, or if the tree is cut down, can the fungus enter the root properly and start growing actively inside it. And a plantation crop such as tea, which is usually considered to be susceptible to *A. mellea*, may carry rhizomorphs on the surface of its roots without suffering any serious attack if it is growing vigorously.[2]

Plant roots have a certain resistance to attack by these fungi, which the fungus must overcome before it can enter. Garrett has introduced the concept of the inoculation potential of the fungus in this context. A fungus with a high inoculation potential will have the energy or

[1] For a fuller discussion of this see L. D. Leach, *J. Agric. Res.*, 1947, **75**, 161. For an example with maize, see J. L. Harper, *Ann. Appl. Biol.*, 1955, **43**, 696, and *New Phytol.*, 1955, **54**, 107, 119; 1956, **55**, 35.
[2] I am indebted to Dr. I. A. S. Gibson for this observation.

ability to overcome a high resistance to attack by the host, and one with a low inoculation potential will only be able to enter a root with a very low resistance. For a given fungus, the better the food supply at the point of attack, the greater is its inoculation potential.

This concept of inoculation potential can be used to illustrate the type of attack caused by three quite different fungi. The fungus of "take-all" in wheat, *Ophiobolus graminis*, only sends out very fine hyphae into the soil and can only infect the fine roots of susceptible Gramineae. The fungus of cotton root rot, *Phymatotrichum omnivorum*, sends out mycelial strands from the root in which it is living and it can infect the thicker roots of herbaceous plants, provided it starts from a fair-sized piece of root. Fungi causing the root rot of trees, such as *Armillaria mellea* and *Fomes lignosus*, send out rhizomorphs starting from a large piece of tree root; and if the root of the tree is relatively resistant to attack, its resistance can only be broken down if it grows fairly close to the source of infection, so the point of attack is not too far away from the food source, and only after the fungus has built up a weft of mycelia on the root which then send a large number of branches down into the root more or less simultaneously—a method which obviously increases the inoculation potential of the fungus very considerably.

A plant root can exist in three conditions in the soil, in each of which it carries a characteristic fungal population. It begins as an actively growing organism, it then becomes senescent though healthy, and it finishes up as diseased or dying. The micro-organisms which multiply round the diseased or dying root are the weak unspecialised pathogens and the saprophytes; whilst around the active growing roots are the true rhizosphere organisms and some of the specialised root parasites, and as the root becomes senescent so the populations change over.

The rhizosphere population on the actively growing root appears to have an important effect on the susceptibility of that root to attack by a parasitic fungus. Thus the roots of those varieties of flax which are resistant to vascular wilt due to *Fusarium oxysporum lini* have a smaller rhizosphere population than those susceptible, but they have a higher population of *Trichoderma viride*, possibly because these roots can maintain a low concentration of hydrocyanic acid around them by excreting the glucoside linamarin, and most of the pathogenic fungi are very sensitive to this; whilst at these concentrations the *Trichoderma* is, if anything, stimulated.[1] *Trichoderma viride* in fact appears to be an excellent root-protecting fungus, partly because it excretes powerful antibiotics, and partly because it can grow over the mycelia of root-inhabiting fungi which are on the root surface and kill them.

[1] E. S. Reynolds, *Ann. Mo. bot. Gdn.*, 1931, **18**, 57, and M. I. Timonin, *Soil Sci.*, 1941, **52**, 395.

There are an increasing number of examples, either proven or by reasonable inference, in which the resistance of crops susceptible to these root-parasitic fungi can be increased by altering the soil conditions around the roots so as to encourage the growth of *Trichoderma*. It is, for example, more resistant to chemical sterilising agents than most pathogenic fungi, so treating a soil with one of these chemicals encourages its development (see p. 221). It grows more strongly in acid than calcareous soils, as has been shown in detail by J. Rishbeth[1] in his study of the susceptibility of pine roots to attack by *Fomes annosus* on some sandy East Anglian soils; for the *Fomes* attack was much more serious, and the growth of *Trichoderma* was much poorer on the calcareous than on the acid soils. Garrett has also suggested that this effect of soil acidity encouraging the growth of *Trichoderma* on root surfaces may be the explanation of some observations made by A. A. Hildebrand and P. M. West.[2] They found that root rots of strawberries and tobacco caused by a complex of weak unspecialised root-parasitic fungi could be reduced by ploughing in soybean tops, which reduced the soil pH, but not by red clover tops, which did not; and they also found that any other soil treatment which reduced the soil pH was beneficial.

Other organisms which are good producers of powerful antibiotics appear to be able to protect plant roots against the root-rot fungi in the same way that *T. viride* can. Thus F. M. Eaton and N. E. Rigler[3] found that varieties of cotton that were resistant to *Phymatotrichum* root rot had roots carrying a much higher number of blue-green fluorescent bacteria of the *Pseudomonas–Phytomonas* group in their rhizosphere than had the roots of susceptible varieties.

A point of great importance in the control of the specialised root-disease fungi of herbaceous and tree crops in the field is that when the plant is cut down, its roots do not die immediately, so for a considerable time the root will maintain its immunity to saprophytic and weakly parasitic fungi whilst becoming a better food source for the specialised parasite; and roots of some tree species that were resistant to infection by these specialised parasites when the tree was alive can lose their resistance and become attacked once it has been felled. Such roots will carry the parasite in the soil for a considerable time, which may be measured in years in the case of trees, and are a source of infection for any new susceptible roots growing in their neighbourhood for this period. This source of infection is of great importance when one is converting natural forest, whose roots may carry a heavy population of *Armillaria mellea* or *Fomes lignosus*, to plantations of susceptible crops such as tea or rubber.

[1] *Ann. Bot.*, 1950, **14**, 365; 1951, **15**, 1, 221.
[2] *Canad. J. Res.*, 1941, **14** C, 183, 199, and see also H. Katznelson and F. E. Chase, *Soil Sci.*, 1944, **58**, 473. [3] *J. Agric. Res.*, 1946, **72**, 137.

The current method of control, which was worked out by R. Leach[1] for the control of *A. mellea* in tea, is to make the roots of the trees an unfavourable environment for the specialised fungus but a more favourable one for the general soil saprophytes. Leach showed that this could be done if the roots were dead by the time the tree was felled, and this could be brought about by ring-barking the tree down to the cambium leaving the outer xylem layers intact. This causes the starch reserves in the roots to become depleted, for the roots must use energy to translocate water and mineral nutrients from the soil to the crown of the tree through the outer xylem layers, but prevents any of the carbohydrates synthesised by the leaves being translocated to the roots, for this translocation is through the phloem layers which have been cut by the ring-barking. When the starch reserves in the roots are depleted the root dies, and when all the roots are dead, so is the tree, though this process may take at least three years for a mature forest tree. When this dead tree is felled, its roots, being dead, are no longer a favourable habitat for the fungus.

The Mycorrhizal Association between Fungi and Plant Roots

Fungi have probably been living symbiotically with the roots of land plants ever since they evolved. When growing in association with algae, the combined organism is a lichen, but they occur in association with the roots of bryophytes, pteridophytes and higher plants, and their associations with the roots of the latter are known as mycorrhizas.[2] They are the fungal equivalents of the bacteria forming nodules on leguminous plants and the actinomycetes forming nodules on a range of other plants. The mycorrhizal associations can conveniently be grouped into four classes: those mainly between some higher Basidiomycetes and Ascomycetes with the roots of many forest trees; those between some Basidiomycetes and orchids and those between a group of fungi and ericaceous plants, neither of which will be considered here; and those between a very characteristic group of fungi and the roots of many higher plants growing in suitable conditions, which are only known as root inhabitants and are in fact very difficult to grow in culture media.

MYCORRHIZA OF FOREST TREES

This association between a Basidiomycete fungus and a tree root is in many ways similar to that between the specialised root-rot fungi, such as *Armillaria* and *Fomes*, and tree roots. They are typically sugar fungi

---

[1] *Proc. Roy. Soc.*, B, 1937, **121**, 561, and *Trans. Brit. Mycol. Soc.*, 1939, **23**, 320.
[2] For a general review of mycorrhizal associations, see J. L. Harley, *The Biology of Mycorrhiza*, London, 1959, and *Ann. Rev. Microbiol.*, 1952, **6**, 367; E. Melin, *Ann. Rev. Plant Phys.*, 1953, **4**, 325.

and ecologically obligate root inhabitants; the attack of a new root commonly begins by their hyphae running over the root surface; their hyphae which enter the root do not initially kill any cortical cells in which they enter; the viable mycelium of at least some of the mycorrhizal and root-rot fungi can remain in the soil in old rotten bits of root for many years[1] and then infect new susceptible roots growing in their neighbourhood; and they may be more sensitive than related saprophytes to antibiotics. They differ in that the mycorrhizal fungi appear to enter susceptible roots more easily than can the root-rot fungi, and to remain a symbiont for a very much longer time. It is possible that there are some fungi which are normally symbiotic but which can become mildly parasitic if conditions for the growth of the tree become unfavourable.

There are, however, species of fungi living in or on roots which show a behaviour intermediate between the specialised saprophytic and the specialised mycorrhizal fungus. In some genera there are species which are purely mycorrhizal, others purely saprophytic decomposing cellulose and lignins, and others which in favourable conditions appear capable of growing by either means.

There are two distinct types of mycorrhizal associations on tree roots with some intermediate types. Some fungi cause the formation of short many-branched structures on the sub-lateral tree roots which take the place of root hairs, as is shown in Plates X and XI for Scots pine and the date palm. This structure is composed of both a mantle or sheath of fungal mycelium enclosing the roots whose cortical cells are enlarged, and also of fungal hyphae filling the intercellular spaces, as can be seen from the cross-section of the mycorrhiza reproduced in Plate XI. The mantle is often coloured, the colours ranging from white through golden brown to black, and usually has a smooth surface, though it may be loose and have many hyphae radiating from it into the soil;[2] and it is these structures that were originally called mycorrhiza, or fungus roots, by B. Frank.[3] This type of mycorrhiza is known as ectotrophic. The other extreme type, the endotrophic, does not normally form a smooth mantle and its hyphae invade the cortical cells of the roots without killing them; and there are transitional types in which some hyphae are within and some between the cells, known as ect-endotrophic.

Little is known of the length of life of a mycorrhiza. On some northern pines, they last a single season only, dying off in the autumn; the fungus

[1] For an example of *Boletus scaber* and *Amanita muscaria* remaining viable in old rotten pine roots and giving mycorrhiza on birch roots, see G. W. Dimbleby, *Forestry*, 1953, **26**, 41.

[2] For descriptions and photographs of different types of mycorrhiza, see M. C. Rayner, *Trees and Toadstools*, London, 1945, and J. L. Harley, *The Biology of Mycorrhiza*, London, 1959. For a histological study of a mycorrhiza on beech see F. A. L. Clowes, *New Phytol.*, 1950, **49**, 248; 1951, **50**, 1.

[3] *Ber. deut. bot. Ges.*, 1885, **3**, 128. Frank spelt the word mycorhiza.

probably rests in the soil over winter and reinfects the short roots of the sub-laterals when growth starts in the spring. In other trees it is probable that the fungus is always present in the root, and it infects new short roots by growing epiphytically over the root surface.

Most species of tree have been found to carry mycorrhiza if grown under suitable conditions, and it is probably true to say that in most existing natural forests and in many plantations on suitable soils, mycorrhiza are normal features of the root system, whatever the tree. The fungi are usually Hymenomycetes, such as species of *Boletus*, *Amanita* and *Lactarius*, but they include at least one member of the Gasteromyceres (puffballs), *Rhizopogon*, and by inference truffles and truffle-like fungi, such as some *Tuberales* and *Elaphomyces* belonging to the Ascomycetes, as well as several fungi whose systematic position is not known because their fruiting bodies have not yet been observed.[1] A given species of fungus will usually form mycorrhiza on a number of tree species, and a given tree can carry mycorrhiza formed from a number of fungal species; and it is possible that most trees and fungi can be classified as carriers and producers either of ectotrophic or of endotrophic mychorrhizas.

Mycorrhizas only develop freely on trees under three fairly definite soil conditions. They need a supply of organic matter in the soil, so develop most freely in the surface litter of the forest floor, and they can often be encouraged in a mineral soil by adding leaf litter or compost to it. They need well-aerated soils and are inhibited by water logging and reducing conditions, so sandy soils are usually more conducive to mycorrhizal formation than clays or peat bogs; and loosening a heavy clay, or draining a bog, often increases mycorrhizal development. They also need a restricted, but not too restricted, supply of nutrients, and in fact mycorrhizal formation appears to be the tree's response to low availability of nutrients. Thus mycorrhiza are more common on tree roots growing in a mor or raw humus layer, when practically every organ carried by the shallower sub-lateral roots is a mycorrhiza, than in a mull layer when mycorrhiza may be relatively few, which is presumably connected with the higher availability of nutrients in the mull. On the other hand there are soils so low in phosphate or available nitrogen that adding a phosphate fertiliser on the one hand,[2] or a nitrogen on the other, will result in a strong development of mycorrhizas and increase in tree growth and vigour.

S. D. Garrett has discussed the ecology of these mycorrhizal fungi in the soil (see p. 228). They typically need simple carbohydrates such as

[1] E. Melin, *Handb. d. biolog. Arbeitsmeth.*, Abt. XI, Teil 4, pp. 1015–1108 (1936), gives lists of fungi forming mycorrhiza on various trees.

[2] For an example with phosphate, see A. L. McComb, *Iowa Agric. Expt. Sta., Res. Bull.* 314, 1943; and with nitrogen, H. Hesselman, *Medd. Skogsförsöksanst*, 1937, **30**, 529.

sugars as their source of energy, whilst closely related non-symbiotic fungi can use cellulose and often lignin. Thus in the field they obtain all their carbohydrates from the roots they are living in and, as E. Bjorkman[1] has shown, they most frequently occur on roots high in carbohydrates, which normally only occurs if protein synthesis is lagging behind carbohydrate synthesis in the tree, and this is likely to be a consequence of a moderate shortage of available soil nitrogen and phosphate. Although most of the fungi probably draw their carbohydrate supply entirely from the tree, yet some may obtain a part of theirs by decomposing some of the cellulose or even lignin in the leaf litter in competition with the saprophytes, because they can draw on a readily available source of energy to increase their inoculation potential which is denied to the saprophytes. Some of the fungi are ecologically obligate root inhabitants and can only remain viable in a suitable tree root, either living or dead; but it is very difficult to prove in what form others remain viable in the soil, and whether they can grow saprophytically there. It is, however, probable that most of them can only grow actively in the soil if they are attached to a tree root, and their fruiting bodies must be attached to a root by a rhizomorph.

The role played by the mycorrhizal fungus in the nutrition of the tree on Garrett's picture is as follows: the fungus is well supplied with energy from the tree, so that part of it which is in the soil can compete strongly for whatever nutrients are in short supply with the soil-inhabiting fungi that are growing slowly on the difficultly decomposable leaf litter. Ecologically this means that the mycorrhiza association will be most strongly developed on soils suitable for the growth of the particular tree except that the nitrogen, phosphate, or some other nutrient element is in rather short supply, which is what is observed. If any nutrient is in too short supply, the tree cannot grow strongly enough to supply the fungus adequately with carbohydrate; and if the nutrients needed for protein synthesis are in good supply, the level of simple carbohydrates in the roots will also be too low for strong fungal growth.

It is very difficult to estimate the quantities of simple carbohydrates the mycorrhizal fungus withdraws from the tree, or to compare this with the carbohydrate requirements of the additional feeding roots which would be necessary if the fungus was not there. There is, however, no need to assume that the effective root system which the fungal hyphae in the soil provides normally makes any larger energy demands on the tree than the root system which it replaces, though this is probably not true on those occasions when the fungus produces a large crop of fruiting bodies (sporophores or toadstools). The amount of fruiting

[1] *Medd. Skogsförsöksanst*, 1941, **32**, 23; *Symb. Bot. Upsaliens.*, 1942, **6**, 191; *Svensk. Bot. Tidskr.*, 1949, **43**, 223.

TABLE 46

Effect of Mycorrhiza on the Mineral Nutrition of Pine Growing in Poor Soil

Per seedling	White Pine[1] Sampled 10/6/36 Non-mycor-rhizal	Mycor-rhizal	Sampled 20/8/36 Non-mycor-rhizal	Mycor-rhizal	Non-mycor-rhizal on soil with complete fertiliser	Virginia Pine[2] on Iowan prairie soil Non-mycor-rhizal	Mycor-rhizal
Dry weight in mgm. .	160	208	181	337	550	152	323
Nitrogen content as per cent of dry weight	1·23	1·48	1·20	1·60	2·50	1·88	1·78
in mgm. . .	1·98	3·09	2·17	5·39	13·75	2·87	5·75
Phosphorus content, as per cent of dry weight	0·08	0·13	0·07	0·21	0·24	0·097	0·184
in mgm. . .	0·13	0·27	0·13	0·72	1·32	0·15	0·60
Potassium content, as per cent of dry weight	0·55	0·50	0·45	0·63	1·10	0·63	0·66
in mgm. . .	0·88	1·03	0·81	2·12	6·05	0·96	2·17
Number of mycorrhizal roots . . .	—	—	—	—	—	7	350
Number of non-mycor-rhizal roots . .	—	—	—	—	—	279	321

bodies formed in any one year, and the proportion of years in which any are formed, depends very much on the climate and other factors which have not been worked out; but L. G. Romell[3] quotes figures for a typical crop under spruce in Denmark in a favourable year. The fruiting bodies contained about 160 lb. dry matter and $4\frac{1}{2}$ lb. of nitrogen per acre, and he estimated that the fungus would need to withdraw at least 350 lb. of carbohydrate from the trees to produce this crop, which is equivalent to one quarter of the organic matter in the annual increment of timber in the trees.

Table 46 illustrates how the mycorrhiza increase the nutrient uptake of pine seedlings compared with uninfected roots growing under comparable conditions; and it also shows that if the soil is well supplied with nutrients, the uninfected roots will take them up quite easily. This last conclusion may not apply to the root systems of all trees, for some have a relatively poor ability to take up phosphates even from fairly readily available sources, and many have a poorer ability than agricultural

[1] H. L. Mitchell, R. F. Finn and R. O. Rosendahl, *Black Rock Forest Pap.* No. 10, 1937.
[2] A. L. McComb, *J. Forestry*, 1938, **36**, 1148.
[3] *Svensk. SkogsvFören Tidskr.*, 1939, **37**, 348.

crops. Thus A. L. McComb[1] found that by adding phosphate to an Iowan prairie soil the growth of jack pine seedlings, as measured by their weight, was increased twenty-eight-fold whilst that of oats in the same soil by only 80 per cent; and this increase in the growth of the pine was brought about through a strong development of mycorrhiza. R. O. Rosendahl[2] likewise found that pine mycorrhiza could extract more potash from orthoclase than could uninfected roots.

A final point on the role of mycorrhiza in tree nutrition concerns leguminous trees in closed equatorial rain forests. C. Bonnier[3] has noted that, in the rain forests around Yangambi in the Belgian Congo, the roots of leguminous trees are covered with mycorrhizas but have no nodules, whilst in the open forest the roots are nodulated but do not carry mycorrhiza. This point deserves more careful study, but if it is found to be correct, the interpretation may be that in the intense competition for all nutrients from the forest floor, only mycorrhiza can compete; whilst in the open forest, where competition will be less severe but where the level of available nitrogen will remain low, the competition is principally for nitrogen, which leguminous trees can bypass through nodulation.

ENDOTROPHIC MYCORRHIZAS

The endotrophic mycorrhizas are far more widespread than the ectotrophic just described. They rarely have characteristic root forms—though the mycorrhizas on ericaceous plants are outstanding exceptions to this[4]—so their presence can only be recognised from a microscopic examination of root sections. They may, however, cause dwarfing and profuse branching of the rootlets carried by the main lateral roots of trees.[5] The fungi producing this widespread type of mycorrhiza cannot easily grow outside the living plant, and have not been observed to form fruiting bodies, nor have their range of host plants been investigated by pure culture inoculations. Hence, practically nothing is known about the number of strains that exist, and only little about their taxonomy.[6] The typical fungi are phycomycetes, classified in the genus *Rhizophagus*, which is probably related to the *Endogonaceae*. The fungus winters in the soil, attacks the plant roots when growth starts in the spring, and sends hyphae through and around the cortical and epidermal cells, but only rarely into the endodermal cells and practically never into the vascular

[1] *Iowa Agric. Exp. Sta., Res. Bull.* 314, 1943.
[2] *Proc. Soil Sci. Soc. Amer.*, 1943, **7**, 477.
[3] *I.N.E.A.C., Sci. Ser. No.* 72, 1957.
[4] For a description of these, see R. Friesleben, *Jahrb. wiss. Bot.*, 1934, **80**, 421, and 1935, **82**, 413; H. F. Bain, *J. Agric. Res.*, 1937, **55**, 811.
[5] H. Bouwens, *Zbl. Bakt.* II, 1937, **97**, 34.
[6] For an account of the taxonomy of this group, see E. J. Butler, *Trans. Brit. Mycol. Soc.*, 1939, **22**, 274.

tissues. The hyphae in some of the cells can take very characteristic shapes, such as vesicles or bladder-like organs, shown in Plate XII, and arbuscules or cauliflower-like organs composed of fine tufts of hyphae, shown in Plate XII, the latter typically occurring in cells near the endodermis. Hence, this group of fungi are often referred to as the vesicular-arbuscular type of mycorrhizal fungi. The vesicles seem to be of universal occurrence, both in the cells themselves and in the soil, and are probably storage organs for fatty substances when first formed. Arbuscules are of more erratic distribution—they are often absent in published descriptions—and rapidly undergo intracellular digestion as is shown in Plate XII. A third type of intracellular occlusion, known as pelotons, consist of coils or skeins of hyphae, and are illustrated in Plate XII, but these probably more often belong to a weakly parasitic *Rhizoctonia* than to a true mycorrhizal fungus. Typically, all the infected rootlets have died by the end of the growing season.

This association can presumably have the same function as ectotrophic mycorrhizas under some conditions and for some plants, but very little quantitative work has been done on it. It has not yet been demonstrated, for example, that its mycelium extends from the root cells into the soil. B. Peyronel found it on nearly all alpine meadow plants, and W. D. Thomas,[1] in Colorado, found it extensively on plants growing above 7,500 feet, but much less commonly below 5,000 feet, observations which suggest it flourishes under conditions of low availability of nutrients, though this cannot be deduced from them. G. Samuel[2] found it extensively on plants growing in phosphate-deficient soils of South Australia, and it was particularly strongly developed on oats growing in manganese-deficient soils.

This association is also commonly found on the roots of a number of trees and shrubs of commercial importance, including the fruit trees, fruit bushes and strawberries of the north temperate regions, and citrus, coffee, tea and rubber in the tropics and sub-tropics, and also on many leguminous plants. Its significance is entirely unknown for most of these crops, though there is no reason to suppose that, when it is beneficial, it differs from ectotrophic mycorrhizas. It does, however, appear to differ in the greater ease with which it can become parasitic if its host plant loses vigour for any reason. Thus, H. S. Reed and T. Frémont[3] found citrus roots in some Californian orchards carried numerous mycorrhizas which were perfectly normal in healthy trees, but were parasitic in trees growing in unfavourable soil conditions. F. R. Jones[4] found leguminous plants, particularly those with a thick cortical layer of cells in their rootlets, such as the clovers, lucerne and peas carried extensive

[1] *Phytopath.*, 1943, **33**, 143.   [2] *Trans. Roy. Soc. S. Aust.*, 1926, **50**, 245.

[3] *Phytopath.*, 1935, **25**, 645; and see *Rev. d. Cytologie*, 1935, **1**, 327, for excellent drawings and photographs of the mycorrhizas.   [4] *J. Agric. Res.*, 1924, **29**, 459.

mycorrhizas, which did not appear to affect nodulation early on in the season. But these mycorrhizal rootlets tended to die off before uninfected rootlets, with the consequence that plant growth was brought to a standstill sooner than on those plants not carrying mycorrhizas.[1] Thus some varieties of lucerne in Wisconsin made practically no growth in late summer as the larger part of their transient rootlets had become mycorrhizal in late spring and were dead by midsummer, leaving practically no absorbing rootlets to produce late summer growth.

The endotrophic mycorrhiza can also be harmful if it weakens the roots sufficiently to allow pathogenic fungi to enter. Peyronel found that the mycorrhizal roots of many plants he examined usually carried a subsequent infection by *Rhizoctonia*, which are weakly pathogenic soil-inhabiting fungi. Strawberries have furnished an excellent example of this effect. At first the mycorrhizal fungus was suspected of being entirely harmful to strawberry plants by its action in depleting the cortical root cells of starch and weakening them so much that the pathogenic soil fungi—*Fusarium, Pythium, Rhizoctonia,* etc.—could gain entry and so cause serious root rot.[2] A. A. Hildebrand[3] was able to show, however, that healthy and vigorous strawberry plants also carried these mycorrhizas, but were sufficiently active to provide enough carbohydrate for the fungus without weakening its root system: it was only when they were unable to produce enough carbohydrate for the fungus that it became parasitic.

It is not easy to distinguish between endotropic mycorrhizal and other fungi in plant roots, as not enough is known about the effects of light infection by these other fungi. But typically they differ from the mycorrhizal in their simpler food requirements: they can usually be grown in pure cultures whereas the mycorrhizal fungi either do not grow at all, or else only very slowly; they often cause discoloured spots on the outside of the infected root, due to necrosis of the cells they attack, whilst the mycorrhizal fungus merely causes a slight yellowing of these cells; and their intracellular mycelia do not usually suffer digestion easily, nor do they usually form organs of large surface, such as arbuscules in the cell, though *Rhizoctonia* may produce pelotons which should be susceptible of digestion, though this only seems to have been described in some orchids,[4] which differ from the other mycorrhizal plants by being definitely parasitic on the fungus.

[1] *J. Amer. Soc. Agron.,* 1943, **35,** 625.
[2] D. G. O'Brien and E. J. McNaughton, *West of Scot. Agric. Coll., Res. Bull.* 1, 1928; J. H. L. Truscott, *Canad. J. Res.,* 1934, **11,** 1.
[3] *Canad. J. Res.,* 1934, **11,** 18; with L. W. Koch, ibid., 1936, **14** C, 11.
[4] A. Burgess, *New Phytol.,* 1939, **38,** 273.

CHAPTER XIV

THE DECOMPOSITION OF PLANT MATERIAL

The Plant Constituents

THESE FORM THE primary material both for the food of the soil organisms and for the production of soil organic matter. They can be divided up into three main groups of material: the cell contents, the reserve food supply, and the cell wall and structural material. The first group is rich in proteins and sugars, and the second in starches, fats and proteins. The third group consists of two fairly distinct materials, the skeletal framework and cementing and encrusting substances.

The skeletal framework is built up from cellulose and cellulosan fibres. Pure cotton cellulose consists of chains of glucose residues linked at the 1:4 β positions, as shown in Fig. 17, but structural cellulose also contains some xylose and glucuronic acid residues similarly linked in the glucose residue chain.[1] The cellulosans of the angiosperms are shorter chains, mainly of xylose and a few uronic acid residues similarly linked, as in Fig. 17, and in the gymnosperms there are also chains of mannose residues, but their linkage has not been definitely established. The architecture of the skeletal framework is still under discussion; it is probably built up of micelles containing about a hundred oriented cellulose chains, each containing several hundred glucose residues with up to 20 to 30 per cent by weight of shorter cellulosan chains similarly oriented.[2]

The cementing and encrusting material consists of two distinct groups of substances: polymerised sugar units and the lignins. The former predominates in the young shoot but the latter in the mature. Initially the lignin only covers the cell walls and the outside of the cellulose micelles, but as the tissue matures it may encrust the fibres in the micelle also. The carbohydrates are normally arbitrarily divided into those substances soluble in water or dilute acids—the pectins, gums and mucilages—and those soluble in dilute alkali—the hemicelluloses—though this group contains some of the cellulosans already mentioned. These substances are built up of either glucose and the corresponding glucuronic

---

[1] A. G. Norman, *Biochem. J.*, 1936, **30**, 2054; with W. H. Fuller, *J. Bact.*, 1943, **46**, 281; S. P. Saric and R. K. Schofield, *Proc. Roy. Sci.*, 1946, **185** A, 431.

[2] See K. H. Meyer, *Natural and Synthetic High Polymers*, New York, 1942, for a description of the present-day views on the constitution of cellulose, and A. G. Norman, *The Biochemistry of Cellulose, the Polyuronides, Lignin, etc.*, Oxford, 1937, for a general discussion of these problems. For a review of the chemistry of the polysaccharides, see A. G. Norman, *Ann. Rev. Biochem.*, 1941, **10**, 65.

acid and xylose residues, or else galactose and the corresponding galacturonic acid and arabinose residues, though mannose and other residues sometimes occur. The gum molecules[1] have probably short main chains with many shorter side-chains; pectin is possibly long chains of galacturonic acid residues linked through the 1 : 4 α positions, as in starch; and the hemicelluloses short chain molecules containing an appreciable proportion of pentose and uronic acid residues. But our

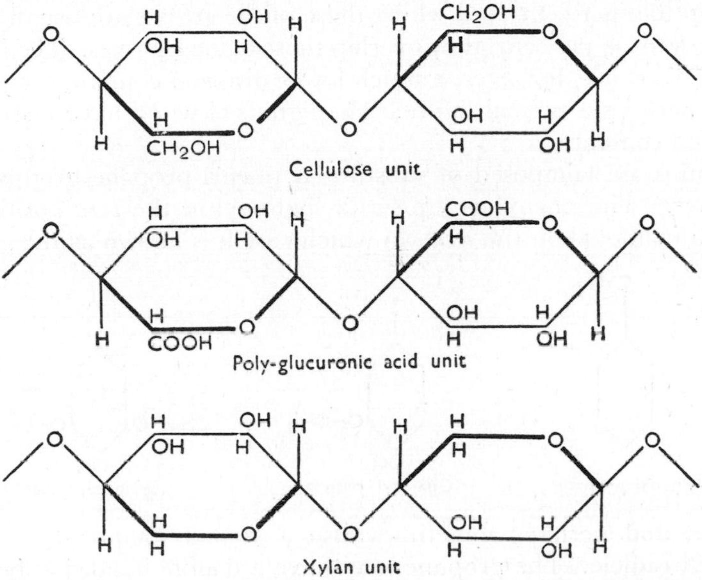

FIG. 17. Formulae of chains built from glucose units through 1 : 4 β linkages.

knowledge of these substances is imperfect, and there are not yet any accepted methods in general use for separating and purifying the individual hemicelluloses, so that the interpretation of experimental results is complicated by the possibility that other molecules may be present besides the type under investigation.

Two of the constituents can, however, be readily determined by boiling the material with 12 per cent hydrochloric acid—the pentose sugar and the uronic acid contents. The former yields furfuraldehyde, which can be distilled off and estimated;[2] and the carboxyl group of the latter is split off and appears as carbon dioxide. Uronic acids, unfortunately, are not the only acids that give the reaction,[3] but no other acid that does has been suspected or isolated in plant material.

[1] For a review of the constitution of plant gums, see E. L. Hirst, *J. Chem. Soc.*, 1942, 70.
[2] For an example of the precautions necessary for the determination of hemicelluloses, see A. G. Norman, *Biochem. J.*, 1929, **23**, 1353.
[3] A. G. Norman and J. T. Martin, *Biochem. J.*, 1930, **24**, 649.

Lignins are richer in carbon and poorer in oxygen than cellulose, their typical analyses being

	Carbon	Hydrogen	Oxygen
lignin	61–64%	5–6%	30%
cellulose	44·5%	6·2%	49·3%

but the lignins of most agricultural crops differ from carbohydrates in containing nitrogen.[1] Thus the lignins of leguminous plants may contain up to 3 per cent, and whilst those of the grasses are usually lower, from 1·5 to 2·0 per cent, they overlap those of the legumes. The lignin of cereal straw has, however, a much lower nitrogen content, 0·5 per cent being perhaps a typical figure. The lignins of wood have a still lower nitrogen content.

Lignins are composed of substituted phenyl-propane groups linked together.[2] The phenyl group has a hydroxyl in the *para*-position and often a methoxyl on the *meta*, in which case it is known as the guaiacyl

Phenyl propane   Guaiacyl radicle   Syringyl radicle

radicle, and perhaps sometimes also a second methoxyl, as in the syringyl radicle. The propane may have a double bond, i.e. be a propene, and also a hydroxyl. The position of the nitrogen is unknown, but it is probably present as a tertiary amine in a linkage similar to that in pyridine. Bondi and Meyer claim to have shown that the lignins of grasses, cereals and legumes are built out of three of these units and hence have a molecular weight of about 650. Further, they showed that grass lignins contained two methoxyls and leguminous lignins one methoxyl per molecule whilst each contained two phenolic and one aliphatic hydroxyls. The third phenolic hydroxyl that should have been present presumably takes some part in the polymerisation process.

The Decomposition of Plant Residues

The biochemistry of the rotting of plant residues in the soil has not been followed in any detail because of the lack of suitable analytical

[1] A. Bondi and H. Meyer, *Biochem. J.*, 1948, **43**, 258; E. R. Armitage, R. de B. Ashworth and W. S. Ferguson, *J. Soc. Chem. Indust.*, 1948, **67**, 241.
[2] For a review of the structure of lignins, see H. Hibbert, *Ann. Rev. Biochem.*, 1942, **11**, 183; E. G. V. Percival, *Ann. Rep. Chem. Soc.*, 1942, **39**, 142.

methods, though the rotting or composting of plant residues, and particularly cereal straws, outside the soil has been studied in more detail. The interpretation of the analytical results is complicated both because of the deficiencies in methods of analysis commonly employed, and also because the rotting process includes the synthesis of microbial protoplasm[1] and the excretion of products of microbial metabolism, both of which may react in the same way to the analytical methods as some of the initial plant products. The difficulty can be serious for substances containing uronic acids or yielding furfuraldehyde on acid hydrolysis, i.e. products of the hemicellulose type; but it is greatest for the organic nitrogen compounds, and no attempt has yet been made to follow the course of their transformations during composting.

The general course of the decomposition of cereal straws under normal conditions is reasonably well understood. Initially, the hemicelluloses encrusting the cellulose fibres are strongly attacked, mainly by fungi, and this attack is accompanied by a considerable evolution of heat and carbon dioxide. The most prominent feature of the attack, once this initial stage is over, is the loss of cellulose, which accounts for the major part of the loss of organic matter. Thus, Norman,[2] working with oat straw rotting aerobically under favourable conditions, found that 100 gm. of oat straw, containing 23 per cent of free hemicelluloses and 44 per cent of pure cellulose, lost 10 gm. of hemicellulose and under 1 gm. of cellulose in the first four days, an additional 1·5 gm. of hemicellulose and 4 gm. of cellulose in the next four, and an additional 1·25 gm. of hemicellulose but 11 gm. of cellulose in the next eight days; the maximum temperature was reached on the seventh day, but the maximum rate of heat production occurred between the second and sixth days. The reason for the slowing down in the rate of hemicellulose decomposition when only half has disappeared is presumably due to the inhomogeneity of this fraction. Finally, the products of microbial activity appear to be the main products undergoing decomposition (Table 47).[3]

A well-rotted compost contains little hemicellulose or cellulose, but the relative times taken for these two constituents to fall to a low level depends on circumstances. Norman[4] found that a chaffed oat straw, rotting at 35°C. under good conditions, lost 99 per cent of its hemicelluloses, but only about a third of its celluloses in nine months' decomposition, but Waksman's[5] results on the whole indicate that the celluloses usually fall to a low level before the hemicelluloses. The

[1] For an account of the composition of the body substances of bacteria, see J. R. Porter, *Bacterial Chemistry and Physiology*, New York, 1946.   [2] *Ann. Appl. Biol.*, 1930, **17**, 575.
[3] A. G. Norman, *Biochem. J.*, 1929, **23**, 1367.   [4] *Biochem. J.*, 1932, **26**, 573.
[5] See, for example, S. A. Waksman and F. C. Gerretsen, *Ecology*, 1931, **12**, 33; S. A. Waksman and F. G. Tenney, *Soil Sci.*, 1929, **28**, 55; J. P. Martin and Y. Wang, *J. Amer. Soc. Agron.*, 1944, **36**, 373.

cause of the discrepancy is not known, but may lie in the different methods used to determine cellulose and hemicellulose.

The course of the lignin decomposition has not been followed in any great detail because of the difficulty of finding specific tests for lignin. Lignin only decomposes slowly, and its rate of decomposition depends on its composition and on its admixture with other hemicelluloses; thus, J. P. Martin and Y. Wang[1] have shown that the lignins in timothy and clover hay appear to decompose more easily than those in oat or

TABLE 47

The Disappearance of Hemicelluloses and Celluloses from Rye Straw during Aerobic Decomposition

Temperature of decomposition 35° C. Extra nitrogen added as ammonium carbonate

All weights calculated on the quantities initially present in 100 gm. organic matter

Duration of decomposition in days	0	4	8	24	84
Organic matter . .	100	97	78	62	49
Cellulose	48	47	33	25	20
Associated Xylan . .	9·0	9·1	8·9	5·4	4·2
Groups in the Hemicellulose fraction:					
Uronic acid . . .	4·5	4·2	3·0	2·3	1·8
Anhydropentose . .	17·0	13·8	7·4	5·5	4·2
Pectin as calcium pectate .	0·35	0·35	0·41	0·62	0·85

maize straw. The importance of the lignin fraction in decomposition lies in the fact that it renders some of the cellulose and possibly other constituents inaccessible to the microflora, hence the higher the lignin content of the material the greater is the proportion of cellulose that is encrusted with lignin and the slower is its decomposition. Thus, 15 per cent of lignin seriously reduces the rate of decomposition of cellulose; 20 to 30 per cent, as is common in woods, slows up the decomposition so much that they cease to have any agricultural value as a source of humus; and a content of around 40 per cent, as occurs in coir, renders the fibre extremely resistant to decomposition.[2]

The course of the decomposition depends on the relative rates at which the heat is produced and dissipated in the initial stages, for these determine the temperatures at which the decomposition takes place,

[1] J. Amer. Soc. Agron., 1944, 36, 373.
[2] See, for example, W. H. Fuller and A. G. Norman, J. Bact., 1943, 46, 291; W. J. Peevy and A. G. Norman, Soil Sci., 1948, 65, 209.

and hence the composition and activity of the microflora. These relative rates are controlled by the decomposability of the substances, the water supply and the aeration; a moist, loose, well-aerated heap decomposes and produces heat more rapidly than a compacted badly aerated heap, but if the heap is too loose it will also lose its heat rapidly.

The effect of the temperature at which decomposition is taking place has not yet been worked out in detail. The general results seem to be that in the temperature range 5° to 30°C.,[1] the lower the temperature of decomposition the slower is the process, and after it has slowed down the smaller is the loss of organic matter and the higher is the organic nitrogen content of the compost. Low temperatures, in fact, as H. L. Jensen[2] has been able to show, directly encourage the accumulation of microbial protoplasm. At very high temperatures,[3] in the range 45° to 75°C., both the loss of organic matter and the organic nitrogen content of the compost decrease with increasing temperature, probably due to the increasing restriction of the microflora to specialised thermophilic organisms, and to their tendency to attack proteins rather than cellulose. In the range 30° to 45° C.,[4] increasing temperature may not have any marked effect on the loss of organic matter, but may allow the organic nitrogen content of the compost to increase.

The results are unfortunately not clear cut, and the effect of the maximum temperatures reached during decomposition on the properties of composts and manures has not been properly worked out.[5] If high temperatures, over 60°C., for example, are reached, it is possible that the humus is formed with less loss of organic matter, and that it is more crumbly, contains fewer volatile substances, i.e. has no smell, and has a higher nitrogen content than if the maximum temperature only reached about 40°C.; and this is the principle used by H. Krantz in his method of composting fresh dairy manure by the hot fermentation or Edelmist process. On the other hand, if the maximum temperature is kept low,[6] possibly under 20°C., the loss of organic matter is reduced and the nitrogen content increased, which forms the basis of the cold fermentation method of strawy manure.

The nitrogen demands of the microbial population during decomposition are of obvious practical importance. On the whole, material containing less than 1·2 to 1·3 per cent nitrogen, on the dry weight basis, when rotting in the presence of ammonium salts will cause some of the ammonia to be taken up and converted into organic nitrogen

[1] S. A. Waksman and F. C. Gerretsen, *Ecology*, 1931, **12**, 33.
[2] *Proc. Linn. Soc. N.S.W.*, 1939, **54**, 601.
[3] S. A. Waksman, T. C. Corden and N. Hulpoi, *Soil Sci.*, 1939, **47**, 83.
[4] A. G. Norman, *Ann. Appl. Biol.*, 1931, **18**, 244.
[5] See, for example, S. H. Jenkins, *Imp. Bur. Soil Sci., Tech. Comm.* 33, 1935 R. Junghähnel, *ForschDienst. Sonderh.* 17, 1941, 103; K. Maiwald, ibid., 45.
[6] R. M. Salter and C. J. Schollenberger, *Ohio Agric. Expt. Sta., Bull.* 605, 1939.

compounds. If the material contains more than 1·8 per cent nitrogen, some of this nitrogen will be converted into ammonia during the rotting process, though if the nitrogen content is not much in excess of this, ammonia may be taken up and fixed in the initial stages of the decomposition. Materials with intermediate nitrogen contents, between 1·2 and 1·8 per cent, tend to have no net effect on the level of ammonia during the decomposition, though they also often take up ammonia initially and release it again later.[1] Fig. 18, taken from some of H. L. Jensen's work,[2] illustrates these points. Thus, the rotting of

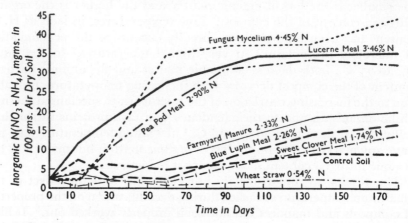

FIG. 18. Rate of accumulation of ammonia and nitrate in a loam soil to which 5 per cent of various organic substances have been added.

nitrogen-poor plant or animal remains in a soil will lower its content of mineral nitrogen, i.e. ammonium and nitrate ions, whilst the rotting of a nitrogen-rich material will increase it. But these effects depend somewhat on the type of material being rotted, and neither the nitrogen content alone, nor the ratio of the carbon in the material to the nitrogen, is a safe guide to the effect of the rotting process on the mineral nitrogen level in the soil.

An experiment of Waksman and F. G. Tenney[3] illustrates these effects well. They added ground-up plant roots of varying nitrogen content to a soil and measured its nitrate nitrogen content during decomposition. They added to 28 lb. of soil sufficient material to contain 600 mgm. of nitrogen, incubated it for three months, then leached the soil well and determined the nitrate nitrogen in the leachates. The results, which are given in Table 48, show that ground clover roots, with a nitrogen content of 1·7 per cent, contains just about

[1] For an example of this, see N. H. Parberry and R. J. Swaby, *Agric. Gaz., N.S.W.*, 1942, **53**, 357. I am indebted to Dr. R. J. Swaby for showing me a fuller report of these experiments containing the nitrogen contents of the various materials used. C. N. Acharya et al. (*Indian J. Agric. Sci.*, 1946, **16**, 178) obtained somewhat similar results.

[2] *J. Agric. Sci.*, 1929, **19**, 71.   [3] *Soil Sci.*, 1927, **24**, 317.

enough nitrogen for its own decomposition, but the other plant roots remove nitrogen from the soil during this process.

The nitrogen demands during the rotting of a material can be specified by its nitrogen factor, which is defined as the number of

TABLE 48

Relation between the Nitrogen Content of Various Plant Roots and the Nitrate Nitrogen in the Soil

Material used	Nitrogen content of material Per cent	Weight of material added Grams	Nitrate nitrogen in leachings Milligrams	Gain or loss of nitrogen Milligrams
Control soil . . .	—	—	947	—
Oat roots	0·45	133	207	−740
Timothy roots . . .	0·62	97	398	−549
Maize roots . . .	0·79	76	511	−436
Clover roots . . .	1·71	35	925	− 22
Dried blood . . .	10·71	5·6	1750	+803

grams of nitrogen, in the form of ammonium or nitrate ions, immobilised during the decomposition of 100 gm. of the material. The nitrogen factor, however, is not a constant for a given material, but depends somewhat on the conditions prevailing during the decomposition. However, E. H. Richards and A. G. Norman,[1] who introduced

TABLE 49

Effect of Duration of Decomposition on the Nitrogen Factor of Oat Straw

Nitrogen content of straw, 0·30 per cent

Duration of decomposition in days	8	16	24	48
Per cent loss of organic matter	13	25	37	50
Nitrogen factor . . .	0·75	0·67	0·75	0·80

it to specify the amount of nitrogen that must be added to heaps of vegetable waste in the field to allow rapid decomposition, found that in farm practice it was sufficiently constant, both during the course of a rot and for a given material rotting in compost heaps under natural conditions, to be of practical value in farm advisory work. In the first place the nitrogen factor is not quite constant during the course of a rot, as is shown both in Table 49, taken from Richards and Norman's

[1] *Biochem. J.*, 1931, **25**, 1769.

work, and also by the fact, already mentioned on p. 246, that materials with a small negative nitrogen factor may remove ammonium and nitrate nitrogen, if available, during the early stages of decomposition and release it later on. In the second place, the nitrogen factor of a

TABLE 50

Effect of Treating Straw on its Decomposability and Nitrogen Factor

Oat straw extracted with	Composition of straw					Decomposition for 48 days	
	Cellulose and associated cellulosans	Hemicellulose as uronic acid anhydride	anhydro-pentose xylose	Lignin	Per cent nitrogen	Loss of organic matter	Nitrogen factor
Control . . .	49	5·4	11·5	18·5	0·30	50	0·80
Hot water . . .	51	6·2	13·3	—	0·27	18	0·51
4 per cent NaOH . .	84	1·0	1·5	11·1	0·12	21	0·16
4 per cent alcoholic NaOH	66	3·2	7·5	8·2	0·11	21	0·36
2 per cent HCl . .	62	2·4	1·0	25·6	0·34	9	0·27

given material cannot be predicted from its nitrogen content. It is usually higher for natural materials, such as straw, than for pure substances, such as cellulose or straw treated to remove some of its constituents, as is shown in Table 50. The nitrogen in a material is not

TABLE 51

Effect of Added Nitrogen on the Nitrogen Factor of Rotting Bean Husks

Nitrogen content of bean husks, 3 per cent.   Duration of decomposition: 48 days

	Loss of organic matter	Nitrogen content of compost	Nitrogen factor
	per cent	per cent	
No added nitrogen . .	48	4·7	− 0·52
With added ammonia . .	41	5·4	+ 0·15

all equally available to micro-organisms: they may use ammonium salts, if present, in preference to difficultly available nitrogen compounds in the material. Thus, Richards and Norman found that bean husks, which had a nitrogen content of 3 per cent, rot to liberate ammonia in the absence of readily available nitrogen, but immobilise some nitrogen in its presence (Table 51).

The rate of decomposition of a material with a low nitrogen content can be increased considerably if a suitable source of nitrogen is added, for the nitrogen supply obviously limits the maximum amount of protoplasm that can be present, and, if it is too low, it limits biological activity. The added nitrogen may also allow a larger proportion of the carbonaceous organic matter to be converted into microbial protoplasm or its by-products, hence it may increase the proportion of the added organic matter that is converted into humic substances.[1] This forms the principle underlying all processes for rapidly obtaining a compost or manure from straw without passing it through a stockyard.[2] Since its nitrogen factor is about 0·8, at least 18 lb. of nitrogen should be added per ton of straw to ensure its rate of decomposition is not limited by nitrogen shortage. This is commonly added as ammonium sulphate, but any other material rich in nitrogen, for example, urine, animal droppings, dried blood, leguminous hays or young green plant material, is equally suitable. It has been claimed that organic nitrogen compounds give a mellow and friable compost in contrast to inorganic nitrogen compounds, which give a more sticky compost, possibly because the former encourage a greater development of fungi compared to bacteria, but there is little critical evidence for this statement.

The actual amount of mineral nitrogen locked up when material with a low nitrogen content is decomposing depends on several factors, not all of which have been well established. For a given carbon and nitrogen content in the decomposing material, the amount of soil nitrogen locked up during the decomposition increases as the speed of decomposition increases. Hence, materials low in lignins typically immobilise more nitrogen than those high in lignins,[3] and decomposition in warm soils immobilises more nitrogen than in cool soils. Thus L. A. Pinck, F. E. Allison and V. L. Gaddy[4] found that under Maryland conditions a ton of wheat straw immobilised about 16 to 18 lb. of nitrogen if decomposing during the winter, but between 21 and 28 lb. during the summer. Again, decomposition under acid conditions appears to lock up more nitrogen than under neutral conditions,[5] though the significance of this result is not known.

The process of decomposition may lock up other nutrients besides nitrogen, or be retarded by their lack. The ash of microbial protoplasm may contain up to 25 per cent of phosphorus and 37 per cent of potassium,[6] so that the micro-organisms may compete with growing crops for the available supplies of these nutrients if the soil or the decomposing organic matter is very low in them. I. P. Mamchenko[7] has brought forward some evidence that increasing the phosphate supply of material

[1] F. J. Salter, *Soil Sci.*, 1931, **31**, 413.
[2] H. B. Hutchinson and E. H. Richards, *J. Min. Agric.*, 1921, **28**, 398.
[3] E. H. Richards and A. G. Norman, *Biochem. J.*, 1931, **25**, 1769; E. J. Rubins and F. E. Bear, *Soil Sci.*, 1942, **54**, 411.
[4] *J. Amer. Soc. Agron.*, 1946, **38**, 410.   [5] H. L. Jensen, *J. Agric. Sci.*, 1929, **19**, 71.
[6] S. A. Waksman, *Principles of Soil Microbiology*, 2nd ed., London, 1931, p. 367.
[7] *Vest. Udob. Agrotekh. Agropoch.*, 1941, No. 3, 5.

well supplied with nitrogen, such as clover residues, increases the proportion of carbonaceous material converted to humic substances by reducing the proportion respired as carbon dioxide. There is also some evidence that the rate of decomposition of tree leaves depends on the base content of the leaves,[1] though whether this is due simply to the effect of the bases in controlling the pH of the rotting material and therefore the composition of the microflora, or to their nutrient effect on the micro-organisms has not been determined.

In conclusion, the conditions favouring rapid decomposition of plant products are:

1. The material should have a low lignin, and probably also a low wax, content.

2. The material should be in as fine a state of comminution as possible; and it is probable that the principal natural agents bringing this about are the larger soil animals.

3. There should be an adequate supply of available nitrogen.

4. The pH should not be allowed to fall too low, otherwise the microbial population becomes unduly restricted and the larger soil animals die out.

5. The aeration should remain good and the moisture supply adequate. Anaerobic conditions or water-logging lead to a restricted population, mainly bacterial, though the nitrogen demands of the population fall.

6. The temperature should be fairly high. Temperatures above 45° C. or below 30° C. give lower rates of decomposition than temperatures in this range.

7. For substances rather difficult to decompose, mixed groups of materials decompose quicker than single groups. Thus, in forest floors, mixed litter from several species of trees usually decomposes quicker than litter from a single type.[2]

Composting

Composting is the term usually applied to the rotting down of plant and animal remains in heaps before the residue is applied to the soil. The chemical processes of decomposition in the compost heap and the soil differ in two respects: the compost heap is usually not so well aerated, and the temperature of the decomposition can be far higher in it than in the soil.

The points of importance in composting are ensuring that the water content and the aeration of the heap are within certain limits: in

[1] W. M. Broadfoot and W. H. Pierre, *Soil Sci.*, 1939, **48**, 329.

[2] See, or example, J. T. Auten, *J. Forestry*, 1940, **38**, 229; F. G. Gustafson, *Plant Physiol.*, 1943, **18**, 704.

practice the rate and type of decomposition is controlled by varying the aeration conditions rather than the water content of the heap. If the heap is too dry, too compacted, or too water-logged, little decomposition takes place, and if it is kept moist and loose, decomposition is at its maximum.

There appears to be no virtue in rotting down materials in the compost heap compared with letting them rot down in the soil itself as far as adding plant nutrients to the soil or increasing its humus content are concerned. The relative value of the two methods depends on circumstances. One cannot always add farmyard manure or waste organic material to the soil when it is available: one must often leave it until it is convenient to put it on the field, and composting is a way of storing these materials until they are required. Again, some soils are naturally very open and free draining, and adding undecomposed material will often exaggerate the harmful consequences of this open structure. Under these conditions it is much preferable to add well-rotted humic material, for this will tend to reduce the openness of the soil. Again, an important difference between the unrotted plant material and the compost is in physical condition. The unrotted material typically holds little water and is coarse and fibrous; the compost holds much water and is friable. On light, sandy soils, which in any case are too open for optimum crop growth, a compost is obviously preferable on this score, whilst on some heavy soils the uncomposted material may be better.

A third difference lies in the consequence of decomposition. A compost, when added to a soil, continues its decomposition only slowly, whilst unrotted material, particularly if it is rather succulent, begins to decompose rapidly, with the consequence that the carbon dioxide content of the soil air is raised, which may be very beneficial on light soils (see p. 533)—that is, on just those soils whose physical condition is most benefited by adding compost. If the decomposition is too rapid, however, the carbon dioxide content of the soil air may rise so high, or the nitrates in the soil temporarily fall so low, that plant growth is inhibited.

A fourth factor, the importance of which has not yet been established, is that rotting a given amount of material in the soil will usually give a larger addition to the humus and nutrient content of the soil than if it is first composted and then added to the soil. Experiments have been made at Rothamsted for a number of years in which a given dressing of straw and nitrogen ploughed into the soil is compared with the same quantity of straw rotted with the same quantity of nitrogen in a compost heap and then applied to the land. The ploughed-in straw has always given a better yield than the compost, as is shown in Table 52.

TABLE 52

Comparison of Straw Composted with Straw Ploughed in on a Three-course Rotation at Rothamsted

| | 12 years, 1934–45 | | | |
| | Year of applying straw | | Year after application | |
	Compost	Straw ploughed in	Compost	Straw ploughed in
Potatoes, tons per acre . . .	7·86	9·40	7·40	7·97
Sugar-beet, sugar cwt. per acre .	37·0	41·2	36·4	38·2
Barley, grain cwt. per acre . .	27·7	31·2	26·5	27·9

The cause of the better crop response to the rotting in the soil compared with rotting in the compost heap may be due to losses of nitrogen during the composting process. Thus C. N. Acharya and his co-workers[1] found that nearly one quarter of the nitrogen in a mixed organic refuse, whose C/N ratio was initially 32, was lost during the first 20 weeks of composting, probably mainly by volatilisation as ammonia, but there was no net loss if some soil was added to the refuse. Presumably the ammonia set free in the decomposition is absorbed by the clay in the soil and then nitrified.

Composting has, however, a considerable farm health aspect. It allows many parasitic organisms in the plant and animal material to be destroyed before the residues are put back on the land, and this destruction is more complete the higher the maximum temperature attained and the better the compost has been made. High temperatures have the further advantage that all the weed seeds present are also killed and decomposed. Hence, if possible trouble from either of these sources is suspected, good high-temperature composting may be well worth while.

Finally, the effect of composting on the content of members of the vitamin B complex[2] and other growth-promoting substances, such as the auxins,[3] has been investigated by many workers, who all find that the amount of these substances in the heap decreases during the course of the decomposition. Composts are, therefore, not rich sources of these substances, but, as has already been mentioned on p. 25, there is no evidence that any farm crop benefits in any way by increasing the levels of these compounds in the soil.

[1] *Indian J. Agric. Sci.*, 1945, **15**, 214; 1946, **16**, 90.
[2] R. L. Starkey, *Soil Sci.*, 1944, **57**, 247.
[3] J. H. Hamence, *J. Soc. Chem. Indust.*, 1945, **64**, 147.

The Micro-organisms Responsible for the Decomposition of Plant Remains

Our knowledge in this subject is not as extensive as might be expected because a considerable amount of the earlier work was based on ideas we now know are inadequate. A search was made for soil organisms which could decompose the various plant constituents in pure culture, and in the case of cellulose often chemically pure cellulose in the form of filter paper was used rather than cellulose in its natural condition associated with hemicelluloses. It was then often implicitly assumed that these organisms carried out the same decompositions in the highly competitive environment of the soil or compost heap. This ignoring of the environment as a whole did not, in fact, lead to as wildly wrong conclusions as might be expected, because they were checked by what had to be rather indirect observations in the field or compost heap itself.

This early work established, for example, that many species of fungi could attack all the principal constituents in a substrate such as oat straw in pure culture, but the decomposition was more rapid if a mixed culture of these fungi were used, as is illustrated in Table 53.[1]

The first group of organisms which multiply when plant remains are mixed with the soil, or start to decompose in a compost heap under aerobic conditions are the sugar fungi (see p. 158), for these can multiply most quickly whilst simple plant cell contents are being decomposed.

TABLE 53

Decomposition of some Plant Constituents brought about by Pure Cultures of Fungi and Actinomycetes

Oat straw rotting at 30° C. for 48 days. Extra nitrogen added as ammonium carbonate

All results are expressed on the basis of 100 gm. of straw

	Dry matter	Cellulose and associated xylans	Anhydro-pentose in hemi-cellulose	Uronic acid an-hydride	Nitrogen factor	Per cent of organic nitrogen
Initial straw . .	100	53	14·4	4·8	—	0·31
Mixed microflora .	49	15	2·2	2·6	0·84	2·37
Aspergillus flavipes .	71	25	5·3	3·5	0·69	1·39
Trichoderma (sp.) .	73	33	9·9	2·6	0·73	1·42
Phoma (sp.) . .	74	29	5·4	3·0	0·50	1·07
Aspergillus niger .	87	42	10·2	3·2	0·82	1·30
Actinomycete (sp.) .	89	41	11·1	4·8	1·03	1.55

[1] A. G. Norman, *Ann. Appl. Biol.*, 1930, **17**, 575; 1931, **18**, 244; 1934, **21**, 454. For another example, see S. A. Waksman and I. J. Hutchings, *Soil Sci.*, 1937, **43**, 77.

The next stage in the soil depends on the soil conditions and the plant material added. If the soil is acid, these fungi are replaced by cellulose decomposing fungi, whilst if it is neutral a general bacterial population appears to become dominant, which often seems to begin on the hyphae of the sugar and cellulose decomposing fungi. But if the plant material contains strongly lignified tissue, fungi remain an important part of the population, for there are no bacteria which will decompose lignins. If the soil is poorly aerated bacteria are dominant from the beginning, with the consequence that the lignified tissues accumulate as peat.

There are a considerable number of species of fungi and actino-mycetes which can decompose cellulosic plant material under aerobic conditions in pure culture, and a considerable number of bacterial species which can do this under conditions of poor aeration, but the number of bacterial species which decompose these tissues in aerobic conditions in the soil appear to be rather limited, although they form a very important part of the microflora in sub-acid and neutral soils.[1]

Certain members of the soil fauna can digest plant cellulose and associated hemicelluloses, but there is no evidence they can digest lignins. Termites can probably be as important as micro-organisms in some tropical soils as cellulose decomposers, and so can some members of the soil faunal population, such as earthworms and possibly some mites and insects, though little critical work has been done on what plant constituents are decomposed by many members of this sapro-phytic population. The fauna probably differ from many of the micro-organisms in that the latter produce appreciable amounts of humus from the decomposition of plant remains, whilst some of the fauna at least, for example termites, produce either little or none.

The products of microbial metabolism include microbial cell-wall components such as polyuronide gums and other polysaccharides, as well as lignin- and humic-like substances. Many bacteria, including some of the cellulose decomposers, also produce polyuronide gums, particularly if they are working under conditions of limited nitrogen supply;[2] for they may have to attack a large amount of polysaccharide to extract sufficient nitrogen for their growth; and since it is nitrogen and not energy supply that is limiting their growth, they have to excrete energy-rich by-products. Some fungi produce dark-coloured products similar to α-humus (see p. 267) when growing on cellulose and other lignin-free plant products.[3] Some bacteria may also produce such pro-ducts, both from the easily decomposable components in recently dead

[1] For reviews of these, see A. G. Norman and W. H. Fuller, *Adv. Enzymol.*, 1942, **2**, 239, and R. Y. Stanier, *Bact. Rev.*, 1942, **6**, 143.

[2] See, for example, S. Winogradsky, *Ann. Inst. Pasteur*, 1929, **43**, 549; A. G. Norman and W. V. Bartholomew, *Proc. Soil Sci. Soc. Amer.*, 1940, **5**, 242.

[3] H. L. Jensen, *J. Agric. Sci.*, 1931, **21**, 81; L. A. Pinck and F. E. Allison, *Soil Sci.*, 1944, **57**, 155.

plant tissue,[1] and also from the mycelia of the fungi that originate the attack on the more resistant plant remains.[2]

Green Manuring

Plant residues can be applied direct to the soil instead of via the compost or manure heap, and the usual method of doing this is to plough in a growing crop. This method of green manuring can have several effects on the soil, depending on conditions: it may increase the organic matter content of, or the available nitrogen in, the soil; it may reduce the loss of mineral nitrogen by leaching; and it may concentrate nutrients likely to be deficient in the surface soil and leave them there in a readily available form. Green manuring normally cannot confer all these benefits on the soil simultaneously, and it may confer none of them.

Green manuring, when properly used, can either increase the humus content or else the supply of available nitrogen in the soil, but rarely can it do both at the same time, and therein it differs from well-made farmyard manure, for the humus content only appears to be increased appreciably if material fairly resistant to decomposition is added to the soil, and resistant plant material is typically low in nitrogen; and the available nitrogen supply is only increased if readily decomposable material high in nitrogen, such as young green plants, are decomposing. Thus, the effect of a given crop as a green manure depends on its maturity when ploughed under. Table 54[3] illustrates this point for rye. Young rye decomposes rapidly with a large production of carbon dioxide, and consequently leaves little residue but much nitrate nitrogen, whilst mature rye decomposes much more slowly, leaving a large residue and making demands on the soil's supply of available nitrogen.

This conclusion has been questioned by F. E. Allison and his co-workers.[4] They concluded that the proportion of carbon added in a green manure crop that gets converted to resistant humic material only depends on the amount of added carbon and not on the stage of maturity of the green crop. On this view immature green manure crops add little carbon to the soil compared with mature crops because of the much smaller weight of carbon they contain when ploughed under. But this conclusion is based on experiments made by adding the green manure to pots containing only 20 lb. of soil and growing five crops

[1] M. M. Kononova, *Pedology*, 1943, No. 6, 27; No. 7, 18; 1944, No. 10, 456; with N. P Belchikova, ibid., 1946, 529.
[2] F. Y. Geltser, *Sovet. Agron.*, 1940, No. 11–12, 22; also see her book *The Significance of Micro-organisms in the Formation of Humus*, Moscow, 1940; J. G. Shrikhande, *Biochem. J.*, 1933, **27**, 1551.
[3] S. A. Waksman and F. G. Tenney, *Soil Sci.*, 1927, **24**, 317.
[4] L. A. Pinck, F. E. Allison and V. L. Gaddy, *Proc. Soil Sci. Soc. Amer.*, 1946, **10**, 230; *Soil Sci.*, 1948, **66**, 39; *J. Amer. Soc. Agron.*, 1948, **40**, 237.

TABLE 54

The Effect of the Maturity of Rye on its Composition and Decomposition

(a) The effect on the carbon dioxide and mineral nitrogen produced during decomposition

Fresh material, containing 2 gm. dry matter, added to 100 gm. soil and incubated at 25° to 28° C. for 27 days

Stage of maturity	Moisture content of material	Per cent of dry matter soluble in cold water	Nitrogen content of dry matter	Carbon dioxide evolved, mgm.	Mineral nitrogen liberated (+) or absorbed (−) mgm.
Plants 10–14 in. high . .	80	34	2·5	287	+ 22·2
Just before heads form .	79	23	1·8	280	+ 3·0
Just before flowering, leaves and stalks . . .	57	18	1·0	200	− 7·5
Grain in milk stage, leaves and stalks . . .	15	10	0·24	188	− 8·9

(b) The effect of maturity on the disappearance of plant constituents

Stems and leaves, decomposing in sand at 25° to 28° C. on a basis of 100 gm. of dry matter initially

Stage of maturity	Just before head forms			Plants nearly mature		
	Initial	After 30 days' decomposition	Per cent loss in 30 days	Initial	After 60 days' decomposition	Per cent loss in 60 days
Water insoluble organic matter .	75	20	73	76	44	42
Pentosans . .	20	4	82	20	8	61
Cellulose . .	26	6	77	31	14	56
Lignin . .	12	8	36	17	15	11
Protein insoluble in water . .	8·2	2·5	69	1·8	5·2	gain 187

of sudan grass or wheat—experiments in which the root residues of the crops per pound of soil would be far higher than in the field—and it was not possible to allow for the contribution made by these resistant root residues to the resistant humic material in the soil. Hence their conclusions may not apply to green manuring in the field.

Green manuring has, in most parts of the world, been applied more successfully to increasing the available nitrogen supply than the humus content of soils. It is, however, only widely practised under certain definite conditions. The crop must be grown as a catch crop between the main cash crops, and consequently the practice is commonly commended in regions where the winters are sufficiently mild and moist to allow the crop to grow during this period. The crop must not compete with the main crops in any way, and in particular not for water, so that this system is not used under dry-farming conditions.

Hence, regions having a long growing season, such as regions with mild winters and with a well distributed rainfall, or else an adequate irrigation system, are well suited to green manure crops. The practice is prevalent in the humid tropics and sub-tropics, and in orchards when the growing season extends into the dormant period of the trees; it is also extensively advocated in the south-eastern states of the U.S.A., where maize and cotton, both summer crops, are the two main cash crops, and where legumes will grow during the winter. Green manure crops can be particularly valuable in saline soils, because in comparison with fallow, they reduce the evaporation from, and hence the salt content in, the surface soil, for they take their water from the subsoil and shade the surface. Further, when they are ploughed in, their residues will help to increase the availability of phosphates and trace elements to the succeeding crop due to the lowering of the soil pH brought about by the carbon dioxide produced in the process of decomposition.

Leguminous crops, such as some vetches, peas and clovers, are commonly used for green manuring as they increase the soil's supply of nitrogen. But these crops will normally only make adequate growth and fix enough nitrogen to make their cultivation worth while if the soil contains an adequate supply of calcium, potassium and phosphates. An example of the need for this is given in Table 55,[1] taken from some experiments made on a soil with pH 5·5 in Mississippi. In this example 28 and 56 lb. of nitrogen in the green manure gave rather more cotton than 18 and 34 lb. of nitrogen in a mixed fertiliser.

The nitrogen liberated during the decomposition of the green manure crop can only benefit the subsequent crop if the latter is sufficiently developed to take up the nitrogen soon after it is released and before the nitrate produced is leached out of the soil; and this period is fairly short, particularly in light soils under warm moist conditions, as the protein of the living green plant decomposes more rapidly than does that in dried or dead plant material. Hence, a long, wet period between the ploughing-in of a green manure crop and the establishment of the following crop, particularly on light soils, can result in much of the nitrifiable nitrogen of the green crop being leached out of the soil with the consequence that the following crop obtains little, if any,

[1] C. D. Hoover, *Proc. Soil Sci. Soc. Amer.*, 1942, **7**, 283.

benefit from the green manure.[1] On the other hand, the main crop should not be sown too soon after the green crop has been turned in, as the period covering the first flush of decomposition is very unfavourable for germination and the growth of very young plants.

TABLE 55

Influence of Fertilisers for Green Manure Crop on the Yield of Cotton

Experiment at Holly Springs, Mississippi. Winter green manure crop: Hairy Vetch

	Yield of seed cotton lb. per acre	Yield of vetch	
		Dry matter lb. per acre	Nitrogen lb. per acre
(a) No green manure before cotton Fertiliser applied to cotton:			
300 lb. 6–8–4	1090	—	—
Ditto, plus 100 lb. nitrate of soda . .	1430	—	—
(b) With green manure, but no fertilisers applied to cotton Fertiliser applied to vetch:			
None	930	460	17
Phosphate	1160	720	28
Dolomitic limestone	1480	1160	56
Limestone and phosphate . . .	1550	1210	57

Green manures do not usually increase the humus content of the soil, and in this respect differ from farmyard manure. Thus, C. A. Mooers[2] found that in a twenty-year experiment in which cow-peas were grown as an autumn catch crop in a continuous winter wheat experiment, the organic matter content of the soil decreased by 0·11 per cent, or by about a ton an acre over the twenty-year period on the plots in which the cow-peas, yielding about a ton of dry matter per acre, had been ploughed under, and increased by about 0·11 per cent on the plots which received 4 tons of farmyard manure, also containing about a ton of dry matter, each year. The 20 tons of cow-pea dry matter, however, reduced the loss of humus from the soil, for the humus content fell by 0·24 per cent on other plots that did not receive either farmyard manure or green manure. Hence, about 20 tons of cow-pea dry matter reduced the humus loss by about 2,600 lb., whilst 20 tons of farmyard manure dry matter reduced it by 7,000 lb.

[1] See E. M. Crowther in *Fifty Years of Field Experiments at the Woburn Experimental Station*, by E. J. Russell and J. A. Voelcker, for a discussion of the causes of the failure of the Woburn Green Manuring Experiment to benefit the soil or the succeeding crop.

[2] *Tennessee Agric. Expt. Sta., Bull.* 135, 1926.

Green manuring is relatively ineffective for two reasons. In the first place, as already noted, immature green plant tissue decomposes more rapidly, leaving less residue, than farmyard manure. But there is an additional effect, for adding an easily decomposable material to a soil so stimulates the soil organisms that they not only attack the readily decomposable material, but they also decompose in the process some of the more resistant organic matter in the soil. This effect has been unequivocally established by F. E. Broadbent[1] using sudan grass as a green manure whose tissues contained a measurable amount of heavy carbon C^{13} and heavy nitrogen N^{15}. He added some of this material to a soil, incubated it, and determined the amount of carbon dioxide given off and ammonium and nitrate nitrogen liberated, and from the C^{13} and N^{15} contents of these products calculated what fraction of each was derived from the humic matter in the soil. His results are given in Table 56, and further results are quoted on p. 290, which show that the presence of the decomposable sudan grass has caused the rate of production of carbon dioxide from the humic matter in the soil to increase threefold, and of mineral nitrogen twofold. This effect obviously limits, very seriously, the effectiveness of green manuring as a means of increasing the organic matter content of the soil.

TABLE 56

The Effect of Additions of Decomposable Matter in increasing the Rate of Decomposition of the Soil Humus

Amounts liberated in milligrams

	Soil plus sudan grass	Soil alone		Soil plus sudan grass	Soil alone
Total CO_2 evolved .	283	19	Total mineral nitrogen released .	4·83	1·40
Part derived from sudan grass .	225	—	Part derived from sudan grass .	1·93	—
Part derived from soil . . .	58	19	Part derived from soil . . .	2·89	1·40

Green manure crops can confer other benefits on the land: by growing during wet off-seasons they reduce the loss of nitrogen and other nutrients by leaching; they can often utilise less available forms of phosphate and zinc than the main crop and, hence, increase the availability of these for the crop; and by decomposing rapidly they liberate large quantities of carbon dioxide in the soil which can increase the availability of phosphates in alkaline calcareous soils. These benefits may be of particular value in deciduous orchards, for they

[1] *Proc. Soil Sci. Soc. Amer.*, 1948, **12**, 246.

have a long dormant season. The practical difficulties in growing these off-season cover crops for green manuring are to get them established without interfering with harvesting or competing with the trees for nutrients before harvest, and to manage them so they are not killed prematurely by the winter sprays and washes used.[1]

Ploughing in a green crop can have another function that has barely been examined yet. It is possible that the best way of ploughing in straw is to under-sow the corn crop with a green manure crop, probably a legume, and under these conditions the benefit conferred by the legume on the succeeding crop appears to be enhanced. F. C. Bauer[2] has given the results of an experiment in Illinois on the three-course rotation, maize-oats-wheat, in which the effect of under-sowing the wheat with sweet clover and returning the straw to the wheat stubble was investigated. The results for the first twelve years of the experiment were:

Residue returned to wheat stubble	Yield of maize in bushels per acre		
	No sweet clover	Sweet clover under-sown in wheat	Benefit of sweet clover
None	58	68	10
Wheat straw and maize . .	59	80	21

and they show that under-sowing the wheat with sweet clover benefited the following maize crop, but this benefit was almost doubled if the wheat and maize straw were put on the sweet clover ley, whilst the straw alone had no effect.

It is a common practice for farmers in several parts of the world who crop their land fairly continuously with a corn or maize crop to under-sow the crop with a legume. Thus, wheat growers in Missouri commonly under-sow their wheat with lespedeza, which can be made both to seed itself for the following year and to provide a hay crop; and Iowan farmers often sow sweet clover or vetch in their maize.[3] English corn growers on chalk and light land soils often under-sow their wheat or barley with trefoil, which not only helps to control "take-all" (*Ophiobolus graminis*) in the corn, but also helps to rot down the straw; for these farmers commonly harvest their corn by combine and plough in the straw. The straw is pressed into the trefoil with a ring roll, and wherever it touches the ground it decomposes, hence it can

[1] For an example of their management in English orchards, see W. S. Rogers and Th. Raptopoulos, *J. Pomol.*, 1946, **22**, 92.
[2] *Proc. Soil Sci. Soc. Amer.*, 1942, **7**, 301.
[3] I am indebted to Dr. A. G. Norman for this information. F. E. Bear (*Soils and Fertilizers* 4th ed., p. 173) quotes a similar practice in Illinois.

be ploughed under more easily. The trefoil thus not only helps the straw to decompose while on top of the ground, possibly by keeping the soil surface damp, but also supplies nitrogen for its decomposition when it is ploughed under.

Green manuring can take another form in the humid tropics for bush crops such as coffee and tea. Here either the crops may be grown under leguminous shade trees,[1] such as species of *Erythrina* (dadap) and *Albizzia* (sau), for example; or leguminous shrubs, such as species of *Tephrosia*, may be interplanted between the bushes. These trees and shrubs are lopped several times a year and the green loppings spread around the bushes and perhaps worked into the surface soil. By this means 10 tons or more of green material, containing possibly up to 60 lb. of nitrogen per ton and rich in bases,[2] are provided as a green manure or a surface mulch. This helps to keep the surface layers of the soil, which contain most of the feeding roots of these bushes, well provided with nutrients and in a porous open tilth. However, nitrogen-rich residues spread over the soil surface as a mulch may increase the available nitrogen in the soil less than if they are ploughed in. Thus T. M. McCalla and J. C. Russel found that the nitrate nitrogen content of a soil was about 10 per cent less under a mulch of sweet clover than when it was ploughed in.[3]

The Decomposition of Green Manures under Water-logged Conditions: Paddy Soils

The course of decomposition of plant residues depends on the aeration of the medium in which they are decomposing, and though in temperate agriculture, decomposition usually takes place under aerobic or slightly anaerobic conditions, yet under some tropical conditions, such as in wet rice or paddy fields, decomposition occurs under water-logged or fairly strongly anaerobic conditions. The main effect of restricting the oxygen supply during decomposition is to encourage the production of organic acids, such as lactic, butyric and acetic, and of gases such as methane and hydrogen, which are themselves probably the decomposition products of the volatile acids under anaerobic conditions. The typical nitrogen end-product of anaerobic decomposition is ammonia, though if alternate oxidising and reducing conditions occur, nitrogen may be set free from the reduction of nitrates.

Some results of C. N. Acharya[4] given in Table 57, illustrate the effects

---

[1] See, for example, C. R. Harler, *The Culture and Marketing of Tea*, Oxford, 1933, for a short description of this practice.

[2] H. E. Macmillan, *Tropical Planting and Gardening*, London, 1935.

[3] *J. Amer. Soc. Agron.*, 1948, **40**, 11. See W. A. Albrecht, *Missouri Agric. Expt. Sta., Res. Bull.* 249, 1936, for a similar result with red clover.

[4] *Biochem. J.*, 1935, **29**, 528, 953, 1116, 1459.

of increasingly severe anaerobic conditions on the rotting of rice straw and on the volume of gas produced. In one set of experiments, he allowed rice straw to decompose at 30° C. for six months, and compared the gas production when the decomposition was strictly anaerobic all the time with that when air was admitted either over the top of the rotting material (moderate anaerobic) or bubbled through it for five minutes (mild anaerobic conditions) once a week.

TABLE 57

The Quantity and Composition of Gas Evolved during the Anaerobic Rotting of Rice Straw

Temperature of decomposition, 30°C.

Litres of gas evolved per 100 gm. of straw in 6 months

Degree of anaerobicity	Mild	Moderate	Strict
Carbon dioxide	32·5	17·4	10·8
Methane	2·1	6·9	10·6
Hydrogen	0·92	5·6	0·10
Loss of dry matter in grammes . .	34·0	37·0	35·0
Nitrogen factor	0·33	0·26	0·07

Table 57 shows that increasing the strictness of anaerobic conditions causes the amount of methane given off to increase, of carbon dioxide to decrease, and the hydrogen first to increase and then to decrease, whilst the loss of dry matter and also the disappearance of cellulose, pentosan and lignin is almost unaffected, though losses are higher under aerobic conditions. The table also shows that decreasing the oxygen supply decreases the nitrogen factor, that is, the amount of ammonium nitrogen immobilised: it decreased from 0·54 for aerobic to 0·07 for strict anaerobic conditions.

The application of these results to the decomposition of green manures in tropical paddy soils is not, however, simple. Paddy soils are water-logged for much of the year but the water should not be stagnant; the soil's permeability should be sufficiently controlled by puddling to allow a slow percolation of water through it, and the land should be adequately drained to let this water get away. W. H. Harrison and P. A. S. Aiyer[1] showed that the principal gas produced in these water-logged soils during the decomposition of green crops was methane with only small amounts of carbon dioxide, hydrogen and perhaps nitrogen, and the gases in the water above the soil are almost

[1] India Dept. Agric. Mem., Chem. Ser., 1913, **3**, 65; 1914, **4**, 1.

entirely oxygen and nitrogen. In the first place, they showed that this difference in composition was due to a film of organisms in the surface layers of the soil. It contained both bacteria that oxidised methane to carbon dioxide and algae that fixed the carbon dioxide photosynthetically and respired oxygen. Hence green manuring could increase the oxygen content of the water percolating through the surface soil, so increasing the oxygen supply to the rice roots, but it seems unlikely that this could be an important reason for the observed benefits derived from green manuring.

Harrison later[1] put forward an explanation of why the soil gases were so unexpectedly rich in methane and poor in hydrogen and carbon dioxide, for he showed that there were bacteria in the soil that could utilise hydrogen to reduce carbon dioxide: a reaction which supplied the bacteria both with energy and a source of carbon, which removed 1·5 to 3·5 parts of hydrogen for every part of carbon dioxide reduced, and which might lead to a production of methane. This is a reaction of great importance for the oxygen régime around the rice roots, for it not only reduces the carbon dioxide content around them, which in itself reduces their oxygen needs, but also removes hydrogen in a way that makes a much lower demand on the oxygen in the soil water than would be made by the hydrogen-oxidising bacteria which he and Aiyer[2] showed were present in the soil.

The nitrogen régime in water-logged soils has not been fully worked out. Nitrates are reduced to nitrogen gas or nitrous oxide via nitrites, and nitrites themselves may accumulate sufficiently to be toxic to crops; consequently nitrate fertilisers are not used on paddy soils.[3] Most organic nitrogen compounds decompose to yield ammonia, but it is not certain if gaseous nitrogen is ever produced during these decompositions: its production is usually characteristic of systems with a widely fluctuating oxygen supply in which nitrates are produced during the aerobic periods and reduced during the anaerobic. Thus ammonia is the typical form of inorganic nitrogen and the typical by-product of bacterial metabolism under water-logged conditions; consequently, ammonium salts, or organic fertilisers, such as green manures that break down readily to give ammonium salts, are the typical nitrogen fertilisers for these soils. It is possible, however, that if the ammonium concentration reaches too high a level in the soil some may be lost by volatilisation from the soil's surface under tropical conditions.[4]

[1] India Dept. Agric. Mem., 1920, **5**, 181.
[2] India Dept. Agric. Mem., Chem. Ser., 1916, **4**, 135. See also S. B. Lee and W. W. Umbreit, Zbl. Bakt. II, 1940, **101**, 354.
[3] M. Nagasko, Bull. Coll. Agric. Tokyo, 1904, **6**, 285; W. P. Kelley, Hawaii Agric. Expt. Sta., Bull. 24, 1911.
[4] A. Sreenivassan and V. Subrahmanyan, J. Agric. Sci., 1935, **25**, 6.

CHAPTER XV

THE COMPOSITION OF THE SOIL ORGANIC MATTER

The Separation of Humus from the Soil Particles

THE COMPOSITION OF the soil organic matter, and in particular of the soil humus, has exercised the minds of soil chemists from the very beginning. The soil organic matter consists of a whole series of products which range from undecayed plant and animal tissues through ephemeral products of decomposition to fairly stable amorphous brown to black material bearing no trace of the anatomical structure of the material from which it was derived; and it is this latter material that is normally defined as the soil humus. The great difficulty in all investigations on the composition of soil humus has been that it can neither be separated from unhumified matter nor from the mineral constituents of the soil. The methods used separate out only a part of the humus, and some may alter the original constitution of the humus into forms that disperse more easily.

The early soil chemists were interested in humus. The work was begun by F. K. Achard[1] in 1786 and by C. Vaquelin[2] in 1797, who found that some of it could be extracted by alkali after the soil had first been treated with an acid. The work was continued by C. Sprengel,[3] a most successful early investigator in agricultural chemistry, who in 1826 had carried his studies so far that little was added during the next hundred years. He distinguished the "acid humus" of peat found in places where bases are lacking from the less acid "mild humus" formed in soils in presence of basic material; the "acid" is much more stable than the "mild" form, being less easily decomposed to carbon dioxide and water. He prepared "humic acid" by extracting the peat with dilute hydrochloric acid for two hours to remove all bases, washing with water, then extracting with a solution of ammonia in a closed vessel, finally adding to the solution hydrochloric acid to precipitate the humus. It did not, however, come down pure, but contained both clay and ferric hydroxides; it was therefore redissolved in sodium

---

[1] *Crells Chem. Ann.*, 1786, **2**, 391. For a detailed account of the history of humus chemistry, see the admirable summary of the literature in S. A. Waksman, *Humus*, 2nd ed., London, 1938.
[2] *Ann. Chim.*, 1797, **21**, 39.
[3] *Kastners Arch. ges. Naturlehre (Nürnberg)*, 1826, **8**, 145.

carbonate solution, filtered and precipitated from the filtrate by cold hydrochloric acid.

The methods in use at the present time[1] for separating the more readily dispersible humus from soils are still based on Sprengel's results, namely, that these substances are negatively charged colloids when in alkaline solution, and are either held on the positively charged spots on the soil or clay particles or are held on the soil or are precipitated as flocs through the agency of cations such as calcium, aluminium and iron. Two groups of methods can therefore be used, that used by Sprengel and the other early workers of increasing the hydroxyl ion concentration, through the use of sodium hydroxide for example, for the high pH raises the electric charge on the humus particles through increasing the dissociation of hydrogen ions, and the hydroxyl ions compete more strongly than many of the humus colloids for the positively charged spots on the soil and clay particles; and modern methods based on the use of anions which form very stable complexes with calcium, aluminium and iron cations.

The first group of methods, based on raising the pH to high values, usually above pH 12, still remain the most efficient if efficiency is judged by the proportion of the organic carbon and nitrogen compounds which are dispersed. Their limitation is that they may cause chemical alteration in the dispersed suspensions both by hydrolysis of some compounds and by autoxidation of others, for the humus extracts absorb molecular oxygen from the air relatively easily when in strongly alkaline solution. Autoxidation can be reduced either by making the dispersion in the absence of oxygen or by adding a reducing agent such as stannous chloride, but there is no clear evidence that the usual laboratory techniques for making the dispersions cause any appreciable chemical alterations in the dispersed colloids. Nor has it been proved that dilute sodium hydroxide solutions at room temperatures cause any appreciable chemical changes. Solutions of lower pH can be used, such as a sodium carbonate-bicarbonate mixture, or sodium carbonate by itself, but it is probably necessary to have a pH of the extracting solution above pH 8·5 if a reasonable yield of humic material is wanted,[2] for the yield increases more or less linearly with pH from about pH 7 to about pH 11.

The second group of methods were really developed because of the fear that these alkaline solutions were causing chemical alterations in the dispersed humus. They are based on treating the soil with a solution capable of forming stable complexes with the humus-bonding cations. J. M. Bremner and H. Lees[3] showed that neutral sodium pyrophosphate

[1] For a review of these see J. M. Bremner, *J. Soil Sci.*, 1954, **5**, 214, and F. E. Broadbent, *Adv. Agron.*, 1953, **5**, 153.
[2] L. T. Evans, *J. Soil Sci.*, 1959, **10**, 110.
[3] *J. Agric. Sci.*, 1949, **39**, 247.

is effective in dispersing significant amounts of humus, up to 20–30 per cent of the organic carbon in the soil, and has the advantage that it introduces no organic anion, and other workers have used organic anions such as oxalate, ethylene diamine tetra-acetate and acetyl acetone, the last one having the advantage that it and its iron and aluminium chelates can be removed from an aqueous solution by shaking it up with ether, itself nearly insoluble in water;[1] but in general these organic anions are less efficient extractors than pyrophosphate in solutions of comparable pH.[2] All these reagents usually extract considerably less humus from a soil than does sodium hydroxide, and in fact their efficiency increases with increasing pH of the extracting solution. The only condition under which they are as efficient is when all the humus is held on soil particles through iron or aluminium ions, as in the B horizon of sandy podsols, in which case all of the humus can be dispersed relatively easily.

A part of the reason that neither sodium hydroxide nor chelating agents can remove all the humus from soils appears to be that some of the humus is held very firmly on the clay particles or on iron and aluminium oxide or hydroxide films. At least a part of this humus can be dispersed, probably without affecting its chemical composition by pretreating the soil with a dilute hydrofluoric-hydrochloric acid solution, if clay absorption is the most important agent, or with sodium hydrosulphite or dithionate if the sesquioxide films are. J. M. Bremner and T. Harada[3] have shown that using the acid treatment alternately with a sodium hydroxide treatment, over 90 per cent of the organic nitrogen could be extracted from Rothamsted soils and subsoils, and in some subsoils a single acid treatment removed a higher proportion of the organic nitrogen than did a single alkali treatment. One cannot rule out in this example, however, the possibility that the treatments were decomposing the organic matter, as the acid was molar in both hydrofluoric and hydrochloric acid and the alkali half molar sodium hydroxide.

These methods separate humic material from the soil particles, but they usually do not give a dispersion only containing humic material. Thus it is very difficult to remove metal-complexing anions, such as pyrophosphate, completely from the dispersion, nor has it yet proved possible to separate the humic material from the large amount of inorganic material which the hydrofluoric acid brings into solution. And only very recently has it been fully appreciated that the humic material obtained by any of these methods may still hold metallic

[1] A. E. Martin and R. Reeve, *J. Soil Sci.*, 1957, **8**, 268, 279.

[2] See, for example, M. B. Choudhri and F. J. Stevenson, *Proc. Soil Sci. Soc. Amer.*, 1957, **21**, 508, and M. Schnitzer, J. R. Wright and J. G. Desjardins, *Canad. J. Soil Sci.*, 1958, **38**, 49.

[3] *J. Agric. Sci.*, 1959, **52**, 137.

cations, such as aluminium, whose presence markedly affects many properties of the humus.

The Fractionation of the Humus Dispersion

The humus dispersions obtained in these ways consist of a mixture of substances, none of which appear to be simple chemical compounds. The earlier chemists had no easy means of testing if these dispersions contained relatively few high molecular weight compounds of fairly definite constitution or not, but they based their methods of fractionation on the assumption that these dispersions did in fact only contain a few fairly definite complex molecules of colloidal dimensions to which they gave names. The method of fractionation commonly used is shown in the following diagram.

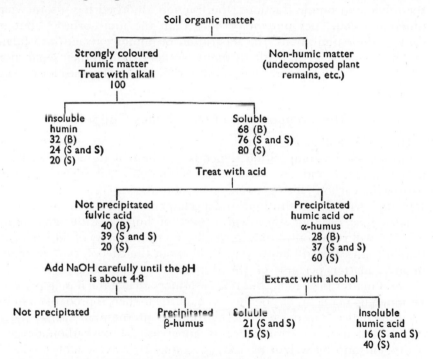

The figures under the fractions show how the carbon is divided amongst them, as determined by M. Berthelot and G. Andre (B),[1] O. Schreiner and E. C. Shorey (S and S)[2] and A. Schmuck (S).[3] These fractions are not, however, pure chemical compounds, but are colloidal sols when dispersed. The following names are still in common use;

[1] *Ann. Chim. Phys.*, 1892, ser. 6, **25**, 364.   [2] *U.S. Dept. Agric. Bur. Soils, Bull.* 74, 1910.
[3] *Pedology*, 1930, No. 3.

humin for the fraction insoluble in alkali; humic acid for that soluble in alkali but insoluble in acid; and fulvic acid for that soluble in both alkali and acid. However, humic acid has sometimes been defined as that part of the alkali-soluble fraction that is insoluble in alcohol. Then the name α-humus has been used for the original fraction.

It is now known that there is no sharp distinction between humin and the dispersible fraction, nor between fulvic and humic acid, and that neither fulvic and humic acids, nor any other acids which have been separated and named are definite substances. The ratio of fulvic to humic acid in a dispersion, for example, can be altered by altering the acid used as precipitant, and in particular one can alter the proportion of the humus dispersion which flocculates by using other simple metallic salts as precipitants, and as will be shown on p. 287, if absorbents such as clays or iron and aluminium oxides or hydroxides are added to the fulvic and humic fractions, the fraction absorbed has a somewhat different colour, per unit of carbon, than the unabsorbed.[1] But in spite of these limitations, the separation of humus extracts into fulvic and humic acids is still made by many workers, though their separation into further groups of acids has, on the whole, been dropped for several decades.

The Composition of the Humus Colloids

Humus is not a single substance, so does not possess a constant composition—its composition depends on the soil from which it has been extracted and the method of extraction used. The elements hydrogen, carbon, nitrogen, oxygen, phosphorus and sulphur enter into its essential constitution, and perhaps no other elements can be regarded as forming an integral part of humus, although humus extracts will commonly contain small amounts of most of the elements in plant ash. We still know very little about the carbon content of soil organic matter because of the difficulty of separating it from the mineral matter in the soil, but it is customary to assume it is 58 per cent although 60 per cent, or possibly even a little higher, is probably a more accurate figure. The oxygen and hydrogen contents of humus are particularly difficult to determine for this same reason, but a carbon, oxygen, hydrogen ratio by weight of 100:55:7 may be a reasonable average. The composition of humic and fulvic acids can be determined more easily; and humic acid has a higher carbon and often higher nitrogen content, about the same hydrogen and a lower oxygen content than fulvic. Thus M. M. Kononova[2] found the mean carbon, oxygen, hydrogen and nitrogen contents of humic and fulvic acids from a

[1] L. T. Evans and E. W. Russell, *J. Soil Sci.*, 1959, **10**, 119.
[2] *Trans. 6th Int. Congr. Soil Sci.* (Paris), 1956, B, 557.

number of soils to be about 61, 31, 3·7 and 4·1 for the humic, and 46, 48, 3·5 and 2·4 for the fulvic acids. The ratios of carbon, nitrogen, sulphur and phosphorus in the organic matter can be more accurately determined and do not usually vary over wide limits in different soils being of the order 100 : 10 : 1 : 1 by weight, as will be discussed in more detail on pp. 280–2.

Most of the particles in the humus dispersion have about the same electrophoretic mobility, and are about the same size in alkaline solutions, namely, 30–100 Å., though they are polydisperse in acid or neutral solutions. They have an average molecular weight of between 5,000 and 50,000, and the larger particles may be elongated rather than spherical.[1] The particles show no crystalline structure in X-ray or electron diffraction cameras.[2]

Humus particles are built up from a number of simple substances as can be proved by suitable methods of hydrolysis. At least 5 per cent, and possibly considerably more of the organic carbon is present as sugar residues,[3] and the following sugars have been recognised in the hydrolysates: galactose, glucose, mannose, arabinose, xylose, rhamnose and ribose, and humus from some soils also yields fucose.[4] A small proportion of these sugars are present as polysaccharide gums which can be isolated as such from soils and are probably produced by the soil bacteria, but Bernier could only extract about 0·5 per cent of the organic carbon in some forest soils in this form. Humus, unlike plants, however, contains no cellulose, and it is naturally difficult to know if the small amounts of polysaccharide which can be isolated from the soil should be considered as part of the soil humus or of the soil micro-organisms. Again acid hydrolysis of soil humus releases amino-sugars, particularly glucosamine and galactosamine; and up to 10 per cent of the organic nitrogen in surface soils, and perhaps up to 20 per cent in subsoils may be present in this form.[5] Part of the humus may be in the form of polyuronides based on glucuronic and galacturonic acids, and at one time a considerable amount of the organic carbon was considered to be in this form owing to the use of an unreliable method for estimating uronic acid, but although these acids certainly occur in humus hydrolysates the older method of determining uronic acid is now known to

[1] F. J. Stevenson et al., Proc. Soil Sci. Soc. Amer., 1952, 16, 69; 1953, 17, 31. J. R. Wright, M. Schnitzer and R. Levick, Canad. J. Soil Sci., 1958, 38, 14; H. Beutelspacher, Ztschr. PflErnähr., 1952, 57, 57, and see also G. Bergold, Ztschr. Naturforsch., 1946, 1, 100, who also finds molecular weights of this order.
[2] W. Flaig and H. Beutelspacher, Ztschr. PflErnähr., 1951, 52, 1.
[3] See, for example, D. L. Lynch, H. O. Olney and L. M. Wright, Soil Sci., 1957, 84, 405, and J. Sci. Food Agric., 1958, 9, 56.
[4] W. G. C. Forsyth, Biochem. J., 1950, 46, 141, and B. Bernier, Biochem. J., 1958, 70, 590.
[5] J. M. Bremner and K. Shaw, J. Agric. Sci., 1954, 44, 152; J. M. Bremner, J. Sci. Food Agric., 1958, 9, 528; F. J. Stevenson, Soil Sci., 1957, 83, 113, and 84, 99; F. J. Sowden, Soil Sci., 1959, 88, 138.

give figures that may be much too high,[1] and more reliable methods have not been introduced long enough for any body of data on the amounts of uronic acids in soils to be available, but it is possible that between 5 and 10 per cent of the organic carbon in a soil is present as polyuronides.[2] Thus taking all these figures together it is likely that well over 10 per cent of the organic matter in humus is present in various polysaccharide forms.

Acid hydrolysis of humus also yields appreciable amounts of amino acids, and in general between 30 and 50 per cent of the organic nitrogen, corresponding to about 15–25 per cent of the organic carbon, can be formed as α-amino nitrogen distributed between twenty amino acids[3] and the amides asparagine and glutamine.[4] The techniques so far used have not been suitable for determining quantitatively the amounts of the sulphur-containing amino acids which could be liberated using suitable methods, but it is known that they are produced during this hydrolysis.[5] The proportion of the nitrogen that can be found as amino acids is rather higher in surface than in subsoils,[6] and its distribution between the various amino acids is reasonably constant for a wide range of temperate soils, unless they belong to widely different great world groups.[7] These amino acids could be, and are commonly assumed to be, derived from the hydrolysis of proteins but there is no other evidence than this for the presence of proteins in humus. If the humus does contain protein it cannot be present as free protein, as this should be readily attacked by the soil micro-organisms, and it should be capable of displaying positive charges in acid solution, which humus does not do. Presumably most of these must have reacted with other groups in the humus, or possibly as Sowden suggests have formed complexes with heavy metal cations. The α-amino nitrogen is not distributed quite uniformly through the various humus fractions, but is usually higher in the humic than the fulvic fraction, and higher in sodium hydroxide than sodium pyrophosphate extracts.[8]

The forms in which the remainder of the organic nitrogen and carbon are present, in each case between 50 and 70 per cent, and the forms in which the organic phosphate and sulphur are present are more difficult to determine. Some of the sulphur is present in amino acids, for cysteic acid is found in the acid hydrolysates and some is almost

---

[1] H. Deuel, P. Dubach and R. Bach, *Ztschr. PflErnähr.*, 1958, **81**, 189, and **82**, 97.

[2] See, for example, D. L. Lynd *et al.*, *Proc. Soil Sci. Soc. Amer.*, 1957, **21**, 160, and *Soil Sci.*, 1959, **87**, 273.

[3] J. M. Bremner, *Biochem. J.*, 1950, **47**, 538; F. J. Stevenson *et al.*, *Proc. Soil Sci. Soc. Amer.*, 1952, **16**, 69.   [4] F. J. Sowden, *Canad. J. Soil Sci.*, 1958, **38**, 147.

[5] J. M. Bremner, *J. Sci. Food Agric.*, 1952, **3**, 497.

[6] F. J. Sowden, *Soil Sci.*, 1956, **82**, 491.

[7] D. I. Davidson, F. J. Sowden and H. J. Atkinson, *Soil Sci.*, 1951, **71**, 347; with D. I. Parker, *Sci. Agric.*, 1952, **32**, 163; and J. Carles, L. Soubiès and R. Gadet, *C.R.*, 1958, **247**, 1229.   [8] See J. M. Bremner, *J. Agric. Sci.*, 1955, **46**, 247.

certainly present as methionine or a related form; and some of the phosphate is present as inositol phosphates. But it seems very unlikely that these can account for the major proportion of the sulphur and phosphates humus contains, and no appreciable amounts of other organic compounds of sulphur or phosphates have been recognised. In particular relatively little either of the nitrogen or the phosphate are present as nucleic acid or its derivatives.[1]

A considerable proportion of the remaining organic carbon is commonly assumed to be based on fused polyphenol rings probably containing quinone and dihydroxy groups both in the ortho- and the para- positions on the phenyl nucleus; and much of the residual nitrogen is assumed to be incorporated in these compounds, partly as amides and partly in forms very resistant to acid hydrolysis, so possibly in heterocyclic rings. These substances are almost certainly derived in part from the products of microbial metabolism,[2] but they could be derived in part from plant lignins during their decomposition, though simple plant lignins do not form any appreciable proportion of the soil organic carbon.[3] However, no methods are yet available for distinguishing between these two possible modes of formation, so their relative importance cannot be quantitatively assessed. Unfortunately the amino-acid based and the polysaccharide-based moieties of the humus cannot be separated from the aromatic based, so the properties and constitution of this group can only be deduced from a study of humus or humus fractions as a whole. But it is this fraction which gives humus its dark colour and probably many other of its properties.

The aromatic-based groups can be characterised by their ultraviolet absorption spectra when in suspension, by the amount of oxygen they will take up under standard conditions, by their buffer curves and the effect of methylation on the curves, by their methoxyl contents and possibly by their ability to form complexes or chelates with heavy metals; and their properties as determined by these methods are consistent with them containing polyphenols. Thus substances formed by condensing quinones with amino acids and the humus-like substances produced by some micro-organisms have very similar ultraviolet absorption spectra.[4] Again humus takes up molecular oxygen when in alkaline solutions in a manner very similar to that in which lignins and many polyphenols of known composition do,[5] and in fact the humus

[1] See, for example, A. P. Adams, W. V. Bartholomew and F. E. Clark, *Proc. Soil Sci. Soc. Amer.*, 1954, **18**, 40, and G. Anderson, *Soil Sci.*, 1958, **86**, 169.

[2] For a review of the theories of the German workers, see J. M. Bremner, *J. Soil Sci.*, 1954, **5**, 214.

[3] S. Gottlieb and S. B. Hendricks, *Proc. Soil Sci. Soc. Amer.*, 1946, **10**, 117, and R. I. Morrison, *J. Soil Sci.*, 1958, **9**, 130.

[4] F. Schaffer and E. Welte, *Ztschr. PflErnähr.*, 1950, **48**, 250.

[5] See, for example, E. C. Shorey, *U.S. Dept. Agric. Tech. Bull.* 211, 1930; E. Juncker, *Kolloid-Ztschr.*, 1941, **95**, 213; and J. M. Bremner, *J. Soil Sci.*, 1950, **1**, 198.

fractions from different soils can be characterised by the amount they take up. This method has been developed by A. G. Norman and W. J. Peevy[1] and by C. D. Moodie[2] using hypoiodite as an oxidising agent.

The chemical groupings necessary for this autoxidation in alkaline conditions to occur include the presence of di- or tri-hydroxy groups on the phenyl nucleus either in the ortho-position as in catechol and gallic and tannic acids, or in the para-position as in hydroquinone; and although the chemical reaction brought about by the autoxidation is not known it probably involves the formation of new carbon rings, possibly sometimes a 7-membered ring;[3] and at the present time it is reasonable to assume that humus fractions can autoxidise because they possess such dihydroxy-phenyl groups. J. M. Bremner[4] found that the humic acid fraction usually took up more oxygen than the fulvic, but on autoxidation some of the fulvic fraction was converted to the humic.

Some information on the constitution of humic acids can be obtained from a study of their buffer curves. W. S. Gillam,[5] for example, studied the buffer curves of humic acid separated from a prairie, a chernozem and a chestnut soil both in their natural condition and after they had been methylated to convert the greater part of the non-carboxylic

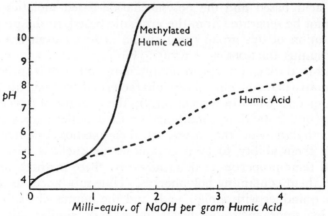

FIG. 19. The effect of methylating humic acid on its titration curve.

hydroxyls into methoxyls. This should remove all those hydroxyls which give the humic acid its very weak acid character, that is, those which dissociate hydrogen ions in neutral and alkaline conditions, but leave the carboxylic acid groups functional. Fig. 19, which is redrawn

[1] *Proc. Soil Sci. Soc. Amer.*, 1939, **4**, 183.   [2] *Soil Sci.*, 1951, **71**, 51.
[3] R. D. Haworth *et al.*, *J. Chem. Soc.*, 1951, 1318, 1325.   [4] *J. Soil Sci.*, 1950, **1**, 198.
[5] *Soil Sci.*, 1940, **49**, 433, and for a further example see F. E. Broadbent and G. R. Bradford, *Soil Sci.*, 1952, **74**, 447.

from his paper, shows that methylation destroys most of the buffering above pH 5 and that the carboxylic acids have a pK about 4·5, which is normal for this group. He determined certain other properties of these acids, which are given in Table 58, and he also compared his results for

TABLE 58

Methoxyl Content and Cation Exchange Capacity of Humic Acids and Lignin before and after Methylation

In milli-equivalents per 100 gm.

Material	Methoxyl content			Cation exchange capacity		
	Untreated	After methy-lation	Gain	Untreated	After methy-lation	Loss
Humic acid, P1 .	33	281	248	394	273	121
P2 .	54	289	235	274	227	47
P3 .	56	255	199	253	246	7
Lignin from Corn cobs .	444	935	491	28	2	26

Composition of the Humic Acids

Acid	Separated from	Per cent ash oven-dry basis	Per cent on ash-free basis			
			Carbon	Hydrogen	Nitrogen	Oxygen
P1	Prairie	6·9	58·3	4·5	5·9	31·2
P2	Chestnut soil	7·8	58·8	5·5	5·5	30·2
P3	Chernozem soil	3·6	55·6	5·2	6·0	33·2

these acids with those he obtained from a maize (corn) cob lignin. Clearly if lignin is the precursor of humic acids in soils, its conversion involves the loss of methoxyls and of hydroxyls which can be methylated and a gain in carboxyls.

It is not yet possible to give a proper interpretation of the type of hydroxyls which cause the buffering from pH 5 to pH 9. Normal aliphatic alcohols are very weak acids, only exerting appreciable buffering in very alkaline solutions, and phenol itself only exerts strong buffering above pH 9. Certain substituted phenols, such as the dinitro-phenols, buffer at a considerably lower pH than this, which shows that the ease with which hydrogen ions dissociate from phenolic hydroxyls depends on the neighbouring groups on the phenyl ring; and in particular it is probable that di- and tri-hydroxy phenols, in which the hydroxyls are adjacent to each other, i.e. on the 1:2 or 1:2:3 positions, begin dissociating hydrogen ions at a pH not much above that at which carboxylic acid buffering ceases. However, it is possible that at least a part of the buffering in the range pH 5 to pH 7 is due to metallic ions such as aluminium which humic acids hold strongly and which have not been removed during their preparation (see p. 284).

One other characteristic of the buffer curves of humic acids may give some additional information on their constitution. It appears to be a characteristic of the titration of humic acid with a strong base, such as sodium hydroxide, that once the solution is above neutrality the pH of the humic acid tends to drop on standing, indicating that new acidic groups are being produced. It is likely that the cause is the conversion of keto groups

$$- \overset{\displaystyle}{\underset{\displaystyle O}{\overset{\|}{C}}} - CH_2 - \quad \text{to enol groups} \quad - \overset{\displaystyle}{\underset{\displaystyle OH}{\overset{|}{C}}} = CH -,$$

a process known as the keto-enol transformation, and known also to go on only very slowly in some compounds. It is also possible, as pointed out by F. E. Broadbent and G. R. Bradford,[1] that humus may dissociate hydrogen ions from groups other than hydroxyls in alkaline conditions, such as the imide group

$$- \overset{\|}{\underset{O}{C}} - \overset{|}{\underset{H}{N}} - \overset{\|}{\underset{O}{C}} -,$$

though this group has not yet been proved present in humus.

There is considerable evidence that at least part of soil humus is derived from lignin. S. Mattson and E. K. Andersson[2] showed that lignin suspended in an ammonia solution would autoxidise in the presence of air, to give a humus-like product that contained nitrogen, and that the number of carboxyl groups it contained, its cation exchange capacity at pH 7, and its nitrogen content all increased linearly with the amount of oxygen taken up. This behaviour is shown by polyphenols such as catechol and hydroquinone as well as by their corresponding quinones, and by gallic and tannic acids, in the same way as by lignins; and amines and amino acids can replace ammonia, and the oxidation can be brought about by polyphenol oxidase as well as by autoxidation.[3]

Mattson and Andersson have discussed some consequences of this theory. Thus chernozem humus, being produced under neutral or slightly alkaline conditions, should be more oxidised and have a higher

---

[1] *Soil Sci.*, 1952, **74**, 447.

[2] *LantbrHögsk. Ann.*, 1943, **11**, 107; 1954, **21**, 389, and W. Laatsch, *Ber. Landtechn.*, 1948, No. 4.

[3] For examples using o-benzoquinone and aniline or some amino acids, see R. H. Hackman and A. R. Todd, *Biochem. J.*, 1953, **55**, 631.

cation exchange capacity and nitrogen content than podsol humus, which is produced under acid conditions. This is in accord with observations. Thus A. G. Norman and W. J. Peevy[1] found that a humus fraction, which they called lignin, from a prairie soil took up much less oxygen from a hypoiodite solution than that from a podsolic soil and had a higher cation exchange capacity. M. D. Ridalevskaya and V. V. Tischenko[2] found that at pH 7 a podsol humus had an exchange capacity of about 280, and a chernozem about 490 milli-equivalents per 100 gm., and M. S. Anderson and H. G. Byers[3] found that the ratio of carbon to nitrogen in the humus of the surface layer of a podsol was about 22, of a podsolic soil about 12·6, of a prairie soil about 12·2 and of a chernozem about 9·0.

No clear picture can yet be given of the way the carbohydrate, the amino acid and the polyphenol moieties are combined together to form the humus particles. The association must be very close because it is not yet possible to remove all the carbohydrate or amino acid moieties from the polyphenol. Further, as the soil humus decomposes, all the major constituents seem to decompose at approximately the same rate, indicating that they are not present as simple mixtures. The way the polysaccharide moiety is incorporated into the humus particle has been little studied, but considerable attention has been given to the form in which the amino acids assumed to be present as protein are held.

As early as 1892 A. Hebert[4] and P. P. Dehérain[5] suggested that the cause of this stability was that humus is an association between lignin and proteins synthesised by the micro-organisms, and this suggestion was revived independently by H. J. Page and R. P. Hobson[6] and by S. A. Waksman and K. R. N. Iyer.[7] Page and Hobson showed that alkaline lignin solutions can be partially oxidised with ease, and in this state can readily combine with proteins to form stable complexes. Waksman and Iyer suggested the reaction was similar to a tanning process, the carbonyls of the lignins condensing with the amino groups of the protein, and they showed that such compounds were resistant to further decomposition. The only alteration one needs to make in this picture since it was originally put forward is that only a part of the humic nitrogen can be present as protein, and the tanning polyphenols must be much more complicated than lignin and may themselves contain nitrogen. But since it has not been possible to prove that there is

---

[1] *Proc. Soil Sci. Soc. Amer.*, 1939, **4**, 183, and see C. D. Moodie, *Soil Sci.*, 1951, **71**, 51, for an extension of their results.
[2] *Pedology*, 1944, 491. For other figures, see P. Schachtschabel, *Bodenk. PflErnähr.*, 1940, **22–23**, 643; *ForschDienst. Sonderh.*, 1941, **17**, 41; Z. Y. Lein, *Trans. Dokuchaev Inst.*, 1940, **23**, 59.
[3] *Soil Sci.*, 1934, **38**, 121.
[4] *Ann. Agron.*, 1892, **18**, 536.
[5] *Traité de Chimie Agricole*, Paris, 1892.
[6] *J. Agric. Sci.*, 1932, **22**, 497.
[7] *Soil Sci.*, 1932, **34**, 43; 1933, **36**, 57.

a protein moiety in humus, it is more probable that it is amino acids rather than proteins which have reacted with the polyphenols.

In conclusion it must be emphasised once again what is the maximum amount of proven knowledge about the composition of soil humus. It contains substances which hydrolyse to simple sugars, amino sugars and uronic acids; it contains substances which hydrolyse to amino acids, but only a proportion of the nitrogen it contains can be accounted for in these acids; it contains carboxylic acids and almost certainly hydroxyl groups in polyphenols. It seems to be exceedingly difficult to make any further progress in our knowledge of its composition, but this is probably what one should expect when it is realised that really nothing is known about the chemical reactions taking place between such simple substances as phenol and ammonia or pyrogallol and oxygen in alkaline solutions, each of which gives a dark-coloured polymer.

THE CARBON-NITROGEN RATIO

The carbon-nitrogen ratio of the organic matter has been frequently determined, both because it is not necessary to separate the organic from the mineral matter, and also because many workers have considered such values helpful in assessing the influence of the organic matter on plant growth. The results of this analysis suffer from the serious limitation that they cannot be definitely interpreted, as the carbon compounds present in the soil are very heterogeneous: they vary from plant remains in various stages of decomposition through humified material to charcoal. Yet such is the lack of appropriate methods for analysing the soil organic matter that the ratio of the total carbon in the soil to the total nitrogen gives as useful a characterisation of the properties of the organic matter in the soil as any other method yet in use.[1]

TABLE 59

Distribution of the C/N Ratio in some British and American Soils

	Percentage of soils examined whose C/N ratio falls in the range				
	below 5·5	between 5·5 and 8·4	between 8·5 and 11·4	between 11·5 and 14·4	above 14·4
British . .	—	6	76	18	—
American:					
Surface . .	—	11	38	21	30
Sub-surface .	4	39	28	15	14
Subsoil . .	23	56	13	6	2

[1] For an account of the early literature on C/N ratios, see *Soils and Fert.*, 1945, **8**, 135.

The carbon-nitrogen ratio of many normal agricultural and natural soils falls within narrow limits, though because of the complications already mentioned, there can be large variations between soils. Table 59 gives an example of this variability for fifty British[1] and sixty-three American[2] soils, which were, however, not selected to show the range of variability that might be expected under extreme conditions. But this variability has often been discounted because in normal fertile arable soils, not containing any pieces of charcoal, as many soils do, the ratio is surprisingly constant and surprisingly independent of soil treatment. Table 60 illustrates this latter point, showing how at Rothamsted very different forms of manuring and cropping have only had a small influence on the C/N ratio, although they have caused large differences in the carbon and nitrogen contents. A C/N ratio of around 10 is, in fact, very common for English arable soils, and for grassland and forest soils whose pH is above 6.

TABLE 60

The Carbon and Nitrogen Contents and C/N Ratio of some Rothamsted Soils

	Per cent C	Per cent N	C/N
Old pasture (3–7 in.)[3]	1·52	0·160	9 5
Old woodland (5–7 in.)[3]	2·38	0·250	9·5
Broadbalk, after 50 years' continuous wheat, 1893:			
No manure since 1839 (0–9 in.) . . .	0·89	0·099	9·0
Complete minerals and 412 lb. of sulphate of ammonia most years since 1843 (0–9 in.) .	1·10	0·12	9·0
14 tons of farmyard manure annually since 1843 (0–9 in.)	2·23	0·22	10·1

A consequence of this relative constancy of the C/N ratio in a soil is that added organic matter decomposes to leave a residue having this C/N ratio. Hence, if organic matter low in nitrogen is added to the soil, the soil population will remove all the available ammonium and nitrates present in the soil to help lower the ratio, whilst if it is high in nitrogen, the decomposition will be releasing ammonium or nitrates into the soil. This is, in fact, the problem discussed on p. 246. But since the soil population attacks the added organic matter to obtain

[1] W. McLean, *J. Agric. Sci.*, 1930, **20**, 348.
[2] W. R. Leighty and E. C. Shorey, *Soil Sci.*, 1930, **30**, 257.
[3] I am indebted to Mr. R. G. Warren for these figures.

energy from it, and since the consequence of this removal of energy, under aerobic conditions, is the production of carbon dioxide, the total carbon content of the material will be reduced, and if there is no loss of nitrogen, or no production of ammonium or nitrate, the C/N ratio will fall. As a consequence there is no strong connection between the C/N ratio of the added material and the level of inorganic nitrogen in the soil, as has already been indicated on p. 248. But if the added material is fairly easily decomposable, such as plant remains, the process of decomposition, in providing a residual product with a C/N ratio of about 10, will release inorganic nitrogen if the C/N ratio of the added material is under 25 and will remove inorganic nitrogen if it is much above 35 in temperate[1] or 50 in tropical regions.[2] On the other hand, if the added material is already partially decomposed, as occurs in the deposits that accumulate on the surface and in the superficial layers of undisturbed soils, the process of decomposition will involve a smaller release of carbon dioxide per unit of carbon, and hence inorganic nitrogen may be taken up from the soil if the C/N ratio is considerably smaller than 35.

F. Hardy[3] has given an example of the value of a knowledge of this ratio in soils coming under cultivation. He found that in the cotton-growing areas of Queensland and the West Indies, if the C/N ratio of the undisturbed soil was below 8·5 in Queensland or below 10 in the West Indies, cultivation released nitrates from the soil organic matter too rapidly for good cotton production: it is only on soils with a higher C/N ratio that good cotton is being grown.

Certain general relations seem to hold between the carbon and nitrogen contents of a soil and the external conditions. The C/N ratio is typically higher under acid than neutral conditions, as would be predicted from Mattson's theory of humic acid formation that the nitrogen content of this fraction increases with its degree of oxidation, which in turn increases with the pH of the soil in which it is being formed. Thus low-moor peats or fens and chernozems, formed in the presence of an adequate lime and mineral supply, typically have a higher nitrogen content, and hence a lower C/N ratio, than high-moor peats and podsols formed under acid conditions. H. Hesselman[4] found the nitrogen content of forest humus tends to increase with increasing pH, and B. D. Wilson and E. V. Staker[5] found a very definite correlation between the C/N ratio of some New York peats and their calcium contents; in fact, their data show that the C/N ratio

[1] L. A. Pinck et al., J. Amer. Soc. Agron., 1946, 38, 410.
[2] C. N. Acharya et al., Indian J. Agric. Sci., 1946, 16, 178.
[3] Trop. Agric. Trin., 1945, 22, 119; 1946, 23, 178.
[4] Medd. Skogsförsöksanst, 1926, 22, 169.
[5] Cornell Agric. Exp. Stat., Bull. 537, 1932.

is more closely related to the calcium content than to the pH of the peat. Again, any conditions that encourage decomposition usually lower the C/N ratio, for the main effect of a rapid decomposition is for much of the carbon to go off as CO_2, leaving the nitrogen in the soil. Thus, cultivating a forest soil typically lowers the C/N ratio, and the C/N ratio of grassland soils under similar conditions of humidity tends to decrease as the mean annual temperature increases,[1] i.e. as the mean rate of decomposition increases.

The constitution of the soil organic matter must also vary down the soil profile, for the C/N ratio decreases with depth and may apparently reach figures as low as 4 under some conditions.[2] An example of this is given in Fig. 20, which shows the fall in the carbon content and C/N ratio down the Rothamsted profile. A part of this apparent fall is due to the inclusion of ammonium ions held by the clay in a form in which they can only be displaced by treatment with a strong acid. But even allowing for this, there is still a marked fall in the C/N ratio, as can be seen from Table 61 which also refers to a Rothamsted profile.[3]

TABLE 61

Effect of Adsorbed Ammonium Ions on the Apparent Fall in the C/N Ratio with Depth

Depth in inches	Per cent carbon	Per cent nitrogen	C/N uncorrected	Per cent organic nitrogen	C/N corrected
1–9	1·04	0·122	8·5	0·113	9·2
18–27	0·37	0·055	6·7	0·044	8·4
46–54	0·14	0·031	4·5	0·024	5·8
73–81	0·14	0·031	4·5	0·024	5·8

The table shows that even allowing for the ammonium ions held by the subsoil, the nitrogen content of the organic matter there is very high, but little is known about its composition. Bremner finds the C/N ratio of the organic fraction which disperses in sodium hydroxide or pyrophosphate actually increases with depth, though the proportion of the organic matter which disperses drops; and so does the proportion of the nitrogen which appears as amino acids on acid hydrolysis. On the other hand, the proportion of the organic nitrogen which disperses after a single treatment with the hydrochloric-hydrofluoric acid increases with depth.

[1] H. Jenny, *Missouri Agric. Expt. Sta., Res. Bull.* 152, 1930.
[2] For an example from Scottish forest soils, see J. M. Shewan, *J. Agric. Sci.*, 1938, **28**, 324.
[3] J. M. Bremner, *J. Agric. Sci.*, 1959, **52**, 147. F. J. Stevenson (*Soil Sci.*, 1959, **88**, 201) has confirmed these results for a variety of American soils.

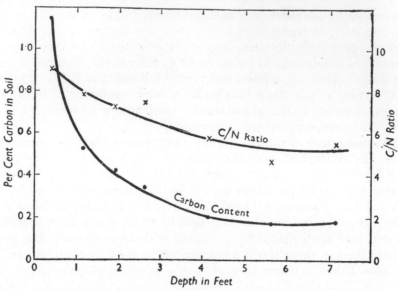

FIG. 20. The percentage of carbon and the C/N ratio in the first 7 feet of Broadbalk soil.[1]

THE PHOSPHORUS COMPOUNDS IN THE ORGANIC MATTER

All soil organic matter contains phosphorus, derived in the first instance from the plant residues returned to the soil. There is not much data on the phosphorus content of organic matter because of the great difficulty of bringing all the organic phosphorus into solution or suspension without breaking it down to inorganic phosphates. Some results of R. W. Pearson and R. W. Simonson[2] for seven Iowa soils indicate that the carbon-phosphorus ratio in the organic matter commonly lies between 100 and 200 and the nitrogen-phosphorus ratio between 8 and 16, though some of their results fell considerably below these limits. P. H. Nye and M. H. Bertheux,[3] however, found much higher ratios than this in the Ghana soils they examined. They found carbon-organic phosphorus ratios up to 500 on gneiss and granitic soils, and up to 350 on sandstones and basic igneous rocks, with nitrogen-organic phosphorus ratios of up to 40 and 25 respectively. They also found that their ratio of carbon to phosphorus was appreciably lower in the subsurface (6–12 inches) than in the surface (0–6 inches) layer, and was about the same in forest as in savannah soils.

The principal organic phosphorus compounds in the soil may not yet have all been recognised. Phytin, which is inositol hexaphosphate,

---

[1] B. Dyer, *U.S. Dept. Agric., Office Exp. Sta., Bull.* 106, 1902.
[2] *Proc. Soil Sci. Soc. Amer.,* 1939, **4**, 162. J. T. Auten (*Soil Sci.,* 1922, **13**, 119), also of Iowa, found similar ratios.
[3] *J. Agric. Sci.,* 1957, **49**, 141.

and other inositol phosphates certainly occur. C. A. Bower,[1] working in Iowa, found that about 40–50 per cent of the organic phosphorus could be hydrolysed to inositol phosphates, of which about two-thirds was phytin and one-third mainly the triphosphate. W. J. Dyer and C. L. Wrenshall[2] also found phytin was present in considerable amounts in a Canadian peat, though R. K. Yoshida's[3] results on some Hawaiian soils indicate that a much smaller preparation of their organic phosphates is combined with inositol.

The second group of phosphorus compounds recognised in the soil organic matter consists of nucleic acid and its nucleotides, but as already mentioned on p. 271, only a small proportion of the organic phosphorus in a soil, possibly up to 0·6 per cent, has been found in forms which could have been derived from nucleic acid or nucleotides.[4] No other compounds have been recognised in appreciable amounts though small quantities of the phospholipid lecithin have been isolated. Thus about half the organic phosphorus present in soils is in forms that have not yet been identified.

It is not known in what form the inositol phosphates occur in the organic matter, nor in which humic fractions they are concentrated. They must be protected in some way from the soil enzymes as they are readily dephosphorylated if mixed with the soil, that is, they have their phosphate groups split off as inorganic orthophosphate anions.[5] This is also shown independently by the fact that these organic phosphates can only be extracted in good yield from the humic material if it is subjected to fairly drastic pre-treatment. However, Dyer and Wrenshall[6] found that iron phytate, which they consider to be the principal phytin compound present in acid soils, is much more resistant to dephosphorylation than the free phytin.

THE SULPHUR COMPOUNDS IN THE ORGANIC MATTER

Very little is known about the sulphur content of organic matter or the forms in which it occurs. C. A. Evans and C. O. Rost[7] found that the sulphur content of the Minnesota soils they examined varied from about one-hundredth of the carbon content in the prairie soils to between one-half and one-quarter of this proportion in the podsolic soils. P. Madonov[8] found that the nitrogen-sulphur ratio in the organic matter of some Kazan chernozem and chestnut soils was between 10·5 and 11·4, agreeing fairly well with the ratio of 8–10 found by Evans and Rost for the Minnesota chernozems. Australian[9] and New Zealand[10]

[1] Soil Sci., 1945, 59, 277. [2] Soil Sci., 1941, 51, 235. [3] Soil Sci., 1940, 50, 81.
[4] G. Anderson, Soil Sci., 1958, 86, 169.
[5] W. J. Dyer and C. L. Wrenshall, Soil Sci., 1941, 51, 159; II. T. Rogers, ibid., 1942, 54, 439.
[6] Soil Sci., 1941, 51, 235. [7] Soil Sci., 1945, 59, 125. [8] Pedology, 1946, 9, 517.
[9] See, for example, C. H. Williams and A. Steinbergs, Aust. J. Agric. Res., 1958, 9, 483.
[10] See, for example, T. W. Walker and A. F. R. Adams, Soil Sci., 1958, 85, 307.

workers have also found nitrogen-organic sulphur ratios of 8 common in their soils, with the possibility that it is rather higher than this in acid soils.

Some of the sulphur occurs in the amino acids produced by acid hydrolysis of the humus, and cysteic acid can be found in these hydrolysates and it is likely that they also contain methionine. But it is unlikely that these can account for more than a small proportion of the sulphur in humus, and nothing is known about the form in which the rest occurs.

Properties of Soil Humus

REACTION OF HUMUS WITH METALLIC CATIONS

There are not yet any universally acceptable methods by which the ability of humus to hold cations can be examined, because one probably cannot yet separate all the humus from the mineral particles without causing some chemical alteration. The types of method which gives useful information are based on one or other of the following principles. First one can use the natural soil and the same soil after as much as possible of the organic matter has been oxidised away by hydrogen peroxide, and assume that the treatment with peroxide has not altered the inorganic soil colloids. This is probably a reasonable assumption for many soils, but would fail if the organic matter is intimately associated with mineral colloids, as for example in allophane-rich surface soils. Secondly one can choose a series of natural soils all having similar mineral composition but because of different systems of land use have different amounts of organic matter. If one can assume that a property is increasing linearly with increase in organic matter then it is reasonable to assume that this property is due directly to the humus, or more probably to the humus when closely intermixed with the soil. The third principle is to study the properties of humic acid dispersions from the soil, and assume that this material represents fairly closely the whole of the soil humus, and that its properties are not appreciably affected by being closely associated with the inorganic colloids.

There seem to be no examples of these three groups of methods being used on the same soil, so it is not possible to discuss how far they all give concordant results. The first two methods have mainly been used to determine the cation exchange capacity of the humus. L. C. Olson and R. H. Bray[1] using the first type showed that for a range of American soils it varied from 30 to 280 milli-equivalents per 100 gm. humus; and E. G. Hallsworth and G. H. Wilkinson[2] using the second for groups of soils from New South Wales found mean exchange capacities of about

[1] *Soil Sci.*, 1938, **45**, 483.   [2] *J. Agric. Sci.*, 1958, **51**, 1.

70 milli-equivalents per 100 gm. humus in acid podsols (mean pH 4·8), 130 for some moderately acid soils (mean pH 5·8), and 300 for some chernozems (mean pH 7·2); whilst L. T. Evans[1] finds the exchange capacity of a humic acid isolated from a neutral old grassland soil at Oxford to be about 300 milli-equivalents per 100 gm.

Most of the detailed electrochemical properties of humus have been determined on humic acids, as this is technically much easier to do. In the first place humic acid, and soil humus, hold certain metallic cations very firmly, and this has complicated the interpretation of some of the older results in the literature, for often what was considered to be a pure acid humus contained in fact aluminium and other metallic cations which affected appreciably the properties being measured. Humus holds di- and tri-valent metallic cations much more firmly than the alkali metal cations, as one would expect. Thus leaching a soil with sodium chloride will not remove all these cations—it is necessary to use the sodium salt of an acid whose anions form stable complexes or chelates with them. Thus leaching a soil with sodium pyrophosphate or oxalate will remove a much larger proportion of di- and tri-valent cations than will a sodium chloride solution, and the sodium humus thus produced disperses relatively easily. This is in fact the reason these salts are such useful dispersing agents for some of the soil humus.

It has been known for a number of years that peats and humic extracts would absorb copper ions strongly from dilute solutions,[2] and H. Lees[3] has even suggested that the amount of copper a soil could absorb under standard conditions could be used as a measure of the active humus in that soil on the basis that one atom of copper is held by every 60 atoms of carbon in the active humus, which corresponds to 80 milli-equivalents of copper per 100 gm. of active humus.

S. G. Heintze and P. J. G. Mann[4] also showed that the humus in soils would hold manganese firmly and that this could be displaced by other metallic ions increasingly strongly in the order calcium, nickel, cobalt, copper and zinc,[5] which is almost the same as the order of the stability constants of normal chelates of the divalent metals, given by H. Irving and R. J. P. Williams[6] as calcium, manganese, ferrous iron, cobalt, nickel, and copper, with zinc usually being a little weaker than copper. This has naturally suggested to several workers that humus can form chelates with suitable metallic cations, but not enough critical work has yet been done to prove if this ability of humus to hold these

[1] *J. Soil Sci.*, 1959, **10**, 110.
[2] For an example, see L. E. De Mumbrum and M. L. Jackson, *Soil Sci.*, 1956, **81**, 353.
[3] *Biochem. J.*, 1950, **46**, 450. [4] *J. Agric. Sci.*, 1949, **39**, 80.
[5] For an earlier paper in which this order was found, see A. Hasler, *Mitt. Lebensm. Hyg.* (Berne), 1943, **34**, 79. [6] *J. Chem. Soc.*, 1953, 3192.

cations is through such a specific method of bonding as chelation, namely, the metallic cation causing the closing of a cyclic ring structure in the organic groups, or if the metallic cations form some other type of co-ordination compound. The bonding appears to be through hydroxyls that can be methylated,[1] which would almost certainly be an integral part of the mechanism if chelation is involved, and R. S. Beckwith[2] showed that the titration curve of an acid humus holding some copper ions was in accord with these ions being in a chelate. A. E. Martin and R. Reeve,[3] however, considered that the metal ion on absorption did not displace sufficient hydrogen ions for simple chelate formation.

Humic acids holding metallic cations in complexes or chelates have a different shaped buffer curve from that of the acid if all the metal has been removed. Martin and Reeve, in the paper just quoted, showed that a humic fraction dispersed from the B horizon of several podsols by treatment with the chelating agent acetyl acetone, a treatment which removes nearly 90 per cent of the organic carbon, contained a large amount of aluminium and had a carbon-aluminium ratio between 5 and 9, which could be increased by stages, through the removal of aluminium with a strong cation exchange resin, to 152; and their results for two of these fractions is illustrated in Fig. 21. The aluminium-containing humus had a buffer curve that was almost a straight line from pH 3·5 to 8, when the pH measured in normal potassium chloride was plotted against the amount of sodium hydroxide added. On removing the aluminium, the total buffering to pH 9 was hardly affected, but a much larger part was displayed at the lower pH end, so the buffer curve became strongly concave. Up to pH 7 the aluminium-containing humic acid required 380 and the low aluminium acid 620 milli-equivalents, though this gain of 240 milli-equivalents was brought about by the removal of 560 milli-equivalents of aluminium. The pH of the humic acid dropped from 3·5 to 2·5, and the apparent pK of the acid fell from 6·2 to 4·1, a figure typical of the stronger carboxylic acids, though this is still considerably higher than the value of 2·95 found by S. P. Saric and R. K. Schofield[4] for the carboxyls attached to polysaccharides such as cellulose, xylans and pectic acid. Beckwith also observed this apparent straightening of the buffer curve if the humus contained complexed cations, and he also showed that if a given amount of any of these cations is added to a mildly acid humic suspension, the drop of pH is greatest with copper and zinc and least for manganese, as one would expect on the chelate picture.

Humic acids separated from acid soils are commonly found to hold aluminium ions, as in the example given by Martin and Reeve and

[1] F. L. Himes and S. A. Barber, *Proc. Soil Sci. Soc. Amer.*, 1957, **21**, 368.
[2] *Nature* 1959, **184**, 745.
[3] *J. Soil Sci.*, 1958, 9, 89.
[4] *Proc. Roy. Soc.*, A 1946, **185**, 431.

described in the preceding paragraph. Thus E. G. Williams and his
co-workers[1] at the Macaulay Institute found that for a number of
Scottish soils both the aluminium extracted by Tamm's acid exalate
solution and the iron extracted by dithionate were closely correlated
with the organic carbon in the soil. This ability of organic matter to hold
aluminium ions by chelation may also explain in part the apparent
differences in the exchange capacity of humus from different types of
soil, which was mentioned on p. 283, for one would expect, on this
picture, that the more acid the conditions under which the humus in a
mineral soil is formed, the greater is its aluminium content likely to be
and the smaller its exchange capacity.

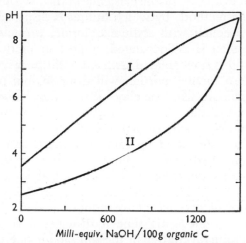

FIG. 21. The buffer curves of a dispersed humus with a carbon-aluminium ratio of 8·5
(Curve I) and 152 (Curve II).

THE CLAY-HUMUS COMPLEX

Humic material has for a long time been known to absorb, or be
absorbed by, clay particles. Thus, Th. Schloesing[2] wrote in 1874 that
"L'argile possède une certaine tendance à s'unir aux humates du
terreau pour former probablement une de ces combinaisons entre
colloides signalées par Graham." He attempted to separate the humus
from the clay by suspending the mixed sol in ammonia and then adding
ammonium chloride which flocculated the clay, but left much of the
humus in suspension. He also found that the quantity of chloride required to flocculate the clay increased with the amount of humus
present, a phenomenon that was first investigated in any detail by
E. Fickendey.[3]

[1] E. G. Williams, N. M. Scott and M. J. McDonald, *J. Sci. Food Agric.*, 1958, **9**, 551.
[2] *C.R.*, 1874, **78**, 1276.   [3] *J. Landw.*, 1906, **54**, 343.

Several lines of evidence have been advanced to show that much or most of the humus in a soil can be in close association with the clay particles. Direct microscopic examination of thin sections of most soils, using the technique of W. Kubiena,[1] indicate that in many mull and arable soils nearly all the humus is closely associated with the clay particles and cannot be seen separately from them, and this is in conformity with electron microscope photographs which also show that in such soils the humus appears to be dispersed evenly throughout the soil aggregates.[2] On the other hand if a humus suspension is shaken up with a pure kaolinite, it is absorbed at the crystal edges and not on the sheets themselves.[3]

A second line of evidence for the existence of the clay-humus complex is derived from the methods by which humus is dispersed from a soil. Thus if a soil is leached with sodium chloride, to convert it into a sodium soil, and then is deflocculated, a portion of the humus will disperse. If the soil is now treated with say sodium pyrophosphate or sodium hydroxide a further portion will disperse, but a portion will still be left in association with the clay. If now the soil be treated with a dilute solution of hydrofluoric acid, or as is more usual with a mixture of hydrofluoric and hydrochloric acids, and a concentration between 0·1 M and 1 M has been used by various workers, and the soil again treated with sodium hydroxide, a further portion of the humus disperses; and this is a part of the so-called humin fraction of the diagram on p. 267.

The interpretation of this effect of hydrofluoric acid in releasing humus is difficult because at the same time it dissolves a very appreciable proportion of the mineral matter in the soil, about one third in J. M. Bremner and T. Harada's experiments;[4] and it is not known what relation, if any, this large amount of dissolved mineral matter has to the humus set free. It is possible that humic acid particles are held on the surface of silicic acid gels through hydrogen bonding in the same way that protein and pectin films can be,[5] although the bonding may be on the surface of a clay particle on which is a silicic acid film. An observation of W. W. Emerson[6] would accord with this possibility, for he showed that removing the humus fraction which dispersed in sodium pyrophosphate from a Rothamsted grassland soil did not reduce the potential stability of its crumbs, whilst Bremner and Harada have shown that these soils contain a considerable proportion of humus which is only dispersible after a dilute hydrofluoric acid treatment.

[1] See, for example, some of the photographs in his *Soils of Europe*, Madrid, 1953.
[2] E. M. Kroth and J. B. Page, *Proc. Soil Sci. Soc. Amer.*, 1946, **11**, 27.
[3] W. Flaig and H. Beutelspacher, *Ztschr. PflErnähr.*, 1951, **52**, 1.
[4] *J. Agric. Sci.*, 1959, **52**, 137.
[5] P. F. Holt and C. W. Went, *Trans. Faraday Soc.*, 1959, **55**, 1435.
[6] *J. Agric. Sci.*, 1956, **47**, 350.

The properties of the clay-humus complex compared with those of a mere mechanical mixture of clay and humus are difficult to study. Thus no real comparison has been made of the properties of a synthetic clay-humus complex, prepared for example by letting a soil clay absorb humic acid, with that of the natural clay-humus complex occurring in the soil. It is known that clays will absorb humic acid prepared from normal soils. H. E. Myers[1] and D. I. Sideri[2] have shown that in dilute dispersions the absorbed humus binds the clay particles into birefringent micelles, indicating that the majority of the clay particles in these micelles have a fairly definite orientation, probably because they are held either face-to-face or edge-to-edge. There is good evidence that humus does not enter between the plates of a montmorillonite clay to give sheets with a regular spacing, but no evidence either way if it will allow sheets with random spacing to build up. The evidence is probably contradictory on whether a normal calcium clay can hold a definite maximum amount of humus, corresponding to a humus-saturated clay or not: E. Jung[3] finding evidence for a fairly definite saturation value and L. T. Evans and E. W. Russell[4] finding no evidence for it.

The clay-humus complex may have a cation exchange capacity a little less than that of the clay and the humus if measured separately. This can be proved by determining the buffer curves of a clay which has absorbed different amounts of a humic acid, and is provable by determining the exchange capacity of a soil before and after treatment with say a sodium carbonate-bicarbonate solution and of the humic acid extracted by the solution, but this does not seem to have been done. If this reduction is a general feature of the clay-humus complex, determining the exchange capacity of the humus from the loss in exchange capacity when a soil is treated with hydrogen peroxide (see p. 282) will underestimate the exchange capacity of the humus.

The type of humus formed in the soil giving the clay-humus complex depends on the type of clay present. As an extreme example in the tropics, montmorillonite clays under conditions of seasonally poor drainage, form what are sometimes known as black cotton soils or grumusols, and their colour is due to some type of clay-humus complex, whilst neighbouring kaolinitic and red earth clays on better drained sites, or even on poorly drained sites close by, have their colour much less affected by comparable amounts of humus.[5] The normal manner in which the clay-humus complex is formed is, however, under conditions

[1] *Soil Sci.*, 1937, **44**, 331.
[2] *Soil Sci.*, 1936, **42**, 461, and 1938, **46**, 267; *Pedology*, 1946, 39. See also S. Henin and J. Dupuis, *Ann. Agron.*, 1952, **3**, 327.
[3] *Ztschr. PflErnähr.*, 1943, **32**, 325.
[4] *J. Soil Sci.*, 1959, **10**, 119.
[5] For an example, see S. Singh, *J. Soil Sci.*, 1956, **7**, 43.

of a good to reasonable calcium supply and an adequate amount of high to medium exchange capacity clay. Thus the normal light loams to clays of the temperate regions can all contain appreciable proportions of their humus in this form, particularly under conditions where earthworms are active, as in deciduous forests and pastures.

The principal points brought out in this section are that two types of clay-humus complex probably exist. The first is due to the attraction of the negatively charged humic colloids for the positively charged spots on the soil surface. Soil conditioners of the polyacrylic acid type behave in the same way as humus on these spots.[1] There is another type of clay-humus complex, whose chemistry has not been determined but involves clays carrying a fairly high electric charge and may involve free silica or silicate surfaces, which is the characteristic complex in pasture and mull forest soils in the temperate regions, and is possibly mainly produced in the gut of the earthworm. This complex may be formed through the hydroxyl rather than the carboxylic acid groups in the humus, and if so the synthetic soil conditioners would not be expected to form it.

In conclusion, by way of summary, a soil may hold humus by five different mechanisms: simple isolated masses of humus, insoluble metal complexes, humus held on positively charged spots in the soil, humus in or on clay interlayers and humus in or on silicates soluble in cold dilute hydrofluoric acid. The first humus group can sometimes be separated from the main mass of the soil by a flotation technique. The second group, which may sometimes include the first, can only be dispersed when the metals have been replaced by, say, sodium ions, which can be done by treating the soil with a salt whose anions form stable soluble complexes with the metallic ions responsible, and which one would expect to be done equally well by the use of suitable cation exchange resins. The third group is displaced by sodium hydroxide, for the alkalinity of this solution decreases the positive charges on the mineral colloids; but since it increases the negative charges on the humus, it will also disperse humus held by other mechanisms. Little can be said about the fourth and fifth mechanisms—this is, the humus released by hydrofluoric acid—but it may include an important part of the clay-humus complex.

THE DECOMPOSABILITY OF SOIL HUMUS

In general soil humus decomposes slowly in the soil, and it may take a very large number of years for, say, 90 per cent of the humus present in a soil to be oxidised away under normal conditions. It has already been noted that if proteins are present in the soil humus they are much

[1] See, for example, B. P. Warkentin and R. D. Miller, *Soil Sci.*, 1958, **85**, 14.

more resistant to decomposition than normal proteins, possibly because their active groups have reacted with the soil polyphenols so there are few sites at which the microbial enzymes can initiate hydrolysis.

However, this may not be the sole reason that proteins if present in the soil are more resistant to decomposition than fresh protein added to a soil. As long ago as 1860 Thomas Graham[1] found that gelatin added to a silicic acid gel was much more resistant to decomposition than the gelatin itself and several workers have shown that proteins absorbed on montmorillonite clays in particular, and to a much less extent on clays of lower cation exchange capacity[2] are more resistant, again probably because their active groups are attached to the clay surface and so become inaccessible to proteolytic enzymes, although part of the reason may be that clays also absorb and inactivate enzymes for the same reason.[3]

The principal result of importance that has been established in the decomposition of soil humus is that at least two separate processes are involved. If a soil is kept warm and moist but well aerated, humus decomposition proceeds at a steady but relatively very slow rate. If the soil is first dried and then moistened, a certain fraction of the humus undergoes very rapid decomposition, and once this is complete, which may take 2–3 weeks, the rate falls to the low steady value just mentioned. The drier the soil and the longer it is kept dry before wetting, the greater the flush of decomposition, and if the soil is taken through a number of such cycles of drying and rewetting, the amount of carbon oxidised to carbon dioxide, and nitrogen oxidised to nitrate, is relatively constant, and only falls off slowly as the number of cycles through which it is carried increases.[4] No completely satisfying reason can yet be given for this flush of decomposition, nor is it known what fraction of the humus is involved, although in part it may be due to that portion which becomes readily dispersible in water each time the dry soil is wetted. A point of importance is that the humus as a whole appears to decompose, not any particular chemical fraction such as the protein or the carbohydrate moieties, which is concordant with the humus in a given soil being a fairly homogenous material and not a mere mechanical mixture of different components.

The decomposition of humus can probably also be increased slightly by adding decomposable organic matter to the soil, although the total amount of humus in the soil is increased. This can be shown by adding

[1] *Phil. Trans.*, 1861, **151**, 183.
[2] See, for example, L. E. Ensminger and J. E. Gieseking, *Soil Sci.*, 1942, **53**, 205, and D. L. Lynch and L. J. Cotnoir, *Proc. Soil Sci. Soc. Amer.*, 1956, **20**, 367.
[3] H. Kabayashi, *Biochem. J.*, 1928, **8**, 205, and M. M. Mortland and J. E. Gieseking, *Proc. Soil Sci. Soc. Amer.*, 1952, **16**, 10.
[4] For recent experimental work on this subject, see H. F. Birch, *Plant and Soil*, 1958, **10**, 9; 1959, **11**, 262; 1960, **12**, 81.

to the soil decomposable organic matter containing radioactive carbon C^{13} or heavy nitrogen N^{15}, and estimating the proportion of these isotopes in the carbon dioxide and nitrate produced. An example of this effect has already been given in Table 56 on p. 259, and a further example, also taken from F. E. Broadbent and A. G. Norman's papers[1] is worth giving. They added 1 and 2 gm. respectively of sudan grass to 100 gm. of soil, incubated the soil for eleven days and measured the CO_2 produced, and since 2·67 per cent of the carbon in the sudan grass was C^{13}, they could compute the proportion of the CO_2 produced that came from the oxidation of the soil organic matter. They found that 49 mgm. of CO_2 were produced from the organic matter when the soil was incubated by itself, but that 216 and 329 mgm. were produced from it when 1 and 2 gm. of sudan grass were added. At the same time 418 and 651 mgm. of CO_2 were produced from the decomposition of the sudan grass. Thus, for about every 100 mgm. of CO_2 produced from the sudan grass by the soil micro-organisms, an additional 40 mgm. is produced from the soil organic matter. So far no quantitative reasons can be given of why the soil organic matter becomes a better source of food for the soil population in the presence than in the absence of readily decomposable organic matter, but an active population can presumably decompose materials which are resistant when the population is working at a relatively low rate.

The Level of Organic Matter in Soils

The carbon compounds in the soil are in a continuous flux: carbonaceous plant residues are continually being added which, by forming the primary food supply of the soil population, suffer a series of decompositions and syntheses. Part of the added carbon is converted into living protoplasm, part into the products of excretion of living organisms and part into forms resistant to decomposition. The main loss of carbon from a soil occurs as carbon dioxide diffusing into the atmosphere or being leached out as carbonic acid or bicarbonate, but some loss may also occur under very acid conditions when mobile organic compounds are formed and leached out of the surface layer. They are typically precipitated in the B horizon in the subsoil, though some are washed out, as the colour of rivers flowing through the pine forests of northern Europe clearly shows.

The proportion of carbon in these various forms, and the rate of loss of carbon from the soil, depends on the soil conditions; and if these conditions remain fairly constant the organic matter also remains fairly constant, both in amount and composition; but if any important change

<hr />

[1] Proc. Soil Sci. Soc. Amer., 1947, **11**, 264; 1948, **12**, 246.

takes place—such as a change in the plant association, or in the aeration or drainage of the soil—this equilibrium is upset.

The organic matter content of a soil increases with the rate at which plant remains are added to the soil, though it also depends on the way they are incorporated with it. Forest soils typically have the bulk of their organic matter close to the soil surface, for the forest litter all falls on the surface, and most of the ephemeral tree roots are concentrated near the surface, so that organic matter can only be brought into the sub-surface layer by worms and other soil animals. Prairie soils, by contrast, have a considerable proportion of their organic matter in the deeper horizons, for not only do they receive grass and other debris on their surface, but many of their grasses produce a deep extensive root system which annually may add a greater weight of organic matter to the body of the soil than the leaves add to the surface.[1] The humus, which the decomposition of these roots yield, is thus produced in the deeper layers of the soil. Plate XXVII illustrates this difference for a prairie and a forest soil in Iowa.

Arable soils receive organic matter from the residues of the crops growing on them. The crop always leaves behind much of its root system in the soil, but except for some grass and leguminous leys, the actual weight of roots is usually very small[2] (p. 457). Most crops also leave a stubble and dead leaves, and the larger the crop the greater the weight of these residues, but the main source of organic matter in well-farmed arable soils that carry no leys is the farmyard manure they are given.

The rate of decomposition of the organic matter depends on the soil aeration, calcium supply and temperature. The more favourable a soil is for animal life, by being well aerated and adequately supplied with calcium, the more rapid in general is the decomposition: poorly drained or very acid soils which can only carry a small animal population nearly always have a higher organic matter content in their surface layers than well-drained neutral soils. High temperatures also encourage high rates of decomposition; the soil micro-organisms certainly decompose organic matter more vigorously at high temperatures, though it has not yet been established if this is also true for the soil animals.

The net effect of climate on the processes of addition and decomposition of the soil organic matter for well-drained pasture soils[3] in the U.S.A. is that the organic matter content increases with increasing

[1] J. Kramer and J. E. Weaver, *Univ. Nebraska Conserv. and Surv. Div., Bull.* 12, 1936, quoted by H. Jenny, *Factors in Soil Formation*, New York, 1941.
[2] C. W. B. Arnold and H. J. Page (*J. Agric. Sci.*, 1930, **20**, 460) came to this conclusion for wheat and mangolds, and F. Hardy (*Trop. Agric. Trin.*, 1944, **21**, 203) showed this also held for sugar-cane.
[3] For a discussion of the effect of climate on these soils, see H. Jenny, *Factors of Soil Formation*.

rainfall and with decreasing temperature—with the former because increasing rainfall favours greater plant growth without having much effect on the rate of decomposition, and with the latter because decreasing temperature both slows down the decomposition processes more rapidly than the growth of the plant, and also because it favours the synthesis of microbial protoplasm (p. 245). Shading the surface of the soil will also increase its organic matter content, for this lowers the maximum soil temperature, and in consequence the rate of oxidation of the organic matter. This effect of shading is seen most strikingly in the tropics, for not only is the difference in day temperature between a bare moist soil, and the same soil under a forest or bush cover appreciable, but oxidation proceeds correspondingly much more rapidly at the higher temperature.

The effect of ploughing out and cultivating a pasture or prairie soil is to reduce its organic matter content, both because the better aeration produced by the cultivations increases the rate of oxidation of the organic matter, and also because of the lower additions of plant remains that usually accompany arable farming. An extreme example of this effect is furnished by peat and fen soils. These soils have accumulated large quantities of organic matter due to them being so badly aerated through water-logging that its decomposition has been inhibited. Draining and cultivating these soils immediately improves the aeration in the soil itself, with the consequence that the organic matter begins to oxidise away and the surface level of the soil sinks; a rate of sinking of 1 to 3 cm. a year is not abnormal. This sinking of the soil surface causes very great complications in the management of the area, for the drainage system must continually be deepened, and the cost of removing the water from the drains will continually rise. O. Djurle[1] has given an example from Sweden, showing how this subsidence can be reduced by keeping the land in grazing leys or pasture as much as possible.

American experience has consistently shown that the soil organic matter content decreases much faster when the land is cropped to wide-spaced crops, such as maize, which receive considerable inter-row cultivation, than to close-spaced crops, such as wheat, which receive none. Hence, a good crop rotation can have the valuable function of conserving the soil organic matter, as is shown by some results, obtained at the Ohio Experiment Station at Wooster,[2] given in Table 62. Whereas nearly two-thirds of the organic matter has been lost from the continuous maize plots, only about one-sixth has been lost from the three-course rotation.

[1] *Svenska Vall-o. MosskFören. Kvartalsskr.*, 1946, **8**, 248.
[2] R. M. Salter and T. C. Green, *J. Amer. Soc. Agron.*, 1933, **25**, 622. H. E. Myers *et al.*, *Kansas Agric. Expt. Sta.*, *Tech. Bull.* 56, 1943, have given another good example of these effects in that State.

TABLE 62

Effect of Crop Rotation on the Organic Matter Content of Arable Soils

Crops grown since 1894 without manure or fertiliser[1]
Weight per acre in top 6⅔ inches of soil

	Carbon in 1,000 lb.	Nitrogen in 100 lb.
Initially (1894)	20·4	21·8
After 30 years' cropping to continuous maize .	7·4	8·4
After 30 years' cropping to continuous wheat .	12·8	13·1
Five-course rotation:		
maize-oats-wheat-clover-timothy . . .	15·5	15·5
Three-course rotation[2]		
maize-wheat-clover	17·1	17·8

These results show that the organic matter content of an arable soil tends to an equilibrium value depending on the crop rotation practiseds for a given soil under given climatic conditions, it is lowest for rotation: containing a high proportion of wide-spaced intertilled crops or culti- vated fallows, and it increases as the proportion of small grains in the rotation increase, and it increases still more as the proportion of grass leys increase. Fig. 23 on p. 319 shows that this is so for grassland at Rothamsted. The normal nitrogen content of Rothamsted arable land is about 0·11 per cent, and for old grassland 0·25 per cent: when land is laid down to grass its nitrogen content increases rapidly at first, and then slowly up to this figure. Again, when grassland or prairie is broken up for arable the organic matter and nitrogen content fall rapidly to begin with, and then more slowly to a figure characteristic for the system of farming on the soil:[3] the losses of nitrogen consequent upon this change in land use are discussed on p. 317.

Adding farmyard manure regularly to an arable soil either increases its organic matter, if it had previously reached an equilibrium value, or else reduces its rate of loss, if that is occurring. Thus, on Broadbalk field, which has been in continuous wheat since 1843, the nitrogen content in the top 9 inches of soil on the unmanured plot and the plot receiving no nitrogen fertilisers has remained steady at about 0·10 per cent, whilst that on the plot receiving an annual dressing of 86 lb. of

---

[1] Some plots received dressings of lime, which appeared to have no effect on the carbon or nitrogen contents of the soil.
[2] Since 1897.
[3] For an example of this from the Waite Institute, Adelaide, see G. B. Clarke and T. J. Marshall, *Aust. J. Counc. Sci. Indust. Res.*, 1947, **20**, 162.

nitrogen as sulphate of ammonia has remained steady at about 0·12 per cent,[1] as shown in Table 63.

TABLE 63

Nitrogen Percentage in the top 9 in. of Broadbalk Soils

Plot	3	5	7	2A	2B
Manuring	None	PK	NPK	Farmyard manure	
				Since 1885	Since 1843
Year					
1865 . . .	0·105	0·106	0·117	—	0·175
1881 . . .	0·101	0·107	0·121	—	0·184
1893 . . .	0·094	0·101	0·115	0·136	0·213
1914 . . .	0·093	0·103	0·115	0·191	0·236[2]
1936 . . .	0·103	0·105	0·120	0·186	0·226
1945 . . .	0·105	0·106	0·123	0·194	0·236

On the other hand, annual dressings of 14 tons per acre of farmyard manure, which contains about 200 lb. of nitrogen, doubled the nitrogen content in fifty years, and brought it to a nearly stable value of 0·24 per cent in 70 years. However, on the neighbouring half plot, which only began to receive 14 tons of manure in 1885, the nitrogen content reached 0·19 per cent in 1914, and has now stabilised at this figure. The apparent discrepancy between the two half plots is probably due to the fallowing that has had to be introduced into this field for weed control since 1925. Since 1930 the land is fallowed one year in five, and this fallowing appears to have slowed up the rate of accumulation of organic matter on plot 2A very appreciably without affecting the level of nitrogen in plot 2B.

These results for the effect of farmyard manure on the nitrogen content of the soil enable one to make rough calculations of the proportion of the carbon and nitrogen in the manure that enters the humus supply in the soil. During the first fifty years of plot 2B the soil gained annually about 50 lb. of nitrogen and about 500 lb. of carbon, and received annually about 200 lb. of nitrogen and 3,800 lb. of carbon in the manure. Thus, over the first fifty years about one-quarter of

[1] E. M. Crowther, *C.R. Conf. Pédol. Méditerr.*, 1947, 123. W. H. Metzger, *Kansas Agric. Expt. Sta., Tech. Bull.* 45, 1939, and J. Elson, *Soil Sci.*, 1943, **56**, 235, have also given illustrations of the ability of nitrogen fertilisers to maintain a higher nitrogen content in the soil due to the larger growth of the crop they produce.

[2] Only one sample; the duplicate sample gave a nitrogen content of 0·266, probably through a bit of manure being included.

The 1945 samples were taken from a larger number of holes per plot, the samples for the other years from a very few.

the added nitrogen and one-eighth of the added carbon remained behind in the soil as slowly decomposable humus, and this fraction was probably 50 per cent higher in the first twenty years.

Crowther has further shown that on the light soil at Woburn, which was cropped to wheat or barley continuously for fifty years, the nitrogen content fell from 0·16 to 0·10 per cent during this period if no farmyard manure was given, but it was maintained at about this level when 6 to 7 tons per acre was given. Again, comparing the plots receiving farmyard manure with those receiving none, about 30 per cent of the nitrogen supplied by the farmyard manure remained in the soil, though in the five years immediately after this period when two fallows and three corn crops were taken without any manure being added, half of the additional nitrogen in the farmyard manure plots was lost. Again, in some Danish experiments at Lyngby,[1] where land was cropped to a six-course rotation and some plots given farmyard manure twice in the rotation, the soils retained 32 per cent of the nitrogen added in the manure during four courses of the rotation. Thus, under normal arable conditions in north-west Europe, soils receiving regular additions of farmyard manure retain between one-quarter and one-third of the nitrogen in the manure, in the form of soil organic matter having a C/N ratio of about 10.

However, under conditions of intensive manuring for short periods of years, a higher proportion of the added nitrogen may be converted into soil nitrogen. Thus H. H. Mann and T. W. Barnes,[2] using a field at Woburn of low humus status, and containing only 0·085 per cent nitrogen, and treated with 15 or 30 tons per acre of farmyard manure annually over a period of nine years, found that the nitrogen content increased by 0·035 and 0·055 per cent respectively, giving a mean conversion of nitrogen from farmyard manure to soil nitrogen of about 50 per cent, even though the land was used for an intensive market garden rotation.

[1] Described by K. Dorph-Petersen, *Tidskr. Planteavl*, 1946, **50**, 555.
[2] *J. Agric. Sci.*, 1956, **48**, 160.

CHAPTER XVI

THE NITROGEN CYCLE IN THE SOIL

The Mineralisation of Soil Nitrogen

MINERALISATION OF SOIL nitrogen is the term used for the process by which nitrogen in organic compounds becomes converted into the inorganic ammonium and nitrate ions. The transformation can probably only take place through the stages

$$\text{organic N} \rightarrow \text{ammonia} \rightarrow \text{nitrite} \rightarrow \text{nitrate}$$

and as far as is known these transformations are predominantly brought about in the soil by micro-organisms.

THE PRODUCTION OF AMMONIA FROM ORGANIC MATTER

The soil microflora typically produce ammonia from organic compounds when they set free more nitrogen from the organic matter on which they are living than they can assimilate into their own protoplasm. Further, ammonia forms their sole important nitrogen excretion product under aerobic conditions, though if the oxygen supply is restricted amines may also be produced. Ammonia production from nitrogen-rich organic matter is thus not confined to a few groups of soil micro-organisms: it is their typical and characteristic nitrogen excretion product. Soil animals, on the other hand, probably excrete either uric acid, as do the insects, or urea as do the mammals.

This concept of ammonia production being the nitrogen waste-product in the conversion of organic matter into microbial tissue and vital energy—originally put forward by E. Marchal[1] in 1893—is fundamental for understanding the effect of adding different types of organic matter on the mineral nitrogen in the soil. Thus, when a protein, such as dried blood, is added to a soil, about 80 per cent of the added nitrogen is liberated as ammonia, the remainder of the nitrogen being retained in microbial tissue; but as increasing quantities of a carbohydrate, such as cellulose, are mixed in with the protein, so the amount of microbial tissue that can be built up is increased, with the consequence that the proportion of nitrogen liberated as ammonia decreases until the ratio of carbohydrate to protein reaches a ratio of

---

[1] *Bull. Acad. Roy. Belg.*, 1893 (3), **25**, 727.

about 5:1 when all the nitrogen in the dried blood is needed by the micro-organisms.

There is some evidence that ammonia can be produced in soils treated with toluene, and therefore presumably not by the action of living micro-organisms. This seems to have been first noted by E. J. Russell and H. B. Hutchinson[1] in 1909, and has been re-examined in more detail by J. P. Conrad,[2] who showed that soils so treated still possess the power to hydrolyse urea and some other amides to ammonium carbonate, presumably through the action of the urease enzymes present in the soil which have been released there during the decomposition of added plant and animal tissues. Whether uric acid—the nitrogen excretion product of most soil invertebrates—is similarly decomposed has not been investigated.

NITRIFICATION IN THE SOIL: THE ORGANISMS INVOLVED

Th. Schloesing and A. Müntz[3] proved in 1877 that nitrification, used here to mean the production of nitrate from ammonia, was mainly a biological process by showing it could be stopped by antiseptics such as chloroform; and this is still the only process that is definitely known to bring about this oxidation in soils.

Various claims have been put forward that nitrate can be produced photochemically from organic compounds, but these have not yet been substantiated.[4] There seems little doubt that ammonia can be oxidised photochemically to nitrite in solution,[5] but it appears that nitrates are more liable to photochemical reduction to nitrites than the other way round. The importance of this photo-oxidation to nitrite even in tropical soils, where it can only be a surface phenomenon, is still undecided.

The only agents that have so far been proved to oxidise ammonia to nitrites and nitrites to nitrates in soil are bacteria, but the technique for isolating the organisms responsible for the oxidation of ammonia to nitrite and nitrite to nitrate is troublesome. Long ago R. Warington at Rothamsted[6] obtained bacterial cultures, which must have been very mixed, that would convert ammonia and some organic nitrogen compounds into nitrites, but not necessarily nitrates, and others that would convert nitrites, but not ammonia, into nitrates; but he could

[1] *J. Agric. Sci.*, 1909, **3**, 111.
[2] *Soil Sci.*, 1942, **54**, 367; *J. Amer. Soc. Agron.*, 1941, **33**, 800; 1942, **34**, 1102; and *Proc. Soil Sci. Soc. Amer.*, 1944, **8**, 171.
[3] *C.R.*, 1877, **84**, 301; **85**, 1018; and 1878, **86**, 982.
[4] For a review, see S. A. Waksman and M. R. Madhok, *Soil Sci.*, 1937, **44**, 361.
[5] G. G. Rao and N. R. Dhar, *Soil Sci.*, 1931, **31**, 379; A. S. Corbet, *Biochem. J.*, 1934, **28**, 1575; B. N. Singh and K. M. Nair, *Soil Sci.*, 1939, **47**, 285.
[6] It is instructive to read his papers on this subject (*Trans. Chem. Soc.*, 1878, **33**, 44; 1879, **35**, 429; 1884, **45**, 637; 1888, **53**, 727; and 1891, **59**, 484) and to realise that in spite of the far better techniques available today many of the problems raised are still unsolved.

not isolate these organisms as pure cultures on gelatine. It was left to S. Winogradsky,[1] to isolate the bacteria responsible. He argued that the organisms should be autotrophic, obtaining their carbon from CO_2 and their energy from the oxidation of ammonia and nitrite, and that therefore they alone of the soil organisms should grow on silica gel plates free from organic matter but containing bicarbonate and ammonium or nitrite salts. Using this technique, he isolated an ammonium-oxidising and nitrite-producing bacterium, which he called *Nitrosomonas*, and a nitrite-oxidising and nitrate-producing bacterium, which he named *Nitrobacter*. He found these bacteria needed free calcium or magnesium carbonate on which to grow and were harmed, in solution cultures, by some organic compounds such as glucose and peptone, though they were stimulated by others such as acetates and a decoction of horse dung. He also found that they were slow-growing and only formed very small colonies, about $0 \cdot 1$ mm. in diameter, and hence would be very difficult to isolate by any other technique, and this technique has been found to require very considerable skill.[2]

These two bacteria have been found by all other workers who have looked for nitrifying bacteria in soils which are known to nitrify, and except that there may be more than one species of each genus, these are usually the only bacteria that are regularly found. Winogradsky described a second ammonium oxidiser, *Nitrosococcus*, in 1904 and subsequently he and his daughter H. Winogradsky described several others, but doubt has been cast on the ability of these to nitrify.[3] A number of claims have also been made for some methane-oxidising bacteria,[4] some heterotrophic bacteria[5] and actinomycetes[6] to oxidise ammonia to nitrite and even for a fungus *Aspergillus flavus* to oxidise organic nitrogen to nitrate,[7] but so far no evidence has been brought forward to show what importance they have in the production of nitrites or nitrates in field soils. There are also present in soils a number of bacteria and actinomycetes that can convert pyruvic oxime $CH_3 . C(NOH) . COOH$ into nitrite, though whether this is on oxidation to give pyruvic acid[8] $CH . CO_3 . COOH$ or a hydrolysis to give propionic acid[9] has not been determined. Further the nitrite produced may

[1] *Ann. Inst. Pasteur*, 1890, **4**, 213, 257, 760; and with W. Omeliansky, *Zbl. Bakt.* II, 1899, **5**, 329, 429; and *Arch. Sci. Biol.* (St. Petersburg), 1899, **7**, No. 3.
[2] For a more recent discussion of the technique with a review of the literature, see J. Meiklejohn, *J. Gen. Microbiol.*, 1950, **4**, 185.
[3] See J. Meiklejohn, *J. Soil Sci.*, 1953, **4**, 59 for a discussion of this problem.
[4] W. E. Hutton and C. E. Zobell, *J. Bact.*, 1953, **65**, 216.
[5] For example D. W. Cutler and B. K. Mukherjee, *Proc. Roy. Soc.*, B 1931, **108**, 384, and T. Fisher *et al.*, *J. Bact.*, 1952, **64**, 596.
[6] H. D. Isenberg *et al.*, *Bact. Proc.*, 1952, 41.
[7] E. L. Schmidt, *Science*, 1954, **119**, 187.
[8] J. H. Quastel, P. G. Scholefield and J. W. Stevenson, *Biochem. J.*, 1952, **51**, 278, 286.
[9] H. L. Jensen, *J. Gen. Microbiol.*, 1951, **5**, 360.

only be a waste product that is utilised by the micro-organism if the medium is enriched in decomposable carbohydrate. If pyruvic oxime occurs as a very fugitive metabolic product in soils, it could be the immediate precursor of some of the nitrite formed.

There is also modern direct evidence that nitrate formation goes through the nitrite stage. H. Lees and J. H. Quastel[1] found that, when circulating a solution of ammonium sulphate through a Rothamsted soil under aerobic conditions, they could delay the onset of nitrate production by adding some potassium chlorate to the solution, and this delay was solely due to stopping nitrite oxidation and not nitrite formation. They showed that this inhibiting effect of the chlorate was due to its power of reducing the rate at which the nitrite-oxidising organisms could proliferate, as the chlorate had no effect on the velocity of oxidation of nitrite to nitrate in the presence of an adequate number of nitrite-oxidising organisms. This inhibiting effect was itself inhibited in the presence of an adequate supply of nitrate. Free ammonia, but not ammonium ions, has a much greater inhibitory effect on nitrate than on nitrite formation, so adding large amounts of ammonia to a soil, as a fertiliser, or of ammonium sulphate to an alkaline soil, causes an accumulation of nitrite to occur.

THE BIOCHEMISTRY OF NITRIFICATION

The biochemistry of the nitrifying organisms is now being worked out.[2] They get their energy from the oxidation of ammonia or nitrite according to the equations

$$2NH_3 + 3O_2 \rightarrow 2HNO_2 + 2H_2O + 79 \text{ Cal.}$$
$$2HNO_2 + O_2 \rightarrow 2HNO_3 + 43 \text{ Cal.}$$

The only proven source of carbon is carbon dioxide, or the bicarbonate ion, and the *Nitrosomonas* group need to oxidise 35–70 moles of ammonia and the *Nitrobacter* group 70–100 moles of nitrite per mole of carbon assimilated. This explains why they appear to be such slow-growing organisms.

The enzymes responsible for these oxidations are now being worked out. The oxidation goes through hydroxylamine, NH_2OH; and a cell-free extract of *Nitrosomonas* in the presence of cytochrome C, which occurs in the cell, will oxidise hydroxylamine to nitrite possibly through hyponitrite.[3] The oxidation of ammonia to hydroxylamine can be selectively suppressed by inhibitors such as allyl thiourea, and of hydroxylamine to nitrite by hydrazine.[4] Thus in the early stages of

[1] *Biochem. J.*, 1946, **40**, 824.
[2] For recent reviews, see J. H. Quastel and P. G. Scholefield, *Bact. Rev.*, 1951, **15**, 1, and J. Meiklejohn, *J. Soil Sci.*, 1953, **4**, 59.
[3] D. J. D. Nicholas and O. T. G. Jones, *Nature*, 1960, **185**, 512.
[4] T. Hoffman and H. Lees, *Biochem. J.*, 1953, **54**, 579.

the oxidation the ammonium ion concentration begins to drop several days before nitrite can be detected.[1]

Nitrification can be suppressed by a number of poisons at low concentrations, such as sodium thiocynate, methionine and guanidine, and at very low concentrations by thiourea and many other compounds containing an active —SH group[2] such as the dithiocarbamates and dimethyl dithiocarbamates, which can be used for weed control; though the concentration needed in the soil for a pronounced effect on nitrification is considerably higher than could arise through their use as a herbicide. It is probable that gelatin, peptone and glucose solutions sterilised by heat are toxic to these bacteria because they contain substances of this type, for in the case of glucose solutions these are not toxic if sterilised by ultra-filtration.[3] A number of insecticides and herbicides also inhibit nitrification, but all appear to be needed at much higher concentrations than would occur in the field if their effect is to be noticeable.[4]

Since the conversion of ammonia to nitrate through nitrite is an oxidation, its rate of conversion must depend on the oxygen supply. Poorly aerated soils cannot nitrify ammonia, but very little work has been done on how low the oxygen tension must fall before nitrification ceases. The problem is difficult to work on experimentally in the field, because it is likely that even if ammonia nitrified in a poorly aerated soil, the nitrate would be rapidly denitrified to a gas, and so would not be easily detected. F. M. Amer and W. V. Bartholomew[5] measured the amount of nitrate produced in a soil to which ammonium sulphate had been added after inoculation for 14 or 21 days when air containing varying amounts of nitrogen was drawn through the moist soil. They added 20 mgm. N per 100 gm. soil, as ammonium sulphate, and found the following amounts of nitrate nitrogen present after 21 days, expressed as a percentage of the added ammonium nitrogen:

O_2 content of air	20	11	4·5	2·1	1·0	0·4
% of added N present as NO_3	46	43	38	28	21	2

These results show that nitrification should be able to take place in very poorly aerated soil, though the interpretation of these figures may need care, as very little is yet known about the effective oxygen supply very close to centres of microbial activity.

[1] See, for example, R. M. Beesley, *Trans. Chem. Soc.*, 1914, **105**, 1014, and W. P. Martin *et al.*, *Proc. Soil Sci. Soc. Amer.*, 1942, **7**, 223.
[2] J. H. Quastel and P. G. Scholefield, *Nature*, 1949, **164**, 1068, and *Bact. Rev.*, 1951, **15**, 1; H. L. Jensen and H. Sorensen, *Acta Agric. Scand.*, 1952, **2**, 295.
[3] H. L. Jensen, *Nature*, 1950, **165**, 974, and J. Meiklejohn, *Plant and Soil*, 1951, **3**, 88.
[4] H. A. Wilson, *W. Va. Agric. Exp. Sta.*, *Bull.* 366 T, 1954, and A. L. Brown, *Proc. Soil Sci. Soc. Amer.*, 1954, **18**, 417.
[5] *Soil Sci.*, 1951, **71**, 215.

NITRIFICATION OF AMMONIUM SALTS IN FIELD SOILS

In general the rate of nitrite oxidation goes faster than that of ammonium oxidation, so in normal soils the level of nitrite nitrogen is very low compared with ammonium and nitrate nitrogen. But nitrites can accumulate in soils whenever the concentration of free ammonia becomes appreciable, as, for example, if heavy dressings of ammonium fertilisers are given on calcareous soils,[1] because of its differential toxicity to the nitrite-oxidising bacteria, and this nitrite may decompose very slowly if the soil temperature is rather low. Thus H. D. Chapman and G. F. Liebig[2] found that with soils of pH 8, concentrations of 90 p.p.m. nitrite-nitrogen could persist for several months at a temperature between 50 and 60°F.

These high concentrations of ammonia in the soil can arise through the use of anhydrous ammonia as a fertiliser, or of heavy dressings of urea, for this ammonifies quickly in many soils. But they can also arise in the urine patches made by grazing sheep and cattle. Thus B. W. Doak[3] found that a sheep excreted about 150 ml. urine per urination, which wetted about 45 sq. in. of pasture, so was equivalent to 430 lb./acre of nitrogen. The composition of the urine was

Total nitrogen		Per cent of total nitrogen as					
	gm. per litre	Urea	Allantoin	Hippuric acid	Creatinine	Amino-N	Ammonia
Average	8·68	76·4	4·1	2·6	1·5	12·4	0·7
Range	5·7–12·6	68–85	2·9–5·2	2·1–3·1	1·0–1·8	10·5–15·9	0·5–0·9

Hence urea was being added at the rate of 700 lb. per acre in the urine patch. In the laboratory he found that urea hydrolysed quicker in urine than if pure, which he could show was due to the presence of the glycine, allantoin and hippuric acid. This rapid hydrolysis could raise the pH of the soil from 5·5 to 9·5 in a few hours, causing both a loss of ammonia as gas, which could amount to about 12 per cent of the nitrogen in the urine, due to the high soil pH (see p. 311) and also an accumulation of nitrite consequent upon this high ammonia concentration.

Nitrification does not take place in strongly acid soils, although they may sometimes contain nitrifying bacteria; but if the pH is above 5 the nitrification rate may be, but need not be, increased by liming. In fact,

[1] G. S. Fraps and A. J. Sterges, *Soil Sci.*, 1939, **47**, 115. A. B. Craster, W. P. Martin and T. F. Buehrer, *Ariz. Agric. Expt. Sta., Tech. Bull.* 96, 1942, and G. Drouineau, P. Gouny and G. Lefèvre, *C.R.*, 1948, **226**, 957.
[2] *Proc. Soil Sci. Soc. Amer.*, 1952, **16**, 276.
[3] *J. Agric. Sci.*, 1952, **42**, 162.

for most soils, there is a considerable pH range in which nitrification rates are almost independent of the pH. However, if a soil is poorly buffered and is given a fairly heavy surface dressing of ammonium sulphate, the pH of the surface soil may easily fall sufficiently to reduce the rate of nitrification of this added ammonia very appreciably. Table 64 gives an example of the way temperature and pH can affect nitrification rates in the laboratory.[1] It shows that ammonium

TABLE 64

Effect of Soil pH and Soil Temperature on the Rate of Nitrification of added Ammonium

100 p.p.m. N added   42 days incubation

Soil	pH	Ammonium added as	p.p.m. N as NO_3 Soil Temperature in °F			
			37	42	47	52
Nixon . . .	4·9	NH_4OH	4·8	17·6	36·0	48·0
		$(NH_4)_2SO_4$	2·4	6·4	12·8	21·6
Nixon . . .	6·8	NH_4OH	4·0	24·0	54·4	58·4
		$(NH_4)_2SO_4$	1·6	29·6	54·4	60·0
Washington . .	5·9	NH_4OH	2	8	29	42
Annandale . .	6·1	NH_4OH	21	45	55	51

hydroxide nitrifies more rapidly than ammonium sulphate in the acid Nixon soil but at the same rate in the neutral; and that there is no very close dependence of the rate of nitrification on temperature in the 47–52° F. range, for with two soils the rates are about the same at both temperatures (neutral Nixon and Annandale) whilst for the other two appreciably more nitrate is formed at the higher temperature. An extreme case, in the field, of the effect of low temperatures depressing the rate of nitrification can be seen in an experiment made by R. L. Fox, R. A. Olson and A. P. Mazurak[2] in Nebraska. They broadcast 80 lb. per acre of ammonium nitrogen, as ammonium nitrate, on 15 November and on 15 April following there was still 60 lb. per acre of ammonium nitrogen left, though by 1 May it had dropped to 25 lb. and had all gone by 15 June.

The effect of the moisture content of a soil on the rate of nitrification now seems to be worked out. J. B. D. Robinson[3] has shown for two Kenya soils that the initial rate of nitrification of an added ammonium salt is similar if the soil is at field capacity or at permanent wilting point,

[1] O. E. Anderson and E. R. Purvis, *Soil Sci.*, 1955, **80**, 313.
[2] *Agron. J.*, 1952, **44**, 509.
[3] *J. Agric. Sci.*, 1957, **49**, 100.

although it falls off in the drier soil after about a week to a rate about half that in the wetter. But once the soil becomes drier than this, the rate drops off very rapidly, and he could detect no nitrification if the moisture content was about five-sixths of the wilting-point moisture, although some of the organic nitrogen compounds can be ammonified at moisture contents below wilting point, and this ammonium accumulates in the soil.

THE LEVEL OF MINERAL NITROGEN IN FIELD SOILS

The mineral nitrogen in the soil is present either as ammonium or nitrate ions. The nitrates are all dissolved in the soil solution, unless the soil dries out, but much of the ammonium is held on the exchange

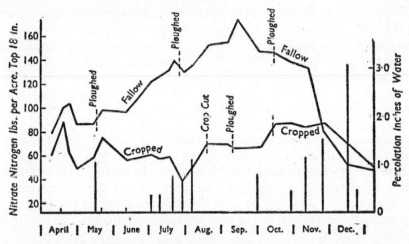

Fig. 22. Amount of nitrate nitrogen in cropped and fallow soils at different seasons of the year and the amount of percolation through the 20-in. bare soil gauge (Broadbalk Field, Rothamsted, 1915).

complex. The total quantity of mineral nitrogen in the soil is the difference between the rate it is being produced from the soil's store of organic matter by the soil population and the rate it is being removed by leaching, by growing crops and by other members of the soil population; and the proportion of nitrate to ammonium depends also on the rate of oxidation of ammonium to nitrates, the uptake of nitrates by the plant and the loss of nitrates by leaching.

Arable soils in the temperate regions, particularly if they are not too acid, have a fairly constant but low content of ammonium nitrogen, but a very variable and higher nitrate content, ranging from 2 to 20 mgm. of nitrogen as nitrate per kg. of soil (i.e. 2 to 20 parts per million of nitrate nitrogen) for normal soils, but rising up to 60 mgm. for rich garden soils. This nitrate content varies throughout the season and, under some conditions which cannot yet be specified, from hour to hour.[1] Fig. 22 shows the nitrate nitrogen content, throughout the growing season of 1915, of two parts of the Broadbalk plot at Rothamsted which receives farmyard manure annually, one part being cropped to wheat and one part fallowed.[2] Not all the details of these curves can be explained, but the figure shows clearly that the fallow soil accumulates nitrate during the spring and summer, whereas the cropped soil does not, and that the fallow appears to have lost all its accumulated nitrate by early winter, presumably due to it being leached down into the deep subsoil.

NITRIFICATION IN FALLOW SOILS

Fallows can only accumulate nitrates under four conditions: there must be decomposable organic matter in the soil to provide a supply of ammonium ions, the fallow must be kept free from weeds, there must not be too much rain otherwise the nitrates are leached out of the soil, and the soil must be moist or be subjected to alternate wetting and drying. F. Crowther,[3] working in the Sudan Gezirah, has given a good example of weeds reducing the accumulation of nitrates in a fallow soil. This heavy clay land is commonly fallowed for several years in preparation for cotton, and Crowther showed that cutting down the weeds that grew during the short rainy season, instead of letting them die as soon as the dry season began, increased the nitrate nitrogen in the top foot of soil from 2–4 p.p.m. to 5–10 p.p.m., and also increased that in the second foot. This led to a 66 per cent increase in the uptake of nitrogen by the cotton and a corresponding increase in the yield of seed-cotton.

Nitrification proceeds more rapidly in soils subjected to alternate wetting and drying than in soils kept permanently moist, because the alternate wetting and drying causes a more rapid oxidation of soil humus (see p. 222). There are many examples of this effect in the literature, and H. F. Birch[4] has recently examined it in considerable detail. He finds that the drier the soil before wetting, the longer it has been kept dry, and the higher the temperature it has been dried, the greater is the amount of nitrogen mineralised; and if the soil is subjected to a standard drying and wetting cycle, very much the same amount of nitrogen is mineralised each cycle, although in the first cycle more may be mineralised if the soil contains some fresh decomposable non-humic

[1] H. G. Thornton and P. H. H. Gray, *Proc. Roy. Soc.*, 1930, **166** B, 399.
[2] E. J. Russell and A. Appleyard, *J. Agric. Sci.*, 1917, **8**, 385. For a further example, see W. A. Albrecht, *Missouri Agric. Expt. Sta., Res. Bull.* 250, 1937.
[3] *Emp. J. Expt. Agric.*, 1943, **11**, 1.
[4] *Plant and Soil*, 1958, **10**, 9; 1959, **11**, 262; 1960, **12**, 81.

organic matter. Nor is it necessary for the soil to be dried: some methods of partial sterilisation have the same effect. His figures show that in the East African soils he studied about 1·5 per cent of the organic nitrogen can be mineralised during each cycle, a figure which is of the same order of magnitude as the estimate of the proportion of the organic matter present as microbial tissue in an English soil (see p. 200).

The benefit to the subsequent crop of drying or heating a soil, particularly under tropical or sub-tropical sunshine, has already been noted on p. 222. In practice, the consequence of this effect in hot regions having a pronounced dry and wet season is that the nitrates are produced most rapidly at the commencement of the rains, and slowly during the rainy season itself. Hence if crops are to benefit from this early flush, they must be planted as early as possible, taking advantage of any showers that fall before the beginning of the main rains, so that they can start growing quickly when the rains break and use this nitrate before it is leached out of the soil. This may be one of the reasons for the failure of most of the ambitious mechanised crop production schemes which have been tried in equatorial Africa, for it has been found that the planting season for profitable crop yields lasts only for two to three weeks; and later plantings give poor to very poor yields, even when neither lack of moisture nor insects appeared to be the cause.

This effect of nitrates being produced more rapidly during the onset of the rains, and more slowly at their end has been observed in fallow soils in the tropics.[1] But since the dry season may last a long time, the total nitrates in the surface of tropical soils at the end of the dry season may be very high. Thus G. ap Griffith[2] found up to 110 p.p.m. of nitrate-nitrogen in the top 6 inches of a fallow soil at Kawanda, Uganda, though levels of 25 p.p.m. were more common; and W. R. Mills[3] showed that it could be over 200 p.p.m. in the top 2 inches there. This compares with 30–40 p.p.m. in the surface soil of the Broadbalk (Rothamsted) plot receiving 14 tons of farmyard manure annually during a summer fallow.

The fact of this accumulation of nitrate in the surface of tropical and subtropical soils during the dry season is accepted by most research workers, but there is still doubt about the causes of this accumulation, and in detail what proportion is produced in the surface soil, what moves up with the subsurface water which is evaporated from the surface soil, and whether any is produced photochemically in the soil

[1] For an example, see D. J. Greenland, *J. Agric. Sci.*, 1958, **50**, 82, who gives an extensive bibliography to earlier work.
[2] *Emp. J. Exp. Agric.*, 1951, **19**, 1, and with H. L. Manning, *Trop. Agric.* (*Trinidad*), 1949, **26**, 108.
[3] *East Afr. Agric. J.*, 1953, **19**, 53.

surface. Unfortunately, although many experiments have been made to investigate this phenomenon, mainly by microbiologists or chemists, not enough observations have been taken either of the pF or suction of the water in the "dry" surface soil, or of the water and nitrate movements in the soil profile, for any critical discussion to be undertaken on the importance of the various processes known to be operative. But it is probable that all the known results can be explained as a consequence of the two processes already mentioned: nitrification in the drying soil which continues till the permanent wilting point is reached, and this takes a long time for the top 9 inches of soil if it is free from vegetation and undisturbed; and some movement of nitrates upwards from below 6 inches with the water that is moving upwards to be evaporated, and although this may only amount to $\frac{1}{2}$–1 inch, yet it can bring appreciable amounts of nitrate into the surface soil.

A further process which may be of importance is the effect of scattered light showers of rain during the dry period, for each will set off a flush of decomposition apparently disproportionate to the amount of water that has fallen. And it is possible, though unproven, that enough moisture may enter the soil surface in regions receiving heavy dew, for nitrification to take place in the surface soil every night.[1]

The direct effect of rainfall on the nitrate content of the soil is to leach it down the profile. If the profile is dry to depth, and the rainfall limited in amount, the nitrates will accumulate lower down in the soil profile, and this accumulation can be very considerable. Thus W. R. Mills[2] found over 400 p.p.m. nitrate nitrogen had accumulated at 3 feet depth in a Kawanda (Uganda) soil under suitable climatic conditions. If the profile is fairly shallow and well drained, and the rainfall adequate, nitrates will be washed into the groundwater or the rivers.

Well-structured loams and clays can, however, hold appreciable quantities of nitrates against leaching. This is because the percolating water moves down principally through the cracks and coarse pores between the crumbs, and most of the nitrates are formed in the crumbs, so the nitrates can only get into this water by diffusion, which is a slow process. This holding of nitrates against leaching is of considerable agricultural importance in British soils, as for example the Rothamsted clay loam,[3] for it means that a part of the nitrates produced in a previous summer fallow is available for the succeeding crop, even if the autumn and winter are wet, although as E. M. Crowther[4] showed, using indirect

---

[1] This has been suggested by G. Drouineau et al. (*Ann. Agron.*, 1951, **21**, 1, and 1953, **4**, 245) as occurring in the south of France.
[2] *East Afr. Agric. J.*, 1953, **19**, 53.
[3] See, for example, R. K. Cunningham and G. W. Cooke, *J. Sci. Food Agric.*, 1958, **9**, 317.
[4] *Trans. 3rd Int. Congr. Soil Sci.* (Oxford), 1935, **3**, 126.

evidence, most of this nitrate must be held in the subsoil rather than in the surface crumbs, possibly because the surface nitrates are lost by denitrification, the surface crumbs being well supplied with decomposable organic matter.

The effect of surface mulches and of shade on the nitrate content of fallow soil in the tropics and subtropics is not fully understood. In general a surface mulch or shading the soil surface reduces the nitrates in the surface soil, though D. J. Greenland gave an example from Ghana when the shading had little effect. No sufficient analysis of the soil conditions prevailing in the covered and bare soil appear to have been made for one to say if factors already discussed are sufficient to explain the facts, namely:

(1) under shade the soil is cooler, so the nitrification should go on at a slower rate than in bare soil;

(2) under bare soil evaporation is initially at least more rapid than under covered, so the soil should dry out sooner and hence nitrification cease sooner;

(3) under bare soil, the surface soil will be dried out more intensively, so if any rain showers occur, or if very heavy dew wets the soil surface, there should be a much greater flush of nitrate production than in the covered soil. Further, if the rain shower is heavy it is possible there will be run off from the surface of the bare soil but deeper percolation of water down the profile in the covered;

(4) denitrification may go on at a faster rate in the moist to wet soil surface under a mulch than in the bare soil.

NITRIFICATION IN ARABLE SOILS

Nitrates are always lower in cropped land than under fallow, as one would expect, because the crop will be taking up nitrates from the soil whilst it is growing. But in addition there is considerable evidence that the crop appears to depress the rate of nitrification in a soil, for the nitrogen present in the cropped soil as nitrate and in the crop is less than the nitrates in adjacent soil kept fallow. Table 65 illustrates the type of data from which this conclusion is drawn, but the correct interpretation of this result is not fully established. Thus in the table only the nitrogen in the above-ground portion of the crop has been determined, that in the roots being ignored, but it is extremely unlikely that there could be enough in the roots to account for the difference. This difference occurs in the earlier part of the crop's growth, for as Table 65 shows, in 1915 the amount of nitrates produced in the fallow and in the cropped land was the same for the period between 26 July and

TABLE 65

Nitrogen as Nitrate in Cropped and Fallow Soil at Rothamsted
Crop—Wheat

As pounds of nitrogen per acre

	Hoosfield		Broadbalk		
			Un-manured	Dunged	
	June 1911	July 1912	July 1915	26th July 1915	17th Aug. 1915
In top 18 in. of fallow soil .	54	46	70	124	150
In top 18 in. of cropped soil	15	13	44	37	69
In crop	23	6	21	70	70
Total	38	19	65	107	139
Deficit in cropped land .	16	27	5	17	11

Expressed as mgm. N per kg. soil

Fallow, 0–9 in. depth . .	12	8
9–18 in. depth .	9	10
Cropped, 0–9 in. depth .	4	2
9–18 in. depth .	2	3

Cropping.   Hoosfield: Alternate wheat and fallow, unmanured since 1851.
Broadbalk: Continuous wheat, but fallow taken over part of this field for the third time since 1843.

17 August, the day on which the wheat was harvested. On the other hand, the deficit only starts to build up when the crop is well established.[1]

This apparent deficit could be due to four causes: the crop could excrete substances into the soil which inhibit or slow down the rate of nitrification, and although this has been postulated for grass roots, there is no evidence that annual arable crops excrete such substances. Then the crop may reduce the rate of nitrification in the soil by its effect on shading the soil, but if so one would expect the effect to be as large at the end of the growing season as earlier on. Then the crop might encourage denitrification or nitrogen losses from its leaves, but this is unlikely because, as is shown in Table 69, one can get a good nitrogen balance sheet for cropped unmanured land at Rothamsted. Finally the rhizosphere organisms on the crop roots, or other micro-organisms close to the root, may extract soluble carbohydrates or other low-nitrogen compounds from the roots, and use the soil nitrates as their

[1] C. A. I. Goring and F. E. Clark, *Proc. Soil Sci. Soc. Amer.*, 1949, **13**, 261.

source of nitrogen, or even use soluble nitrogen compounds from the roots, and converting these soluble compounds to insoluble organic soil nitrogen compounds; and there is direct evidence, using N^{15}, for this last process.[1]

NITRIFICATION IN GRASSLAND SOILS

Grassland appears to have a different mineral nitrogen economy from arable, for as Table 66 shows for grass leys and pastures at Rothamsted, a greater proportion of their mineral nitrogen is ammonium than nitrate. This ammonium content, as H. L. Richardson[2]

TABLE 66

Average Ammonium and Nitrate Contents of Rothamsted Grassland Soils

Years under grass	Depth of sampling in cm.	Nitrogen in parts per million of dry soil	
		Present as ammonium	Present as nitrate
Ley, under I	20	1·1	0·5
Ley, under 2	20	2·2	1·1
Pasture, 59	10	4·7	1·3
Pasture, over 200	20	5·4	1·1

showed, remains fairly constant between 3 and 9 p.p.m. ammonium-nitrogen throughout the year, yet if an ammonium or nitrate fertiliser is added, this mineral nitrogen very soon disappears from the soil and has presumably been taken up by the grass. No satisfactory explanation has yet been put forward to explain why the grass cannot reduce the ammonium level below this fairly high level, nor why this ammonium is not nitrified. Richardson showed that there was nothing in the soil of the old Rothamsted pastures that inhibited nitrification, for on incubating these soils all the ammonium produced was readily nitrified, unless the soil was too acid or too low in phosphate—a result which has been confirmed by other workers. Further, if an old pasture is ploughed out, the usual British experience is that the following crop is over-well supplied with soil nitrates.

Pastures in the tropics behave similarly. The nitrate and ammonium

[1] W. V. Bartholomew and F. E. Clark, *Trans. 4th Int. Congr. Soil Sci.* (Amsterdam), 1950, **2**, 112 and A. E. Hiltbold, W. V. Bartholomew and C. H. Werkman, *Proc. Soil Sci. Soc. Amer.*, 1951, **15**, 166.
[2] *J. Agric. Sci.*, 1938, **28**, 73.

levels are very low,[1] though not enough data has been published to establish if the ammonium is usually higher or equal to the nitrate concentration; and the soils will nitrify added ammonium if put in a soil perfuser in the laboratory, provided the soil conditions are otherwise suitable. They may differ from temperate soils in that the rate of nitrification when a ley or natural pasture is ploughed in is more dependent on the type of grass in the tropics than in temperate regions. Ploughing out native grass or savannah may lead to very low levels of available nitrogen for the next year or so,[2] and ploughing out planted leys will only give good levels of available nitrogen after some grasses, such as elephant grass (*Pennisetum purpureum*) and much poorer after others, such as some of the paspalum grasses,[3] although under some conditions, it may take two years for the nitrate level in the soil to reach normal levels after an elephant grass ley.[4]

The cause of the very low nitrate levels in old pastures compared with the low levels of ammonium nitrogen is not fully known, because, as shown above, there does not seem to be anything inherent in the soil preventing nitrification. J. J. Theron[5] tried to explain the low nitrate level by assuming the roots of the grasses excreted some soluble compound which inhibited nitrification, but this hypothesis runs into difficulties because one would expect a microbial population to be built up, perhaps slowly, around the grass roots which would decompose this product, so allowing nitrification to proceed normally.

NITRIFICATION IN FOREST SOILS

The level of mineral nitrogen in forest soils, and the forms in which it is present, depends on the pH of the soil and on the type of humus in the forest floor. C. H. Bornebusch[6] found in Danish forest soils with pHs in the range 4 to 5·5 that the rate of nitrification exceeded that of ammonification under mull though it did not under mor, as is shown in Table 67. The reason for this is possibly that the mull is better supplied with bases and phosphates than the mor, but this may not be the whole reason, for the mull is a form of humus produced by earthworms, and N. V. Joshi[7] noted that the introduction of earthworms into some India black cotton soils well supplied with bases and phosphate increased the rate of nitrification though this could also be because they increase the rate of decomposition of the organic matter.

Very few observations have been made on the level of ammonium

---

[1] For an example from the savannah region of Ghana, see D. J. Greenland, *J. Agric. Sci.*, 1958, **50**, 82.

[2] See, for example, W. G. Wells, *Queensland Agric. J.*, 1951, **73**, 109, and *Emp. Cotton Growing Corp. Rev.*, 1952, **29**, 94, and P. H. Nye, *Emp. J. Exp. Agric.*, 1951, **19**, 275.

[3] See W. R. Mills, *East Afr. Agric. J.*, 1953, **19**, 53.

[4] G. ap Griffith, *Emp. J. Exp. Agric.*, 1951, **19**, 1.   [5] *J. Agric. Sci.*, 1951, **41**, 289.

[6] *Forstl. Forsoegv. Danmark*, 1930, **11**, 1.   [7] *Bull. Nat. Inst. Sci. India*, 1954, **3**, 115.

and nitrate ions in tropical forest soils, but the evidence such as it is points to the similarity between tropical and temperate conditions. Thus D. J. Greenland,[1] in Ghana, found fairly high and fluctuating nitrate levels but low and fairly constant ammonium levels in the floor of a natural forest. He also found relatively high levels of readily nitrifiable nitrogen in these soils, as did H. Jenny[2] in Columbian forest soils and Y. Dommergues[3] in West African forest soils.

TABLE 67

The Effect of Type of Humus on Nitrification

Parts per million of ammonium and nitrate nitrogen in the soil

Mull Soils				Raw Humus Soils			
			Under	Beech			
Layer:	pH	NH$_4$	NO$_3$	Layer:	pH	NH$_4$	NO$_3$
Old leaf litter	. 6·1	84	1200	Old leaf layer	. 5·6	252	20
Wormcasts .	. 5·8	8	264	Upper raw humus.	4·3	388	trace
Upper mull .	. 5·4	4	48	Middle raw humus.	3·7	95	trace
Lower mull .	. 5·2	2	7·5				
			Under	Spruce			
Mull layer .	. 4·3	80	26	Upper raw humus .	3·6	115	0·8
Upper top soil .	. 4·1	2	5	Middle raw humus .	3·5	32	trace

Losses of Inorganic Nitrogen from the Soil

The inorganic nitrogen compounds—ammonia and nitrates—suffer several types of loss from the soil. They may be taken up by growing plants, they may be assimilated into the bodies of micro-organisms and so brought back into the organic nitrogen reservoir, they may be converted into volatile compounds and lost into the air, or they may be leached out of the soil. It is only the last two losses that will be considered here.

Ammonium can be lost to the atmosphere, in the form of ammonia, but probably only when an ammonium fertiliser is added to the surface of a calcareous soil.[4] Hence on such soils, particularly when the fertiliser is applied in hot dry weather, a nitrate fertiliser is more efficient than an ammonium, and if an ammonium fertiliser is used it

[1] *J. Agric. Sci.*, 1958, **50**, 82.   [2] *Soil Sci.*, 1949, **68**, 419.
[3] *Trans. 6th Int. Congr. Soil Sci.* (Paris), 1956, E, 605.
[4] For examples, see F. Crowther, *Emp. J. Expt. Agric.*, 1941, **9**, 125, and T. N. Jewitt, *Soil Sci.*, 1942, **54**, 401 (Sudan), D. A. van Schreven, *Trans. 4th Int. Congr. Soil Sci.* (Amsterdam), 1950, **1**, 259 (Holland), S. Tovborg Jensen and B. Kjaer, *Ztschr. PflErnähr.*, 1950, **50**, 25, and W. H. Willis and M. B. Sturgis, *Proc. Soil Sci. Soc. Amer.*, 1945, **9**, 106.

should be incorporated as deep as practicable in the soil. It is possible also that such losses can occur if readily decomposable organic matter high in nitrogen is added to alkaline soils in hot wet conditions, such as occur in some paddy fields; but there appears to be no experimental evidence to show if this is of any importance. The general practice in paddy cultivation is to use such organic fertilisers rather than ammonium sulphate as the nitrogen fertiliser when possible in such conditions, though if the ammonium sulphate is incorporated with a reasonable depth of soil, there is no reason to suppose it is any less efficient (see p. 263).

There must be processes for returning nitrogen from soil organic matter back to the air as nitrogen gas, and the only processes which have been proved to be of significance are the biological, and probably only the bacteriological reduction of nitrates or nitrite to nitrogen gas or to nitrous oxide, which breaks down in the atmosphere to nitrogen. Nitrogen can be liberated in the laboratory by the reaction between amines and nitrites in acid conditions:

$$R.NH_2 + NO_2^- \rightarrow R.OH + N_2 + OH^-$$

but work with ammonium and nitrites enriched with N^{15} have shown that this reaction is of no significance in field soils.[1] Nitrous oxide can be produced by the reaction between hydroxylamine and nitrites in conditions such as could occur in the soil

$$NH_2\,OH + NO_2^- \rightarrow N_2O + H_2O + OH^-$$

and this reaction was examined in the laboratory by P. W. Arnold[2] who put it forward to explain the production of nitrous oxide from ammonium ions in conditions when nitrates appeared not to be denitrified.

The biochemistry of denitrification in the soil is not yet fully understood, and it is best to describe the probable processes for nitrates and for ammonia separately. The denitrification of nitrates is a bacteriological reduction: the bacteria responsible obtaining from the nitrates part of the oxygen they need for the oxidations of the organic matter which they carry out; and the products of denitrification are primarily nitrogen gas and nitrous oxide, although it is possible that under some conditions ammonium ions may be produced as well. The poorer the aeration, the lower the level of microbiological activity needed for the reduction, and the better the aeration, the higher. Thus soils very well supplied with decomposable organic matter, as for example soils

[1] F. E. Allison and J. H. Doetsch, *Proc. Soil Sci. Soc. Amer.*, 1951, **15**, 163, and *Soil Sci.*, 1952, **74**, 311, E. J. Jones, *Soil Sci.*, 1951, **71**, 193, and A. Wahhab and F. Uddin, *Soil Sci.*, 1954, **78**, 119.
[2] *J. Soil Sci.*, 1954, **5**, 116.

receiving large dressings of farmyard manure, will denitrify nitrates readily even if they are well aerated, probably because there are many pockets of soil in which the micro-organisms are using up the soil oxygen at a greater rate than it can be replenished by diffusion from the atmosphere. The bacteria responsible for this include species of *Pseudomonas* and *Micrococcus* and a number of aerobic spore formers.[1] The proportion of nitrous oxide to nitrogen gas produced increases as the pH of the soil drops and as it becomes drier.[2]

Ammonium ions can be converted into nitrous oxide and nitrogen gas in moderately well aerated soils by being converted to nitrates, which are denitrified, and both processes can go on simultaneously in the same soil.[3] It is likely that the ammonium ions do not need to be oxidised as far as the nitrate stage, and in some acid soils it is possible that only a fraction need be oxidised to the nitrite, which then reacts with some fugitive product, possibly hydroxylamine, to give nitrous oxide, or with some amine to give nitrogen gas.[4] Further, as the soil becomes drier, the production of nitrous oxide from nitrates drops more rapidly than from ammonium salts, again indicating that the ammonium ions do not need to be oxidised to nitrates to be converted to nitrous oxide.[5] What has not been established is the lower limit of aeration at which this conversion of ammonium ions to nitrous oxide ceases, for it does not take place under anaerobic conditions; nor has it definitely been established if ammonium ions can be converted to nitrogen gas without first being oxidised to nitrite.

Various estimates can be made of the magnitude of denitrification in soils as a whole. Nitrous oxide occurs in the atmosphere, and it is being destroyed there at a rate corresponding to about 10 lb. per acre per year of nitrous oxide nitrogen.[6] If the most important source of nitrous oxide is denitrification of mineral nitrogen on land and sea, this must be the average production over the earth's surface, and since about equal amounts of nitrogen gas and nitrous oxide are produced during the denitrification of nitrates, this implies that the average rate of conversion of organic nitrogen compounds to gaseous nitrogen products is about 20 lb. per acre per year of nitrogen.

P. W. Arnold[7] has examined the rate of production of nitrous oxide

[1] J. Meiklejohn, *Ann. Appl. Biol.*, 1940, **27**, 558, W. Verhoeven, 'Aerobic spore forming nitrate reducing bacteria' (thesis), Delft, 1952, R. O. Marshall *et al.*, *J. Bact.*, 1953, **66**, 254.
[2] W. Verhoeven, thesis, 1952, F. E. Broadbent and B. F. Stojanovic, *Proc. Soil Sci. Soc. Amer.*, 1952, **16**, 359, J. Wijler and C. C. Delwiche, *Plant and Soil*, 1954, **5**, 155.
[3] For an example, see H. Loewenstein, L. E. Engelbert *et al.*, *Proc. Soil Sci. Soc. Amer.*, 1957, **21**, 397.
[4] F. C. Gerretsen, *Trans. 4th Int. Congr. Soil Sci.* (Amsterdam), 1950, **2**, 114 and with H. de Hoop, *Canad. J. Microbiol.*, 1957, **3**, 359. N. R. Dhar (*J. Ind. Chem. Soc.*, 1949, **26**, 227) also observed this.   [5] P. W. Arnold, *J. Soil Sci.*, 1954, **5**, 116.
[6] R. M. Goody and C. D. Walshaw, *Quart. J. Roy. Met. Soc.*, 1953, **79**, 496.
[7] *J. Soil Sci.*, 1954, **5**, 116.

nitrogen from some good English arable and pasture soils, and found that they could lose about one-tenth of their mineral nitrogen as nitrous oxide per day if the soil was wet, about one-hundredth if moist and one-thousandth if fairly dry. If such soils contain 10 p.p.m. of mineral nitrogen in the top 9 inches, these losses work out at about 3 to 0·03 lb. per acre per day of nitrous oxide, or if it was maintained at this level throughout the year, between 1,000 and 10 lb. per acre annually. As will be shown later some soils which are probably always well aerated, but which are high in readily decomposable organic matter, appear to lose between 50 and 150 lb. per acre annually, and this when the soil is cropped most of the time, so the nitrate content will remain low.

TABLE 68

The Nitrogen Balance Sheet of a Soil kept Free from Vegetation but Exposed to Rain and Weather[1]

Year	Per cent N in soil, top 9 in.	N in soil, top 9 in. lb. per acre	Loss of N from top 9 in. lb. per acre	N recovered as nitrate 1870–1915 lb. per acre[2]
1870 . . .	0·146	3500	—	—
1905 . . .	0·102	2450	1050	987
1915 . . .	0·098	2350	1150	1223

These figures therefore indicate that at least a part of the nitrous oxide in the atmosphere may have come from the soil, and it is not impossible that a considerable part has.

J. M. Bremner and K. Shaw[3] have studied the conditions which affect the rate of loss of nitrate nitrogen from soils, and as with Arnold's results, find that a normal Rothamsted soil supplied with nitrate and glucose, could lose about 85 per cent of the nitrate in five days. This rate of loss was slow in acid conditions, especially below pH 4·8, and was high in slightly alkaline conditions, pH 8–8·6. It was slow in cold soils, increased rapidly with rise in temperature up to 25°C. and was an optimum at 60°C. They found no loss in moist well-aerated soils.

Turning to the field, nitrogen losses from the soil can take three forms: nitrogen compounds in crops harvested from the soil, nitrates leached out from the soil, and unaccounted losses presumably in the

[1] Constructed from data given in N. H. J. Miller, *J. Agric. Sci.*, 1906, **1**, 377; and E. J. Russell and E. H. Richards, ibid., 1920, **10**, 22.
[2] After deducting the amount brought down in the rain. No significance should be attached to the difference between the last two columns owing to the assumptions involved in obtaining, and the uncertainties in interpreting, the figure for the weight of nitrogen in the top 9 inches of the soil.
[3] *J. Agri. Sci.*, 1958, **51**, 22.

TABLE 69

Losses of Nitrogen from a Cultivated Soil
Broadbalk, Rothamsted, 49 years, 1865-1914

Pounds per acre in top 9 inches of soil

	Farmyard manure (Plot 2B)	No manure (Plot 3)	Complete Artificials (86 lb. N as sulphate of ammonia annually)	
			(Plot 7)	(Plot 13)[1]
N in soil in 1865, lb. per acre . .	4850	2960	3390	3320
per cent . .	0·196	0·114	0·123	0·121
N in soil in 1914, lb. per acre . .	5590	2570	3210	3240
per cent . .	0·236	0·092	0·120	0·122
Total change in 49 years, lb. per acre	+740	−390	−180	− 80
N added in manure, seed and rain, per annum	208	7	93	93
N removed in crops, per annum .	50	17	46	44
N retained (+) or lost (−) by soil per annum	+15	− 8	− 4	− 2
N unaccounted for, per annum .	143	(gain 2)	51	51

form of nitrogen gas and nitrous oxides. In general, if the mineral nitrogen status of a soil is low, the only two losses of nitrogen appear to be loss by leaching and loss in the crop, whilst if it is high, and particularly if it is being maintained high by good husbandry so the microbiological activity is also high, there can be very large unaccounted losses.[2]

The Rothamsted drain gauges give a good example of the losses from a bare uncropped soil being accounted for almost entirely as nitrates leaching out of the soil. These gauges, each 1/1,000 acre in area, have been kept free from vegetation since 1870, and by 1915 had lost one-third of the nitrogen originally present in the top 9 inches of soil. As Table 68 shows, practically all this nitrogen was found as nitrate.

The unmanured plot on Broadbalk, the permanent wheat field at Rothamsted, gives an example of the full nitrogen loss from the soil being accounted for by the nitrogen in the crop removed, as shown in Table 69. But this table shows that when nitrogen is added either as sulphate of ammonia, or as farmyard manure, very large losses occur, no less than 70 per cent of the nitrogen in the farmyard manure being unaccounted for. Some of this loss undoubtedly occurs in the drainage

[1] These plots are almost duplicates, plot 7 receiving 100 lb. each of the sulphates of soda and magnesia in addition to the 3½ cwt. of superphosphate and 200 lb. sulphate of potash given to plot 13.   [2] For a recent review, see F. E. Allison, *Adv. Agron.*, 1955, **7**, 213.

water, which cannot be estimated accurately in the field experiment, but it is very unlikely it could account for any appreciable proportion of it.

TABLE 70

Loss of Nitrogen from Soil under Crops Liberally Supplied with Inorganic Nitrogen (Cornell, N.Y.)

	Nitrogen changes in pounds of nitrogen per acre			
	Timothy (9-year period)		Market garden crops (15-year period)	
			Nitrogen as	
	High nitrogen	Low nitrogen	Sulphate of ammonia	Nitrate of soda
Lost from soil	—90	—40	470	710
Added as fertiliser and rain . .	1860	700	2230	2230
Total	1770	660	2700	2940
Removed in crop	1290	640	1400	1640
Removed in drainage water . .	40	20	630	690
Total	1330	660	2030	2330
Unaccounted for	440	—	670	610
As per cent added as fertiliser . .	24	—	31	28

Lysimeter experiments with growing crops can, however, give more detailed information about this loss, because the amount of nitrogen lost in the drainage water can be measured.[1] Table 70, due to J. A. Bizzell[2] at Cornell University, shows that provided the level of available nitrogen in the soil is low, there is no unaccounted loss, but if it is raised by manuring it is appreciable.

These unaccounted losses also occur when grassland is converted to arable, or when virgin prairie soil is broken up for cropping. Oxidation of the organic matter and nitrification both proceed rapidly in the initial years, but only a small part of the loss of soil nitrogen can be

[1] For a review of results obtained from lysimeters see H. Kohnke, F. R. Dreibelbis and J. M. Davidson, *U.S. Dept. Agric., Misc. Publ.* 372, 1940.
[2] *Cornell Agric. Expt. Sta., Mem.* 252, 1943; *Mem.* 256, 1944. For an example from California, see H. D. Chapman *et al., Hilgardia,* 1949, **19**, 57.

TABLE 71

Losses of Nitrogen Consequent on Breaking up of Prairie Land
Top 9 inches

	Per cent	Lb. per acre
Nitrogen present in unbroken prairie . . .	0·371	6940
Nitrogen present after 22 years' cultivation . .	0·254	4750
Loss from soil		2190
Recovered in crop		700
Deficit, being dead loss		1490
Annual dead loss		68

accounted for in the crop. Table 71 gives an example of this at Indian Head, Saskatchewan,[1] where the rainfall is sufficiently low for there to be very little drainage from the soil. These large losses occur in the early years after breaking up the prairie, for E. S. Hopkins and A. Leahey,[2] continuing Shutt's work at Indian Head, found that in the next sixteen years almost the whole of the loss of soil nitrogen could be accounted for by the nitrogen in the wheat. H. E. Myers and his co-workers[3] in Kansas have shown that this loss of nitrogen is proportional to the nitrogen content of the soil in excess of its equilibrium value for the rotation adopted; thus for the wheat and barley rotations used, nitrogen losses only occurred if the nitrogen content of the soil exceeded 0·10 per cent.

All these results and conclusions can be readily explained by Arnold's results on denitrification, already discussed. The observed losses could all be proportional to the average level of mineral nitrogen in the soil, and though they are higher than the calculated mean annual loss of nitrogen for the world as a whole, this would be expected as the examples have all been chosen from soils whose nitrogen status is well above their equilibrium levels.

Gains of Nitrogen by the Soil

Most soils are continuously losing nitrogen by one or more of the processes so far described; they must possess, therefore, some methods for gaining it to balance these losses. Arable soils in the temperate

[1] F. T. Shutt, *J. Agric. Sci.*, 1910, **3**, 335.
[2] *Dom. Canada Dept. Agric.*, *Publ.* 761, 1944.
[3] *Kansas Agric. Expt. Sta.*, *Tech. Bull.* 56, 1943. For an example from the Canadian prairies, see J. D. Newton *et al.*, *Sci. Agric.*, 1945, **21**, 718; and for the Great Plains, H. J. Haas *et al.*, *U.S. Dept. Agric.*, *Tech. Bull.* 1164, 1957.

regions, if allowed to revert either to natural forest or to pasture, rapidly gain nitrogen and organic matter. On Broadbalk field, for example, a third plot adjacent to the two quoted in Table 69 carried a wheat crop in 1882 which was never harvested: the plot was allowed to revert to natural prairie by cutting out all bushes and trees at regular intervals. A. D. Hall[1] found that in 1904, after twenty-two years, the vegetation consisted of 60 per cent grasses, 15 per cent miscellaneous herbs and 25 per cent legumes, mainly meadow vetchling (*Lathyrus pratensis*). The gains in nitrogen and organic matter during this period were considerable, as shown in Table 72. The nitrogen is all in organic compounds, for the nitrate and ammonium remain at low levels—the nitrate well below that of arable land and the ammonium a little above it. The gain in nitrogen in a neighbouring field, Geescroft, which carried clover in 1885 and was then allowed to go derelict, is also given

TABLE 72

Gain in Nitrogen in Soils Permanently Covered with Vegetation
Rothamsted Soils Left to Run Wild for over Twenty Years

	Broadbalk: $CaCO_3$, 3·32 per cent				Geescroft: $CaCO_3$, 0·16 per cent			
	Carbon, per cent		Nitrogen, per cent		Carbon, per cent		Nitrogen, per cent	
	1881	1904	1881	1904	1883	1904	1883	1904
1st 9 inches .	1·14	1·23	0·108	0·145	1·11	1·49	0·108	0·131
2nd 9 inches .	0·62	0·70	0·070	0·095	0·60	0·63	0·074	0·083
3rd 9 inches .	0·46	0·55	0·058	0·084	0·45	0·44	0·060	0·065
Approximate gain in nitrogen, lb. per acre				2200	. . . . .			1400
Lb. per acre per annum . . .				92	. . . . .			60

in Table 72. This soil contains much less calcium carbonate, has about the same mechanical analysis, but it is much worse drained and lies water-logged for long periods. It also had a very unkind tilth for a number of years previously. In 1904 the grass *Aira caespitosa* composed 86 per cent of the plants present and legumes were almost entirely absent, composing only 0·4 per cent of the plants present; yet its annual gain of nitrogen was only about 35 per cent less than that of the Broadbalk plot.

In the same way arable land laid down to pasture increases in nitrogen content: the typical nitrogen content of Rothamsted arable soils is about 0·11 per cent and of old grassland about 0·25 per cent, and H. L. Richardson[2] estimated it takes about twenty-five years for

[1] *J. Agric. Sci.*, 1905, **1**, 241.   [2] *J. Agric. Sci.*, 1938, **28**, 73.

half this gain to take place, as is shown in Fig. 23. This rate of gain works out at about 70 lb. per acre per year of nitrogen in the top 9 inches of soil over this period, but these pastures will contain clovers.

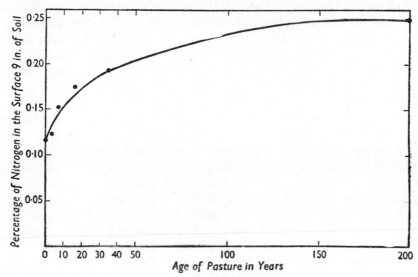

FIG. 23. The rate of accumulation of nitrogen in the top 9 in. of soil at Rothamsted when old arable land is laid down to grass.

But land laid down to grass can accumulate nitrogen in the soil even if the pasture contains no clovers. Thus, T. L. Lyon and H. O. Buckman,[1] at Ithaca, found the soil under a grass ley, apparently free from legumes, accumulated 40 lb. of nitrogen per acre per year if the ley was cut and the grass left on the surface, but lost a few pounds if the hay, which contained about 20 lb. of nitrogen per year, was removed. Similarly, J. W. White, F. J. Holben and A. C. Richer,[2] working in Pennsylvania, found the soil under a grass ley described as free from leguminous plants, gained 15 to 30 lb. of nitrogen per year.

Soils can gain small amounts of nitrogen from the rain which falls on them. Thus at Rothamsted[3] rainwater carries down annually about 4 lb. per acre of nitrogen as ammonia and nitrates, at Cornell[4] the figure is about 5 lb. and elsewhere in the world[5] it varies from 2 to 20 lb. per acre. These quantities are clearly quite inadequate to give the gains of soil nitrogen just quoted, although in some stable and mature ecological regions, such as undisturbed natural forests, it may be sufficient to balance the losses of nitrogen by leaching.

[1] *The Nature and Properties of Soils*, 4th ed., New York, 1943, p. 393.
[2] *J. Amer. Soc. Agron.*, 1945, **37**, 21.   [3] N. H. J. Miller, *J. Agric. Sci.*, 1905, **1**, 280.
[4] E. W. Leland, *Agron. J.*, 1952, **44**, 172.
[5] See, for example, E. Erikson, *Tellus.*, 1952, **4**, 215, for a collection of published data.

The most important natural process for increasing the nitrogen content of soils in temperate agriculture is through bacteria living in the nodules of leguminous plants, a process discussed later on in this chapter. Thus on p. 348 it is shown that a good clover or lucerne crop will increase the organic nitrogen in the soil by over 100 lb. per acre annually—a quantity which can be measured without much difficulty. Symbiotic nitrogen fixation is also brought about in root nodules on certain trees and shrubs, probably by actinomycetes though this has not been adequately proved; and this process appears to be of importance in the colonisation of land after it had been freed from the ice-sheets which covered much of the Northern Hemisphere, or of sandy land left by the retreat of the sea. This process is discussed in more detail on pp. 325–6, but it has not yet been used in agriculture. It is also possible, but not yet properly proven, that nitrogen fixation may take place in nodules on the leaves of certain plants, or even by bacteria living on their leaves, processes mentioned again on p. 326.

Nitrogen fixation can also take place in soils by processes which do not involve living plants. A number of pigmented bacteria capable of photosynthesis are also capable of nitrogen fixation, and indeed these two properties may be very closely linked.[1] But these micro-organisms are all anaerobes and the only ones for which there is any evidence that they may be of importance for agriculture are the non-sulphur purple bacteria (Athiorhodaceae) which occur in many water-logged paddy soils.[2] The blue-green algae also fix nitrogen in sunlight, as described on p. 163, but they can function in aerobic as well as anaerobic conditions, and whilst of importance in paddy soils and in the water lying on the soil, they may also be of minor importance on the surface of moist soils under some conditions. There are also a number of bacteria which fix nitrogen in the soil itself, of which the *Azotobacter* and *Clostridia* groups are of most importance, or at least have been most intensively studied; but there may be many other groups, occurring in much higher numbers in the soil than these two, which can take some part in the process.

One further point that should be emphasised once again in this introduction is this. Biological nitrogen fixation only appears to take place in soils when the vegetation is not in equilibrium with the soil and climate, or when nitrogen compounds are being removed from the land. Thus agriculturally biological nitrogen fixation is always likely to be going on, to a greater or lesser extent, unless the farmer is regularly using appreciable amounts of farmyard manure or other organic or inorganic nitrogen manures or fertilisers.

[1] For a review, see J. L. Stokes, *Ann. Rev. Microbiol.*, 1952, **6**, 29.
[2] A. Okuda *et al.*, *Soil and Plant Food*, 1957, **2**, 131, and *6th Int. Congr. Soil Sci.* (Paris) 1956 C, 521.

Non-symbiotic Fixation of Nitrogen

Soils contain a number of free living nitrogen-fixing organisms, and though most investigations have been confined to two groups of bacteria and some blue-green algae, modern techniques based on the use of air enriched with either the stable isotope N^{15} or the radio-active N^{13} have demonstrated conclusively that a number of other organisms can convert atmospheric nitrogen into organic compounds. Excluding the blue-green algae and the photosynthetic bacteria, the organisms which have been proved to fix nitrogen appear to be:

1. Bacteria of the genus *Azotobacter*. The common soil species are *chroococcum, beijerinckii* and *vinelandii*, and are relatively large organisms encased in bacterial gum. They are aerobic, and usually confined to soils well supplied with phosphate and not more acid than pH 6,[1] though species have been found in acid soils.[2] Though widely distributed, they do not occur in many soils that are apparently suitable for them.

2. Bacteria of the genus *Beijerinckia*. The first species discovered was originally described as an *Azotobacter* (*A. indicum*), but H. G. Derx[3] separated it from *Azotobacter* on morphological grounds, and subsequently H. L. Jensen[4] showed they differ in their nutritional requirements, for *Beijerinckia* has a lower calcium demand than *Azotobacter* and it cannot use vanadium in place of molybdenum. It appears to be a tropical genus for Y. T. Tchan[5] could only isolate it from Australian soils collected north of latitude 18°S., and A. J. Kluyver and J. H. Becking[6] failed to find it in any of a large number of temperate soils they examined. However, T. Suto[7] isolated it from a Japanese volcanic soil in latitude 38°N.

Three species of *Beijerinckia* have been recognised, all of them very acid tolerant though they are not confined to acid soils. They have been isolated from many different parts of the tropics, but details of their distribution are not yet known. J. Ruinen[8] has also recorded them as occurring in large numbers on the leaves of some tropical forest trees and lianas (p. 327).

3. Many bacteria belonging to the *Clostridium* group, and perhaps all that occur in soils. These differ from the two preceding in being

---

[1] H. L. Jensen (*Tidsskr. Planteavl*, 1950, **53**, 622) and A. Kaila (*Maataloust. Aikak.*, 1954, **26**, 40) find none occur below pH 5·8. T. McKnight (*Queensland J. Agric. Sci.*, 1949, **6**, 177) finds a few in soils between pH 5·5 and 6·0.
[2] For example by Y. T. Tchan, *Proc. Linn. Soc. N.S.W.*, 1953, **78**, 83, and H. L. Jensen, *Acta Agric. Scand.*, 1955, **5**, 280.
[3] H. G. Derx, *Meded. Konink. Ned. Akad. Wetens.*, 1950, **53**, No. 2.
[4] *Bact. Rev.*, 1954, **18**, 195.
[5] *Proc. Linn. Soc. N.S.W.*, 1953, **78**, 171.   [6] *Ann. Acad. Sci. Fennicae*, 1955, **60**, 367.
[7] *Sci. Rep. Res. Inst. Tohuku Univ.*, Sec. D, 1954, **6**, 25.   [8] *Nature*, 1956, **177**, 220.

found in nearly every soil in which they have been adequately looked for. They have only been proved, in the laboratory, to fix nitrogen under conditions of low oxygen tension, but these conditions are likely to occur in isolated pockets for short periods in soils normally considered well aerated.

4. P. W. Wilson and his co-workers have recently shown that a number of common soil bacteria, belonging to the genera *Aerobacter*,[1] *Achromobacter* and *Pseudomonas*[2] can also fix nitrogen, to a small extent under aerobic conditions, but better under conditions of low oxygen tension. Although they appear to be far less efficient nitrogen fixers than the previous groups they are present in far larger numbers in the soil, so their overall importance may be much greater.

5. A few other soil bacteria[3] have been claimed to be nitrogen fixers.

6. Two yeasts, one a *Saccharomyces* and one a *Rhodotorula*, found in the subsoils of acid heaths of pH 4·5 under *Betula* and *Calluna* in Kent have been proved to be nitrogen fixers, but being subsoil organisms they were only present in very small numbers.[4]

There are at present no techniques for estimating the relative contributions made to the nitrogen compounds in the soil by these groups. *Azotobacter* appear to be relatively rare organisms in most agricultural soils, although commoner in clay soils than sands.[5] Thus J. Meiklejohn only found up to 200 cells per gram of soil from eight Broadbalk plots, and even these low numbers showed considerable seasonal variation; H. L. Jensen[6] found under 1,000 per gram of soil in 90 per cent of the 264 Danish soils in which he looked for them, and G. R. Anderson[7] found similar results in the Palouse region of Washington. *Clostridia* are present both in a wider range of soils and in larger numbers, usually from tens to hundreds of thousands per gram of soil. These numbers are extremely low compared with total population of several thousand million. Unfortunately there is still considerable doubt about the efficiency of the counting techniques employed for these two groups,[8] and they may be very considerably under-estimated.

The chemistry of the nitrogen fixation process is not known. The four organisms that have been investigated in detail—blue-green algae,

---

[1] With P. B. Hamilton, *Ann. Acad. Sci. Fenn.*, A II Chem., 1955, **60**, 139.

[2] With M. H. Proctor, *Nature*, 1958, **182**, 891.

[3] For example by Y. T. Tchan and J. Pochon, *C.R.*, 1950, **230**, 417, and Y. T. Tchan, *Proc. Linn. Soc. N.S.W.*, 1952, **77**, 92, F. D. Sisler and C. E. Zobell, *Science*, 1951, **113**, 511.

[4] G. Metcalfe and S. Chayen, *Nature*, 1954, **174**, 841, and E. R. Roberts and T. G. G. Wilson, *Nature*, 1954, **174**, 842.

[5] See, for example, T. McKnight, *Queensland J. Agric. Sci.*, 1949, **6**, 177.

[6] *Trans. 4th Int. Congr. Soil Sci.* (Amsterdam), 1950, **1**, 165.

[7] *Soil Sci.*, 1958, **86**, 57.

[8] For a discussion of some of the problems involved, see F. M. Collins, *Aust. J. Exp. Biol.*, 1952, **30**, 587, and C. A. Parker, *Aust. J. Agric. Res.*, 1954, **5**, 90.

Azotobacter, *Clostridia* and the nodule bacteria—may all use the same process. All four use an enzyme reaction that is suppressed by carbon monoxide or hydrogen gas, and all need small amounts of molybdenum for efficient working although larger quantities of vanadium will allow them to work less efficiently;[1] and all four only fix nitrogen when the level of available nitrogen salts is low. The first product of nitrogen fixation is not known for certain, but presumptive evidence is that it is ammonia which then reacts with α-ketoglutaric acid to give glutamic acid.[2] *Clostridia* in pure cultures excrete soluble nitrogen compounds into the surrounding medium during their period of active growth, whereas *Azotobacter* usually only do this after their rapid growth has ceased.[3]

Nitrogen fixation goes on more actively under conditions of poor than of good aeration, provided no hydrogen gas is being produced. Thus C. A. Parker[4] found that his strains of *Azotobacter*, which are usually regarded as aerobic organisms, fixed about 22 mgm. N per gm. of sucrose used when the oxygen content of the air was 4 per cent, but only 8 mgm. when it was 20 per cent. Again it will grow symbiotically with facultative anaerobes under partially anaerobic conditions on plant residues, such as cellulose, hay or straw: there must be an inadequate supply of nitrogen compounds for the facultative anaerobes, and there must be an air supply sufficiently restricted for the fermenting bacteria to convert a considerable proportion of the cellulose into simple acids, such as lactic, butyric or acetic.[5] Thus, under water-logged conditions H. L. Jensen and R. J. Swaby[6] found that *Azotobacter* could fix about 14 mgm. of nitrogen per gm. of cellulose decomposed, and most of this nitrogen was taken up by the other bacteria. C. J. Lind and P. W. Wilson[7] also found that under these symbiotic conditions *Azotobacter* could fix nitrogen efficiently with a much more restricted supply of available iron than in pure culture.

Clostridia have usually been claimed to be less efficient fixers of nitrogen in pure cultures than *Azotobacter*, fixing only 6·8 mgm. per gm. of sugar decomposed compared with about 20 mgm., but E. D. Rosenblum and P. W. Wilson[8] showed this was principally due to the conditions in the medium not being favourable to high fixation rates, and when these were assured, the efficiencies of the two organisms were similar. They also showed that using proper techniques all the soil

---

[1] This last result does not apply to *Beijerinckia* for some reason (p. 321).

[2] For reviews see R. H. Burris and P. W. Wilson, *Ann. Rev. Biochem.*, 1945, **14**, 685, and *Bact. Rev.*, 1947, **11**, 41, and A. I. Virtanen, *Ann. Rev. Microbiol.*, 1948, **2**, 485.

[3] D. Burk and R. H. Burris, *Ann. Rev. Biochem.*, 1941, **10**, 587.

[4] *Nature*, 1954, **173**, 780. For earlier examples, see D. Burk, *J. Phys. Chem.*, 1930, **34**, 1195; H. L. Jensen, *Proc. Linn. Soc. N.S.W.*, 1940, **65**, 1.

[5] E. H. Richards, *J. Agric. Sci.*, 1939, **29**, 302.   [6] *Proc. Linn. Soc. N.S.W.*, 1941, **66**, 89.

[7] *Soil Sci.*, 1942, **54**, 102.   [8] *J. Bact.*, 1949, **57**, 413, and 1950, **59**, 83.

Clostridia which could be made to grow actively in their media were active nitrogen fixers.

The efficiency of fixing nitrogen by *Achromobacter* and *Pseudomonas* in aerobic conditions is lower than these figures, being between 1 and 4 mgm. nitrogen fixed per gm. of sugar decomposed,[1] and although Proctor and Wilson state that poor aeration increases the rate of nitrogen fixation, they gave no figures for its effect on the efficiency of fixation.

The soil conditions favouring non-symbiotic nitrogen fixation conform with expectations based on these results, for this nitrogen fixation only seems to be an important factor in soils whose organic nitrogen content is below the equilibrium value for the current system of cropping and in which the ammonium and nitrate levels are low, a good example being old arable land going to a low legume grass or scrub vegetation. There is a return, small at first and then larger, of dead plant tissues low in nitrogen, and the greater the return of dead plant material, that is, the better the soil is supplied with nutrients or the better drained the soil, the more rapid the fixation, as can be seen from the figures for Broadbalk and Geescroft Wildernesses given in Table 72 on page 318.

TABLE 73

Effect of Glucose and Sucrose on the Productiveness and Nitrogen Content of the Soil

Sugar added per 100 gm. of soil in Spring 1905	Crops obtained				Total N removed in both crops	Nitrogen left in soil, Spring 1906	
	Oats, 1905		Sugar-beet, 1906		Gm.	Total N per cent	N as nitrate, parts per million
	Dry matter	Yield of N	Dry matter	Yield of N			
None . . .	100	100	100	100	0·591	0·093	10
2 gm. glucose . .	32·8	62·5	186	190	0·681	0·105	17
2 gm. sucrose . .	33·3	58·7	179	195	0·680	0·105	15
4 gm. sucrose . .	37·7	78·1	283	339	1·099	0·119	37

Non-symbiotic nitrogen fixation also occurs when high levels of readily decomposable carbonaceous matter is added to the soil, such as sugar for example. The first effect of adding sugar is to reduce the ammonium and nitrate production, with a consequent reduction in plant growth at this period, but later on the increased nitrogen content

[1] M. H. Proctor and P. W. Wilson, *Nature*, 1958, **182**, 891.

of the soil gives an increase in the readily nitrifiable nitrogen compounds. Table 73, taken from some pot experiments of A. Koch,[1] gives an example of this effect. Adding carbonaceous matter to the soil does not always give this effect. Ploughing in straw without the addition of extra nitrogen usually reduces the yield of the following crop and does not increase the yield of the next.

Russian workers have claimed that the nitrogen economy of the soil can be improved by suitably inoculating it with *Azotobacter*, without adding any additional energy-containing material. This practice appears to be widespread in Russia at the present time and has already been mentioned on p. 227.

Symbiotic Nitrogen Fixation in Non-leguminous Plants

Symbiotic nitrogen fixation takes place in plants belonging to families other than the Leguminoseae. A group that has been intensively studied are typically plants of moist or wet lands belonging to several families.[2] They include alder (*Alnus glutinosa*),[3] bog myrtle (*Myrica gale*),[4] species from the three genera belonging to the family Elaeagnaceae, namely, sea buckthorn (*Hippophae rhamnoides*),[5] *Sheppardia* spp.[6] and *Elaeagnus* spp. and to the genera *Coriaria*,[7] *Ceanothus* and the sub-tropical and tropical *Casuarina*. The nodules are similar to leguminous nodules in being red inside, though the colour is due to an anthocyanin[8] and not to a haemoglobin being present. They differ from leguminous ones in that the symbiont or symbionts have not been grown in pure culture, nor is it certain to what group of organisms they belong. In the nodules they give the appearance of actinomycete hyphae,[9] but L. E. Hawker and J. Fraymouth[10] have made out a case for their belonging to the Plasmodiophora or slime fungi. The symbiont is not the same for all the plants in this group, and appears to be different for each family. It is different for *Alnus*, *Myrica* and *Hippophae*, as these cannot be cross-inoculated, but may be the same for the three genera in the Elaeagnaceae, as these can be cross-inoculated.[11] The

[1] *J. Landw.*, 1907, **55**, 355.
[2] For an extensive review of this subject, together with lists of species on which nodules have been found, see E. K. and O. N. Allen, *Handb. Pfl. Physiol.*, 1958, **8**, 48.
[3] G. Bond, *J. Exp. Bot.*, 1956, **7**, 387, and *New Phytol.*, 1956, **55**, 147.
[4] G. Bond, *Ann. Bot.*, 1951, **15**, 447, and 1952, **16**, 467.
[5] G. Bond and his co-workers, *Plant and Soil*, 1954, **5**, 309, and *Ann. Bot.*, 1956, **20**, 501.
[6] I. C. Gardner and G. Bond, *Can. J. Bot.*, 1957, **35**, 305.
[7] G. Bond and P. Montserrat, *Nature*, 1958, **182**, 474.
[8] G. Bond, *Ann. Bot.*, 1951, **15**, 447.
[9] For pictures of this, see K. Shibata, *Jahr. wiss. Bot.*, 1902, **37**, 643, and with M. Thaharo, *Bot. Mag. Tokyo*, 1917, **31**, 157, and R. Schaeder, *Planta.*, 1933, **19**, 389.
[10] *J. Gen. Microbiol.*, 1951, **5**, 369.
[11] M. Roberg, *Jahrb. wiss. Bot.*, 1934, **79**, 472, and G. Bond and his co-workers, *Plant and Soil*, 1954, **5**, 309, and *Canad. J. Bot.*, 1957, **35**, 305.

nodules have a much less regular shape than are usually found on leguminous roots. If the plant is growing in wet conditions, the nodules often send up roots devoid of root hairs to the surface, though whether their function is to increase the oxygen supply to the symbiont has not yet been proved. G. Bond and J. T. MacConnell[1] have, however, shown that a fairly good oxygen supply is necessary for high rates of fixation: for alder a reduction of oxygen content from 21 to 12 per cent nearly halves the rate of nitrogen fixation. Further, some of these plants will fix nitrogen when growing in very acid soils. Thus G. Bond[2] finds *Myrica gale* can fix nitrogen actively at pH 5·4, probably at pH 4·2, and doubtfully at pH 3·7.

The chemistry of the nitrogen fixing processes in these nodules is not known, but it is probably as efficient a process as in leguminous nodules. Further, it continues to go on in isolated nodules for a much longer time and much more efficiently than in isolated leguminous ones.[3] The rate of fixation per gram of nodule is similar to that in legumes, *Alnus* nodules fixing about 800 mgm. and *Myrica* and *Casuarina* about 400 mgm. nitrogen per gram of dry matter during the growing season compared with about 700 mgm. for field beans and red clover and 250 mgm. for soybeans.[4]

Other groups of plants have also been claimed to carry symbiotic nitrogen-fixing mechanisms either on their roots or leaves. Thus R. Douin[5] has claimed that certain members of the Cycadaceae have roots bearing nodules containing the nitrogen-fixing blue-green alga *Anabaena cycadeae*. One species, *Cycas circinalis*, which he claimed to have this property, occurs in rather dry thickets and coastal forests in East Africa, and is even cultivated along the coastal strip. This family is a relict from the end of the Triassic period.

A number of tropical shrubs have knots or swellings on their leaves which contain bacteria and which have been claimed to fix nitrogen. Most of the shrubs belong to the family Rubiaceae,[6] although *Dioscora*,[7] a monocotyledon, also possesses them. These claims for nitrogen fixation were all made many years ago, and no work appears to have been published in which this possibility has been re-investigated using modern techniques. These claims, if well founded, would be of great ecological interest, as many tropical rain forests contain numerous tree species belonging to the Rubiaceae as well as to the Leguminoseae, and the leguminous trees are, on the whole, not nodulated possibly because the Rubiaceae are the principal source of new nitrogen compounds for

[1] *Nature*, 1955, **176**, 606. [2] *Ann. Bot.*, 1951, **15**, 447.
[3] G. Bond, *J. Exp. Bot.*, 1955, **6**, 303.
[4] G. Bond, *Ann. Bot.*, 1957, **21**, 373. [5] *C.R.*, 1953, **236**, 956.
[6] F. C. Faber, *Jahrb. wiss. Bot.*, 1912, **51**, 285; K. A. Rao, *Agric. J. India*, 1923, **18**, 132.
[7] M. Y. Orr, *Edinb. Roy. Bot. Gardens*, Notes, 1924, **14**, 57.

this type of vegetation (but see p. 237). J. Ruinen[1] has found species of the non-symbiotic nitrogen-fixing bacterium *Beijerinckia* very common inhabitants of the leaf surface of many such plants, and has suggested that this bacterial genus is not a true soil inhabitant but a leaf inhabitant, and this is the reason it is confined to soils in tropical areas. If this picture is correct, it is an example of a bacterium occupying a half-way house to specialised symbiotic activity.

Symbiotic Nitrogen Fixation in Leguminous Plants

Certain leguminous plants are very extensively cultivated in temperate agriculture, and correspondingly their ability to fix nitrogen has been equally extensively investigated. But D. O. Norris[2] has emphasised that any general discussion on symbiotic nitrogen fixation must be based on the fact that the great majority of leguminous genera and species are tropical, and that the ancestral ecological niche was probably on fairly strongly leached soils in tropical rain forests. The temperate and sub-tropical legumes developed from these, and some of them, particularly certain species belonging to the Trifolieae, which includes the genera *Trifolium*, *Medicago*, *Melilotus* and *Trigonella*, and the Vicieae, which includes the genera *Vicia*, *Pisum*, *Lens*, *Cicer* and *Lathyrus*, have become adapted to neutral or calcareous soils of higher nutrient status. A high proportion of the leguminous crops cultivated in temperate agriculture belong to these groups, and a very considerable proportion of the research work done on legumes has been confined to a few species having this untypical demand for fertile soils of high calcium saturation. A great many of the statements made in this chapter may therefore be of limited validity: how limited cannot be known until far more work has been done on the tropical species.

A typical statement often heard is that leguminous crops carry nodules on their roots, which fix nitrogen, and therefore legumes raise the nitrogen status of the soil. This statement is only doubtfully true for the cultivated large-seeded crops, such as peas, beans, soybeans and groundnuts because, even if their roots are well nodulated, which is often not so when they are grown under good farming conditions, a large proportion of the nitrogen they have fixed is removed from the land in the seed crop, and nearly all the rest is in the vines or straw which again is usually removed at harvest time. And in the tropics many legumes, grown for the ostensible purpose of raising the nitrogen status of the soil, are not even nodulated for most of the growing season. It is not known if there are genera or sub-families which never carry nodules on their roots, and the problem is complicated because a

[1] *Nature*, 1956, **177**, 220. 　　　　[2] *Emp. J. Exp. Agric.*, 1956, **24**, 247.

leguminous plant growing in one habitat, for example, high tropical rain forest, may rarely be nodulated, yet it may be commonly well nodulated in another habitat, for example, on the fringes of the forest.[1]

The nodules, which are found on the roots of leguminous crops, vary widely in their shape and size, but typically they are excrescences on the outside of the root, which can be easily broken off; in fact one can often only tell if a plant is nodulated by digging it up and carefully removing the soil from around its roots. The nodules may be spherical, though they are usually elongated, or flat and grooved, or may have finger-like projections, or they may be irregular and sometimes convoluted, though they usually have a smooth surface. Their size may vary from that of a pin head to over 1 cm., but the larger nodules are never spherical but have shapes giving a high ratio of surface area to volume, possibly to ensure an adequate supply of nitrogen gas to the active nodule cells and an adequate means of disposal of the carbon dioxide produced in the nodule. Typical shapes on clover and lucerne roots are illustrated in Plates XII and XVI.

Nodules contain bacteria living symbiotically with the plant; the plant leaves supplying the carbohydrate and the bacteria the amino acids for the combined organism. But the bacteria become parasitic if for any reason the carbohydrate supply is restricted, as, for example, by keeping the plant in the dark,[2] or by restricting the boron supply[3] so that the vascular strands supplying carbohydrates to the nodule fail to develop, for the nodules form close to the vascular strands, as can be seen in Plate XIV. This parasitism also occurs normally in old nodules, resulting in their decay, and in nodules of some annuals such as peas and vetches at the time of flowering or setting of seed.[4]

THE BIOCHEMISTRY OF NITROGEN FIXATION

The biochemistry of the nodule is only partially understood, the great experimental difficulty being that the bacteria can so far only be made to fix nitrogen effectively when living in nodules attached to the living plant, although they will fix a little nitrogen for a short time after the nodule is cut off from the root.[5]

Symbiotic fixation also differs from non-symbiotic in that a substance similar to haemoglobin, and sometimes called leghaemoglobin, is essential for the process;[6] for there is a good correlation between the

[1] For an example from the Yangambi forests (Belgian Congo), see C. Bonnier, *I.N.E.A.C.*, *Sci. Ser., Publ.* 72, 1957.
[2] H. G. Thornton, *Proc. Roy. Soc.*, 1930, **106** B, 110.
[3] W. E. Brenchley and H. G. Thornton, *Proc. Roy. Soc.*, 1925, **98** B, 373.
[4] J. S. Pate, *Aust. J. Biol. Sci.*, 1958, **11**, 366, 496.
[5] M. H. Aprison and R. H. Burris, *Science*, 1952, **115**, 264.
[6] H. Kubo, *Acta Phytochim.*, Tokyo, 1939, **11**, 195; D. Keilin with Y. L. Wang, *Nature*, 1945, **155**, 227 and with J. D. Smith, ibid., 1947, **159**, 692.

amount of haemoglobin in the nodule and the rate of nitrogen fixation;[1] and some ineffective nodules have a pale light green colour and do not contain it. Nodules containing haemoglobin are bright red on sunny days, but brown on cloudy days because the haemoglobin is converted to methaemoglobin. The role and mode of formation of the haemoglobin is unknown: it is only produced in nodules containing bacteria, and it is presumably dispersed in the cytoplasmic fluids or the vacuole, because it can easily be washed out of the crushed nodules.[2] Otherwise the chemistry may be similar to non-symbiotic fixation, for the first product in both processes seems to be ammonium which is converted to glutamic acid presumably by reacting with α-ketoglutaric acid. This apparently becomes converted in the nodule to the amino acids characteristic of the proteins of the plant, for the distribution of amino acids in the nodule and in the plants is otherwise similar.[3]

Nodules can only fix nitrogen actively if the plant is adequately supplied with all the mineral elements essential for active growth. But in addition all nodulated plants probably have a higher molybdenum requirement than un-nodulated, and some species have a higher calcium or higher pH requirement, and a few a higher boron and sulphur requirement. Thus W. E. Brenchley and H. G. Thornton[4] in 1926 showed that the symbiosis between the nodule of the plant could only be complete with broad beans (*Vicia faba*) if it was adequately supplied with boron, as otherwise the vascular tissue between the nodule and the root did not develop properly; and it is probable that this need is higher with broad beans than many other legumes, though this point does not seem to have received detailed investigation. Again lucerne and groundnuts may have a higher sulphur demand than many other legumes. On the calcium requirement or pH requirement, some plants, for example, lucerne and red clover, only grow well on soils of fairly high pH or calcium status, and in general they need soils of pH 6 or above for optimum growth. On the other hand, some white clovers and subterranean clovers can fix nitrogen in soils of pH 4·2–4·5[5] although they usually respond to liming if the soil is as acid as this, whilst other plants, and particularly many tropical legumes, can fix nitrogen actively at these low soil pHs, provided they can extract calcium from the soil. Thus W. A. Albrecht[6] found that

---

[1] A. I. Virtanen, *Biol. Rev.*, 1947, **22**, 239. *Acta Chem., Scand.*, 1947, **1**, 861; A. Novotny-Mieczynska, *Bull. Acad. Pol. Sci.*, B 1949, 53, and J. D. Smith, *Biochem. J.*, 1949, **44**, 591.

[2] J. D. Smith, *Biochem. J.*, 1949, **44**, 585.

[3] G. E. Hunt, *Amer. J. Bot.*, 1951, **38**, 452 and I. Zelitch, P. W. Wilson and R. H. Burris, *Plant Physiol.*, 1952, **27**, 1.

[4] *Proc. Roy. Soc.*, 1925, **98** B, 373.

[5] See, for example, H. L. Jensen, *Proc. Linn. Soc. N.S.W.*, 1947, **72**, 265.

[6] *J. Amer. Soc. Agron.*, 1933, **25**, 512, and with C. B. Harston, *Proc. Soil Sci. Soc. Amer.*, 1942, **7**, 247.

soybeans could nodulate well and fix nitrogen actively in a soil of pH 4·2 provided the calcium supply was adequate. So far no quantitative study seems to have been made on the ability of acid-tolerant temperate legumes, for example, lupins or gorse (*Ulex europaeus*) to fix nitrogen in acid to very acid soils.

The reason for this difference in pH or calcium requirements of the various legumes is not completely known. It is partly due to the nodule bacteria of lucerne, and presumably other high pH legumes, having an appreciable calcium demand for their multiplication, whilst those of the acid-tolerant type, for example, soybeans, have only a very small demand, though these may have a larger magnesium demand.[1] It is also possible that the acid-tolerant legumes have a greater ability than the acid-sensitive ones to extract calcium from relatively unavailable forms. Thus D. O. Norris[2] has shown that on some strongly leached acid soils in Queensland the typical tropical legumes could take up adequate amounts of calcium for active growth and nodulation, whereas temperate species of *Trifolium* and *Medicago* failed to grow properly, yet a dressing as low as 2 cwt. per acre of calcium carbonate was sufficient to give reasonable, and 10 cwt. per acre good, growth and nodulation. It is, incidentally, because clovers respond to such very low dressings of calcium carbonate in parts of Australia that the practice of pelleting clover seed with calcium carbonate and the correct nodule bacteria can be so effective; and it is also probable that clovers and lucerne on these soils are suffering from a pure calcium deficiency and not from any other possible consequence of soil acidity.

The molybdenum requirements of leguminous plants are entirely, or almost entirely, for the nitrogen-fixing mechanism; for the plants will grow perfectly well, and their roots will be well nodulated, in soils very low in molybdenum, but the nodules will fix no nitrogen.[3] Again, if the molybdenum is in short supply, the molybdenum in the plant will be concentrated in the nodules rather than in the roots or tops. H. L. Jensen and R. C. Betty,[4] for example, found the nodules of lucerne contained 6–20 p.p.m. of molybdenum in the dry matter, which was 5–15 times as much as the rest of the root system, which in turn had a higher content than the tops. It is only when the supply is adequate that the molybdenum content of the tops begins to rise. In Australia and New Zealand there are some soils on which subterranean clover will not grow unless it is given a dressing of a molybdenum salt.

[1] T. M. McCalla, *Missouri Agric. Exp. Sta., Res. Bull.* 256, 1937, and D. O. Norris, *Emp. J. Exp. Agric.*, 1956, **24**, 247, and *Nature*, 1958, **182**, 734.
[2] *Nutrition of Legumes*, ed. E. G. Hallsworth, London, 1958.
[3] A. J. Anderson, *Aust. Counc. Sci. Indust., Res. Bull.* 198, 1946; and H. L. Jensen, *Proc. Linn. Soc. N.S.W.*, 1945, **70**, 203.
[4] *Proc. Linn. Soc. N.S.W.*, 1943, **68**, 1; see also K. G. Vinogradova, *C.R. Acad. Sci. (U.S.S.R.)* 1943, **40**, 26.

Dressings of a few ounces per acre of molybdenum as sodium molybdate[1] are common, but examples of appreciable responses to 1/32 oz. (about 1 gm.) and $\frac{1}{4}$ oz. have been reported.[2] If the concentration of molybdenum in the soil is too high, it accumulates in the leaves of the leguminous plants and causes the soil to become "teart"[3] (see p. 56).

The bacteria in the nodules must be supplied with energy if they are to fix nitrogen, and hence with oxygen for the oxidation of the carbohydrate. G. Bond[4] has estimated that, in some of his experiments with soybeans, 16 per cent of the total carbohydrates synthesised by the plant were respired by the nodules, and of the total respiration from the plant, 57 per cent was from the tops, 18 per cent from the roots and 25 per cent from the nodules. Hence a well-nodulated leguminous crop in the field needs a better oxygen supply to its roots, which respire more carbon dioxide than does a cereal or root crop, as is shown in Table 80 on p. 363. P. W. Wilson[5] calculates that for a crop fixing 1 lb. of nitrogen per acre per day in summer, nodular respiration should amount to 3·3 gm. per sq. m. per day of carbon dioxide, a figure that should be compared with the normal rates of soil respiration given in Table 80. Bond[6] also showed that if soil aeration is reduced, the growth of soybeans given nitrates or ammonia is not much affected, but it is definitely reduced if they are nodulated plants receiving no nitrogen fertiliser.

Nodules are more efficient fixers of nitrogen than the non-symbiotic bacteria, for nodules fix 1 gm. of nitrogen for every 15–20 gm. of carbohydrate oxidised, whereas the non-symbiotic bacteria use about $2\frac{1}{2}$ times as much carbohydrate. Further fixation in the nodules takes place when the bacteria are in the resting phase (see p. 336), so all the nitrogen fixed must be passed into the plant; and this also is quite different from the non-symbiotic bacteria which only fix nitrogen when they are growing, and the nitrogen compounds are initially incorporated into their new cells.

Nodules can be very active fixers of nitrogen. A healthy lucerne nodule can fix up to 100 milligrams of nitrogen daily per gram of dry matter, which corresponds to 1·36 times its own nitrogen content, and nodules of subterranean clover can fix up to 50 milligrams daily, though for each crop the average fixation per unit of dry matter in the

[1] H. C. Trumble and H. M. Ferres, *J. Aust. Inst. Agric. Sci.*, 1946, **12**, 32.
[2] See, for example, A. J. Anderson, *Aust. J. Counc. Sci. Ind. Res.*, 1946, **19**, 1.
[3] For the margin between optimum molybdenum contents for nitrogen fixation and the minimum for teartness, see H. L. Jensen, *Proc. Linn. Soc. N.S.W.*, 1946, **70**, 203.
[4] *Ann. Bot.*, 1941, **5**, 313.
[5] *The Biochemistry of Symbiotic Nitrogen Fixation*, Madison, 1940.
[6] *Ann. Bot.*, 1950, **15**, 95. For the corresponding work with red clover, see T. P. Ferguson. and G. Bond, *Ann. Bot.*, 1954, **18**, 385.

nodules is usually about half of these rates.[1] For these rates to be possible, the lucerne nodules must contain 10–25 p.p.m. and the clover 4–8 p.p.m. of molybdenum in the dry nodule tissue.

THE NODULE BACTERIA

The nodule bacteria are classified in the genus *Rhizobium*, though they were formerly called *Bacillus radicicola*. The bacteria are typically rod-shaped when grown on suitable media and when actively growing in healthy nodules, but they may have a shape like an X, Y, T or club if growing in unfavourable conditions in media or in the nodule,[2] and they have characteristic banded and branched shapes in the older cells of the nodule. They seem to have affinities with *Agrobacterium* (*Achromobacter*) *radiobacter*, a soil bacterium found near the roots of many plants and particularly legumes, and with *Agrobacterium* (*Phytomonas*) *tumifaciens*, a soil bacterium which is often parasitic on plant roots, producing swellings and tumours on them.[3]

Nodule bacteria can be grown fairly easily in simple culture media, though some species need some of the vitamin B group for active growth.[4] They fall into two fairly well defined groups; those which grow rapidly and are large, and those which grow slowly and are very small on these media, the former typically being rhizobia isolated from the nodules of temperate legumes, e.g. clovers, lucerne and peas, and the latter from the nodules of tropical legumes.[5] C. Bonnier and J. Seeger[6] have made the interesting observation that the large fast-growing type sometimes accompany the slow growers, but if they are isolated and inoculated on to a sterile root of that legume they do not form effective nodules. It is not yet known if this very characteristic difference in behaviour has any significance inside the nodule.

Nodule bacteria exist in a number of species or strains which differ in the host plants they can infect, and in their serological reactions, their resistance to different phages, their production of gum, their growth rates in standard media, and in other properties; but unfortunately there is little detailed correlation between most of these properties, and there are still no generally accepted criteria for classifying them into distinct species.

Some of the nodule bacteria have for practical purposes been divided into groups according to the host plants they infect. E. B. Fred

[1] H. L. Jensen, *Proc. Linn. Soc. N.S.W.*, 1947, **72**, 265.
[2] C. Bonnier, *I.N.E.A.C. Sci. Ser., Publ.* 72, 1957.
[3] For a discussion of these affinities, see H. J. Conn, G. E. Wolfe and M. Ford, *J. Bact.*, 1940, **39**, 207, and 1942, **44**, 353. They put these two groups into a new genus *Agrobacterium*.
[4] For a review, see E. K. and O. N. Allen, *Bact. Rev.*, 1950, **14**, 273.
[5] D. O. Norris, *Emp. J. Exp. Agric.*, 1956, **24**, 247.
[6] *I.N.E.A.C. Sci. Ser., Publ.* 76, 1958.

and his Wisconsin co-workers[1] recognised six so-called cross inoculation groups based on the assumption that all bacteria in one group will infect all plant species in that group and none outside it. Fred considered the bacteria in each group belonged to a different species, and gave them the following names:

(1) *R. meliloti* which infect lucerne and sweet clover (*Medicago, Melilotus* and *Trigonella*).

(2) *R. trifolii* which infects clovers.

(3) *R. leguminosarum* which infects peas and vetch (*Pisum, Lathyrus, Vicia* and *Lens*).

(4) *R. lupini* which infect lupins and serradella (*Lupinus* and *Ornithopus*).

(5) *R. japonica* which infects soybeans.

(6) *R. phaseoli* which infect a few species of *Phaseolus*, e.g. *P. vulgaris, P. coccineus* and *P. angustifolia*.

It is doubtful if there are any theoretical grounds for accepting this classification as it stands,[2] which in any case is confined to crops cultivated in the temperate regions. It probably has a certain validity for the first three groups, but is probably invalid for the last three; and it is of little help in practice because, if a bacterial strain is to have any agricultural value, it must form nodules capable of fixing appreciable amounts of nitrogen; and it is probable there is no single strain which can form effective nodules on all plant species in any of the first three cross-inoculation groups. But it does emphasise that there are bacterial strains which will form nodules on many plant species in one of the groups and on few if any species in any other group. If one pays attention to the production of effective nodules, the first two groups are too large and should be broken down to several sub-groups, in each of which a bacterial strain may be able to form effective nodules on all plants in the sub-group but on none in the other sub-groups. Thus Australian experience has shown that the species of *Trifolium* can be divided into three sub-groups,[3] namely

(1) *T. repens, pratense, hybridum, procumbens*, and *fragiferum*,

(2) *T. subterraneum, incarnatum, glomeratum* and *alexandrinum*,

(3) *T. ambiguum*,

and experience in Kenya is that the indigenous clovers of the African equatorial highland areas, such as *T. semipilosum* (which corresponds

---

[1] *Root Nodule Bacteria and Leguminous Plants*, Madison, 1932.

[2] See, for example, J. K. Wilson, *J. Amer. Soc. Agron.*, 1939, **31**, 159, 934; *Cornell Agric. Expt. Sta., Mem.* 221, 1939, and *Soil Sci.*, 1944, **58**, 61.

[3] See, for example, J. M. Vincent, *Proc. Linn. Soc. N.S.W.*, 1954, **79**, 4, who also breaks down the *Medicago-Melilotus* group into three sub-groups, species from each genus occurring in two of them.

to *T. repens* of the temperate regions) and *T. ruppelianum* (which corresponds to *T. pratense*) have their own group of bacteria and cannot be effectively nodulated, and probably not nodulated at all, by any strain which nodulates the first two sub-groups.

A much clearer understanding of the relationship between bacterial strain and plant species can be obtained by studying it in the tropics, where there is a very wide range of indigenous leguminous plants. There is no good evidence for the existence of any cross-inoculation groups amongst this vast collection of species. What has been found is that amongst many of the cultivated and semi-cultivated tropical and sub-tropical legumes, the ability of different bacterial strains to form effective nodules, or any nodules at all varies very widely. Some strains can nodulate a wide range of species and genera, whereas others can only form nodules on a few species of a single genus.[1] The pattern of effectiveness can also vary considerably. Cowpeas, for example, can be effectively nodulated by a wide range of bacterial strains, whilst others, such as *Leucaena glauca*, have become specialised and can only be effectively nodulated by a few strains, which themselves may be specialised to a restricted range of plants.

THE FORMATION AND MORPHOLOGY OF NODULES

This is a subject on which our knowledge is still limited, in spite of a vast amount of research which has gone into it, and only a brief account, possibly only applicable to the legumes of temperate agriculture, can be given here.[2]

Actively growing roots of leguminous plants secrete substances into the soil which stimulate the multiplication of nodule bacteria, and related species such as *Agrobacterium radiobacter*, in their rhizosphere.[3] The nodule bacteria, in their turn, produce a substance, probably 3-indolyl acetic acid,[4] possibly from tryptophan excreted by the legume roots.[5] This causes a proportion of the root hairs of leguminous, but not other plants to curl, and if the nodule bacteria belong to a suitable strain, they will enter a proportion of these curled root hairs. Again in a proportion—sometimes only a small proportion[6]—they will grow down through an infection thread and enter certain parenchymatous cells in the cortex causing them to swell and multiply to form a

---

[1] See, for example, O. N. and E. K. Allen, *Soil Sci.*, 1939, **47**, 63, and *Bot. Gaz.*, 1940, **102**, 121, and J. C. Burton, *Proc. Soil Sci. Soc. Amer.*, 1952, **16**, 356.

[2] For a detailed discussion, see E. K. and O. N. Allen, *Handb. Pflanzenphys.*, 1958, **8**, 48, and P. S. Nutman, *Biol. Rev.*, 1956, **31**, 109.

[3] H. Nicol and H. G. Thornton, *Proc. Roy. Soc.*, 1941, **130** B, 32.

[4] K. V. Thiman, *Proc. Natl. Acad. Sci. Wash.*, 1936, **22**, 511; *Trans. 3rd Comm. Int. Soc. Soil Sci.*, New Brunswick, A 1939, **24**; and H. K. Chen, *Nature*, 1938, **142**, 753.

[5] A. D. Rovira, *Plant and Soil*, 1956, **7**, 178.

[6] E. McCoy, *Proc. Roy. Soc.*, 1932, **110** B, 514.

nodule. These cells are surrounded by vascular tissue which is joined to the central stele of the root.

The roots only secrete their characteristic substance when the plant is in certain stages of development. Thus for lucerne it is only after the first true leaf has opened,[1] but the actual stage may be hereditarily determined, as for clover.[2]

The primary infection of the seedling clover root takes place some time before the nodules are visible, and generally some time after a large population of nodule bacteria has been built up in the rhizosphere. In some leguminous species, and with some strains, the number of primary infections corresponds closely to the number of nodules formed,[3] whereas in others there is a large excess of root hair infections which do not develop into nodules. In this case the initially infected root hairs tend to occur at widely separated points along the root, and later infections form at first near these points and then more generally along the root. At this period the number of infected root hairs is then in-creasing exponentially with time, but as soon as the first nodule appears the rate of infection drops off very rapidly. Thus nodules reduce the rate of formation of new nodules; and the larger the nodule, the larger is the area of un-nodulated root, and hence the fewer nodules on a root system of a given extent. For a given variety of subterranean clover, for example, different strains of bacteria give widely different numbers of nodules on its root system, but the nodule volume is relatively con-stant. If these nodules are removed, new ones will begin forming, if the soil and plant conditions are suitable.[4]

If a root ceases to grow actively, further infection also ceases; and for many plants infection only takes place for a relatively short period of growth, sometimes only 2–3 weeks, and this particularly applies to annuals which tend to grow their principal superficial root system fairly early on in their life. For perennial crops, such as some white clovers, new nodules are forming throughout most of the growing season. These nodules are sometimes annual growths shed every autumn, but this is not invariable for some trees and shrubs keep their nodules for a number of years, the nodule usually growing for a period in each year.[5]

This description of the nodule starting by infection of a root hair is true for most of the cultivated crops that have been examined, but it is uncertain if it is generally true for all legumes. Thus O. N. and E. K.

---

[1] H. G. Thornton, *Proc. Roy. Soc.*, 1929, **104** B, 481.

[2] P. S. Nutman, *Ann. Bot.*, 1953, **17**, 95.

[3] H. F. Purchase, *Aust. J. Biol. Sci.*, 1958, **11**, 155.

[4] This account is taken from P. S. Nutman, *Nutrition of Legumes*, ed. E. G. Hallsworth, London, 1958.

[5] For some references and illustrations of this, see E. K. Allen, K. F. Gregory and O. N. Allen, *Canad. J. Bot.*, 1955, **33**, 139.

Allen[1] consider that infection in the groundnut takes place at root axils, possibly through splits in the cortical cells due to the emergence of the new rootlet.

The mature nodule consists of a cap of uninfected cortical cells, behind which is a region of rapidly dividing uninfected cells, and behind these are the much larger cells filled with rhizobial bacteria. The recently infected cells contain rods and coccoid forms, whereas the older larger cells contain the banded and branched "bacteroids", as illustrated in Plate XV. It is the bacteria in these resting stages that are the ones active in nitrogen fixation and it is the cells containing them that contain haemoglobin. As the nodule ages the cells lose their haemoglobin, become brown in colour and a large vacuole appears in each, crowding the bacteria and the cell contents into a dense mass around the periphery of the cell wall, and finally the bacteria digest the remaining cell contents and attack the cell wall—the nodule becomes necrotic and sloughs off, and the bacteria are released into the soil. The period of maximum development and haemoglobin content in the nodules of annual legumes is probably normally just before flowering.[2]

This description of infection and nodule formation only applies if the bacterial strain can form an effective or fully healthy nodule. But this process can fail to be completed for a number of reasons, and since these have been studied in more detail with red clover than with other legumes, the various causes of failure will be described for this species.[3]

The establishment of an effective symbiosis in clover can be blocked by incompatability at any of the following stages of development:

(1) At the primary infection of the root hair.
(2) In the growth of the infection thread.
(3) In the release of the bacteria from the infection thread.
(4) In their multiplication within the cytoplasm of the host cell.
(5) In bacteroid formation.
(6) In bacteroid persistence.
(7) In the functioning of the bacteroids.

In some of these, the cause has been traced to a bacterial defect, in others to a hereditary defect in the host plant, and in still others it involves a specific interaction between the bacteria and the host plant.

The lack of bacteroid persistence appears to be the commonest cause of the nodules being ineffective. Nodules which are ineffective for this reason differ from effective ones in that they are very much

[1] *Bot. Gaz.*, 1940, **102**, 121.
[2] D. C. Jordan and E. H. Garrard, *Canad. J. Bot.*, 1951, **29**, 360.
[3] F. J. Bergensen, *Aust. J. Biol. Sci.*, 1957, **10**, 233, and P. S. Nutman, *Soc. Exp. Biol. Symp.*, 1959.

Plate XIII

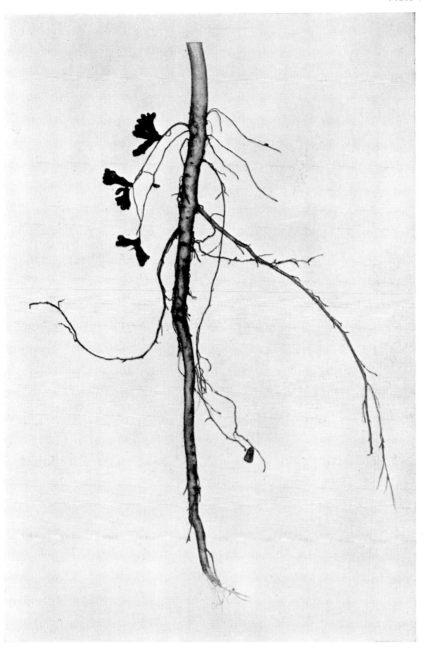

Healthy nodules on lucerne rootlets (natural size)
(*p. 328*)

Plate XIV

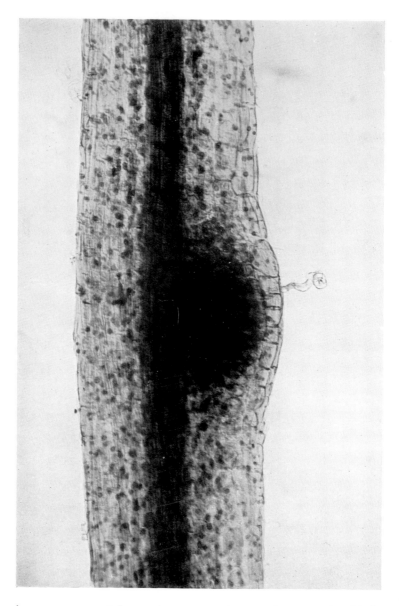

A very young nodule on a lucerne rootlet seen by transmitted light. The dark lines across the centre of the rootlet are the vascular bundles (x 250)

(p. 328)

Plate XV

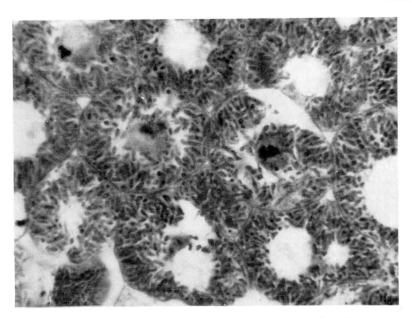

The nodule bacteria inside the cells of a clover rootlet. The black areas in some cells are their nuclei (x 1,500)

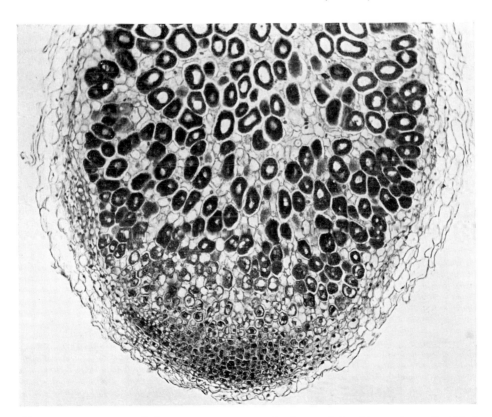

Transverse section of the meristematic end of a nodule. Note the cells filled with bacteria (x 180)

(p. 336)

Plate XVI

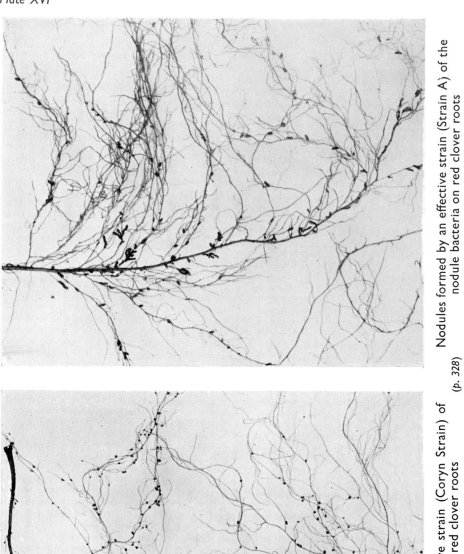

Nodules formed by an ineffective strain (Coryn Strain) of the nodule bacteria on red clover roots

Nodules formed by an effective strain (Strain A) of the nodule bacteria on red clover roots

(p. 328)

smaller, often short lived and, although they are typically far more numerous than effective ones on the roots, yet the total volume of bacteroid, or red nodular, tissue per plant is very much smaller. However, the rate of nitrogen fixation per unit volume of red tissue appears to be about the same for this type of ineffective nodule as for an effective one.[1] Plate XVI illustrates white clover roots carrying these two types.

Other types of ineffective nodules which can occur in the field have not been fully studied. In equatorial Africa, lucerne at Muguga (Kenya) and groundnuts at Yangambi (Belgian Congo) sometimes have swellings on their roots which look like nodules, but their colour is white or pale green, and they appear to be a proliferation of cortical parenchyma without the cellular differentiation of the normal nodule.[2]

The process of infection and nodule formation can be disturbed if the nitrate or ammonium concentration around the plant roots is too high. A high nitrate concentration reduces the proportion of root hairs that can be infected, though this reduction can in part be counteracted by adding a suitable quantity of glucose to the solution.[3] Nitrate not only reduces the number of nodules, it also decreases their volume. The volume can, in fact, be halved by a concentration of nitrate insufficient to affect the number of nodules.[4]

A legume root can carry nodules formed by several bacterial strains though each nodule usually only contains one bacterial strain, at least for the temperate legumes. The root can normally only carry a limited number of nodules per unit length; hence, if root growth ceases fairly early in the season, as it may do with peas for example, the root system can become saturated with nodules, and once this has happened no further bacteria of any other strain can produce additional nodules on the root. Root saturation will not be shown by plants such as clovers whose root system continues to develop through much of the growing season.

The number of nodules produced on unit length of root depends on the bacterial strain, the genetic constitution of the plant and the density of plant roots in the soil. P. S. Nutman[5] has shown that clovers possess several genes which determine the number of nodules a given bacterial strain can produce and the period in the growth of the plant when they are produced; and he also found that clovers selected for abundant nodulation produce a larger number of lateral roots than those selected for sparse nodulation, whether or not the plants were nodulated. He[6]

[1] H. K. Chen and H. G. Thornton, *Proc. Roy. Soc.*, 1940, **129** B, 208.
[2] C. Bonnier, *I.N.E.A.C. Sci. Ser., Publ.* 72, 1957.
[3] H. G. Thornton, *Proc. Roy. Soc.*, 1936, **119** B, 474.
[4] H. G. Thornton and H. Nicol, *J. Agric. Sci.*, 1936, **26**, 173.
[5] P. S. Nutman, *Ann. Bot.*, 1948, **12**, 81, and 1949, **13**, 261; *Heredity*, 1949, **3**, 263; *Proc. Roy. Soc.*, 1952, **170** B, 176.
[6] *Ann. Bot.*, 1953, **17**, 95, and 1952, **16**, 79, and E. R. Turner, *Ann. Bot.*, 1955, **19**, 149.

also showed that the number of nodules produced on a root of clover or lucerne is greater on plants grown singly than in pairs or larger groups, and that this depressing effect of high root density could be reduced if charcoal were added to the rooting medium. When this charcoal was extracted with suitable organic solvents it was found that it had absorbed substances secreted by these roots which when added to the rooting medium sometimes depressed but sometimes stimulated nodulation.

The full significance of the role of charcoal around the roots on nodulation is not yet known. J. T. Vantsis and G. Bond[1] earlier noted that $\frac{1}{2}$–2 per cent of activated charcoal added to sand cropped to peas increased the efficiency of nitrogen fixation, though in this example the number of nodules was diminished though their size was increased. They also obtained evidence that several substances were being excreted, for if animal charcoal was used the growth of the peas was depressed. Nor is this effect confined to the laboratory, for A. J. Anderson and D. Spencer[2] in Australia, and C. Bonnier[3] in the Belgian Congo have both noted that clovers in one case, and *Puereria javanica* in the other, were much better nodulated, and the plants were stronger with a darker green colour where wood charcoal was present in the soil; and Bonnier also noted that charcoal was not necessary, for where the roots grew through rotten wood, there also were they well nodulated.

Under some conditions, some of the soil micro-organisms appear to excrete substances into the soil which prevent both the rhizobia and the rhizosphere bacteria from multiplying on the surface of legume roots, and this toxic principle can be de-activated by heat and is probably absorbed on the charcoal.[4] If this observation is correct, it may well supply part of the explanation of this beneficial effect of charcoal.

Bentonite or fuller's earth in the rooting medium also can have the same stimulating effect on nodulation and growth, but the clay close to the root changes colour, going blue-green close to a red clover root, faint orange near a lucerne, and orange or brown near a vetch. This colour change is not confined to leguminous roots, for flax roots coloured the bentonite saffron yellow; nor is it confined to nodulated red clover plants, for un-nodulated but non-inoculated plants also produce it; nor do all inoculated red clover plants produce it. The colour developed depends on the pH, but it is not known what the compounds responsible for these colours are.[5]

Nodules already present on the roots of clover can affect the number

[1] *Ann. Appl. Biol.*, 1950, **37**, 159.   [2] *J. Aust. Inst. Agric. Sci.*, 1948, **14**, 39.
[3] *I.N.E.A.C. Sci. Ser., Publ.* 72, 1957.
[4] F. W. Hely, F. J. Bergensen and J. Brockwell, *Aust. J. Agric. Res.*, 1957, **8**, 24.
[5] P. S. Nutman, *Nature*, 1951, **167**, 288, and E. R. Turner, *J. Soil Sci.*, 1955, **6**, 319.

of new nodules produced. Roots infected by ineffective strains of bacteria carry far more but much smaller nodules than those infected by effective strains. Initially nodulation is as rapid with either strain, but the effective nodules inhibit further nodulation as soon as nodule growth is properly started.[1]

THE LONGEVITY OF NODULES

The amount of nitrogen fixed by a leguminous crop depends very largely on the longevity of the nodules on its roots. Four factors affect longevity: the physiological condition of the plant, the moisture content of the soil, parasites in the nodule, and the strain of bacteria forming the nodule.

The longevity of a nodule depends on the physiological condition of the plant. The nodules of annual plants tend to die at flowering and seed set, presumably because at this time the flowers and developing seeds are drawing on the carbohydrate reserves of the plant very heavily, and the young seeds may also be drawing on the nitrogen compounds in the nodules.[2] Again the cutting or hard grazing of clovers, for example, may cause the death of the nodules, presumably because the carbohydrate supply to the nodules is interrupted. Some perennial legumes shed their nodules during winter, when they cease to make any growth but this may be of more importance in winters which are long and cold and all plant growth ceases completely, and be less noticeable in years of mild winters.

Nodules only seem to remain on the roots of many leguminous crops if the soil is kept moist, and the first effect of the onset of drought is for the crop to shed its nodules; though unfortunately no systematic work has been done on the moisture deficit in the plant, or the suction of the water in the soil, at which shedding is severe. This effect is very noticeable on exotic legumes in parts of Africa, for even quite moderate breaks in the rains can cause the nodules of exotic legumes to be shed.

Nodules can also be short-lived through being parasitised by the larvae of insects. Thus E. G. Mulder[3] in Holland, and G. B. Masefield[4] in Great Britain, found that the nodules of pea and field bean crops can be heavily attacked by the larvae of the pea weevil *Sitona lineata*.

THE RELATION BETWEEN RHIZOBIA IN THE SOIL AND
NODULATION: SOIL INOCULATION

This relation is quite straightforward if the soil only contains rhizobial strains all of which form effective nodules on the roots of the legume

[1] P. S. Nutman, *Ann. Bot.*, 1949, **13**, 261, and 1952, **16**, 79.
[2] See J. S. Pate (*Aust. J. Biol. Sci.*, 1958, **11**, 366, 496) for a description of this on the roots of field peas and field vetch.
[3] *Plant and Soil*, 1948, **1**, 179.　　　　[4] *Emp. J. Exp. Agric.*, 1952, **20**, 175.

considered; in such cases no problems of getting good nodulation arise. This typically happens with white clover in good British pastures, and doubtless also for the indigenous annual leguminous crops such as vetches, peas, beans and red clover. But when this does not happen, one of three problems may arise in agricultural practice:

(1) the soil may contain no bacteria which can form nodules on the legume,

(2) the soil only contains bacteria which form ineffective nodules on the legume,

(3) the soil contains a mixture of bacteria, some forming effective and some ineffective nodules,

and in each case it is desired to grow a leguminous crop which will carry as large a number as possible of effective nodules.

The first problem arose in England in the early 1920s when an attempt was made to increase the area under lucerne in the Eastern Counties, and it was known that lucerne was only naturally nodulated on a few soils on which it had frequently been grown in the past. Similar problems arose at about the same time in Western Europe and America, and an intensive study was made on the problem of inoculating soils with suitable strains of bacteria. It was found that this could be done most effectively by inoculating the seed at sowing time, which is done by mixing the seed with a suspension of the correct bacteria just before the seed was sown. It was also found worth while adding a little phosphate and sometimes skimmed milk to the suspension, as this probably encouraged a high proportion of the bacteria to develop flagellae, and so become motile, about the time the young roots could be infected.[1] This technique is now used very widely in temperate agriculture; but in the tropics it may be preferable to absorb the bacteria on peat, or on a suitable grade of vermiculite, and mix this with the seed before sowing.[2]

The choice of bacterial strain for inoculation is not quite straightforward, for several strains can be equally effective when tested under laboratory conditions, but can differ greatly in performance in the field for two reasons. In the first place the relative effectiveness of a group of strains in the field may depend on the level of soil fertility; but since, on the whole, the differences are greater the poorer the soil, this is a problem more in subsistence than high farming regions.[3] In the second place, strains can differ greatly in their ability to infect roots. This is a different property from their ability to form effective nodules:

[1] H. G. Thornton and N. Gangulee, *Proc. Roy. Soc.*, 1926, **99** B, 427.

[2] C. Bonnier, *I.N.E.A.C. Sci. Ser.*, Publ. 72, 1957, and 76, 1958.

[3] D. L. Lynch and O. H. Sears, *Proc. Soil Sci. Soc. Amer.*, 1949, **14**, 168, and 1950, **15**, 176 (for Bird's-foot trefoil) and see also O. N. Allen and I. L. Baldwin, *Soil Sci.*, 1954, **28**, 415.

it is their ability to multiply just outside the young growing root and so to give a heavy infection when the root is ready.[1] This is of relatively little importance in pure culture work in the laboratory, either because enough bacteria are usually added to ensure infection, or because there are no other soil or rhizosphere micro-organisms to produce toxic substances inhibiting their multiplication (p. 338). Thus J. M. Vincent[2] compared the effect of inoculating subterranean and crimson clover in nine field trials with five strains which were all equally effective in the laboratory, and found that one strain gave nodules on 42 per cent of the young plants and another one on only 9 per cent, with corresponding effects on the dry matter yields; but the relative order of the strains, as measured by the proportion of clover plants nodulated depended somewhat on the soil type.

Nodule bacteria, once established in a temperate soil, can live there many years without any host legume being grown. Indigenous strains seem to be very long-lived, and introduced strains can probably live for at least ten years in the field.[3] They therefore apparently form the exception to the rule that introduced species of soil-inhabiting bacteria cannot compete with the indigenous soil inhabitants unless the soil conditions are altered in their favour. This happens whilst the leguminous plant is growing, but the introduced bacteria continue to exist along with the indigenous population for many years after the leguminous plants have ceased to be present. In tropical soils, introduced strains for exotic legumes may be very short-lived. Thus at Muguga, Kenya, lucerne bacteria appear to live only for a very short time in the soil, even if the land is in lucerne, for reasons that are not yet known.

The second problem, that of soils predominantly containing bacteria which form ineffective nodules, occurs both in parts of Great Britain and of the Tropics. Some of the hill lands of Great Britain which are in poor to very poor pasture, contain a few white clover plants carrying nodules formed by ineffective strains of bacteria.[4] M. P. Read[5] showed that if such poor grazings were ploughed out, and the land properly fertilised and sown to white clover which was inoculated with an effective strain of bacteria, the roots of the young clover plants were very well nodulated. Unfortunately these experiments did not contain a control treatment where the soil was properly fertilised but the clover was not inoculated with an effective strain, for the general experience in the hill lands of Great Britain has been that if the land is given a

[1] H. Nicol and H. G. Thornton, *Proc. Roy. Soc.*, 1941, **130** B, 32.
[2] *7th Int. Grassland Congr.* (N.Z.), 1956.
[3] A. L. Whiting, *J. Amer. Soc. Agron.*, 1925, **17**, 474.
[4] H. G. Thornton, *Sci. Progress*, 1954, **49**, 185, and K. J. Baird, *Nature*, 1951, **168**, 116.
[5] *J. Gen. Microbiol.*, 1953, **9**, 1.

good dressing of basic slag, and if necessary drained, and white clover sown, it grows very well and is well nodulated without any inoculation.

The problem in the Tropics arises when typical tropical crops, such as groundnuts, are grown, which can be infected by a large number of strains adapted to many other plants. C. Bonnier[1] found in the Belgian Congo that groundnuts typically carry a rather sparse and erratic nodulation early in the season which becomes more abundant later on, but they vary in effectiveness and have not the time to make a really useful contribution to the crop before it is harvested. Inoculation with a suitable strain of bacteria will allow these plants to nodulate much earlier and carry effective nodules, so increasing considerably the amount of nitrogen fixed, and consequently the crop yield.

The third group of problems, when the soil contains both effective and ineffective strains of bacteria, has not yet become of agricultural importance, and if it does, the simplest way of increasing the proportion of effective nodules on the plants will probably be by raising the fertility of the soil, or the standard of farming, and it is really the position that occurs when a soil containing ineffective strains is inoculated with an effective one. But this condition occurs naturally amongst wild legumes and possibly amongst some indigenous tropical legumes, as has already been mentioned, and can be of importance if one is trying to isolate effective strains of bacteria from nodulated plants. Thus J. T. MacConnell and G. Bond[2] found, in the neighbourhood of Glasgow, that nearly half the Rhizobia isolated from the nodules of wild plants of black medick (*Medicago lupulina*), formed ineffective nodules, in the sense that these nodules fixed no appreciable amount of nitrogen, whilst all the Rhizobia isolated from gorse (*Ulex europaeus*) growing wild gave effective nodules.

Bacteriophages of Rhizobia: Clover and Lucerne Sickness of Land

Nodule bacteria, when living in the soil, can be attacked by several strains of bacteriophage, but the individual phage strain can only attack its own characteristic group of nodule bacteria which often consists of bacterial strains from more than one of the Wisconsin cross-inoculation groups.[3] The typical method of attack is that the phage lyses most members of the susceptible bacteria, but usually a few are left unlysed[4] which produce a secondary growth of bacteria resistant to the particular phage if the cultures are kept long enough. They may show other differences from the original strain, sometimes being converted from an ineffective mutant back to the original effective strain.

[1] *I.N.E.A.C. Sci. Ser.*, Publ. 72, 1957, and 76, 1958.   [2] *Ann. Bot.*, 1957, **21**, 185.
[3] For a review of this subject, see E. K. and O. N. Allen, *Bact. Rev.*, 1950, **14**, 273.
[4] J. Kleczkowska, *J. Bact.*, 1945, **50**, 71, 81; 1946, **52**, 25.

These phages have been assumed to be a cause of clover and lucerne sickness[1] in soils, but there is little positive evidence for this assumption; indeed, J. Kleczkowska found that pea-bacteria phages occur in soils giving no sign of pea sickness, and also that the unknown cause of clover sickness can be removed much more easily than phages from soils.

The Amount of Nitrogen Fixed by Leguminous crops in the Field

The amount of nitrogen fixed per acre by a leguminous crop depends on the number of nodules per acre, their size and longevity, and the bacterial strains in them. In turn it also depends on the conditions of growth and management of the crop, and in particular on the availability of water and the nutrient status of the soil. Little is known about the effect of drought on the rate of fixation of nitrogen by a leguminous crop, except that the nodules are shed from the roots of many legumes shortly after the onset of a drought, and this effect is particularly marked for a number of leguminous crops grown in tropical and sub-tropical regions.

The rate of nitrogen fixation should be dependent on the total volume of active nodule tissue the crop is carrying, but very few field observations have been made on this. G. B. Masefield[2] has begun some studies on the weights of nodules carried by some crops both in temperate and tropical regions, though he worked on the weight of nodules per plant rather than per acre. On the whole British crops tend to have a higher weight of nodules per plant than tropical crops, possibly because of the lower soil temperatures and higher soil moistures. Thus broad beans (*Vicia faba*) and dwarf beans (*Phaseolus vulgaris*) in England were found to carry 4·5 gm. nodules per plant, whilst groundnuts in West Africa had between 1·5 and 3 gm., soybeans in Malaya up to 3·3, and cowpeas up to 4 gm.; and plants having these weights of nodules typically have between 100 and 1,000 nodules, so the individual nodules vary between 1 and 40 mgm. in weight. Some plants such as lupins in Kenya can have nodules weighing very much more than these, but they will have very few per plant and probably they are relatively inefficient per gram of nodule, as they usually show a large volume that is only pale pink in colour.

Nitrogen fixation can only go on actively if the crop is healthy and the nutrient supply adequate. A good supply of calcium or magnesium, potassium, phosphate, sulphate, borate and molybdate is probably essential, but the leguminous crops differ considerably in their requirements for these nutrients. In addition, an adequate ammonium or

[1] A. Demolon and A. Dunez, *C.R.*, 1933, **197**, 1344; 1934, **199**, 1257; *Ann. Agron.*, 1935, **5**, 89. [2] *Emp. J. Exp. Agric.*, 1952, **20**, 175; 1955, **23**, 17; and 1957, **25**, 139.

nitrate supply is necessary for rapid establishment of the crop from seed, particularly if the seed is small, and if a leguminous crop is to be sown on worn-out land it is nearly always desirable to give an initial dressing of a nitrogen fertiliser to help it get established.

Whilst a high level of soil nitrates may depress the amount of nitrogen fixed by crops such as clovers and lucerne, it may be essential for high yields of crops such as soybeans and groundnuts. Some results obtained by A. H. Bunting on the black cotton soil of the Rainlands Research Station, Sudan, illustrate this very clearly. Table 74 shows that groundnuts responded to 0·4 cwt. of N, in this particular year very profitably, but sorghum only responded to 0·2 cwt. N and sesame did not respond at all. P. H. Le Mare[1] has also shown that groundnuts responded to nitrogen at Kongwa and Nachingwea in Tanganyika, although oddly enough not on the nitrogen-deficient soil of Urambo. Unfortunately no observations were taken on the nodulation, or of the effectiveness of the nodules, on these crops.

TABLE 74

Response of Groundnuts, Sorghum and Sesame to Nitrogen. Rainlands Research Station, Sudan, 1954–5

Yields: grain or seed in cwt. per acre
Nitrogen given as Ammonium Nitrate

	Cwt. per acre N				
	0	0·2	0·4	0·6	0·8
Groundnuts	7·1	8·3	9·7	10·1	10·4
Sorghum	20·0	23·8	23·4	23·4	21·4
Sesame	4·3	4·2	4·2	3·9	4.3

The reasons for this response to nitrogen have not been worked out, but in the examples quoted for groundnuts, it may have been due to poor nodule development because of droughts. But it could also be due to an effect of bright sunlight, for E. B. Fred[2] at Wisconsin has shown that the amount of nitrogen fixed by soybean plants growing in pots and exposed to bright sunlight increased as the amount of nitrogen fertiliser added to the pots was increased, yet if the plants started in the shade until well established, and then transferred to the sun, even in the absence of added nitrogen, the plants were fixing nitrogen very actively. This is illustrated in Table 75. It is possible, however, that

[1] *Emp. J. Exp. Agric.*, 1959, **27**, 197.
[2] E. B. Fred, *Proc. Natl. Acad. Sci. Wash.*, 1938, **24**, 46.

Fred misinterpreted the results of this experiment, and that it is more correctly interpreted as showing the depressing effect of a high soil temperature on nodule fixation. Thus D. R. Meyer and A. J. Anderson[1] showed that the nodules of subterranean clover fixed nitrogen actively at 20°C. and at its maximum rate at 25°C. but hardly at all at 30°C., and they give reasons for assuming this effect is not due to carbohydrate starvation in the nodule. And this observation may in part explain the common observation that a mulch applied to the surface of the soil around a legume increases its nodulation, although this is certainly sometimes due to the higher soil moisture content under the mulch. J. C. Lyons and E. B. Earley[2] also found that in a hot dry season in Illinois, nitrogen fertiliser increased the yields of soybeans, but it had little effect in a cool moist one, though this was probably due to the much poorer nodulation in the former than the latter seasons.

TABLE 75

Effect of Nitrogen Supply and Shade on Nitrogen Fixation by Soybeans at Madison, Wisconsin

5–8 plants per pot. Sown, 1/7/37. Harvested, 30/8/37
Nitrogen added or pots put in shade, 28/7/37

Nitrogen added per pot as $Ca(NO_3)_2$ mgm.	Where pot kept	Dry matter in plants, gm.	Per cent nitrogen in dry matter	Nitrogen fixed, mgm.
0	in sun	4·2	1·14	2·6
5		20·7	1·26	35·6
10		28·5	1·28	43·7
25		30·8	1·45	63·3
50		37·7	1·72	67·7
0	in shade	8·9	2·20	25·6
0	in shade till 9–8–37 then in sun	18·7	1·98	54·7

The actual amounts of nitrogen fixed by leguminous crops in the field is difficult to estimate, because of the difficulty of determining accurately the nitrogen content of a soil on the one hand, and the amount of denitrification taking place during the growing season. Some typical figures have been given by T. L. Lyon and J. A. Bizzell[3] at Cornell. They found that two courses of a rotation consisting of one-year clover cut for hay, and four years' grain crops added 200 to

[1] *Nature*, 1959, **183**, 61.   [2] *Proc. Soil Sci. Soc. Amer.*, 1952, **16**, 259.
[3] *J. Amer. Soc. Agron.*, 1933, **25**, 266; 1934, **26**, 651.

300 lb. of nitrogen per acre to the soil and 300 to 400 lb. to the harvested crops, compared with a similar rotation in which timothy grass replaced the clovers, indicating that each clover crop had fixed between 250 and 350 lb. of nitrogen per acre, and this is comparable with the amount of nitrogen other workers have found a good crop of lucerne can fix in a year.[1] Soybeans, field beans (*Vicia faba*) and peas harvested for grain on the other hand, depleted the soil of nitrogen as much as ordinary cereal crops: they fixed between 100 and 200 lb. of nitrogen, but it all appeared in the harvested material. Table 76 gives some of their results for five courses of a two-year rotation of legume-cereal,[2] the cereal being either rye or barley, and it shows that the yield of the following cereal crop largely depends on the amount of nitrogen the legume adds to the soil.

TABLE 76

Amount of Nitrogen Fixed by Leguminous Crops, and their Influence on a following Cereal Crop

Mean of two experiments, each five courses of legume-cereal (rye or barley) rotation

	Nitrogen harvested in		Gain or loss of nitrogen in the soil per rotation lb. per acre	Total nitrogen fixed by legume lb. per acre	Yield of cereal grain cwt. per acre
	Leguminous crop lb. per acre	Cereal crop lb. per acre			
Lucerne . .	299	66	122	450	23·2
Clover . .	125	51	115	260	19·4
Sweet clover .	170	51	84	270	18·9
Soybeans . .	176	29	−8	160	11·8
Field beans .	103	25	−20	70	10·6
Cereal every year	—	22	−10	—	8·7

These results show in the first place that leguminous crops fix very varying amounts of nitrogen, in this particular experiment, from about 70 to 450 lb. per acre, and even the figure of 70 lb. per acre is probably high for some crops, for A. G. Norman[3] found that soybeans growing on Iowan prairie soils and giving good yields, often fixed no more than 20 to 25 lb. of nitrogen. The second result established by these experiments is that because a leguminous crop fixes nitrogen it need not enrich the soil in nitrogen. There is a general tendency for leguminous crops grown for their seed—peas, field beans, soybeans and

[1] See, for example, R. C. Collison, H. G. Beattie and J. D. Harlan, *New York Agric. Expt. Sta.*, *Tech. Bull.* 212, 1933; E. S. Hopkins and A. Leahey, *Canada Dept. Agric.*, *Publ.* 761, 1944.
[2] T. L. Lyon, *Cornell Agric. Expt. Sta.*, *Bull.* 645, 1936.
[3] *Proc. Soil Sci. Soc. Amer.*, 1947, **11**, 9.

groundnuts—to reduce the nitrogen content of the soil, and legumes grown for their leaf—clovers, sweet clovers and lucerne—to increase the nitrogen content, though they do not necessarily.[1] Naturally if the large-seeded legumes are grown as a green manure and ploughed in, all the nitrogen they fix is returned to the soil. However, there may be exception to this rule, for the statement is continually being made in farming journals and text-books that field beans grown for seed enrich the soil in nitrogen, a statement that is discussed in more detail on p. 541.

Little is known about the amount of nitrogen tropical and sub-tropical crops fix, and it is probable that in general all that nitrogen is transferred to the tops and seed, for there is no good evidence that they increase the nitrogen content of the soil any more than non-leguminous crops. Most of the field experiments the author has seen both in the wetter regions of West Africa as well as in the drier regions of West and East Africa do not indicate that resting land under a leguminous crop raises its fertility, as judged by the yields of succeeding un-fertilised crops, any more than under some grasses or some non-leguminous bush fallows; although unfortunately none of these experiments is really satisfactory as the experiments were usually begun before enough was known to ensure all the crops could be grown successfully. However, G. H. Gethin Jones[2] showed that if land was rested under *Glycine javanica*, a creeping cover crop, which was allowed to cover the land but was not harvested in any way, the nitrogen content of the surface soil increased under the litter and green crop at a rate of 160 lb. per acre annually for the first five years and at about 100 lb. per acre annually for the next. This experiment was made on the deep Kikuyu Red Loam outside Nairobi, Kenya, and nothing is known of the rate at which humus will accumulate under grass or natural vegetation in this area. E. R. Orchard and G. D. Darby also found that under wattle (*Acacia mollissima*) plantations in Natal, the nitrogen in the topsoil (0–9 inches) could increase at a mean annual rate of 180 lb. per acre over a 30-year period, if the soil started low in nitrogen,[3] and this was in a strongly weathered and leached soil of pH 4·8. This rate of build-up is comparable to that found under a good clover or lucerne crop growing in a fertile soil in the temperate regions.

The processes by which leguminous crops add organic nitrogen compounds to the soil are difficult to study in detail. On the whole crops which have a very extensive root system, particularly a system continually sending out new roots which can later carry nodules, appear

[1] For an example from Utah where the nitrogen content of land under lucerne for 16 years remained about the same, see J. E. Greaves and L. W. Jones, *Soil Sci.*, 1950, **69**, 71.
[2] *E. Afric. Agric. J.*, 1942, **8**, 48.
[3] *6th Int. Congr. Soil Sci.* (Paris), 1956 D, 305.

to leave more nitrogen behind in the soil than those with a restricted root system, particularly when nearly all the nodules are formed during a relatively short part of the growing season. Clovers and lucerne in the temperate regions, for example, may add between 150 and 200 lb. of nitrogen per acre per year to the soil, and they are making new roots which become nodulated throughout the growing season. As a consequence they can add between 2 and 3 tons of root fibre per acre to the soil annually and this can easily contain the 150 to 200 lb. of nitrogen they add to the soil. Peas and beans, on the other hand, have a far smaller root system, so the weight of root fibre is very much less, and the nodules are nearly all formed within a few weeks. Further, very few experiments seem to have been made on the proportion of the nitrogen fixed by a leguminous crop that remains in its root system, but in some pot experiments by J. S. Pate[1] in Northern Ireland, up to 90 per cent of the nitrogen in the nodules of peas and vetches had been transferred to the tops before the plant died, a result confirmed by I. E. Miles[2] in Mississippi, who further found that the subtropical summer forage legumes—velvet beans, lespedeza and kudzu—retained 20–30 per cent of the nitrogen they fixed in their root system.

Another factor which affects the amount of nitrogen a legume adds to the soil is the rate of mineralisation of the nitrogen in its root residues. The roots of annual legumes, such as Korean lespedeza grown as a summer crop in areas with moist warm winters may decompose so rapidly that all the nitrogen in their roots has been converted into nitrates and leached out of the soil by the time the next summer crop is planted,[3] whereas the roots of a perennial crop such as lucerne may leave a higher proportion of the nitrogen they contain as soil organic nitrogen.

There is little doubt, however, that leguminous crops can add nitrogen to the soils by processes other than the death of their root systems. One process, which may only be minor, is the sloughing-off of dead nodules from the roots, and this process is probably encouraged by the grazing or cutting of the legume.[4] This may be an important method of transferring nitrogen to the soil and thence to grasses in well-grazed pastures. But in addition to this, there is the probability that the nodules actually excrete soluble organic nitrogen compounds, possibly the amino acids, aspartic acid and β-alanine.[5] This excretion has been very difficult to prove both in the laboratory and in the field,

[1] *Aust. J. Biol. Sci.*, 1958, **11**, 366, 496.
[2] *Miss. Agric. Expt. Sta., Circ.* 126, 1946.
[3] P. E. Karrakar, C. E. Bortner and E. N. Fergus, *Kentucky Agric. Expt. Sta. Bull.* 557, 1950.
[4] J. K. Wilson, *J. Amer. Soc. Agron.*, 1942, **34**, 460.
[5] A. I. Virtanen. For an account of his work on this subject, see his book *Cattle Fodder and Human Nutrition*, Cambridge, 1938.

but it seems to occur when nitrogen fixation is taking place more rapidly than carbohydrate synthesis.[1]

Pot experiments, in which the legume and non-legume are grown in a nitrogen-poor sand, however, can give clear examples of the non-legume using nitrogen fixed by the legume, and although the experiments cannot prove that any of the nitrogen used by the non-legume was excreted by the legume, this is the simplest explanation of the results. Thus H. G. Thornton and H. Nicol[2] at Rothamsted grew lucerne and Italian ryegrass together in sand, and found at the end of July, four months after sowing, that the lucerne, which contained 1,000 mgm. of nitrogen, had apparently transferred 80 mgm. to the ryegrass, and a month later, when it contained 1,300 mgm. it had transferred 250 mgm. to the grass. They considered it was unlikely any appreciable amount of nitrogen had been transferred as a result of the death and decomposition of nodules. This result, however, probably only holds if the combined crop is grown in a sand or a sand-soil mixture low in available nitrogen, and even then one may have to choose the leguminous crop carefully. Thus G. Gliemeroth[3] using oats and peas in a nitrogen-poor soil, found nitrogen transfer only took place late in the season, and then only if the peas nodulated well early on. He considered, therefore, that the transfer of nitrogen was a direct consequence of the disintegration of the nodules.

It is very difficult to determine if and when any transfer of nitrogen from a legume to a non-legume occurs in the field, when arable cropping is used. Table 77, which gives the result of a field experiment at Rothamsted[1] using a mixture of oats and vetches, shows the typical

TABLE 77

Yields and Nitrogen Contents of Different Oats-Vetch Mixtures

Field experiment at Rothamsted

Weight of seed sown per acre in lb.		Yield of dry matter per acre in lb.			Per cent nitrogen in dry matter		Yield of nitrogen in lb. per acre		
Oats	Vetches	Oats	Vetches	Total	Oats	Vetches	Oats	Vetches	Total
200	—	4800	—	4800	1·14	—	55·0	—	55·0
150	50	4100	1230	5330	1·33	2·70	54·5	33·3	87·8
100	100	3420	2060	5480	1·29	2·72	44·0	56·2	100·2
50	150	2430	2680	5110	1·40	2·86	34·0	76·7	110·7
—	200	—	3200	3200	—	3·06	—	98·0	98·0

[1] For a discussion, see P. W. Wilson, *The Biochemistry of Symbiotic Nitrogen Fixation*, Madison, 1940.
[2] *J. Agric. Sci.*, 1934, **24**, 269, and see also J. Nowotnowna, ibid., 1937, **27**, 503.
[3] *Ztschr. Acker. u. PflBau.*, 1951, **94**, 106.   [4] *Rothamsted Ann. Rept.*, 1932, 148.

results that have been found in temperate regions. Mixed cropping causes the yield per acre of both the oats and the vetches to be reduced, though the total yield per acre is increased for certain mixtures. It reduces the total uptake of nitrogen by the oats but increases the nitrogen content of its dry matter, whilst reducing that in the vetches. This result does not prove that no transfer of nitrogen from the legume to the cereal takes place, but the simplest explanation is that the legume, by fixing its own nitrogen, does not need to draw on the soil nitrates, so that as the number of cereal plants is reduced, the nitrate supply per plant is increased. Further, the higher the number of cereal plants, the more the legume is shaded and hence the amount of nitrogen fixed per plant is reduced, although if any excretion of nitrogen did take place, shading should encourage it. This problem of mixed arable cereal-legume cropping is discussed in more detail on pp. 548-9, from the agricultural point of view.

The other type of mixed cropping in the field is the grass-clover association in pastures or meadows. Here the most important agency for transfer is the urine of the animals grazing the pasture, but there is an important transfer even if the ley is only mown for hay. Table 78, taken from some work of J. Melville and P. D. Sears[1] with ryegrass and white clover pastures at the Grasslands Stations, Palmerston North, New Zealand, illustrates the amount of transfer that can occur both

TABLE 78

The Distribution of Clover Nitrogen between Clover and Grass

Palmerston North. Yield of Nitrogen in lb. per acre

Age of sward	Mown				Grazed, urine and dung returned			
	N in grass	N in clover	Total N	Per cent har- vested N in grass	N in grass	N in clover	Total N	Per cent har- vested N in grass
First year .	110	412	522	21	254	230	484	51
Second year .	136	387	523	26	276	312	588	47
Third year .	188	346	534	35	379	271	650	58
Grass alone without clover	about 50 lb. per year				about 75 lb. per year			

when the pasture is mown only and the mowings removed, and when it is grazed by sheep. This table shows how as the sward on the mown area ages, so a greater proportion of the nitrogen fixed by the clover appears in the grass, although the total amount of nitrogen harvested

[1] *N.Z. J. Sci. Tech. A*, 1953, **35**, *Suppl.* 1, 30.

annually remains constant at about 520 lb. per acre. This result, therefore, does not support the theory that the clover roots are excreting soluble nitrogen compounds into the soil, though it does not disprove it.[1] The results do, however, show that the clover is fixing 480 lb. per acre of nitrogen per year, which is harvested in the grass and clover leaf, and if, as T. W. Walker[2] suggests, as much as 50 per cent of what appears in the tops is left behind in the soil as grass and clover roots, the white clover must be fixing about 700 lb. of nitrogen per acre annually. In the grazed series, with the return of urine, a greater proportion of the nitrogen fixed by the clover appears in the grass, as the urine is an effective nitrogen fertiliser.

These rates of nitrogen fixation by white clover are much higher than are usually considered operative in the United Kingdom, possibly because white clover grows for nearly every month of the year in New Zealand. But some experiments made by W. Holmes and D. S. MacLusky[3] at the Hannah Dairy Research Institute, Ayr, on a very well-fertilised ryegrass and white clover sward, receiving no nitrogen fertiliser but repeatedly mown for high-protein dried grass and a corresponding pure grass sward receiving varying levels of a nitrogen fertiliser, also repeatedly mown for dried grass, showed that the yield of dry matter and of protein in the grass of the grass-clover sward was only equalled on the grass-alone plots if it received 160 lb. and 290 lb. per acre respectively of fertiliser nitrogen, given naturally as a number of dressings throughout the growing season. These experiments indicate, therefore, that even in the United Kingdom very large transfers of nitrogen from clover to grass can occur, and R. E. Hodgson[4] at Beltsville has found very similar results there.

This discussion shows, therefore, that whilst there is very little evidence that crops such as peas and vetches can transfer any nitrogen to a cereal crop growing with them, there is very firm evidence that clover, in a well-managed grass clover sward, can transfer over 100 lb. per acre of nitrogen to the grass annually, probably through decomposition of its ephemeral roots. This figure is naturally only found under very good conditions, and transfers of the order of 20 to 50 lb. is probably more common in English leys, though in many cases the transfer is less and may be negligible.[5] In normal pastures, which are grazed and not mown, the transfer is higher, through the return of the urine of the grazing animal.

[1] For a discussion and analysis of the nitrogen transfer in this experiment, see T. W. Walker H. D. Orchiston and A. F. R. Adams, *J. Brit. Grassland Soc.*, 1954, **9**, 249.

[2] *J. Sci. Food Agric.*, 1956, **7**, 66.

[3] *J. Agric. Sci.*, 1955, **46**, 267.

[4] *Better Crops and Plant Food*, Nov. 1953.

[5] T. W. Walker, H. D. Orchiston and A. F. R. Adams, *J. Brit. Grassland Soc.*, 1954, **9**, 249.

CHAPTER XVII

THE TEMPERATURE OF THE SOIL

THE SOIL DERIVES its heat almost entirely from the sun, the small amounts due to oxidation of organic matter and to radioactivity being, so far as is known, negligible in influencing plant growth. The temperature of the soil depends, therefore, on the amount of heat received by the surface and the way in which this heat is dissipated.

The quantity of radiant energy reaching the soil depends on the position of the sun, the opacity of the atmosphere, the aspect of the land and the vegetation cover. The atmosphere absorbs nearly all the short-wave ultra-violet radiation, but if the air is clear and dry and the sun is overhead, it transmits most of the visible and heat rays. Water vapour, however, absorbs much of the long-wave radiation, particularly that with a wavelength around 10 μ, and water droplets scatter and absorb much of the general radiation; and even if the sky appears to be clear, these absorptions can be very noticeable when the sun is low in the sky. Hence, more of the incoming radiant energy reaches the surface of the earth in arid climates than in humid; and more when the sun is high in the sky, as in the equatorial regions, than when low, as in the polar. The effect of topography is simply due to the fact that a surface at right angles to the sun's rays receives more energy than an equal area sloping in any other direction. Hence, in the Northern Hemisphere a south slope is warmer than a north slope, and is sufficiently so to produce marked vegetation differences.

The effect of cloud on the incoming energy reaching the earth's surface at Rothamsted can be seen in Fig. 24.[1] The maximum amount of energy that could be received per day increases from about 100 calories per sq. cm. in mid-December to 700 in mid-June, whilst the actual mean daily values increase from about 40 to 400 calories during this period. Table 79 gives the mean daily and monthly figures for the ten years 1931–40, and shows that at Rothamsted about 64,000 calories are received per sq. cm. for the seven months of the growing season, from March to September, and about 76,000 calories for the year.[2] If all this energy were used to evaporate water from the

---

[1] W. B. Haines, *Quart. J. Roy. Met. Soc.*, 1925, **51**, 95.

[2] Using the acre instead of the square centimetre as the unit area, this is equivalent to 3½ million units of electricity (kilowatt hours), to 4½ million horse-power hours, or to the heat developed by burning some 400 tons of coal. Only about 0·5 per cent of this is recovered in the crop.

land surface, about 50 inches of water per year would be evaporated. This figure can be compared with the actual evaporation of about 18 inches per year by an actively growing crop and of about 14 inches per year from a bare soil, given in Table 91, on page 396.

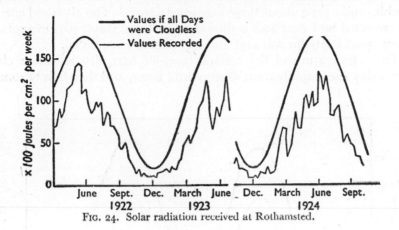

FIG. 24. Solar radiation received at Rothamsted.

TABLE 79

Mean Value of the Daily and Monthly Radiation at Rothamsted

Period: 1931-40

Months						cals. per cm.² per day	cals. per cm.² per month	
January .	.	.	.	.	.	54·2	1680	
February	.	.	.	.	.	97·6	2733	
March .	.	.	.	.	.	202·5	6277	
							——	10690
April	.	.	.	.	.	260·8	7824	
May	.	.	.	.	.	353·2	10949	
June	.	.	.	.	.	405·2	12156	
							——	30929
July	.	.	.	.	.	361·3	11200	
August .	.	.	.	.	.	306·0	9486	
September	.	.	.	.	.	227·7	6831	
							——	27517
October	.	.	.	.	.	129·4	4011	
November	.	.	.	.	.	63·6	1908	
December	.	.	.	.	.	39·9	1237	
							——	7156
Total for year	.	.	.	.	.			76292

The Heat Balance of a Soil

Of the radiation falling on a soil or crop, part is absorbed and the rest is reflected back. A bare wet soil reflects back about 7 to 10 per cent of the incident energy on a sunny day, a bare dry soil about double, and a crop about three times this figure.[1] The absorbed energy is converted into heat and is dissipated in three ways: part evaporates water, part heats the soil and air, and part is re-radiated.

The temperature of the surface layer of bare dry soil on a clear sunny day rises rapidly from sunrise until noon, and then falls to sunset,

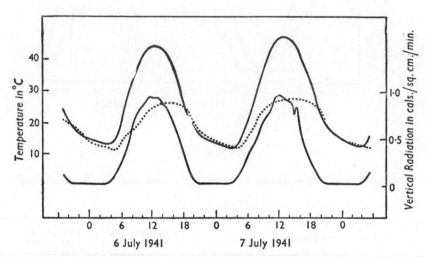

FIG. 25. Relation between incoming solar radiation and the air and soil surface temperatures on two cloud-free days at Rothamsted.

Upper Full Curve: The temperature of the surface of the soil.
Lower Full Curve: The solar radiation received by the soil surface.
Middle Dotted Curve: The air temperature 4 feet above the ground (in the screen).

following very closely the rate of absorption of incident radiation; after sunset it continues to lose heat at a slower rate until sunrise, as is shown in Fig. 25.[2] This is because the soil is re-radiating heat to the sky. If the atmosphere absorbed none of the re-radiated heat, the rate of loss of heat from the soil would be proportional to the fourth power of its absolute temperature, and since this is about 280° to 300°K., the wavelength band at which the maximum amount of energy is being re-radiated is around 10 μ. Now this is just the wavelength band that water vapour molecules absorb strongly, and having absorbed energy

[1] A. Ångstrom, *Geograf. Ann.*, 1925, p. 323.
[2] H. L. Penman, *Quart. J. Roy. Met. Soc.*, 1943, **69**, 1.

at this wavelength, they then re-radiate it at the same wavelength, but in all directions equally. Thus, at a given level in the atmosphere, the water vapour there effectively reflects half the outgoing radiation in this wavelength band back towards the earth, and if there is a thick belt of moist air very little of the radiation of this wavelength that leaves the earth's surface will penetrate into space. No exact calculations can yet be made of the effect of cloud and water vapour in the atmosphere on this loss, but D. Brunt[1] has shown that to a useful approximation it is reduced by a factor

$$(0.56 - 0.092 \sqrt{e}) \, (1 - 0.09m),$$

where e is the water vapour pressure in millimetres of mercury in the air 6 feet above the soil and $m/10$ is the fraction of the sky covered with cloud. Thus, desert regions are characterised by great inflows of radiant energy during the day and great outflows during the night, with the consequence that the daily variation of surface soil temperature is very great. The conditions differ in the humid regions, because they can still receive large amounts of radiant energy during the day, for this radiation comes from the sun, which has an effective radiation surface temperature of $6,000°$ K., so that the wavelength band at which the maximum amount of energy is being radiated is about $0.5 \, \mu$. But the soil surface cannot lose much energy during the night because of the blanketing effect of the water vapour in the atmosphere. At Rothamsted in clear summer weather this daily fluctuation is about $35°$ C. when the surface soil is dry, and it exceeds $50°$ C. in subtropical deserts. If the soil is wet, about half the absorbed energy is used for evaporating water, so that although the shape of the diurnal surface temperature curve is unaltered, the daily variation at Rothamsted is reduced from about $35°$ C. to about $20°$ C.

It is possible to control the surface temperature of a soil somewhat by altering its colour, so altering the proportion of the incoming radiation that is reflected. Whitening the surface, for example, by spreading a thin film of chalk on it, increases, and blackening it,[2] as, for example, with soot, decreases the amount of energy reflected; and hence the soil should be cooled by the one and warmed by the other. Other methods of increasing the soil temperature, which is often very desirable in the temperate regions, are to improve the drainage of the soil, so decreasing the amount of water that has to be evaporated before the air content of the surface soil becomes appreciable.

---

[1] *Physical and Dynamical Meteorology*, 2nd ed., Cambridge, 1939.
[2] E. Wollny, *Forsch. Geb. Agrik. Phys.*, 1878, **1**, 43; 1881, **4**, 327; R. K. Dravid, *Indian J. Agric. Sci.*, 1940, **10**, 352. See *Indian Farm.*, 1941, **2**, 47, for a Canadian experiment on increasing the yield of cantaloupe melons by the use of black paper.

The Influence of Vegetation on Soil Temperatures

The fundamental effect of a crop, or of crop residues, on the surface temperature of a soil is to reduce both the diurnal and the seasonal fluctuations. This is because during the daytime most of the incident radiation is absorbed by the vegetation above the soil level, so that the main supply of energy to the soil is the long-wave radiation of the plant leaves, for the air that is heated by the absorbing leaves transports very little of this heat to the soil. Correspondingly, at night the soil cannot radiate energy into space, for it is absorbed and radiated back by the vegetation. The main region of energy loss by radiation is the plant leaves and, in so far as the air cannot supply energy by condensing water vapour as dew, it becomes cooled, and so sinks to the soil level; but air because of its low heat capacity is a poor transporter of heat from the soil to the leaves, so again the heat lost from the soil surface is low. Thus, in clear weather the air temperature over a crop is higher than the soil surface temperature during the day, but lower during the night; whilst the air temperature over a bare soil is lower than the soil surface temperature during the day, but higher during the night.

One aspect of the control of air temperature by vegetation, of great importance to fruit growers, is the production of cold air during clear spring nights. When radiation takes place from vegetation, such as long grass, for example, the heat is lost from the grass leaves which cool the air in contact with them. This air becomes heavier as it cools and, if the grass is thick, it will be entrapped between their blades and form a stationary layer which, since it has a low heat conductivity, will transport little heat from the soil surface to the cooling blades of grass. The air temperature just above the grass will, therefore, cool very rapidly, and if it is fairly dry, it will have to be cooled below the freezing-point before water vapour begins to condense out and to supply heat to the grass for radiation. If, however, the vegetation is fairly thin, small convective air currents between the radiating leaves and the soil surface will be present, so that heat can be transferred from the soil to the radiating surfaces, and the fall of air temperature above the vegetation will be correspondingly reduced. Thus, C. E. Cornford[1] found that the minimum air temperatures 3 feet above the ground on some flat land in Kent, after a clear, still night at the end of May, were: above bare soil, 49·5°F.; in a wood, 49°F.;[2] in a short-grass meadow, 45·7°F.; and over a longer grass meadow, 43°F.

[1] *Quart. J. Roy. Met. Soc.*, 1938, **64**, 553.
[2] The reason for the small fall in the wood is that the radiation takes place at tree-top or canopy level and the cold air formed there sinks and mixes with the large volume of air in the wood itself, thus only causing a small drop in temperature.

Surface mulches, such as layers of straw, have the same effect as a cover crop of preventing the exchange of heat between the soil surface and the air. Thus, W. S. Rogers[1] found in some Kent strawberry beds that there could be a 13·5°F. temperature difference on either side of a straw mulch on a clear spring night, and the minimum air temperature might be 7°F. lower over a straw mulch than a bare soil.

This blanketing effect of vegetation or mulches may have an important effect on the vegetation in winter, for it reduces the penetration of frost into the soil. Thus, E. J. Salisbury[2] quotes an example where frost penetrated a sandy loam to a depth of 5·5 to 8·5 cm. if bare, to a depth of 2·5 to 3·5 cm. under rough grass, to less than 2 cm. under some bushes, to 1·5 cm. in open hazel copse, where there was no litter,

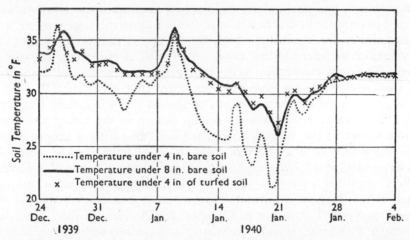

FIG. 26. The effect of a turf covering on the sub-surface temperature of the Rothamsted soil during a hard frost.

and did not enter at all where there was litter. R. K. Schofield[3] found at Rothamsted and Woburn that a grass cover was even more effective, being equivalent to 4 inches, or 10 cm., of soil, as is shown in Fig. 26: that is, if frost penetrated 8 inches in bare soil it only penetrated 4 inches under short grass. F. A. Post and F. R. Dreibelbis,[4] in Ohio, have given another example; they found that soil became frozen to a depth of 2 inches or more many times during the winter when under wheat, only a few times under grass, and not at all under forests.

Snow also protects the soil against penetration of frost, with the consequence that the soil may be warmer and frozen to a less depth

[1] *Imp. Bur. Hort., Tech. Comm.* 15, 1945.   [2] *Quart. J. Roy. Met. Soc.*, 1939, **65**, 337.
[3] *Quart. J. Roy. Met. Soc.*, 1940, **66**, 167.   [4] *Proc. Soil Sci. Soc. Amer.*, 1942, **7**, 95.

in an extremely cold winter if there is much snow than in a not so cold winter without snow.

Vegetation and mulches thus reduce the fluctuations in the temperature of the surface soil, and the thicker the vegetation the smaller the temperature fluctuations in the soil. Forests, by ensuring that the absorbers and emitters of radiant heat, i.e. their leaves, are high above the soil, give a deep column of fairly still air in which convection can readily take place and which, therefore, acts as a buffer between absorption and emission of radiation. The plants in a grass pasture, on the other hand, merely remove the emitters and absorbers of radiation a small distance from the soil, and hence give a small depth of stagnant air above the surface.

This power of vegetation to reduce fluctuations of the soil surface temperature, and particularly to lower its maximum day temperature, is used in practice in the tropics to protect shallow-rooting crops, such as cacao and coffee, against the high temperatures that occur during the dry season by interplanting these crops with deep-rooting tall shade trees. The daily fluctuation in the temperature of the surface few inches of a soil under forest is often only one-third that of a bare soil.

Vegetation affects the seasonal changes in the soil surface temperature. Soil under vegetation warms up slower in the spring and cools down slower in the autumn than bare soil. But little is known about the magnitude of this effect or how it varies from year to year. At Rothamsted, at a 4-inch depth below the surface, bare soil is always cooler than turf, except in June and July, and the difference between these two is largest in autumn. On a ten-year average (1930–9) soil under turf is 2°F. warmer in October and November than bare, but is only 1°F. warmer during the winter and spring, whilst from May to August it is within 0·5°F. of the bare soil temperature.

The Variation of Soil Temperature with Depth

The daily fluctuation of temperature in the surface soil causes a daily temperature wave to penetrate into the soil. This wave is heavily damped, as is shown in Fig. 27 for a number of cloudless summer days at Rothamsted, and becomes very small below 12 inches; and as it penetrates, the time the maximum value is reached becomes later in the day. The thermal conductivity of the soil controls the rate of damping—the lower the conductivity the smaller the diurnal variation at a given depth. Thermal conductivity is very dependent on soil tilth,[1] for soil particles and water have about a hundred and about twenty-five times the thermal conductivity of still air respectively, so

[1] W. O. Smith and H. G. Byers, *Proc. Soil Sci. Soc. Amer.*, 1938, **3**, 13.

that the smaller the area of contact between soil crumbs the lower the thermal conductivity. For the undisturbed subsurface soil it is only slightly dependent on moisture content, rising a little as the soil becomes wet, though this dependence will probably be more marked on coarse than fine-textured soils. Thermal conductivity depends also to some extent on the texture of the soil, being rather higher for sandy soils than for clay soils. Thus, R. K. Schofield[1] found that the sandy Woburn soil cools down quicker in frosty weather than the heavier Rothamsted soil. It also warms up quicker in the spring, thus it is on the average 1°F. warmer at 4 inches and 1·5°F. at 8 inches during the spring months, whilst during the autumn the mean soil temperatures are the same.

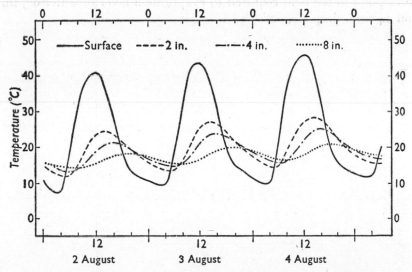

FIG. 27. The damping of the daily temperature wave with depth in a bare Rothamsted soil.

The temperature of some soils in the spring can be increased by improving their drainage, but it is not quite clear how far this is due to an increase in their air content—thus decreasing their heat conductivity—or to a decrease in their water content—thus decreasing their specific heat—and how far to increasing their maximum daily surface temperature through a smaller proportion of the incoming radiation being used for evaporating water, so leaving a larger proportion for warming the soil.

The seasonal variation of temperature at a given depth is complex, for during the summer heat is moving from the surface downwards and there is a regular downward temperature gradient; during winter

[1] Quart. J. Roy. Met. Soc., 1940, 66, 167.

heat is moving upwards and there is then a regular upward gradient; whilst in the spring, heat is moving downwards from the surface and upwards from below, and during the autumn there is a zone above which it is moving upwards and below which it is moving downwards. But the range of temperature variations naturally decreases at increasing depth, and the mean annual temperature in the root zone is probably independent of depth.

The actual net changes in the amount of heat held by the soil are only small. Thus, H. L. Penman estimates that at Rothamsted the heat content of the top 4 feet of soil rarely changes by as much as 30 calories per day, or probably by 800 calories during the year. These correspond to the heat required to evaporate a layer of water 0·5 mm. and 14 mm. deep respectively.

CHAPTER XVIII

THE SOIL ATMOSPHERE

THE SOIL PORES that are not filled with water contain gases, and these gases constitute the soil atmosphere. But its composition differs from that of the free atmosphere because the plant roots and organisms living in the soil remove oxygen from it and respire carbon dioxide into it. Thus, it is richer in carbon dioxide and poorer in oxygen than the free atmosphere.

Most crops can only make vigorous growth if the carbon dioxide concentration around their roots is not too high, nor the oxygen concentration too low (see p. 449). Hence, the rate of transfer of carbon dioxide from the root zone to the atmosphere and of oxygen from the atmosphere to the root zone is a soil property of fundamental importance to the crop, and in humid soils the rate of oxygen penetration probably limits root growth more often than the rate of carbon dioxide removal: the oxygen supply is as important in humid soils as is the water supply in arid.

The principal paths along which the carbon dioxide and the oxygen move in the soil are those pores containing the soil atmosphere that form a continuous system throughout the depth of a well drained soil. Good aeration can only occur in well drained soils which have an adequate proportion of their volume occupied by such pores, and several workers have shown that this proportion should be at least 10 per cent.[1] There are, however, some soils, such as the Rothamsted clay loam,[2] which when wet but well drained appear to have very little air in the continuous pores, but on which plants do not seem to suffer from bad aeration. The reason for this difference in behaviour from other clay soils is not known, but presumably must be due in part at least to their subsurface soil being filled with cracks down which oxygenated rain-water can percolate fairly quickly in the deeper subsoil. Aeration problems thus fundamentally arise either in soils with a high water table or in heavy soils when wet; they do not arise in well drained sandy soils or in heavy soils that have been partially dried out by the plant roots.

---

[1] J. Kopecky, *Int. Mitteil Bodenk.*, 1914, **4**, 138 (for cereals); L. D. Baver and R. B. Farnsworth, *Proc. Soil Sci. Soc. Amer.*, 1941, **5**, 45 (sugar-beet on a heavy soil in Ohio); R. E. Stephenson and C. E. Schuster, *Soil Sci.*, 1937, **44**, 23 (walnuts on a heavy soil in Oregon).

[2] For another example, see A. Woodburn, *Agric. Engng.*, 1945, **26**, 193, who showed cotton would grow satisfactorily in pots filled with a heavy black Houston clay having no air content when wet but well drained.

The proportion of the total volume of a soil occupied by air is difficult to determine in many soils. One method, which is only applicable to stone-free soils that are coherent and not too compacted, is to push a hollow metal cylinder or box into the soil in such a way that the sampling tool neither loosens nor compresses the soil inside it; the air content is then determined either directly,[1] or by the difference between the volume of the sampling tool and the volume of soil plus water in the sample. This method fails with loose sands or stony soils; the air space in the former, and in the latter if it is open, can, however, be determined fairly readily by impregnating the soil with a hot molten wax,[2] for example, paraffin wax, whilst there are no really satisfactory methods for stony loams or clays.[3]

The volume of air in a well drained soil at field capacity (see p. 381) decreases as the soil becomes heavier, that is, as the silt and clay content increase, but there is no simple relation between it and the mechanical analysis of the soil. It also increases as the soil dries. For sandy soils and light loams in the field, the increase of air content is approximately equal to the amount of water removed from the soil, for every cubic centimetre of water transpired is replaced by one cubic centimetre of air, and this replacement takes place in the same small volumes. But in clay soils the increase in air content is less than the decrease in the volume of water held, and much of the new air space does not occupy the actual pores from which the water was removed. For clays shrink on drying and this shrinkage causes a general subsidence of the soil surface relative to a fixed plane in the moist subsoil, which for English clays may be 2–3 inches in a dry summer.[4] But the shrinkage is not uniform throughout the soil mass; it takes place round many centres, and the more centres around which the contraction takes place, the greater will be the number of cracks that will open, so the better distributed will be this new air space and in consequence the better will be the aeration in the subsoil due to its being dried.

The composition of the soil air is determined by the difference between the rate of production of carbon dioxide in the soil by the plant roots and micro-organisms and the rate of its removal from this zone either into the deeper subsoil or into the atmosphere. The rate of production under natural conditions is not too well established, but a selection of figures is given in Table 80, which shows that up to 10 to 12 grams, or 5 to 10 litres of carbon dioxide can be produced per square metre per day, and a corresponding volume of oxygen is then

[1] As, for example, by W. C. Visser's method (*Soil Sci.*, 1937, **44**, 467).
[2] As, for example, by N. F. Mishchenko's method (*Soil Res.*, 1932, **3**, 24).
[3] For a discussion of the best available methods, see E. W. Russell and W. Balcerek, *J. Agric. Sci.*, 1944, **34**, 123.
[4] W. H. Ward, *Proc. Conf. Biology and Civil Engng.*, London, 1949, 181.

needed.[1] Romell points out that if carbon dioxide is being produced at 7 litres per square metre per day throughout the top 20 cm. of soil, and if gas exchange were prevented, the CO_2 content of the soil in an average soil would double in one and a half hours and would increase tenfold in fourteen.

TABLE 80

CO_2 Evolution and Oxygen Absorption in Natural Field Soils

	CO_2 evolved per sq. metre per day Grams	Oxygen absorbed per sq. metre per day at 15°C. Litres
Broadbalk, dunged plot	4·2[2]	2
J. Stoklasa and A. Ernest[3] (Wheat field) .	7·5	4
L. G. Romell[4] (August)	13–20	7–10·5
H. Lundegårdh[5] (August) . . .	2·6–50	1·4–26
P. Hasse and F. Kirchmeyer[6]		
Bare ground	1·6–4·8	—
Rye	5·4–10·2	—
Potatoes	11·8–12·7	—
Lucerne	9·0–21[7]	—
H. Humfield[8]		
Bare ground	1·8	—
Cropped	2–4·4	—

The carbon dioxide produced in the soil can find its way into the atmosphere by a variety of means. In the first place, since the concentration of carbon dioxide is higher in the soil than in the atmosphere, some of it will diffuse into the atmosphere at a rate calculable from the well established theory of the diffusion of gases. Besides this process, changes in soil temperature and in the barometric pressure of the atmosphere will cause the soil atmosphere to expand and contract, and will, in fact, make the soil "breathe", in an amount dependent on

[1] This figure can be compared with the absorption of 10 c.c. of nitrogen per sq. m. per day needed by a lucerne crop fixing 1 cwt. of nitrogen per acre in three months.

[2] Annual evolution divided by 365. Stoklasa and Ernest assume only 200 "active" days, at which rate this value becomes 7·7, closely agreeing with theirs. But at Rothamsted there are more than 200 active days.

[3] *Zbl. Bakt.* II, 1905, **14**, 723. Their total evolution is 13·5, but of this 6 is assumed to come from the roots of the wheat, leaving 7·5 to come from the soil.

[4] *Medd. Skogsförsöksanst.*, 1922, **19**, 125. Forest soils, tree roots included. Summer values only.

[5] *Klima und Boden in ihrer Wirkung auf des Pflanzenleben*, Jena, 1925. English translation from 2nd German ed., *Environment and Plant Development*, by E. Ashby, London, 1931. See also *Soil Sci.*, 1927, **23**, 417.

[6] *Ztschr. Pflanz. Düng.*, 1927, A **10**, 257.

[7] It was estimated that 80 per cent of this was due to root respiration.

[8] *Soil Sci.*, 1930, **30**, 1 (Sept. values).

the change of pressure or temperature. Rain also, by bringing dissolved oxygen into the soil (Table 81), will first of all carry oxygen into the upper subsoil and then carbon dioxide into the deeper as it percolates down to the water table.

TABLE 81

Dissolved Oxygen Brought Down in Rain[1]

	Average rainfall (inches) at Rothamsted (28 years)	Dissolved oxygen	
		Parts per million	Lb. per acre
Summer	13·32	9·0	27·12
Winter	15·50	11·2	39·27
Year	28·82	—	66·39

The relative importance of these various processes is still under discussion,[2] but L. G. Romell,[3] in a classic paper published in 1922, showed that the process of diffusion appears to be adequate to effect the exchange at the rates observed. Now the rate of diffusion of carbon dioxide from the soil to the atmosphere is proportional to the CO_2 concentration gradient, and is dependent on the volume of the soil atmosphere. G. Buckingham[4] showed that, to a first approximation, it was solely dependent on this volume and not on the size of the empty pores making up this volume. He considered the rate of diffusion was proportional to the square of the air space in the soil, though H. L. Penman[5] has recently shown that, in the range of air spaces usually met with in agricultural soils, a linear relation between the rate of diffusion and the air space fits the experimental data better than the quadratic, and that Buckingham's formula under-estimates the diffusion rates in this range. This result means that good aeration is directly dependent on the magnitude of the air space: any soil treatment that increases the air space, such as ploughing, cultivating or subsoiling, provided the increase lasts for a period of time, reduces the carbon dioxide content and increases the oxygen content of the soil. Conversely, any operation that reduces the air space, such as rolling the soil, increases the carbon dioxide content, and hence often lowers the pH of the soil (see p. 106)—an effect that may be of importance in calcareous loam and sandy soils, and may explain the experience of

[1] E. H. Richards, *J. Agric. Sci.*, 1917, **8**, 331.
[2] See B. A. Keen, *Physical Properties of the Soil*, London, 1931, for a quantitative discussion of the relative importance of these processes.　　[3] *Medd. Skogsförsöksanst.*, 1922, **19**, 125.
[4] *U.S. Dept. Agric., Bur. Soils, Bull.* 25, 1904.　　[5] *J. Agric. Sci.*, 1940, **30**, 437, 570.

farmers that heavy rolling and good consolidation are so essential on
them.

The composition of the soil air depends on the relative rates of two
opposing processes: the rate of production of carbon dioxide in the
soil and its rate of removal from the soil. This rate of removal is continuously fluctuating with every change in structure, moisture content
and temperature of the soil, whilst the rate of production is probably
much less sensitive to these ephemeral changes; with the consequence
that both the CO_2 and the oxygen concentrations in the soil air are
continuously fluctuating, and their fluctuations do not necessarily
follow each other closely. Fig. 28[1] shows these fluctuations in the air

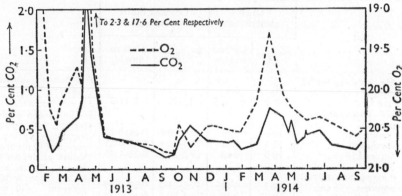

FIG. 28. The oxygen and carbon dioxide content of the soil air in the dunged plot of
Broadbalk under wheat.

drawn from a 6-inch depth out of the dunged wheat plot on Broadbalk
over a period of twenty-one months. It can be seen that while, on the
whole, the carbon dioxide concentration follows the inverse of the
oxygen concentration fairly accurately, yet there are occasions when
both increase or decrease together (i.e. they have opposite slopes in
the figure). But the figure also shows that when diffusion is restricted
by the soil being very wet, as in early May 1913 and early April 1914,
the oxygen content falls by much more than the carbon dioxide rises.
This result, which appears to be generally true,[2] is probably due, as
will be explained on p. 369, to much of the carbon dioxide being
dissolved in the soil water whilst little of the oxygen is; it is unlikely to
be due to the plant roots or soil micro-organisms respiring less carbon
dioxide than could be produced from the amount of oxygen they
consume.

[1] E. J. Russell and A. Appleyard, *J. Agric. Sci.*, 1915, **7**, 1.
[2] This is shown both in the New York apple orchard results in Fig. 29 and the cacao
soils in Table 83.

The composition of the air in the surface layers of arable soil does not usually differ widely from that of the atmosphere when the main fluctuations in composition are smoothed out. The oxygen content is usually over 20·3 per cent, the nitrogen about 79 per cent, and the carbon dioxide between 0·15 and 0·65 per cent, compared with 20·96, 79·01 and 0·03 per cent respectively in the atmosphere. Table 82 gives some typical figures for the composition of the air in the surface soils of north-western Europe.

TABLE 82

Composition of the Air in Soils, per cent by Volume

Soil	Usual composition		Extreme limits observed		Analyst
	Oxygen	Carbon dioxide	Oxygen	Carbon dioxide	
Arable, no dung for 12 months . . .	19–20	0·9	—	—	J. B. Boussingault and Lévy[1]
Pasture land . .	18–20	0·5–1·5	10–20	0·5–11·5	Th. Schloesing *fils*[2]
Arable, uncropped, no manure:					E. Lau,[3] mean of determinations made frequently during a period of 12 months. Values at depths of 15 cm., 30 cm. and 60 cm., not widely different. (30 cm. values given here.)
sandy soil . .	20·6	0·16	20·4–20·8	0·05–0·30	
loam soil . .	20·6	0·23	20·0–20·9	0·07–0·55	
moor soil . .	20·0	0·65	19·2–20·5	0·28–1·40	
Sandy soil, dunged and cropped:					
potatoes, 15 cm. .	20·3	0·61	19·8–21·0	0·09–0·94	
serradella, 15 cm. .	20·7	0·18	20·4–20·9	0·12–0·38	
Arable land, fallow .	20·7	0·1	20·4–21·1	0·02–0·38	
unmanured	20·4	0·2	18·0–22·3	0·01–1·4	E. J. Russell and A Appleyard[4]
dunged .	20·3	0·4	15·7–21·2	0·03–3·2	
Grassland . . .	18·4	1·6	16·7–20·5	0·3–3·3	

Under tropical conditions the CO_2 content of the soil air may rise much higher, and the oxygen content fall lower, than these figures during the warm rainy seasons,[5] presumably because of the very rapid evolution of carbon dioxide by the soil organisms on the one hand, and the heavily restricted air space in the soil on the other.

The carbon dioxide content of the soil air usually increases, and the oxygen content decreases, with depth; and this can be very marked during wet periods in heavy or badly drained soils. Fig. 29[6] shows this variation for a well-drained sandy soil and a badly drained heavy soil in the apple orchards of Cornell, and Table 83[7] shows it for a

[1] *Ann. Chim. Phys.*, 1853, **37**, 5.   [2] *C.R.*, 1889, **109**, 618, 673.
[3] *Inaug. Diss.*, Rostock, 1906.   [4] *J. Agric. Sci.*, 1915, **7**, 1.
[5] For some results at Pusa, see J. W. Leather, *India Dept. Agric. Mem. Ser.*, 1915, **4**, 85.
[6] D. Boynton and O. C. Compton, *Soil Sci.*, 1944, **57**, 107.
[7] H. Vine, H. A. Thompson and F. Hardy, *Trop. Agric. Trin.*, 1942, **19**, 175, 215; 1943, **20**, 13.

cacao soil in north-west Trinidad during the rainy and the dry seasons. These show that the carbon dioxide content can rise to very dangerous heights in a subsoil where the crop roots ought to be active. Hardy

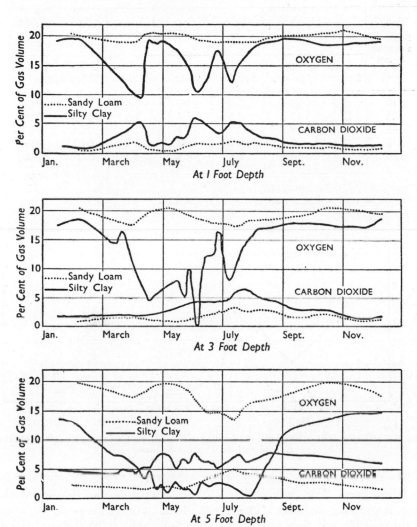

Fig. 29. The oxygen and carbon dioxide contents of the soil air at three depths in a sandy loam and a silty clay apple orchard (Cornell).

also showed, in more detail than is given in Table 83, that the CO_2 gradient was nearly constant down the profile during the dry season, but was much higher in the surface than subsurface layers during the wet.

TABLE 83

The Oxygen and Carbon Dioxide Content of Soil Air under Cacao
(Rivers Estate, Trinidad)

Depth of sampling in cm.	Oxygen content		Carbon dioxide content			Carbon dioxide gradient per cent per cm.	
	Wet Oct.–Jan.	Dry Feb.–May	Wet Oct.–Jan.	Early dry Feb.	Late dry April–May	Wet Oct.–Jan.	Dry April–May
10	13·7	20·6	6·5	1·0	0·5	0·65	0·05
25	12·7	19·8	8·5	2·1	1·2	0·13	0·06
45	12·2	18·8	9·7	4·3	2·1	0·04	0·07
90	7·6	17·3	10·0	6·7	3·7	0·01	0·06
120	7·8	16·4	9·6	8·5	5·1	—0·01	0·06
Observed CO_2 diffusion rate from the soil in litres per sq. m. per day . .			6·8	7·5	17·7		

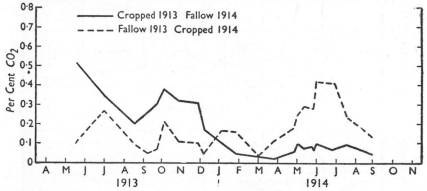

FIG. 30. The effect of a wheat crop on the carbon dioxide content of the soil air (Rothamsted, Hoosfield, wheat and fallow).

The carbon dioxide content of the soil air is higher in cropped than in fallow land (Fig. 30), and this effect is most noticeable when the crop is growing actively. The effect of the type of crop on the composition of the soil air is not well established, as the short period fluctuations in composition and changes in the tilth of the surface soil consequent upon growing the crops usually swamp any differences between them. There is, however, as shown in Table 82, little doubt that the air in soils carrying lucerne or permanent pastures is richer in carbon dioxide than that in arable soils.

The effect of dressings of farmyard manure on the carbon dioxide content of the soil air is less than one might expect, presumably because although the rate of production of carbon dioxide is increased, the air space in the soil, and hence the rate of diffusion of the carbon dioxide into the atmosphere, is also increased. Fig. 31 shows the carbon dioxide contents of two neighbouring plots on Broadbalk, one of which has been unmanured since 1843, and the other which has received 14 tons of farmyard manure practically every year since then. The main difference between them lies in the carbon dioxide contents when the soil is wet and diffusion slowed down. The soil was wet throughout the period April–May 1913, whereas it was dry throughout this period

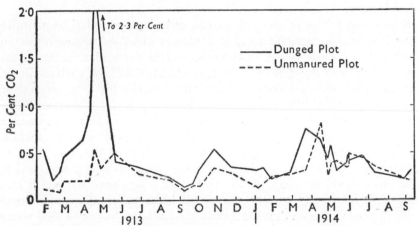

Fig. 31. The effect of annual dressings of farmyard manure on the carbon dioxide content of the soil air (Broadbalk, wheat).

in 1914, and this is the probable cause of the much greater difference between the carbon dioxide contents of the two plots in the former spring.

Green manuring, particularly if the crop is fairly succulent, will also put up the carbon dioxide content of the soil air. This may have two consequences. If seeds are sown too soon afterwards, the carbon dioxide may inhibit germination or harm the very young root system of the seedling. On the other hand, if it is done on land carrying an established crop, such as an orchard, it will lower the pH of the soil; and if the soil is calcareous and very well aerated, it may enable the crop to take up sufficient phosphate and other elements whose availability is very low in these alkaline conditions, to make several months good growth.

Not all the gases present in the soil are in the soil atmosphere: some are dissolved in the soil water. Russell and Appleyard examined the composition of the dissolved gases and found that they consisted mainly of nitrogen and carbon dioxide, and the dissolved nitrogen could be pumped out much more readily than the dissolved carbon dioxide. No oxygen could be found, presumably because all dissolved oxygen would be immediately used by the soil micro-organisms. Unfortunately no estimates have been made of the distribution of the gases between the liquid and gas phases, but presumably the absolute amount of carbon dioxide, and possibly also the amount relative to that in the gas phase, increases as the moisture content increases; and this may be the cause of the result already noted, that in wet conditions the oxygen content of the soil air falls by much more than the carbon dioxide rises.

The composition of the soil air can only be controlled to a limited extent by the farmer; his control is mainly exercised through varying the porosity, or air space, in the soil, and in particular in the surface layers of the soil, for this controls the rate at which the carbon dioxide produced in the root zone diffuses out into the air. As an extreme example, puddling the surface of a soil when it is wet is a very efficient method for reducing the aeration in the subsoil, and this is an essential operation in much paddy rice cultivation, though its main importance in this example is to reduce the permeability of the soil. But the same effect can sometimes be seen in irrigation practice and perhaps also in ordinary farming. If the surface of a fine-textured soil is compacted, most of the surface pores will hold water against drainage, with the consequence that for several days after it has been well wetted there will only be few empty pores through which the carbon dioxide can diffuse out from the subsoil, so its concentration there will build up considerably. If this happens during a spell of hot weather the absorbing roots of the crop will very soon be killed. This effect is of proved importance in irrigation agriculture, hence the need to lightly cultivate the surface of any such soils as soon after irrigation as possible.[1] And it may be the reason why some farmers in the temperate regions are quite certain that root crops such as sugar-beet benefit from surface hoeing in hot weather, for if a moderately light rain did come it would have much less chance of sealing the soil surface against diffusion of the carbon dioxide from the soil. Further, soils liable to have their surface air space much reduced by rain or irrigation would be expected to benefit from a surface organic mulch, for this maintains the soil surface underneath it in a good crumbly condition.

The main problem facing the farmer in humid regions is that of increasing the oxygen content, and decreasing the carbon dioxide content in the subsoil of heavy or wet soils. This can be done readily

[1] For an example, see S. R. Ray and J. B. Shanks, *Proc. Amer. Soc. Hort. Sci.*, 1947, **49**, 420.

in light or medium soils having a high water table simply by draining them so that the air space is increased down to the capillary fringe above the water table. Draining also improves the aeration of heavy soils, even if it does not appreciably increase the air space of the subsoil, both because it increases the air space in the surface by letting soil rain-water drain through quicker, and also probably in part by preventing the water in the subsoil from becoming too stagnant and the attendant strongly anaerobic conditions from arising. This problem is, however, discussed again in more detail on p. 412.

The aeration in the deeper layers of a clay soil are probably very dependent on the amount and depth of the cracks that develop during periods of drought. In tropical climates with a pronounced wet and dry season, or desert soils under irrigation, clay soils will develop cracks 3 feet or more in depth and up to 3 inches wide at the surface, and these cracks may occupy between one-fifth and one-third of the superficial area of the soil.[1] When the rainy season first begins these cracks will maintain adequate aeration for the roots of the crop in the subsoil to continue the function after the surface soil has become impermeable to air.

Only a few methods are available for increasing the number and stability of the channels or cracks going from the surface into the subsoil of impermeable silt and clay soils. If the land is in arable, deep cultivation and subsoiling help, provided the structure of the subsoil is stable so the cracks last for an appreciable time and do not fill up immediately. On the whole, clay soils have stable, and silts unstable, subsoil structure, hence this method is mainly applicable to clay soils. If the soil is not in arable, deep-rooting crops, such as lucerne or even meadow hay in dry years, will open up the subsoil considerably. Very long leys may also encourage an increase in the population of deep-burrowing earthworms, such as *Lumbricus terrestris* and *Allelobophora nocturna*, whose burrows will help the aeration in the subsoil. But the population of these species is usually low in arable land, and their population only builds up slowly when such land is put down to grass (p. 188); hence, it may be found economically worth while to hasten their natural rate of increase by adding a large number of their cocoons to such soils when they are first put down to a long ley after being old arable.

[1] For an example from Egypt, see V. Mosseri and C. A. Bey, *Sultanic Agric. Soc., Bull.* 11, 1923; from Trinidad, F. Hardy and L. F. Derraugh, *Trop. Agric. Trin.,* 1947, **24**, 76.

CHAPTER XIX

THE WATER IN SOILS

Where and How the Water is Held

Soil holds water in two ways: in the interstices or pores or capillaries between the solid particles, and by adsorption on the solid surfaces of the clay and organic matter particles. The mechanism of the adsorption of water on the clay particles has already been discussed in Chapter VIII; the mechanism of capillary condensation will be considered here. But at the outset it is important to realise that the water held in even a fairly dry soil cannot be sharply separated into capillary and adsorbed water.

The soil capillaries are not straight uniform tubes, and for that reason it may be best to drop this word and use the words interstices or pores to describe the spaces between soil particles. Soil particles have irregular shapes and so leave irregular spaces between them; they aggregate in crumbs and clods which are separated from each other by spaces; and the soil is filled with channels or tunnels made either by the roots of plants which have since decayed, or by the larger soil fauna, e.g. earthworms and insects. These spaces form an interconnected system filling the whole soil—the pore space of the soil—whose geometry in most soils is characterised by very rapid changes in the width of the space: relatively wide spaces may only connect with other wide spaces through necks which are much narrower.

The water in the soil thus exists in thin films or sheets of very irregular shape and thickness, sometimes bounded by solid particles and sometimes by air menisci. The properties of such thin films, or sheets of water, are dealt with under the heading of capillary phenomena in many books of physics, physical chemistry or colloid science. For the present purpose the following properties of these films are relevant.

Consider a liquid in a capillary tube having a boundary with air. The boundary layer between the liquid and the air is called the meniscus. The meniscus is usually curved; it may make a definite angle —the angle of contact—with the walls of the tube; and it puts the liquid column under a tension T, given by

$$T = \frac{2\sigma}{r} \cos \alpha$$

if the liquid is in a circular tube of radius r, where σ is the surface tension of the liquid and α is the angle of contact, which is usually zero for the system soil particles-water-air.

This tension which the meniscus exerts on the water column may control the minimum size of pore in which water can exist; for once the tension corresponding to a particular pore size causes a tensional stress in the water that exceeds its cohesion—i.e. the force of attraction between neighbouring water molecules—the water column in the capillary will become unstable. Unfortunately the cohesion of water in fine capillaries cannot yet be measured experimentally or calculated theoretically, so no exact estimate of the minimum size of pore capable of holding water can be made. There is no question that the cohesion of water exceeds 30 atm., so that it can certainly exist in capillaries of 0·1 μ diameter,[1] and R. K. Schofield[2] has collected together evidence to show it almost certainly exceeds 100 atm., corresponding to capillaries of 0·03 μ or about 100 water molecules in diameter, and that it probably exceeds 1,000 atm. Hence there is no theoretical reason against water existing as liquid in capillaries only a few water molecules across.

A study of the detailed processes of adsorption and capillary condensation thus shows that it is not even theoretically possible to divide up the water held by a soil into adsorbed and capillary water for three reasons. Water, unlike alcohols and in particular the long-chain alcohols, does not form a definite monomolecular layer on the clay particles; it has a zero angle of wetting with clay particles and with the adsorbed water films on them, and it can probably exist in capillaries only a few molecules in thickness—so narrow that, for most soils, the water would be in adsorbed multimolecular films. Hence, concepts such as that of hygroscopic water, which is meant to represent the total amount of adsorbed water a soil can hold, are without theoretical foundation.

Suction and pF Curves for Soils

The intensity with which water is held by a soil can be measured in units based on the concept of suction. If water rises a height h cm. in a capillary tube standing in water, one can speak of the air-water meniscus exerting a suction of h cm. on the water; alternatively, a suction of h cm. of water must be applied to the base of the tube to suck the water down to the same level as the water outside. Thus water, held by a soil at a suction of h cm., can only be removed from that soil if a suction greater than this is applied to it.

[1] For a discussion of the cohesion of water, particularly when it contains some dissolved air, see H. N. V. Temperley and L. G. Chambers, *Proc. Phys. Soc.*, 1946, **58**, 420, 436.
[2] *Trans. 1st Comm. Int. Soc. Soil Sci.*, Bangor, 1938, p. 38.

The intensity with which a liquid is held in a capillary can also be defined in terms of the difference between the free energy of the liquid in the capillary and in bulk. This difference can either be expressed in absolute units, such as ergs per gm., or, as R. K. Schofield[1] has suggested, in the more practical units of a potential difference in the earth's gravitational field, i.e. a height in centimetres, obtained by dividing the absolute units by the acceleration due to gravity; or it can be expressed in a variety of indirect units such as depression of vapour pressure, or freezing-point of the liquid.[2] Schofield also suggested that since the range of free energy changes between a dry, a damp and a wet soil are so large, the logarithm of the free energy difference, expressed in centimetres, which he called pF, would be a more convenient unit. The range met with varies from about pF 7 for an oven-dry soil through pF 4 for a soil in the wilting-point range to about pF 2 for a wet soil when well drained.

The suction scale and Schofield's pF scale are seen to be two different scales, for the units of suction correspond to a pressure, and therefore involve the density of the water, whereas the units in Schofield's scale do not include this density as they are derived from a free energy difference. These two scales are nearly equal when the soil water is at normal temperature and under a low suction: but they differ to an unknown extent as the suction increases, for very little is known about the density of water in fine pores: it is decreased by the tension which the water is under, but increased in the neighbourhood of the electrical charges on the clay surfaces and of the ions that have dissociated from it into the water; and no determinations are available of the resultant effect of these two opposing tendencies on the density of the water at different moisture contents.

Each scale has its greatest utility in different moisture ranges—the direct suction scale in regions of low suctions, and the free energy and pF scales in regions of high suctions, for the simplest method of determining the free energy difference in the low suction region is by a direct determination of the suction that must be applied to move water out of the soil, whilst for the high suction region other methods, such as lowering of vapour pressure or freezing-point, from which free energy differences can be calculated, must be used. The suction range that can be easily covered by direct suction measurements certainly extends up to $\frac{1}{2}$ atmosphere[3] (pF 2·7 or 500 cm. of water); and L. A. Richards[4] has shown it can be extended up to 15 atm. (pF 4·2). Above about

---

[1] *Trans. 3rd Int. Congr. Soil Sci.*, Oxford, 1935, **2**, 37.

[2] For a discussion of the thermodynamical relationships between these measurements and free energy, see N. F. Edlefsen and A. B. C. Anderson, *Hilgardia*, 1943, **15**, 31.

[3] See L. A. Richards, *Soil Sci.*, 1942, **53**, 241, for the details of his technique.

[4] L. A. Richards and M. Fireman, *Soil Sci.*, 1943, **56**, 395, for suctions up to 2 atm., and L. A. Richards and L. R. Weaver, *J. Agric. Res.*, 1944, **69**, 215, for suctions up to 15 atm.

½ atmosphere, however, indirect methods of measuring suction or free energy differences are usually more convenient to use.

There is no unique relationship between the suction or pF of the water in a soil and its moisture content. In the first place, if the moisture content remains constant but the temperature of the soil increases, the suction of the water in the soil decreases, because the surface tension in the air-water meniscus decreases with increasing temperature. An example showing the possible importance of this effect

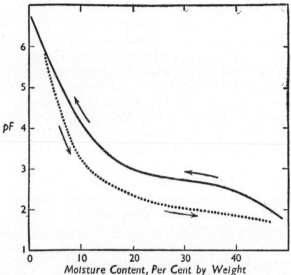

FIG. 32. The pF-moisture content curve for a Rothamsted soil.

is given on p. 380. Again, at constant temperature, the suction of the soil water at a given moisture content depends upon whether the moisture content is increasing or decreasing. This can be shown by constructing the suction or pF-moisture content curve for a dry soil allowed to wet slowly, and then for the wet soil as it is allowed to dry slowly, as is shown in Fig. 32 for a Rothamsted soil.[1] This figure shows that the wetting and drying curves are different, and hence that there is no unique pF-moisture content curve for a soil. The suction or pF-moisture content curve also depends on the soil structure in the range of low suctions, as will be discussed in more detail on p. 427.

This dependence of the soil's pF-moisture content curve on its past history is due to two causes, one of which gives a fairly reproducible hysteresis loop and the other an irreversible displacement of the curve. The first type can best be studied in a rigid system, i.e. in a system

[1] R. K. Schofield, *Trans. 3rd Int. Congr. Soil Sci.*, Oxford, **2**, 37.

whose volume does not depend on its moisture content, as, for example, a mass of sand grains in closest packing.[1] In this system the space between continuous sand particles is connected to its neighbours through necks that have a smaller effective diameter than the main volume of the space. When the moisture content of the sand is falling, i.e. when water is being sucked out of the sand, the effective diameter of the pore is that of its largest bounding neck in contact with the air, for the pore space cannot be emptied of water until the suction is sufficient to break the water meniscus in this neck. On the other hand, when the sand is being wetted the effective diameter of the pore is that of its widest part, for it cannot fill until the meniscus of maximum surface has been created, after which the rest of the pore fills immediately. Thus, the sand holds more water at a given suction when water is being withdrawn than when it is being added.

This hysteresis loop is reversible in the sense that one can take the system round a series of identical wetting and drying cycles and obtain the same hysteresis curve each time. The appearance of this loop for a non-swelling soil block is a sign that the pore space being filled with water has a cellular shape, such as is bound to occur between spherical or irregularly shaped continuous particles. The existence of this loop has the consequence that the actual moisture content of a soil holding water at a given suction can vary very widely depending on how this moisture content was arrived at. Thus the suction of the water in a soil with a changing moisture content may change appreciably with little alteration in moisture content if the direction of change is reversed.

A second cause for the dependence of a soil's pF curve on its past history can only operate when the volume of the soil depends on its moisture content. Swelling involves the constituent soil particles sliding over each other during the process, and the soil particles need not come back into the same relative position with respect to their neighbours after being taken round a wetting and drying, or a swelling and shrinking, cycle. Whenever these shearing movements, set up during drying, result in a repacking of the soil particles, such as occurs with the cylinder of moulded soil illustrated in Fig. 13 on p. 130, the pF or suction curve will be shifted bodily, for the pore space has been irreversibly altered, and in general reduced, by this repacking.

These two types of effect are illustrated in Fig. 33, which shows, for a Rothamsted subsoil, both the typical hysteresis loop and also the bodily shift of the whole curve, consequent upon subjecting the soil particles to the intense suction forces generated by drying the sample to 200° C.[2]

The pF curve for a soil gives the pore size distribution in that soil

[1] For a detailed discussion of this system, see W. B. Haines, *J. Agric. Sci.*, 1927, **17**, 264; 1930, **20**, 97; also B. A. Keen, *Physical Properties of the Soil*, London, 1931.
[2] R. K. Schofield, *Trans. 1st Comm. Int. Soc. Soil Sci.*, Bangor, 1938, A, 38.

provided the volume of the soil does not alter with change of moisture content, a condition that is usually only fulfilled in sandy soils. It does not give this information for soils which swell appreciably on wetting; but the concept of a pore size distribution for such soils has no unique significance, for swelling and shrinking can only occur when an appreciable proportion of the soil particles are surrounded by layers of water whose thickness depends on the moisture content of the soil.

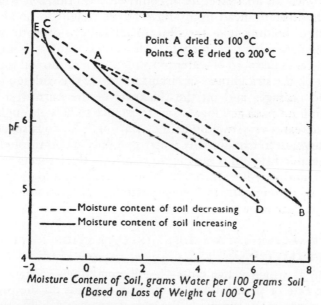

FIG. 33. Hysteresis due to wetting and drying, and to high temperature drying of a Rothamsted soil. The curve was obtained in the direction A B C D E.

Thus, when swelling and shrinking occur, the geometry of the spaces between the soil particles depends on the moisture content.

The suction-moisture content curves for a soil are, in theory, dependent on its tilth or structure. In practice, the dependence on structure, or on the effects of cultivation, is important for suctions under about 20 cm. of water, and very important for suctions much lower than this. In the field, cultivation operations probably barely affect the suction curve for values above 50 cm. of water; but if the soil is brought into the laboratory, air-dried, ground up and passed through a 2-mm. sieve, its suction-moisture content or pF-moisture content curve will depend on the method of packing into the measuring apparatus, or its method of being worked before measurement, up to pF values as high as 5·4.[1]

[1] M. D. Thomas, *Soil Sci.*, 1928, **25**, 409. He stated his result in the form that the vapour pressure curve for the soil depended on the method of working it for relative humidities above 85 per cent.

The Movement of Liquid Water in Soils

Water can move in soils under gravity (drainage) and under a suction gradient (capillarity), and the rate of movement is controlled by the size and continuity of the pores containing the water, by the pressure or suction gradient, and by the viscosity of the water. Water can only move through existing water-filled passages: it cannot move across or down an air space, for it could only do this if it were under sufficient hydrostatic head from above for its weight to break the air-water menisci holding it in the film, so allowing a drop to break off. Thus, water can only move freely in wide pores if water is being applied to the surface. The speed of water movement in a damp soil is thus very dependent on the straightness or circuitousness of the widest continuous water-filled passages and on the thickness of the narrowest parts of these continuous passages, for viscous resistance to flow through narrow passages increases very rapidly as they narrow.[1] Viscous resistance by itself is adequate to explain why water can only move through soils at any appreciable rate if it is moving in relatively thick sheets or through wide pores, and why flow through the main body of a loam or clay soil when wet, or through any soil when partially dry, is so slow as to be of no practical significance.

ENTRY OF WATER INTO A SOIL: INFILTRATION RATE OR PERMEABILITY

The rate at which water enters a soil, sometimes spoken of as the infiltration rate or permeability of the soil, depends on the proportion of coarser pores in the surface of the soil. It seems probable that rapid movement is confined to pores that are emptied by a suction of 10 cm. of water, though those requiring 40 cm. take some part and possibly also those requiring 100 cm.,[2] corresponding to an "equivalent diameter" of 30 μ.

The rate of entry is thus controlled by every factor which affects the number and stability of these larger pores, and is therefore dependent on the shape of the suction-moisture content curve of the soil in its natural condition at low suctions. It is heavily reduced if the pores at the surface become filled with mud, as may happen if muddy water flows over the land or, during heavy rain storms, if the surface crumbs are not protected from the mechanical shattering effect of fast-falling

---

[1] The quantity Q of liquid of viscosity η flowing through a tube of internal radius r and length l under a pressure difference p is given approximately by $Q = \frac{\pi p r^4}{8 l \eta}$. Hence halving the diameter of the tube reduces the flow sixteenfold.

[2] R. M. Smith, D. R. Browning and G. G. Pohlman, *Soil Sci.*, 1944, **57**, 197. See also G. R. Free, G. M. Browning and G. W. Musgrave, *U.S. Dept. Agric., Tech. Bull.* 729, 1940; L. D. Baver, *Proc. Soil Sci. Soc. Amer.*, 1938, **3**, 52.

heavy drops of water.[1] It may also be reduced if for any reason an appreciable number of these pores become sealed by entrapped air pockets,[2] if the soil crumbs swell appreciably on wetting, and if the subsoil structure of the soil is unstable (see p. 427).

DRAINAGE OF WATER

After all surface water has seeped into a soil, the water redistributes itself by downward drainage, and in many soils this redistribution takes place very rapidly. It can be followed easily in drain-gauges or lysimeters. Thus, the Rothamsted 1/1,000-acre drain-gauge containing 20 inches of bare uncultivated soil, after it has just been filled full of water by a rain storm, i.e. when water is just not standing on the surface of the gauge when the rain ceases, will only lose a third of an inch of water by drainage and nearly all this drainage loss will occur within twenty-four hours, although a trickle of the order of one or two thousandths of an inch a day will go on for a few days longer. This figure of a third of an inch for the total drainage loss gives an estimate for the air content—or to be more exact of the air space that can be filled with water—of the top 20 inches of the fully drained Rothamsted soil, which works out at 1·6 per cent of the total volume. A well-drained Rothamsted soil—like many well-drained heavy loams and clays—does not in fact possess any appreciable volume of air. The Rothamsted gauge containing 60 inches of soil loses 0·43 inch of water in corresponding circumstances, and though most of this loss is completed in two to three days, the gauge continues to discharge water at the rate of a few thousandths of an inch a day for a further two to three days in summer and ten to twelve days in winter.

H. L. Penman and R. K. Schofield[3] have shown that the results are consistent with the idea that the rate of water flow is controlled by the width of the pores and the viscosity of the water, and that flow ceases because of the great viscous resistance to movement in the thin films remaining. Many deep loess and alluvial soils, however, do not show this sharp cut-off of drainage. Thus, W. W. Burr[4] in Nebraska, O. W. Israelson[5] in Utah, and N. E. Edlefsen and G. B. Bodman[6] in California have all worked with soils that continue to show the phenomenon of slow or delayed drainage for many months. Edlefsen and Bodman, for example, heavily irrigated a deep silt loam, protected its surface from evaporation and determined the amount of water in each 6-inch

[1] See J. O. Laws, *Agric. Engng.*, 1940, **21**, 431, for photographs of this effect.
[2] J. E. Christiansen, *Soil Sci.*, 1944, **58**, 355.
[3] *J. Agric. Sci.*, 1941, **31**, 74.
[4] *Nebraska Agric. Expt. Sta., Bull.* 114, 1910.
[5] *Hilgardia*, 1927, **2**, 509; with F. L. West, *Utah Agric. Expt. Sta., Bull.* 183, 1922.
[6] *J. Amer. Soc. Agron.*, 1941, **33**, 713.

layer down to 9 feet at increasing intervals of time after the soil surface had ceased to be water-logged, which was on 3 October, 1934. Some of their results are given in Table 84, which shows that from the fourteenth to the fifty-eighth day after the commencement of the experiment 4 inches of water had drained out of the profile, of which 1·6 inches had come from the first 4 feet, that drainage almost ceased throughout the winter and spring, but as the soil warmed up in the summer another 5·3 inches left the profile, whilst during the next summer a further 1·3 inches left.[1] This experiment shows that these silt soils can lose water by drainage during warm summer weather two and a half years after an irrigation.

TABLE 84

Inches of Water draining out of a Silt Loam Soil
(Davis, Calif.)

Sampling dates	3/10/34– 6/10	6/10– 17/10	17/10– 30/11	30/11/34– 8/5/35	8/5– 31/8	31/8/35– 22/1/37
No. of days of drainage . .	3	11	44	159	115	510
Inches of water draining out of the top 4 ft. of soil . . .	9·6	1·5	1·6	0·2	2·7	0·4
9 ft. of soil . .	17·6	4·1	4·0	0·8	5·3	1·3

The phenomenon of the effect of soil temperature on the amount of water a soil can hold against drainage, which is shown up so well in Edlefsen and Bodman's experiment, is due not only to viscosity but, at least in part, to the effect of temperature on the surface tension of water, as mentioned on p. 375. As the temperature increases the surface tension decreases, hence the pore diameter that can just hold water against a given suction decreases, with the consequence that a volume of water, equal to the pore volume between the two pore diameters, will drain away. Whether this effect is adequate to explain Edlefsen and Bodman's results—and other workers elsewhere have obtained the same result[2]—is not known, as it has not yet been systematically investigated.

The process of the movement of water into soils can be seen clearly when a limited amount of water is allowed to percolate into a deep, dry soil. As the water penetrates, a fairly sharp boundary can be seen

---

[1] A sampling was made in the spring of 1936, but the results are erratic, as the top layers 0–4 feet and the bottom layers 7½–9 feet on the whole appeared to lose water and the middle layers 4–7½ feet to gain water.

[2] See, for example, L. A. Richards and L. R. Weaver, *J. Agric. Res.*, 1944, **69**, 215; H. Roseau, *C.R.*, 1947, **225**, 320.

moving downwards, the soil being wet on one side and dry on the other. A short time, usually a few days, after water is withheld from the surface the boundary becomes stationary, and this sharp division between unwetted and wetted soil persists for a long time.[1] The reason why the bounding surface persists for so long hinges, once again, on the control viscous resistance imposes on the movement of water, for the water has to flow in very thin sheets from the wet boundary into the dry soil. L. A. Richards[2] has given an example of the slowness of the process: he found it took over three months for equilibrium to be reached when 3 inches of air-dry soil were wetted with water under a suction of 150 cm. (5 feet), though if the soil was previously damp, equilibrium was attained in two to three days. Water can, in fact, only distribute itself through soils at rates as high as a thousandth of an inch per day through an inch of soil if the soil is definitely moist.

FIELD CAPACITY

The moisture content of many well-drained soils falls to a fairly definite value after rain or irrigation has ceased, provided evaporation is prevented, and a soil in this condition is said to be at its field capacity.[3] Some, probably most, soils possessing a well-defined field capacity reach this moisture content in the course of two to three days, when the water in the surface soil appears to be under a suction of 20 to 40 inches, or 50 to 100 cm., though the range of suctions has not been extensively investigated.[4] But soils which show the phenomenon of delayed drainage strongly, such as some deep uniform moderately silty soils, cannot be said to possess a field capacity, for drainage continues to remove appreciable quantities of water from them over periods of several months.

The difference between these two types of soil lies in their pore space distribution. Soils possessing a definite field capacity have two fairly distinct pore space systems—a continuous system of coarse pores extending round the main structural units through which water can

[1] R. E. Moore, *Hilgardia*, 1939, **12**, 383, has described the corresponding effects for the upward rise of water from a water table.

[2] *J. Amer. Soc. Agron.*, 1941, **33**, 778. For another example, see F. Shreve and W. V. Turnage, *Soil Sci.*, 1936, **41**, 351. Again, F. J. Veihmeyer and A. H. Hendrickson (*Plant Physiol.*, 1926, **2**, 71) packed a 2-foot long cylinder of soil at field capacity (22 per cent moisture content) between two 2-foot cylinders of the same soil just above its wilting point (14½ per cent moisture content) and found that after 139 days moisture had only moved 6 inches into the dry soil.

[3] Field capacity is here defined as a condition of the soil; but many workers define it as the moisture content, expressed as a weight percentage, at this condition.

[4] If a soil sample is air-dried, and passed through a 2-mm. sieve, and then wetted in some laboratory apparatus, it needs to be put under a suction of 3–10 metres of water (⅓–1 atm.) to bring it down to the same moisture content as the field capacity of the soil in its natural field structure. This does not prove, however, that the water at field capacity in the natural soil is at this suction. See L. A. Richards and M. Fireman, *Soil Sci.*, 1943, **56**, 395, for an example.

move rapidly, and another continuous system of fine pores extending throughout the interior of these units through which water movement is practically inhibited by the viscous resistance to flow in such thin sheets.

The existence of a definite field capacity implies that the rate of water movement under a definite suction gradient, the capillary conductivity of a soil, must fall very rapidly as the suction of the water In a soil increases from about 10 cm. to about 100 cm. This can be illustrated by an example of L. A. Richards.[1] Table 85 shows that the

TABLE 85

Relation between the Suction of Water in a Soil and its Mobility

Suction of water in the soil, cm. of water	Moisture content per cent, air-dry basis	Rate of flow of water under standard conditions[2]
	Sandy Soil	
20·3	13·0	930·0
138·0	6·3	16·4
243·0	5·4	6·95
	Greenville Loam	
32·1	34·0	342·0
161·0	22·4	310·0
248·0	19·9	257·0
393·0	17·2	178·0
597·0	15·4	72·7
	Preston Clay	
14·3	63·3	460·0
27·1	59·0	135·0
149·0	42·2	3·29

capillary conductivity of the Greenville loam, which is a soil possessing no definite field capacity, falls off slowly through the suction range 30 to 600 cm., whilst that for the Preston clay, which possesses a definite field capacity, is reduced a hundred and fifty-fold for an increase of suction from 14 to 150 cm. R. E. Moore[3] has extended this work somewhat and concluded that, on the whole, the capillary conductivity usually sinks to very low values at lower suctions in sands (80 to 90 cm. suctions) than in loams or clays (100 to 140 cm. suctions), and interprets this by saying that the water films become discontinuous, or very thin in places, at lower tensions in sands than in clays; but the generality of this for a wide range of soils has not yet been investigated.

[1] *J. Amer. Soc. Agron.*, 1936, **28**, 297. For a further illustration, see G. J. Bouyoucos, *Soil Sci.*, 1947, **64**, 71.
[2] Capillary conductivity secs. × 10^{11}. The unit of capillary conductivity is 1 cm. water crossing 1 sq. cm. of soil per second under a force of 1 dyne per gram.
[3] *Hilgardia*, 1939, **12**, 383.

Evaporation of Water from a Bare Soil

The rate of loss of water from a damp soil is controlled by the evaporating power of the air and the heat energy falling on it, and so long as the soil can supply water to the surface fast enough to keep it moist, this rate of loss persists. The rate falls sharply, however, as soon as the rate of loss sufficiently exceeds the rate of supply for the surface to become dry, for then instead of the water vapour being produced at the soil surface, and diffusing immediately into the air to be rapidly removed by the air currents, it is produced below the soil surface and must diffuse through the soil pore space under a small concentration gradient before it reaches the atmosphere. Even a dry layer 1 to 2 mm. thick can appreciably reduce the rate of evaporation.[1]

The magnitude and rate of evaporation losses from soils with deep water tables can be illustrated with results obtained during the last seventy years from the fallow drain gauges at Rothamsted. The rate of loss of the first $\frac{1}{2}$ inch of water is controlled by the evaporating power of the air, and in summer this lasts for about five days, and the rate then drops rapidly from $\frac{1}{10}$ inch per day to about $\frac{1}{12}$ to $\frac{1}{20}$ inch per week, so that it is only after a six-week drought that an inch has been lost by evaporation from the bare soil; and the three-month drought of 1921, which lasted from June to August, only caused a total loss of 1·3 inch,[2] and it is unlikely that more than $\frac{1}{4}$ inch of water moved up from the soil layer below 9 inches in depth into the layer 0–9 inches deep. Fig. 34 illustrates this result for the moisture content of a bare soil at Rothamsted on 27 June, 1870, after a prolonged drought. Within the accuracy of the determination no water had moved up from below 18 inches and only about $\frac{1}{4}$ inch from below 9 inches. The figure also gives the moisture distribution in a neighbouring plot carrying barley, and shows by way of contrast how the crop reduced the water content of the layer 45 to 54 inches deep. The figure further illustrates the importance of specifying the moisture contents on a volume and not a weight basis—a point that will be stressed later on—for the fallow plot happens to have a larger average pore space than the cropped, and hence can hold more water; so that if the comparison was made between moisture contents calculated on a weight basis, the barley would be judged to have removed much more water from the subsoil than it in fact had done.

This result, that a bare Rothamsted soil can only lose about $\frac{1}{2}$ inch of water rapidly by evaporation is not necessarily true in the laboratory, for there H. L. Penman[3] showed that it could lose about $1\frac{1}{4}$ inches at

[1] H. L. Penman, *J. Agric. Sci.*, 1941, **31**, 454.
[2] H. L. Penman and R. K. Schofield, *J. Agric. Sci.*, 1941, **31**, 74.
[3] *J. Agric. Sci.*, 1941, **31**, 454.

FALLOW SOIL

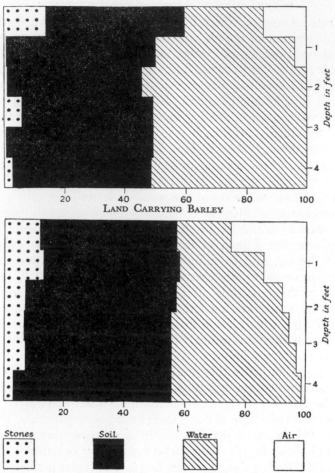

LAND CARRYING BARLEY

FIG. 34. Volumes of soil, water and air at different depths of a fallow and of a cropped soil at Rothamsted on 27 June, 1870, after a prolonged drought (R. K. Schofield).

the rate of $\frac{1}{10}$ inch per day, that is, at the same initial rate as the drain-gauge on typical June days but for over twice as long. But after it has lost about $1\frac{1}{4}$ inches its rate of loss falls very rapidly to the $\frac{1}{12}$ inch or less per week, just as with the drain-gauge. This behaviour is shown graphically by the curve A D in Fig. 39, on p. 409, though in this figure the potential evaporation instead of the number of days is plotted as abscissa, but, as already mentioned, the potential evaporation on a typical June day at Rothamsted is about $\frac{1}{10}$ inch. The differences in behaviour between the drain-gauge and the laboratory soil is, in fact, due to the effect of high evaporation rates in drying out the soil surface.

and in consequence of preventing water moving to the surface at an appreciable rate; for the laboratory results were obtained by keeping the column of soil continuously in a constant-temperature room. But if the surface of this column was heated by shining an electric fire over it for 12 hours a day, to simulate the effect of a sunny June day, the soil then behaved like the drain-gauge soil—it could only lose about $\frac{1}{2}$ inch of water at the rate of $\frac{1}{10}$ inch a day before the rate of loss dropped rapidly to the $\frac{1}{12}$ inch or less per week.

The estimates of the loss of water from a bare soil at Rothamsted are not widely different from those made in subtropical arid climates. R. K. Dravid[1] has given a figure in which the moisture content of a bare soil at different depths is plotted against time for the seven months' dry season at Poona. After four months the surface soil had under 5 per cent moisture, the soil at 4 inches depth 10 per cent, at 8 inches 20 per cent, and at 12 inches 25 per cent moisture. The moisture contents barely altered during the next three months, the main alteration being a slight fall at 4 inches, due to evaporation, and at 12 inches, due to drainage. This loss of water from the subsoil by slow drainage downwards was overlooked by many of the early workers, who concluded, quite wrongly, that this loss of water represented loss by evaporation. A. T. Sen,[2] by following the movements of the soluble salts in the soil, showed quite clearly that at the end of a seven-month drought at Pusa there had been a little upward movement of water from above the three-foot deep level, and a continuous drainage of water out of the soil from below this level; and R. K. Schofield has calculated that the total loss of water by evaporation from this soil during this period did not exceed 2 inches.

A direct consequence of these results is that hoeing a soil, to maintain a dust mulch, cannot appreciably reduce the rate of evaporation of water from the soil once a dry layer has been formed;[3] for the existence of this layer, even if only a millimetre thick, involves the water having to be vaporised below the soil surface and then having to diffuse through the pore space before it can be removed into the atmosphere; and the rate of transfer of water vapour through a dry layer is much slower than the rate of flow of liquid water through a corresponding thickness of damp soil. The rate of loss of water is, in fact, relatively insensitive to the thickness of this dry layer. It is possible, however, that hoeing a wet soil, particularly during periods of slow evaporation, might reduce the loss a little by giving a loose surface which will be able to dry out quicker and hence stop surface evaporation.

[1] Indian J. Agric. Sci., 1940, **10**, 352.
[2] Mem. Dept. Agric. India, Chem. Ser., 1930, **10**, 221.
[3] For an example which illustrates this point, see F. J. Veihmeyer, Hilgardia, 1927, **2**, 236.

The further consequence of these results is that during the winter half-year at Rothamsted, from October to April, the evaporation from the soil is controlled by the evaporative power of the air, or by the amount of radiation received from the sun; for this is sufficiently low, and the rainfall sufficiently frequent, for the soil surface never to be properly dried out. But during the warmer months, from May to September—and even in some years in March, April and October— the evaporation is normally controlled by the number of days the soil surface remains wet, which in turn depends on the frequency of the rain showers and on their intensity, if they are only light, because the showers are usually sufficiently infrequent and the evaporative power of the air, or the energy absorbed by the soil, sufficiently great for the soil surface to be dry for an appreciable number of days per month.[1]

This rainfall distribution effect is of great practical importance in arid countries having summer rainfall, as in the dry farming wheat belt of the Canadian prairies, when summer fallows are taken to store water for a succeeding crop. Frequent light falls of rain on such fallows are evaporated soon after they fall and so cannot contribute to the soil moisture supply. Thus, J. W. Hopkins[2] has computed that at Swift Current, Saskatchewan, if 1 inch of rain falls on one day, $\frac{2}{3}$ inch remains in the soil ten days afterwards, whereas if it falls as five separate showers, each of $\frac{1}{5}$ inch, on five consecutive days only $\frac{1}{3}$ inch remained ten days afterwards.

Evaporation from saline soils differs a little in detail from non-saline soils, for evaporation from them leaves a saturated salt solution, and eventually, a salt efflorescence on the surface. A saturated salt solution, by having a lower vapour pressure than a dilute solution, takes longer to evaporate, and hence longer for the dry surface layer to form; it allows, in fact, solution to move up for a longer time to the surface, and hence more solution to move up than if no salt was at the surface. This has the consequence that once a salt patch has formed in such a soil it grows at the expense of the neighbouring soil, so that instead of a small amount of salt being spread over a large area, it tends to get concentrated in all the hollows of the land, as is illustrated in Plate XXXI. Hence the great importance on all irrigated fields of an absolutely level surface to prevent water standing in pools, and of a water table too deep to influence the moisture régime of the surface soil; for, as will be discussed in Chapter XXXIV, salt accumulation is the constant menace of all arid irrigation projects.

[1] R. K. Schofield and H. L. Penman, *J. Agric. Sci.*, 1941, **31**, 74; H. L. Penman, *Quart. J. Roy. Met. Soc.*, 1940, **66**, 401.
[2] *Canad. J. Res.*, 1940, **18** C, 388.

CHAPTER XX

WATER AND PLANT GROWTH

WATER IS AN essential nutrient for plant growth, and it is needed in much larger quantities than any other; but whereas a large proportion of every other nutrient absorbed by the plant is retained, the outstanding characteristic of the water is its continuous one-way flow from the soil through the roots up the stems into the leaf surface, where it is evaporated mainly inside the stomata, through which it diffuses into the air.

The rate at which water is transferred from the soil into the air by the plant is controlled by four separate processes: the transfer of water from the soil through the protoplasm of the cells of the absorbent rootlets into the vascular system; the transfer from the vascular system through the protoplasm of the leaf cells bounding the stomata; the energy supply falling on the leaves that can be used for evaporating the water in the stomata and from the surface of the leaf; and the transfer of the water vapour from inside the stomata into the main body of the air by diffusion and convection. The transfer of the water up the vascular system from the rootlets to the leaves always appears to be more rapid than its transfer through the protoplasm of living cells, so never controls the speed of water movement. Plants growing in damp soil under normal English summer conditions usually have their rate of water loss controlled either by the amount of energy available for evaporating the water or by the rate of diffusion of this vapour into the air: they normally transfer water from the soil to the leaf cells faster than it is dissipated from the leaves as vapour. But under conditions either of high evaporation, due to strong sunlight or hot drying winds, or of limited water supply in the soil, the root cells may no longer be able to transfer water from the soil to the vascular system as fast as the leaf cells are dissipating it: the leaves will then begin to lose water, causing those of many species to lose turgor and wilt.

Shortage of water in the leaf has several effects besides causing it to wilt: the stomata close almost entirely, thus cutting down transpiration losses, but also photosynthesis, very considerably—and this is normally the first effect to be manifest; the leaf cells lose water, causing first the osmotic pressure of the cell sap to rise, and later the death of the cells, and hence of the leaf.

Most farm crops react to prolonged drought by shedding their leaves, thus reducing the amount of water they transpire and hence their demands on the soil water; but they differ very considerably in the severity of drought they can withstand before all the leaves have been lost or have died. All young plants are very dependent on an adequate supply of water and are unable to withstand any appreciable drought; but as the plant grows older, it can usually survive periods of water shortage without any serious injury, particularly if the drought occurs during overcast weather. It is only during the later stages of growth that marked differences in the ability of different crops to withstand drought become important. Sorghums, such as durra, kafir and milo —the characteristic summer cereals of the semi-desert—can, when well established, withstand droughts that would kill most semi-humid crops, because their leaves are so constructed that they can become dormant during spells of weather hot and dry enough to kill the leaves of non-desert crops.

The direct effect of drought on a crop is thus fundamentally on the amount of leaf the crop is able to carry. Its effect can be well studied on cereals, for their growth in many parts of the world is limited by water shortage. Moderate drought on an established cereal crop can cause an appreciable loss of leaf, and hence of straw, without any great loss of grain, though it tends to bring the crop to maturity earlier. As the drought becomes more severe the crop will come to maturity increasingly earlier and the grain yield will fall more rapidly than the straw, until a condition is reached when there is not enough water for the crop to form any grain. On the other hand, if a crop grown under moderately dry conditions is irrigated, increasing the amount of the irrigation water will increase the amount of leaf, and hence the straw yield much more than the grain, as is shown by some experiments of J. A. Widtsoe,[1] given in Table 86.

The effect of water above the minimum required to allow a normal plant to develop depends on the time at which this additional water is

TABLE 86

Yield of Wheat with Increasing Quantities of Irrigation Water (Greenville Farm, Utah)

Irrigation water: inches	5	7.5	15	25	50
Yield of grain, cwt. per acre	19·7	21·3	22·8	23·0	23·5
Yield of straw, cwt. per acre	25	28	33	37	48
Ratio grain/straw . .	0·80	0·76	0·69	0·63	0·49

Average rainfall during growing period, 5·0 in.

[1] *Utah Agric. Expt. Sta., Bull.* 116, 1912.

given. When the plant is young the extra water is not only usually wasted, but may have incidental harmful effects on the soil structure and the air supply to the roots. This is illustrated by the results of some experiments of A. T. Bartel and C. Hobart[1] with wheat in the arid Salt River Valley of Arizona, which are given in Table 87. They show that water in excess of 6 inches, of which 3 inches came from rainfall, early in the life of the crop appears to be harmful, whilst during the period of maximum growth, from the commencement of rapid shoot growth until the soft dough stage of the grain, the crop has a very considerable water demand. This harmful effect of excess

TABLE 87

Effect of Distribution of Irrigation Water on Yield of Wheat
(Salt River Experiment Station, Arizona)

Inches of irrigation water given up to tillering	3	6	3	9	6	12
Inches given after tillering . . .	15	12	9	9	6	6
Yield of grain, bushels per acre . .	43	39	39	37	34	30
Yield of straw, cwt. per acre . .	66	56	57	46	46	39

Average rainfall for the three months before tillering, 3·0 in.; and for the three months from tillering to harvest, 0·5 in.

irrigation water can be seen on the yield of a perennial crop such as lucerne hay, and two examples from California are given in Table 88. Clearly, water in excess of 36 to 42 inches is unnecessary, and the efficiency of each inch of water used, up to 30 inches on the heavier and 36 inches on the lighter soils, either remains constant or slightly increases.

These results appear to be fairly clear cut, but the optimum supplies of water found in these experiments may be in excess of the plant's needs owing to the difficulty of ensuring uniform penetration of the water, and it is probable that the same maximum yields could have been obtained with less water if it had been uniformly sprayed over the crop. Many field experiments have, in fact, given less consistent and reliable results due to the large number of complicating factors that can enter, and many examples showing the very variable response of the crop to additional irrigation water can be found in B. A. Etcheverry and S. T. Harding's book on Irrigation Practice.[2]

The water supply affects the amount of nutrients taken up by the plant, for as it increases so does the adsorption of mineral matter,

[1] *Arizona Agric. Expt. Sta., Bull.* 151, 1935.   [2] Vol. I, 2nd ed., New York, 1933.

particularly calcium, increase, as is shown for wheat in Table 90.[1] On the other hand, the uptake of nitrogen appears to be almost independent of the water supply, so that since the yield increases with increasing water supply, the nitrogen content of the plant decreases, and this decrease is reflected in both the grain and the straw.

TABLE 88

Effect of Amount of Irrigation Water used on Yields of Lucerne Hay (California)

Soil	Fine sandy loam[2]		Fine sand[3]	
Inches of water supplied	Inches of water per irrigation	Yield, tons per acre	Inches of water per irrigation	Yield, tons per acre
0	—	3·9	—	—
12	6	5·6	4	5·3
18	6	6·8	6	5·7
24	6	7·9	6	6·3
30	7·5	9·0	6	7·2
36	9	9·3	6	8·2
42	—	—	7	8·7
48	12	9·0	8	8·4
60	15	8·4	10	8·2

TABLE 89

Percentages of Nitrogen, Ash, Phosphorus, Potassium, Calcium, and Magnesium in Wheat Grain Grown under Irrigation (Logan, Utah)

Amount of Irrigation water	Calcium		Magnesium		Nitrogen		Phosphorus		Potassium		Ash	
	Per cent	lb. per acre	Per cent	lb. per acre	Per cent	lb. per acre	Per cent	lb. per acre	Per cent	lb. per acre	Per cent	lb. per acre
None	0·103	2·31	0·170	3·82	2·39	53·8	0·295	6·64	0·396	8·92	1·56	35·1
5 inches	0·107	2·02	0·171	3·54	2·16	44·9	0·301	6·38	0·414	8·97	1·56	34·2
10 ,,	0·122	2·63	0·172	3·65	2·18	47·1	0·306	6·38	0·439	9·49	1·57	35·9
15 ,,	0·165	3·53	0·172	3·23	1·99	42·4	0·323	6·87	0·491	10·47	1·71	36·4
20 ,,	0·195	3·78	0·198	3·77	1·98	37·7	0·371	7·08	0·490	9·35	2·01	38·5
35 ,,	0·211	4·72	0·207	4·64	2·01	45·1	0·458	10·24	0·534	11·95	2·28	51·1
67·5 ,,	0·262	5·64	0·224	4·80	2·06	44·7	0·424	9·12	0·535	11·50	2·19	47·1

This result is of special interest for wheat and barley, since the nitrogen content of the grain affects their market value: high nitrogen

[1] J. E. Greaves and E. G. Carter, *J. Biol. Chem.*, 1923, **58**, 531. See also J. E. Greaves and D. H. Nelson, *J. Agric. Res.*, 1925, **31**, 183.
[2] S. H. Beckett and R. D. Robertson, *Calif. Agric. Expt. Sta., Bull.* 280, **1917.**
[3] S. H. Beckett and M. R. Huberty, *Calif. Agric. Expt. Sta., Bull.* 450, 1928.

content in wheat usually gives a strong flour and a good loaf, whilst low nitrogen content in barley usually gives a good malt and a bright beer. General field experience shows, in accordance with this rule, that the quality of a given variety of wheat is usually highest in dry years and of barley in wet ones. Thus, in C. H. Bailey's[1] examination of the data for spring wheat, gathered in sixteen counties of Minnesota, the results were:

Rainfall: Apr. 1–Sept. 1, inches	12–14	14–16	16–18	18–20	20–22	22–24
Nitrogen, per cent in grain .	2·62	2·41	2·14	2·35	2·26	2·04

and in F. T. Shutt's[2] comparison of wheat grown under irrigation at Invermere, British Columbia, and under dry land conditions at Lethbridge, Alberta, the percentages of protein in the wheat grain were:

	1st Year	2nd Year	3rd Year
Irrigated . . .	14·02	16·93	13·91
Dry Land . . .	16·70	18·47	18·18

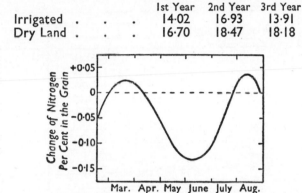

FIG. 35. The effect of an additional inch of rain above the average in any month on the nitrogen content of barley grain at Woburn.

In England the nitrogen content of barley grain is reduced by rain falling during the growing season, particularly in May and June, as is shown in Fig. 35;[3] the relation between these two is, in fact, sufficiently close for a reasonable forecast to be made of the nitrogen content of the grain about two months before harvest.[4]

The Amount of Water Transpired by a Crop

Much interest has been taken in determining the weight of water a plant must transpire to produce a unit weight of dry matter in its aerial parts, i.e. excluding the dry matter in the roots; and this weight of water has been called the transpiration coefficient or ratio of the

[1] *Minnesota Agric. Expt. Sta., Bull.* 131, 1913.
[2] *Trans. Roy. Soc. Canada*, 1935, **29**, Sect. 3, 37.
[3] E. J. Russell and J. A. Voelcker, *Fifty Years of Field Experiments at the Woburn Experiment Station*, London, 1936.   [4] E. J. Russell and L. R. Bishop, *J. Inst. Brew.*, 1933, **39**, 287.

crop. As long ago as 1850 J. B. Lawes[1] published the results of some experiments made at Rothamsted, in which he found that wheat, barley, clover, beans and peas all used about 200 to 270 lb. of water for each pound of dry matter produced, and subsequent workers in western Europe have obtained similar figures.[2] On the other hand, workers in the semi-arid regions of the U.S.A. have found much higher values, as is shown in Table 90, which summarises many results obtained by L. J. Briggs and H. L. Shantz[3] at Akron, Colorado. These variations clearly show that plants do not have unique transpiration coefficients.

TABLE 90

Transpiration Coefficients of Various Crops in Colorado

Crop	Extreme values for different varieties	Mean value for crop
Proso	268 to 341	293
Millet	261 to 444	310
Sorghum	285 to 467	322
Maize	315 to 413	368
Wheat	473 to 559	513
Barley	502 to 556	534
Oats	559 to 622	597
Flax	—	905
Sugar-beet	—	397
Potato	—	636
Cow-pea	—	571
Clover	789 to 805	797
Lucerne	651 to 963	831
Grasses	—	861
Various native plants (i.e. weeds)	277 to 1076	—

The amount of water transpired by a crop is controlled by the meteorological conditions prevailing—the rainfall and the evaporating power of the air—rather than by the amount of growth it makes. An extreme example of this is furnished by some results obtained on the permanent hay plots at Rothamsted in 1870. The spring was very dry—the rainfall during the period April to June being only 2·8 inches —which is well under half the average for this period. The amount of water left in the soil shortly after the hay harvest was determined

[1] *J. Hort. Soc. London*, 1850, **5**, 38.

[2] For a very full review of the results obtained before 1913, see L. J. Briggs and H. L. Shantz, *U.S. Dept. Agric., Bur. Plant Indust., Bull.* 285, 1913, and for a more recent summary, see C. H. Lee's contribution in *Physics of the Earth*—IX *Hydrology*, ed. by O. E. Meinzer, New York, 1942.

[3] *J. Agric. Res.*, 1914, **3**, 1. See also H. L. Shantz and R. L. Piemeisel, ibid., 1927, **34**, 1093.

on three plots: that receiving no manure and which yielded 5¾ cwt. of hay per acre, about a quarter of its average yield; that receiving complete minerals and about 80 lb. of nitrogen as ammonium salts each year and which yielded 30 cwt. of hay, about a half of its average yield; and that receiving complete minerals and about 85 lb. of nitrogen as nitrate of soda each year, and which yielded 56 cwt. of hay, about its average yield. The water deficit in the soil, i.e. the amount of water the crop took from the soil over and above that received during the growing season from the rain was, however, surprisingly independent of the yield of hay; it was about 3 inches, confined to the top 27 inches of soil, on the unmanured plot and about 4 inches, confined to the top 36 inches of soil, on the manured.[1] Thus, the nitrate of soda crop used about 7 inches of water—3 inches from the rainfall and 4 inches from the soil—to produce 56 cwt. of hay, whilst the unmanured crop used about 6 inches of water—3 inches from the rainfall and 3 inches from the soil—to produce just one-tenth the weight of herbage; and the reason it did not transpire the extra inch of water is probably because it was too starved to send its roots down as deep as the manured plants did, so its leaves were dying or dead when those of the manured plants were transpiring the last inch. This result appears to be out of line with the general result of arid farming, namely, that unmanured grain crops are more drought-resistant than those fully manured, but the explanation probably lies in the reduced drought resistance of the more succulent leaves of the manured crop rather than in its increased water demands.

The amount of water a crop transpires depends on the amount of water available to the crop, on the period of the day in which the stomata of the leaves of the crop are open and on the solar energy falling on the crop. For turgid crops with open stomata, the amount of water transpired depends on the energy available, for most of the energy absorbed by the leaves that is not reflected or re-radiated is used to evaporate water.

H. L. Penman[2] has shown that it is possible to calculate the amount of water evaporated from an open water surface or a wet, bare soil or an actively growing crop from considerations of the energy balance and the evaporative power of the air at the evaporating surface, and he has derived equations connecting the rate of evaporation with data obtained or obtainable by meteorological observations. Of the solar energy falling on a wet surface, part is reflected back, part is re-radiated as long-wave radiation (see p. 354), part is used to heat up the absorbing

[1] J. B. Lawes and J. H. Gilbert, *J. Roy. Agric. Soc.*, 1871, **7**, 1. The figures given here have been recalculated on a volume basis by Dr. R. K. Schofield, to whom I am indebted for them.
[2] *Proc. Roy. Soc.*, 1948, **193 A,** 120.

material and the air around it, part is used in photosynthesis, and the remainder evaporates water at the rate of approximately 1 gm. per 590 calories, the exact amount depending on the surface temperature of the leaf. The part used by crops for photosynthesis is negligible, being about one-half of 1 per cent. The part used for heating the soil or the plant itself is small if taken over a period of several days, though not over shorter periods (see p. 360). The part reflected back can be determined experimentally, and the parts re-radiated as long-wave radiation and used to heat the air can be approximately calculated from meteorological observations. Again, the power of the air to carry away the water vapour that evaporates from the wet surface depends on the temperature of the evaporating surface, on the temperature and water vapour content of the air, and on its rate of movement over the surface; and it can also be calculated approximately from meteorological data.

Penman made the calculation in three ways, and has given semi-empirical results so that they could be expressed in terms of quantities that are either measured by meteorological stations or could be so measured. The simplest of his results connects the evaporation E from an open water surface with the speed of the wind and the saturation deficit of the air, namely:

$$E = 0.35 \ (e_s - e_d) \ (1 + 0.0098u_2) \text{ mm. per day}$$
$$\doteqdot 0.37 \ (e_s - e_d) \ B \text{ mm. per day}$$

where e_s is the vapour pressure of the water at the water surface, e_d is the vapour pressure of the air in bulk at the dew-point, u_2 is the speed of the wind 2 metres above ground-level in miles per day, and B is the mean force of the wind on the Beaufort scale. The quantity most difficult to measure, and least commonly measured is e_s, which depends on the temperature of the water surface. For a crop e_s depends on the temperature of the transpiring leaf, and is not only a quantity very difficult to measure, but also varies with the position of the leaf on the plant. One could determine a mean exposed leaf temperature; but this problem can be circumvented, as this term can be eliminated and replaced by the vapour pressure of saturated air at the mean air temperature, a quantity that can easily be determined, but the resulting equation is far more complicated than the simple one given above.

These calculations give results for the amount of water evaporated from an open water surface or a wet, bare soil that are in satisfactory agreement with observation, considering the limitations of the equations used. However, if applied directly to a growing crop they give transpirations definitely in excess of those observed. Thus, the actual transpiration from turf is only about 80 per cent of the computed in summer, about 70 per cent during the spring and autumn, and about 60 per cent in winter. This difference is due to the behaviour of the stomata. When the stomata are open, the leaf behaves as an open water surface because the rate of removal of water vapour from the surface of the leaf into the body of the atmosphere is usually slower than the rate of diffusion of water vapour through the stomatal openings, even though they only occupy 1 to 3 per cent of the leaf area. This is the normal condition of a turgid leaf during the day-time. But at night-time the stomata close, and then the resistance to the diffusion

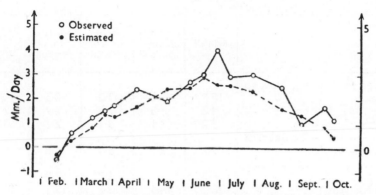

FIG. 36. The observed and computed evaporation from a turf soil at Rothamsted.
(Water table 16 in. below the surface.)

of water vapour from the inside of the leaf to the outside limits the rate of transpiration. Hence, the shorter the hours of daylight, the shorter the proportion of the day that the leaf behaves as an open water surface, and the greater the difference between the amounts of water lost by an open water surface and the crop, in accord with Penman's findings. Fig. 36 gives an example of the concordance between the measured and the calculated transpiration from a turf surface at Rothamsted, and also of the difficulties of making an accurate calculation because the divergence between the two curves could easily be due to inaccuracies in the estimates of some of the physical quantities in the equation.

A consequence of Penman's work is that the transpiration from an actively growing, or a turgid, crop is primarily dependent on meteorological conditions, and only dependent on the crop in so far as the behaviour of stomatal openings and closing vary. But this calculation is only valid if the crop covers an appreciable area of land: it is not valid for individual plants in isolation nor for crops in small areas with unusual exposures. It enables one to compute, from standard meteorological data, the amount of water a turgid crop will transpire; and the values so calculated for the average seasonal transpiration of a turgid crop at Rothamsted are given in Table 91, along with the average rainfall and drainage through a bare soil.

TABLE 91
Evaporation from a Bare Soil and Transpiration by Grass at Rothamsted
(Average for 1931–40)
In inches of water

	Rainfall	Drainage through bare soil	Evapora-tion from bare soil	Calculated trans-piration	Rainfall minus trans-piration
Winter (4 months), Nov. to Feb.	10·8	8·6	2·2	0·5	10·3
Spring, March–April . .	4·0	1·8	2·2	2·7	1·3
Autumn, Sept.–Oct. . .	5·2	2·1	3·1	2·1	3·1
Total for the 4 equinoctial months	9·2	3·9	5·3	4·8	4·4
Summer (4 months), May–Aug.	8·2	2·0	6·2	12·9	—4·7
Total for year . . .	28·2	14·5	13·7	18·2	10·0

The table shows that a deficit is built up under a continuously growing crop in the summer, which is not made up on the average until some time in November. The figures given for the transpiration are, however, a little uncertain, particularly for the winter period, where the transpiration is probably somewhat under-estimated, but they are of the right order of magnitude, for D. Lloyd[1] has calculated, from rainfall and river discharge data, that the average annual evaporation and transpiration from the watershed of the Lea, near which Rothamsted is situated, is about 19 inches, though this estimate is known to be a little too high, as not all the rain-water entering the ground-water under the watershed finds its way into the river.

The table also allows one to calculate how much water a crop must be able to take from the soil to remain turgid for any specified seasonal rainfall, or, alternatively, how much water must be removed by drainage.

One consequence of the amount of water used by crops depending primarily on the energy supply or the evaporative power of the air, is that all the water falling on the crop, whether as light drizzle or dew

[1] Quart. J. Roy. Met. Soc., 1941, 67, 33.

or whether as a definite rain storm, is as effective in contributing to the water requirements of the crop as is the water removed from the soil. There is no question here of light showers contributing nothing to the water requirements of the crop, in the way that they usually contribute nothing to the water supplies of the soil—every thousandth of an inch of rainfall, however long it take to fall, on being evaporated from the plant leaves or stems reduces the plants' demands on the soil water by this amount.

The total water used by different plants or crops in a year depends on the periods at which crops are making active growth: broad-leaved evergreen crops near a water table, or in a high rainfall region, will transpire more water per year than deciduous crops or crops which are only growing for short periods of the year, and then either mature or become dormant. C. H. Lee[1] has collected together many different estimates of the amount of water actually transpired by crops. They reach 5 to 6 feet a year for evergreen trees and marsh grasses in tropical swamps and river bottoms, such as in the Nile Sudd, and are about 24 to 36 inches for perennial crops, such as lucerne and pastures, in the typical irrigated areas of the world, and about 18 to 30 inches for short season crops, such as the small grains and deciduous orchards.

Plants can transpire up to $\frac{1}{4}$ inch of water in a summer's day at Rothamsted, and they will certainly transpire more than this in hot, dry climates. In Saskatchewan[2] wheat can transpire 0·2 inch of water daily over a seventy-day period, and in windy weather during the heat of summer up to 0·3 inch a day.

Some of the methods employed for reducing the effect of droughts are immediately obvious from these results. The earlier in summer a crop matures the less water it will need, as it will be maturing at a time of high or increasing daily water demands. Crops growing throughout the summer and maturing in autumn, e.g. sugar-beet in this country, will tend to have heavy water demands, as they have to grow throughout the period of maximum transpiration; and for these crops early maturity is of limited value, as it will only save days in late autumn, a period of rapidly decreasing daily water demands. Permanent crops, such as pastures and leys, make the heaviest demands of all if they are to grow throughout the year, which they can only do if the annual rainfall is in excess of the transpiration, and also if a considerable proportion of it falls during the summer months.

---

[1] *Hydrology*, ed. O. E. Meinzer, chap. viii ,1942.
[2] *Soil Res. Lab., Swift River, Sask., Rept.*, 1943.

CHAPTER XXI

THE TRANSFER OF WATER FROM SOIL TO PLANT

The Wilting Range in Soils

THE ROOTS OF the plant supply it with the greater proportion of the water it uses during its lifetime, hence the rate the root system can extract water from the soil during dry periods is of fundamental importance in the development of the crop. During hot, dry weather the leaves of many plants wilt whenever water is not being supplied to their cells quickly enough: they can wilt at midday in hot sunny weather when the plants are growing in damp soil because water cannot pass through the protoplasm of the root and leaf cells quickly enough, but they normally recover turgor early in the afternoon under these circumstances; or they can wilt because the roots cannot move water out of the soil quickly enough, in which case they may not recover turgor until the late afternoon or evening. As the soil around the roots becomes drier, water moves into the roots more slowly, and it takes longer for the leaves to regain their turgor, until a time is reached when first the mature leaves and later the younger leaves cease to regain turgor before transpiration begins again next day.

Plant roots can only extract water from a soil if they can apply a sufficiently great suction to move it out of the pore space. As the soil dries, so the suction needed to extract water rises and the rate of movement of water into a given length of root decreases, which may sometimes have the consequence that if the crop is growing in conditions conducive to high rates of transpiration, the actual maximum rate it can reach will decrease as the soil dries.[1] The maximum suction roots can exert on the soil water does not appear to be a very definite quantity, but if the water is held at suctions higher than about 7 atm.[2] —the first permanent wilting-point of the soil[3]—the roots appear to be unable to extract sufficient water to keep the whole plant of most farm crops turgid when placed in a saturated atmosphere, i.e. in an atmosphere where transpiration cannot take place; and if above about 20 to 30 atm.—the ultimate wilting-point—to keep any leaves

[1] S. I Dolgov, *C.R. Acad. Sci. (U.S.S.R.)*, 1947, **55**, 449.
[2] L. A. Richards and L. R. Weaver, *J. Agric. Res.*, 1944, **69**, 215.
[3] J. R. Furr and C. A. Taylor, *U.S. Dept. Agric.*, *Tech. Bull.* 640, 1939; J. R. Furr and J. O. Reeve, *J. Agric. Res.*, 1945, **71**, 149.

turgid. The water held between these two suctions is sufficiently available to the roots for the maintenance of life, but not for growth; that held at suctions less than that corresponding to the first permanent wilting-point may be, but is not necessarily, readily available for growth.

This conception of a permanent wilting range in the soil has not been used by all workers, although L. J. Briggs and H. L. Shantz, in their classical paper[1] on the subject, clearly stated that such a range exists; they defined the wilting coefficient of a soil as the moisture content that would no longer support plant growth: most plants growing in drier soil than this could still extract enough water to maintain life.

The great difficulty of determining any permanent wilting-point for a soil lies in the uncertainty of deciding exactly when the plant remains wilted in a saturated atmosphere. The difficulty, however, is of less importance than one might expect, for the moisture content of most soils does not vary very much between suctions of 10 to 20 atm., or roughly between pF 4·0 and 4·3. Nor does the wilting-point depend very much on the plant, for again, although the maximum suctions different plant roots exert differ somewhat, this does not greatly alter the moisture content at which wilting takes place for the same reason. The suction at wilting-point is commonly taken as either 15 atm.,[2] or pF 4·2[3] (16 atm.), and it must be accepted with the provisos that there should be a fairly rapid drop in the availability of the soil water to the plant in the neighbourhood of this suction; that no two observers necessarily agree exactly when a plant has reached its wilting-point; and that different plants exert different suctions before they reach their wilting-points.

The discussion in the previous paragraphs has implicitly assumed that the water in the soil is present as pure water; but in fact it contains dissolved salts, which cause it to have an osmotic pressure. The osmotic pressure of a solution is the pressure one must exert to force pure water through a membrane permeable to water but not to salts into the solution. The cell sap in the roots also contains dissolved substances, so can exert an osmotic pressure against pure water, and the root can only extract water from the soil if the osmotic pressure in the root cells is appreciably higher than that in the soil solution, which is the name given to the water in the soil. This fact must not be taken to mean that the transfer of water from the soil solution to the plant root is purely an osmotic phenomenon, for it only takes place if the roots are properly aerated, implying either that the roots expend energy in making the transfer or in maintaining their semi-permeable membranes.

[1] U.S. Dept. Agric., Bur. Plant Indust., Bull. 230, 1912.
[2] L. A. Richards and L. R. Weaver, Soil Sci., 1943, 56, 331.
[3] See J. V. B. da Costa, J. Agric. Sci., 1938, 28, 630, for a discussion on this figure.

Now the osmotic pressure of the cell sap of agricultural crops appears to be between 10 and 20 atm., and is probably rather higher for plants that have been growing in conditions of water shortage or in solutions having an appreciable osmotic pressure than for those that have been growing with a good supply of fairly pure water. Now no crop can make any appreciable growth in a solution having an osmotic pressure of 10 atm., and some crops have their growth affected if the osmotic pressure of the solution exceeds 2 atm., and their growth may be reduced in proportion as the osmotic pressure rises from 2 to about 10 atm.[1]

The osmotic pressure of the soil solution depends on the amount of salt and the amount of water present in the soil; hence, as the soil dries, so the osmotic pressure of the soil solution increases. For normal soils in the temperate regions the osmotic pressure of the soil solution at the wilting-point is under 2 atm., although it may be above this on sandy soils which have been given large dressings of soluble fertilisers, as happens sometimes in intensive market-garden areas.[2] But in many semi-arid areas the soil may contain enough salts for the osmotic pressure of the soil solution to be well above 2 atm. even when the water is held at a suction well below the 15 atm. of the normally defined wilting-point.

The soil water is only at a suction of between 10 and 15 atm. or over in a soil carrying a permanently wilted crop if the osmotic pressure of the soil solution is low. If it is appreciable, the plants wilt permanently when the soil water is at lower suctions than this. The ease with which plant roots extract water from the soil seems to depend, not on the suction of the water in the soil, but on its free energy; and these two are only equivalent when the water contains no dissolved substances. The free energy of a solution in a soil is approximately the sum of the free energy change due to the dissolved salts and that due to the curved air-water menisci bounding the solution in the soil pores. Both of these quantities can be measured in units of atmospheres. Hence, if the osmotic pressure of the solution is 3 atm., and it is under a suction of 3 atm. in the soil pores, then plant roots will have at least the same difficulty in using the water from this solution as they would if the soil contained pure water at a suction of 6 atm.

Some work of C. H. Wadleigh and his co-workers illustrates these points well. Thus Fig. 37[3] shows the effect of the free energy of the water supply on the growth of beans. The plants were grown in a loam soil to which no sodium chloride or 0·1, 0·2 or 0·4 per cent of

[1] F. M. Eaton, *J. Agric. Res.*, 1942, **64**, 357; O. C. Magistad and R. F. Reitemeier, *Soil Sci.*, 1943, **55**, 351; C. H. Wadleigh and A. D. Ayers, *Plant Physiol.*, 1945, **20**, 106.
[2] L. M. White and W. H. Ross, *J. Agric. Res.*, 1939, **59**, 81.
[3] With A. D. Ayers, *Plant Physiol.*, 1945, **20**, 106.

sodium chloride had been added, and were watered when the average moisture content of the soil had fallen half-way, two-thirds way and nine-tenths way from field capacity to the wilting-point, as determined in the salt-free soil. Again, they showed[1] that beans, maize, lucerne and cotton could extract water from soils with free energy reductions of 8 to 9, 10·5 to 11·5, 12 to 13 and 16 to 17 atm. respectively when

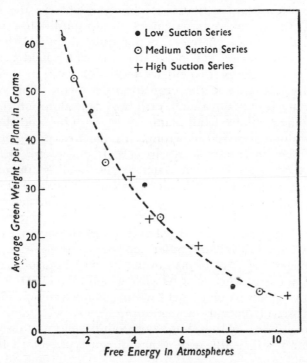

Fig. 37. The relation between the green weight of beans and the mean free energy of the water supply.

only about 2 atm. was due to the suction with which the soil held the solution, and the remainder to the osmotic pressure caused by the dissolved salts, in this case sodium chloride at concentrations of 0·1, 0·15, 0·25 and over 0·25 per cent respectively. However, at these high salt concentrations the actual growth of cotton and lucerne was much restricted. The effect of salts on plant growth will, however, be discussed in Chapter XXXIV, but here it is relevant to mention that plants do not wilt so sharply when growing in salt solutions, and the leaves keep their turgor even when very little water is being transpired and when the moisture stress is so high that all growth has ceased.

[1] *Soil Sci.*, 1947, **63**, 341.

The Available Water in Soils

Plants growing in soils of low salt content under drought conditions can dry the soil in their root zone considerably below field capacity before they begin to suffer from lack of water. Veihmeyer and his associates,[1] working mainly with irrigated orchard crops, have maintained that all the water in the root zone held at a suction less than the permanent wilting suction is readily available to the crop, and that there is no advantage in irrigating a crop until it has used up all this water. They could, therefore, define quite definitely the quantity of available water a soil can hold: it is the water held between the field capacity and the permanent wilting-point; and, in their view, it is all equally available to the crop for its growth. This concept of available water is only of value if Veihmeyer's assumption that all this water is equally available to all plants is correct: it becomes meaningless if the assumption is seriously wrong. In the first place plants have varying abilities to extract water from soil: maize and potatoes, for example, cannot take as much water as the small grains or lucerne. In the second place, the actual values for the available water obtained by Veihmeyer are subject to an uncertainty, for he determines the permanent wilting-point of the soil not when it is in its natural condition, but only after it has been dried and passed through a 2-mm. sieve. Hence, his values for available water depend on the additional assumptions that the salt content of his sample in the laboratory is the same as the soil in the field when near its wilting-point, and that the moisture content of the soil at its permanent wilting-point is independent of the actual structure of the soil—an assumption that is certainly approximately correct for many soils, but whose validity has not been critically examined for a sufficiently wide range of soil types for its limitations to be known.

Veihmeyer's assumption appears to be valid for a wide range of crops and soils in the field, and it has been extensively used to predict when irrigation is necessary, and how much water should be given at each irrigation. But it is not universally true in the field, and the conditions under which it fails are not yet clearly defined. The surprising feature, however, is that it should be of any practical value, for, as already shown in Fig. 37 for beans, and as both C. H. Davies[2] and J. L. Haynes[3] have shown for maize, when these plants are grown in controlled laboratory conditions, their growth is roughly inversely

---

[1] For prune and peach trees, see *Hilgardia*, 1927, **2**, 125; *Calif. Agric. Expt. Sta., Bull.* 479, 1929, and 573, 1934; for apples and pears, *Bull.* 667, 1942; for cotton, *Bull.* 668, 1942; for grapes, *Proc. Amer. Soc. Hort. Sci.*, 1931, **28**, 151; for walnuts, 1937, **35**, 289; and for growth rates of fruit on pears, peaches and prunes, 1942, **40**, 13; for sugar-beet, L. D. Doneen, *Ann. Amer. Soc. Sugar-Beet Tech.*, 1942.

[2] *Bot. Gaz.*, 1940, **101**, 791.   [3] *J. Amer. Soc. Agron.*, 1948, **40**, 385.

proportional to the suction of the water in the soil, decreasing continuously as the suction rises from about 1 atm., i.e. just drier than field capacity.

Veihmeyer's assumption will fail whenever the plant roots cannot ramify throughout the soil zone sufficiently uniformly to extract all the usable water fairly rapidly, for once the soil in the immediate neighbourhood of the plant root is in the wilting range, water can only move very slowly from moister soil through this zone. Hence the tendency for crops which make a great weight of root system, and which therefore can ramify through the whole soil mass, to extract more water from a soil than those which have a smaller system.[1] Again, M. R. Lewis and his co-workers,[2] studying pears in some heavy Oregon soils, and J. R. Furr and C. A. Taylor,[3] studying lemons in some heavy Californian soils, found that the trees suffered from water shortage when only one-third of the available water in the top 3 to 4 feet had been used, but they also found that in these soils the tree roots were very unevenly distributed throughout the root zone.

Veihmeyer's assumption can also fail on light soils. Thus, Furr and Taylor in California, and H. R. Oppenheimer and D. L. Elze in Palestine,[4] working with citrus—lemons, oranges and grape-fruit—on light soils found that the rate of fruit growth could be limited by lack of water before the transpiration rate was affected and whilst the moisture content of the soil in the top 3 to 4 feet was above the wilting-point under conditions when the roots were evenly distributed throughout the soil.

These failures could be due to a wrong value of the wilting-point moisture being used through the soil having a lower salt content when brought into the laboratory for the determination of its wilting-point than when it is near its wilting-point in the field. However, it is unlikely this is the sole cause of the failure, even if it is of any importance, for K. Mendel[5] found that the stomata of orange leaves close during the heat of the day, and they remain closed all day when the suction of the water in the soil has risen to 3·5 atm.

The Amount of Available Water held by a Soil

The amount of water held by a soil that is available to plants depends on the amount held per unit volume of soil and on the depth of soil from which plants can extract their water. All measurements and calculations of available water should always be made on the volume

[1] For example, see R. D. Lane and A. L. McComb, J. Forestry, 1948, 46, 344.
[2] U.S. Dept. Agric., Tech. Bull. 432, 1934; Plant Physiol., 1935, 10, 309.
[3] U.S. Dept. Agric., Tech. Bull. 640, 1939.   [4] Rehovoth Agric. Res. Stat., Bull. 31, 1941.
[5] Rehovoth Agric. Res. Stat., Bull. 37, 1945.

basis; for it is only available water per unit depth of soil that is of significance for plant growth, not available water per unit weight of soil. In practice, however, one has often to measure available water on the weight basis and, if so, it is then essential to measure, and not to assume, the weight of unit volume of soil. Table 92 demonstrates how moisture contents calculated on a weight basis can give quite a different picture from those on a volume basis: the water content of this Greenville soil, which is a deep uniform loess, decreases with depth on a weight basis, but remains almost constant per unit depth of soil.

TABLE 92

The Variation of Moisture Content with Depth in a Well-drained Loess Soil on a Weight and on a Volume Basis[1]

Moisture contents measured 68 days after flooding, with evaporation prevented
Fallow Soil, Greenville Farm, Logan, Utah

Depth of soil In feet	0–2	2–4	4–6	6–8
Water per 100 gm. of dry soil[2] . .	17·6	16·6	15·9	15·75
Density of soil particles[3] . . .	2·695	2·745	2·755	2·755
Grams of dry soil per c.cm. of soil[3] .	1·25	1·295	1·335	1·37
Pore space, per cent of total volume .	53·6	52·8	51·5	50·3
Water per 100 c.cm. of soil . .	22·0	21·5	21·2	21·6

The amount of available water per unit volume of soil, usually measured in inches of water per foot of soil, is calculated as the difference between the volume of water held per foot at field capacity and at the permanent wilting-point. It is not very dependent on the texture of the soil, although very light soils can only hold small quantities of available water. Table 93, referring mainly to irrigated soils from the western U.S.A., shows how little the texture controls the available water present, and how a heavy soil may hold less available water than a light loam.

Available water can be increased to some extent by adding organic matter to the soil. An extreme case shows the limited amount of increase possible. On Broadbalk, at Rothamsted, one plot has received ninety-three dressings of farmyard manure at 14 tons per acre between 1843 and 1943, and its neighbour has received no manure at all during this period, and the field is ploughed to about 6 to 8 inches deep. Table 94 shows that the available water in the top 9 inches has been

[1] I am indebted to Dr. R. K. Schofield for this table.
[2] O. W. Israelsen, *Hilgardia*, 1927, **2**, 516.
[3] J. A. Widtsoe and W. W. McLaughlin, *Utah Agric. Expt. Sta.*, Bull. 115, 1912, p. 201.

increased from 2·0 to 2·7 inches, or by 35 per cent, due to these ninety-three dressings of manure, but has barely been affected in the 9 to 15 inch layer. The high figure for the unmanured plot in the 15 to 21 inch layer is due to it having a higher clay content (53 per cent) than the

TABLE 93

The Field Capacity, Wilting Point and Available Water in Certain American Soils[1]

Soil	Field capacity[2] on oven-dry weight basis	Permanent wilting-point on oven-dry weight basis	Available water, inches per foot
Yuma sand	4·8	3·2	0·3
Delano sandy loam . . .	9·1	4·2	0·8
Fresno sandy loam . . .	11·1	3·1	1·3
Salinas fine sandy loam . .	28·2	20·0	1·3
Wooster silt loam . . .	23·4	6·1	2·9
Aiken clay loam . . .	31·1	25·7	0·7
Gila clay	30·4	16·0	2·4

TABLE 94

The Effect of Repeated Dressings of Farmyard Manure on Available Water in Broadbalk Soil[3]

Available water in the 9- or 6-in. sample in inches

Depth in inches	With farmyard manure	Unmanured	Difference
0– 9	2·68	1·97	+ 0·71
9–15	1·17	1·04	+ 0·13
15–21	1·13	1·54	− 0·41

other samples (23 to 31 per cent). Hence, this large amount of farmyard manure has not increased the available water in the top 9 inches by more than 0·7 inch, though in period of dry springs this increase can be of great importance for shallow-rooted seedlings. American experience, with less extreme dressings of farmyard manure, indicates that a given series of dressings of farmyard manure raises the available water rather more in light than in heavy soils.[4]

[1] From J. H. MacGillivray and L. D. Doneen, *Proc. Amer. Soc. Hort. Sci.*, 1942, **40**, 483.
[2] Measured as the moisture equivalent.
[3] E. W. Russell and W. Balcerek, *J. Agric. Sci.*, 1944, **34**, 123.
[4] G. J. Bouyoucos (Michigan), *Soil Sci.*, 1939, **47**, 377; L. Havis (Ohio), *Proc. Amer. Soc. Hort. Sci.*, 1943, **42**, 497.

The depth from which plants take their water is very variable. Wheat and barley rarely take water from below 6 feet, even in the Great Plains of the U.S.A., whilst they can sometimes suffer from drought on well-drained deep soils when they are drawing water from a depth of only 3 to 4 feet. Maize probably cannot take water from quite such a depth as wheat and barley, but the sorghums can probably take it from a rather greater depth. Grasses, i.e. pastures, meadows and prairies, in general take their water from smaller depths than wheat and barley, whilst sugar-beet probably goes deeper. Some of the leguminous crops, such as sweet clover, but in particular lucerne, can go down to very considerable depths; thus, on the loess soils of Kansas and Nebraska, lucerne can dry out the subsoil to 20 to 30 feet in three to six years,[1] though its behaviour here seems exceptional.

Orchard trees on permeable, well-drained soils can certainly take water from 9 to 12 feet depth, though, as Veihmeyer[2] has shown, they can wilt and suffer from drought if the top 6 feet of soil is dried to the wilting coefficient. On heavy soils, however, they often cannot get much water below 3 feet, even in arid regions. Some authors have reported water being taken by orchard trees and vegetable crops from depths of 16 to 20 feet, but these reports are mainly from the loess soils of the Great Plains of the U.S.A.—soils which, as Israelsen and others have shown, are characterised by displaying the phenomenon of slow or delayed drainage very strongly (see p. 379), and the authors making these claims do not appear to have considered seriously this alternative explanation of their results. However, it appears that under some forest and grassland conditions, as, for example, in the hills of California, the soil may be dried down to 10 feet or more, and the water deficit may be as high as 20 inches.[3] A soil with such a deficit, if its surface is properly protected, is ideally suited to absorb the water from cloudbursts, such as sometimes occur in these hills during the winter season.

Plants take water easiest from directly underneath them, and tend to dry out the superficial layers before going deeper. In dry periods the soil in this superficial layer under the plant can be dried out to under the wilting-point, whilst the roots are taking water rapidly from soil either deeper down or farther away laterally.[4] Fig. 38,[5] taken from some results of H. H. Nicholson for the drying out of a heavy soil under pasture in Cambridge during the summer, illustrates this

[1] T. A. Kiesselbach, J. C. Russel and A. Anderson, *J. Amer. Soc. Agron.*, 1929, **21**, 241; 1934, **26**, 422; H. E. Myers, ibid., 1936, **28**, 106; C. O. Grandfield and W. H. Metzger, ibid., 1936, **28**, 115.   [2] *Hilgardia*, 1927, **2**, 125.
[3] M. Donnelly, *Trans. Amer. Geophys. Un.*, 1942, 544; J. W. Tourney, *U.S. Dept. Agric. Yearbook*, 1903, p. 279.
[4] M. B. Russell, F. E. Davis and R. A. Blair, *J. Amer. Soc. Agron.*, 1940, **32**, 922.
[5] I am indebted to Dr. R. K. Schofield for this figure.

effect. Almost the full deficit is built up in the top 10 inches before much water is removed from greater depths. This figure also shows the condition of the soil after a dry autumn and winter, when the rainfall was not sufficient to make good the deficit built up during the preceding summer.

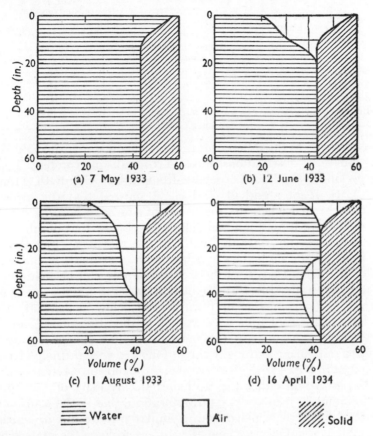

FIG. 38. The distribution with depth of water deficit in the soil during a drought. (Gault clay pasture, Cambridge University Farm.) The actual water deficits are: 7 May 0·0 in., 12 June 2·8 in., 11 August 5·0 in., 16 April 1·0+1·7=2·7 in.

There is very little difference between deep- and shallow-rooting crops in the early stages of drying out the soil, and this can be illustrated by comparing the depths from which deep-rooting lucerne and shallow-rooting citrus take their water under standard conditions of irrigation on light soils in California and Arizona, as is shown in Table 95. The correspondence between the levels from which these two crops take their water under normal irrigation practice appears to be surprising

TABLE 95

Depth from which Lucerne and Citrus Trees take their Water under Standard Irrigation Practice

Soil—Sandy Loam in California

Depth	Proportion of water taken from these depths	
	Lucerne	Citrus[1]
0–2 ft.	62	66
2–3 ft.	15	16
3–4 ft.	12	10
Below 4 ft. . . .	11	8

when compared to the differences that they show under drought conditions. But these observations must be correctly interpreted. Lucerne can grow under conditions of severe drought, but its growth is limited. Thus, A. S. Hunter and O. J. Kelley[2] showed that the growth of lucerne is checked when the top 3 feet of soil have become dried out even when there is an abundant supply just below that depth.

Plants can use not only the water in the root zone, but also some water from the soil immediately below, and an estimate of the amount of water the deeper layers of the soil can supply can be made experimentally, for if the roots are removing water from the base of the root zone, water is moving up from the soil below in the same way as if the base of the root zone was exposed to the atmosphere and water was evaporating from it at the same rate. The change in moisture deficit in a soil during a drought can be followed with the help of a curve such as that in Fig. 39.[3] This curve shows the moisture deficit in a well-drained pasture on either the Rothamsted clay loam or the Woburn sandy loam for a given potential transpiration, that is, the transpiration that would have taken place from a similar pasture but in which the water table was sufficiently near the surface to keep the grass roots in moist soil. The curve A D shows the rate of loss of water by evaporation from the moist soils under low temperatures and slow drying rates, as explained on p. 384, and therefore represents the amount of water that can move up by capillarity into the root zone from below. The total amount of water available to the crop is therefore the amount of water present in the root zone plus that which can move up by capillarity. In

---

[1] Similar figures were obtained for citrus in Salt River Valley, Arizona, by K. Harris *et al.* (*Arizona Agric. Expt. Sta.*, *Bull.* 153, 1936), who concluded from this that citrus must be irrigated as soon as the top 2 foot of soil is dry.

[2] *Soil Sci.*, 1946, **62**, 441.   [3] H. L. Penman, *J. Soil Sci.*, 1949, **1**, 74.

Fig. 39 the straight line portion A'A represents the amount of this root-zone water, all of which is considered to be equally easily available. The figure shows that in this example, although there are only 3 inches of water in the root zone, the transpiration of the crop does not begin to be affected until after the crop has transpired 4 inches. After that, however, the soil rapidly ceases to be able to provide water for transpiration. For the next inch of potential transpiration the soil will only

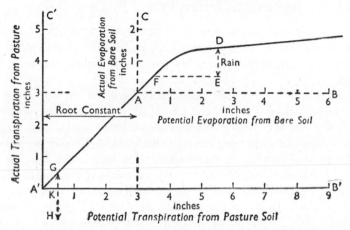

Fig. 39. The relation between the actual loss of water by transpiration from a well-drained pasture during a drought and the potential loss if there had been an adequate water supply within the root range (Rothamsted and Woburn Soils). (For explanation of the letters, see text.)

be able to provide a third of an inch, and afterwards for each inch of potential transpiration the soil can only supply about one-twelfth of an inch.

This curve, together with Penman's formula for computing the transpiration of a turgid crop from meteorological data, given on p. 394, allows one to calculate the water conditions in the soil at any time. Thus, if the soil had a water deficit represented by the point D, and rain fell equal to D E, the moisture deficit in the soil would then be represented by the point F. Similarly if it had a deficit represented by G, and a rain equal to G H fell, then a quantity of water equal to K H would have to drain out of the soil. Penman has given examples of the kind of information one can compute from this curve such as the prediction of the date at which drains under a pasture field will begin to run in the autumn.

CHAPTER XXII

THE CONTROL OF SOIL MOISTURE IN PRACTICE

Removal of Excess Water by Drainage

ARTIFICIALLY DRAINING A soil is a necessary operation under two distinct conditions: if the soil has a high water table, or if excess surface water cannot penetrate reasonably rapidly to below the root zone of the crop.

Soils having a water table sufficiently high for the capillary fringe, i.e. for the soil that is kept wet by capillarity above the water table, to reach the surface always need to have their water tables reduced. The minimum allowable depth of the water table below the soil surface depends on the crop to some extent: thus fruit trees need a deeper water table than grass, for if the water table is too high their root system is too shallow to anchor them firmly against high winds when the soil is wet. It is probable that agricultural crops can only be cultivated easily in temperate regions if the water table never rises to within 24 to 30 inches of the surface, but it is usually reckoned that it should be below 3 feet, though rather higher water tables are allowable for pastures or meadows.[1]

The optimum depth of the water table, however, depends on circumstances. On peat and fen soils, which oxidise away rapidly on cultivation, it is usually considered desirable to have as high a water table as possible, for the higher the water table the slower the rate of oxidation of the peat.[2] However, English fen farmers, for some reason that has not been established, do not agree with this: they like the water table to be as deep as possible. Again, if the ground-water contains enough dissolved salts to harm the root system of the crop, it should be sufficiently deep for its capillary fringe to be below the bottom of the crop's root system, and depths of less than 10 feet are considered undesirable.

The second type of soil needing draining is that in which surface water will not drain away through the soil quickly enough, with the consequence that it either stands in pools on the field, or else it fills all

---

[1] For experimental results on the effect of depth of water table on crop yield, see R. Schwarz, *Kulturtech.*, 1932, **35**, 448, for canary grass; H. B. Roe, *Minnesota Agric. Expt. Sta., Bull.* 330, 1937; H. Burgevin and S. Hénin, *Ann. Agron.*, 1943, **13**, 288.

[2] For an example from the Florida Everglades, see B. S. Clayton and J. R. Neller, *Proc. Soil Sci. Soc. Flor.*, 1943, **5** A, 118; J. R. Neller, *Soil Sci.*, 1944, **58**, 195.

the main soil pores and prevents the plant roots being adequately aerated. The main principle to bear in mind when rectifying defects of drainage under these conditions is that water can only move at an appreciable rate through cracks or other discontinuities in the soil structure: it cannot move through the constitutional pores, i.e. the pores between the constituent soil particles forming the soil structure, of even light loams rapidly enough for practical purposes. Drainage can, therefore, only take place through cracks and spaces between soil crumbs in medium and heavy soils; and soils can be in need of drainage either because there are not sufficient coarse pores to let the water through the superficial layers quickly enough, or because the permeability of the deeper subsoil is too low to let the surface water drain away down to the water table. If the cause of the bad drainage is due to the water being unable to percolate through the surface layers of the soil because of insufficient coarse pores, then proper cultivation or soil management is adequate to remedy this defect. The cause of this trouble may be due either to muddy water running over the land and depositing its load of mud into the coarser pores, or to rain breaking up the surface tilth with the consequent filling up of these pores: preventing muddy water entering the area in the first case, and protecting the surface against the rain in the second, are the proper methods to be employed. If a compact subsoil is the trouble, deep cultivation, or deep ploughing to get underneath the compacted layer, is required. If the cause of the bad drainage is that the deeper subsoil is too impermeable to allow water to percolate below the root range of the crop quickly enough, then the field must be drained artificially. This is done by digging a suitable system of ditches and, if necessary, underdraining the land between them, using either a system of tile or mole drains.[1] Thus, the water falling on the surface of the soil can flow through cracks in the soil into the drains and through the ditches away from the area. If, but only if, the drainage system allows surplus subsoil water to be removed rapidly, its efficiency can often be increased by deep tillage, either ploughing or subsoiling, as this increases the number of channels the water can seep through from the surface into the drains.

The success of a drainage system depends on the stability of the soil structure, i.e. both on the length of life of the various fissures and wide pores in the soil that let the water through into the drains, and also on the clearness of the water entering the drains. Clay soils typically have a stable structure in England and troubles due to silting up of the drains and blocking up of the wide pores are unusual. Their

[1] For a discussion of the principles of field drainage, see M. G. Kendall, *Practical Field Drainage* (a series of articles in *Farm Implement and Machinery Review*, 1944, **70**); H. H. Nicholson, *The Principles of Field Drainage*, Cambridge, 1942; J. L. Russell, *J. Agric. Sci.*, 1934, **24**, 544.

stability may be increased by liming the soil, as the drainage water from unlimed clay soils may be more turbid than from limed,[1] and decreased by heavy dressings of sodium nitrate, using the same criterion of the increased turbidity of the drainage water.[2] The great difficulties in England arise with silt soils, for these have a weak, unstable structure. So much silt enters the field drains that devices such as silt traps are essential, and very careful management of the land is needed to keep the wide soil pores open, for they are rapidly filled up with muddy water unless considerable skill is used. The permeability of these soils can be maintained by proper cropping and in particular by the use of potentially deep-rooting crops such as lucerne. Such crops not only open up new channels through the soil but they also tend to stabilise the soil structure. It has not yet been established whether lucerne leys will be helpful on the silty wealden clays of South-East England where they are now being tried, but they can improve the permeability of silt loams in Iowa.[3]

Drainage improves the fertility of a medium to heavy soil for many reasons. It improves the aeration of the soil if the soil contains any appreciable volume of coarse pores that are emptied as a consequence of the draining; but it also improves the aeration of heavy soils having practically no air-space when drained, for it removes all stagnant water from the crevices and cracks in the soil, and allows oxygenated rain-water to penetrate rapidly into the subsoil. In consequence of this im-proved aeration of the subsoil, and removal of stagnant unoxygenated water, crops can develop a deeper root system, and this is particularly important during the winter when transpiration is low. A young plant of winter wheat can, for example, carry a well developed root system in these cracks on a heavy soil, so that as soon as the warmer weather of spring comes, it can start growing quickly as its extensive root system can tap a large volume of soil for nutrients. The corresponding plant on the undrained clay will only carry a very restricted root system, of which only a small proportion is capable of absorbing water and nutri-ents, as explained in Chapter XXIV, so it will make very slow growth in the spring, as it will not be able to tap a sufficient volume of soil for an adequate nutrient supply. The stronger plant on the drained soil will also be able to withstand periods of rapid transpiration during a drought much better than the weaker plant on the undrained, because of its much more extensive root system at the onset of the dry period. This effect of deeper rooting and greater vigour of the crop will also allow it to dry out the soil more during the drought, hence increase the amount

[1] E. C. Childs (*J. Agric. Sci.*, 1943, **33**, 136) found 260 parts per million of silt and clay in the drainage water from an unlimed clay pasture and only 70 parts per million from an adjacent area recently limed.   [2] A. D. Hall, *Trans. Chem. Soc.*, 1904, **85**, 964.
[3] G. W. Musgrave and G. R. Free, *J. Amer. Soc. Agron.*, 1936, **28**, 727.

of cracking that occurs in the subsoil, and hence again allow water to drain through the soil more easily in the following wet weather. Thus, vigorous crops on heavy land can help create, and stabilise when created, the cracks and fissures which are essential for the downward movement of water and the improvement of the aeration.

Draining surplus water away has other desirable consequences. Drained land may warm up quicker in spring than undrained, particularly if drainage removes an appreciable proportion of the water in the soil, i.e. if the soil has an appreciable specific yield. The surface soil will warm up quicker because its specific heat is reduced by the surplus water being removed, but the same result applies to the subsurface soil, though there appears to be very little information available on the magnitude and importance of this warming-up at depths of, say, 4 inches or 1 foot. The combined effect of improved aeration, and possibly higher temperatures, encourages microbiological decomposition of plant residues, leading eventually to an increased rate of nitrification.

Draining can have one other important effect for autumn-sown crops or for leys and grassland. The surface of a water-logged soil tends to heave, or be lifted upwards, when it becomes frozen, with the consequence that if any plants are growing in the soil they get lifted up with the surface and may have all their roots broken in the process. Heaving of soil in frosty weather is almost confined to soils containing an appreciable volume of water held in the coarser pores, hence draining a soil always reduces the liability of the surface to heave, and its magnitude if it does.

Irrigation

Irrigation consists in applying water to the land in such a way that a reasonable proportion of the root zone of the plant is moistened. The water can be applied either as a spray or artificial rain, or it can be run over the land as a sheet of water—flood irrigation—or it can be introduced into the subsoil through leaky pipes—subsurface irrigation. Spray irrigation is preferable where only small amounts of water need be given, as, for example, by market gardeners in England; flood irrigation in one form or another is the typical method used in the irrigation projects of the arid regions; and subsurface irrigation is still in its infancy owing to the technical difficulties involved. Little detailed work has been done on the relative advantages of these methods, but, as recent work in Palestine has shown, good crops can be grown with less water if spray rather than flood irrigation is used, due to the more even distribution of water so achieved. Spray irrigation is, however limited to areas in which soluble salts cannot accumulate in the soil surface: it is excellent for supplementary irrigation when at another period of the year there is enough rain to wet the subsoil to well below the depth of the root zone.

The fundamental problem underlying all irrigation projects in arid regions is preventing soluble salts accumulating in the surface soil,[1] and this problem is discussed in more detail in Chapter XXXIV. Soluble salts accumulate because the irrigation water itself usually contains them, and since most of the water applied is evaporated, either directly or through the plant, the salts tend to remain behind. Thus, if the irrigation water contains 100 parts per million of salt, which is a good sample of water, each acre foot transpired leaves behind nearly $2\frac{1}{2}$ cwt. of salt per acre; and much irrigation is practised with water containing 500 parts per million and 3 acre-feet may be used per year, thus salts may accumulate at the rate of about 2 tons per acre per year. They have, in consequence, to be washed away either into the subsoil below the root zone of the crop or into drainage canals and so back into the river below the area, and in either case a part of the irrigation water must be used to carry away these salts—the proportion needed for this purpose increasing with the concentration of undesirable salts in the water. C. S. Scofield,[2] for example, found that in three irrigated areas in the south-west of the U.S.A. which were supplied with water containing about 500 parts per million of salts—a fairly high concentration—one-quarter of the water applied to the land had to be used just for carrying away these salts.

The second danger is that the ground-water, which in arid districts always contains soluble salts, often derived in part from salts initially present in the superficial layers of the soil profile, may rise if too much water is applied, or if water can seep out of the canals carrying the irrigation water, and once this comes near the surface the zone of plant roots becomes very limited, and in depressions the capillary fringe may come up to the surface of the soil. Thus, salts may very rapidly accumulate in the surface at such high concentrations that successful crops can no longer be grown.

The three essential features of a successful irrigation scheme are, therefore, adequate control of the ground-water level, the ability to move soluble salts from the surface soil down below the root zone or into drainage canals, and the ability to get the water spread and absorbed evenly over the land.

Ground-water levels should never be allowed to rise higher than 6 feet below the surface and should, preferably, be below 10 feet. If this

[1] For a bulletin on this subject, see H. E. Hayward and O. C. Magistad, *U.S. Dept. Agric., Misc. Publ.* 607, 1946.   [2] *J. Agric. Res.*, 1940, **61**, 17.

level cannot be adequately controlled by careful use of water, then either a suitable system of drainage or interceptor ditches must be constructed to remove the water, or the ground-water must be pumped into drainage canals.

The soil must also be kept permeable both to help leach the salts down into the ground-water and also to allow the applied water to penetrate reasonably rapidly and uniformly. Slow penetration of irrigation water gives temporary water-logging, and under the high temperatures that often prevail in most irrigated regions, very short periods of water-logging may deplete the oxygen in the soil air so much that the roots are weakened sufficiently for them to be killed or attacked by root-rot fungi. Thus, V. A. Wager,[1] in California, found that water-logging the roots of an Avocado for one day allowed them to be attacked and killed by the fungus *Phytophthora cinnamomi*, although if the fungus was absent from the soil, water-logging for nine days did no serious harm to the tree. For relatively impermeable soils a suitable system of husbandry must be adopted as, for example, one including deep-rooting crops, such as lucerne, and the keeping of dairy cows to provide manure. A system producing farmyard manure is also often advisable on very permeable land, for the manure both decreases its high permeability and also increases its low water-holding power. In general, for all irrigation projects it is, in fact, desirable to maintain a high level of organic matter in the surface soil; hence, leys, green manuring, cover crops and farmyard manure are all desirable adjuncts of irrigation rotations.

The principles used to decide when and how much water should be applied have already been discussed; they depend on putting back into the soil the water deficit that exists in the root zone just before the crop begins to suffer from lack of water, with sufficient excess to ensure any accumulated salts are washed down into the subsoil or the drains. On many soils, as Veihmeyer and his associates have shown, this can be calculated as the number of inches of water held by 4 to 6 feet of soil between its field capacity and permanent wilting-point; but not all soils can be allowed to build up such a large deficit as this, and so need more frequent and lighter irrigations, but, in consequence of the difficulties inherent in distributing water evenly over the land by all methods of flood or furrow irrigation, they need a correspondingly greater total quantity of water.

If land is plentiful and water scarce, the most efficient way of using the water is to apply small amounts of water over large areas rather than large amounts over small. This is illustrated by some results of J. A. Widtsoe,[2] given in Table 96, for dry land farming in Utah, where

[1] *Hilgardia*, 1942, **14**, 519.   [2] *Utah Agric. Expt. Sta., Bull.* 116, 1912.

using $7\frac{1}{2}$ inches of water on 4 acres gives about three times the yield of 30 inches applied to 1 acre. Naturally, if land is scarce and water plentiful, the 30 inches per acre, which gives a greater yield per acre than the $7\frac{1}{2}$ inches per acre, constitutes a more intensive and, therefore, a preferable use of the land.

The methods of applying irrigation water are fully treated in the literature and will not be discussed here; but it is important to ensure that the irrigation water does not run rapidly enough over the land to cause erosion, as not only is this directly harmful but it also makes the water muddy, and hence hinders its rapid entry into the soil.

TABLE 96

Yield of Crops for a Given Quantity of Water used over Different Areas

Greenville Farm, Utah

Crop	Yield from 30 acre in. of irrigation water given over	
	I acre	4 acres
Wheat, grain in bushels. .	47·5	166
Maize, in bushels . . .	97	317
Lucerne, hay in tons . .	3·6	14·3
Sugar-beet, roots in tons .	20·8	64·8

The quality of the water used in irrigation is of fundamental importance for the permanence of every irrigation system. All water contains salts, whose cations are mainly calcium, magnesium and sodium, and whose anions are sulphates, chlorides and bicarbonates; and, whilst high concentrations of calcium, for example, are desirable, high concentrations of sodium or chloride ions in particular, and to a less extent sulphate ions, are very undesirable.

The maximum permitted salt content of irrigation water depends on the soil. It is safe to use low-quality water on permeable soils well supplied with calcium carbonate and having a deep ground-water surface, for any excess salts in the surface can easily be leached to below the root zone. On the other hand, relatively pure water, or water very low in sodium and chloride ions, is essential on heavy soils, for then nearly all the salts in the irrigation water remain in the root zone of the plant, and if any appreciable concentration of sodium or chloride ions is allowed to build up, the soil will soon become unsuited to plant growth. This problem is, however, discussed in more detail on p. 607.

Dry Farming

Dry farming is farming under conditions of water shortage when irrigation cannot be used, and it includes the systems of agriculture in use throughout the semi-arid regions of the world. The outstanding characteristic of most of these regions is that the limited rainfall is usually concentrated in a fairly well-marked rainy season, but the total amount of rain falling in the season, and its length, are extremely variable from year to year; and crops are often liable to almost complete loss through catastrophes, such as plagues of leaf-eating insects—e.g. locusts and chinch-bugs—violent hailstorms and complete failure of the rains. Table 97 gives a comparison of the variation in the yield of wheat from year to year in the wheat-growing areas of the Great Plains of the U.S.A. with that of the unmanured plot on Broadbalk, Rothamsted. The mean yield of wheat is about the same, but whereas yields of below 5 bushels per acre occur on the average one year in six in the dry-farming area, they only occur in one year in thirty under humid conditions, with a correspondingly far greater probability of famine occurring among populations subsisting under dry than under humid farming conditions.

TABLE 97

Variability of Wheat Yields in Semi-Arid and Humid Regions

Range	Per cent of year's yield, in bushels[1] per acre, within the following ranges							Mean Yield
	Failure	0–5	5–10	10–20	20–30	30–40	Over 40	
Great Plains[2]	4	13	18	29	23	11	2	16
Broadbalk[3] (unmanured)	—	3	24	70	3	—	—	13

The fundamental object of all systems of dry farming is to allow the crops to make the best use of the available water. This can be done in three ways: using crops that make the main part of their growth during the rainy seasons; reducing all unnecessary waste of water by run-off or weeds; and, if need be, by storing rain from one rainy season for use in the next by means of suitable fallows.

The crops normally grown between the region of mixed farming and the desert are grain crops, and they are usually only taken during

[1] The American figures are in Winchester, and the Broadbalk in Imperial, bushels. (1 Winchester bushel = 0·97 Imperial bushel.)
[2] E. C. Chilcott, *U.S. Dept. Agric., Misc. Circ.* 81, 1927. This is based on 218 crop yields at 16 field stations.   [3] Sixty-year mean, 1852–1911.

the period of the year when rain is expected. Wheat and barley are the typical grains of the cooler regions and sorghums and millets of the hotter. Wheat needs a longer growing period and rather heavier soils than barley, so barley is the most suitable, and also the typical, crop grown on the edge of deserts having winter rainfall, such as those in North Africa and Arabia. But wheat is the preferred bread corn of the world, so it is much more widely cultivated, and is often taken in places where barley would do better.

The sorghums can withstand hot summer droughts that would shrivel up wheat and barley without coming to much harm by becoming semi-dormant, and they resume growth as soon as more rain falls. They are the typical summer cereals of the Arabian and Indian semi-deserts, and are the most reliable grain crop in the southern Great Plains of the United States; but again they are only used as human food when wheat is not available. However, they only give good yields if they can draw on an adequate supply of water during the weeks they are forming their heads. Thus Table 98[1] shows that at Dalhart, Texas, the sorghum, milo, will only produce a good crop if it can find at least 4 inches of water, in the soil or from rain, during the five weeks of heading time.

TABLE 98

Effect of Available Water at Heading Time on the Yield of Milo

Total water available from the end of July to early September	Continuous grain		Alternate grain and fallow	
	Per cent of years	Mean yield bushels per acre	Per cent of years	Mean yield bushels per acre
Under 4 in.　.　.　.	47	10	28	10
4 in. and over　.　.　.	53	28	72	39

Crop yields are not proportional to the rainfall or to the available water; the crop must use a considerable quantity of water before it is able to give any yield at all. In the wheat-growing areas of Kansas the first 8 to 10 inches of rain per year are only sufficient to keep the plant alive, but every inch of rain above this gives, on the average, 2 bushels of wheat per acre;[2] hence the great importance of even quite a small extra supply of water in years of deficient rainfall, as, for example, by fallowing, which supplies, on the average, an extra 3·7 inches. Extra water is even more efficient if the summer temperatures

[1] O. R. Mathews and B. F. Barnes, *U.S. Dept. Agric.*, *Circ.* 564, 1940.
[2] J. S. Cole, *U.S. Dept. Agric.*, *Tech. Bull.* 636, 1938; O. R. Mathews and L. A. Brown, *U.S. Dept. Agric.*, *Circ.* 477, 1938.

are lower than occur in Kansas; in Saskatchewan, 10 inches of water gives about 14 bushels of wheat, and every additional inch increases the yield on the average by 7 bushels per acre.[1] It is interesting to note that in some years there wheat after fallow takes over half the water it uses from the soil.[2]

The period in the development of the crop at which additional rainfall, or additional water in the soil, is most beneficial depends on the crop. For sorghums in the Great Plains it is, as already shown in Table 99, around heading time; for winter wheat in the same region it is before the winter dormancy sets in,[3] the reason probably being that adequate water in this early stage encourages good germination and a well-developed root system, so that the plant is better able to withstand adverse conditions later on. Hence, the extra water retained by a fallow is available for wheat just at the period the wheat is most responsive to extra water.

The function of fallows is to store water, and they can only do this under certain definite conditions. Rain must fall during the fallow period; there must be sufficient rain to increase the soil's moisture content below 4 to 8 inches deep, otherwise it will all be lost by evaporation; the soil must be heavy enough to store a useful amount of water in its first 4 to 6 feet, but not so heavy that the plant roots cannot go down and get it, that is, it should be neither a coarse sand nor a heavy clay; and there must be no weeds. Fallows are ineffective on soils having a high water-holding power when the rain only falls in light showers, so only wetting the top 2 to 4 inches of soil. Fallows are, therefore, inefficient users of rainfall—they can rarely store more than one-quarter of the rainfall in semi-arid regions—though in Saskatchewan[4] they averaged 25 per cent over an eighteen-year period, varying from 2 to 50 per cent of the spring and summer rainfall in individual years. Fallow differs in this respect from crops: crops make full use of all the rainfall however light—a thousandth of an inch of rain falling on a crop reduces the water demands the crop is making on the soil by just this amount.

The great difficulty in managing fallows is to keep a loose, deep tilth in the surface of the soil, which is essential for weed control and for allowing the water to penetrate rapidly, without at the same time exposing it unnecessarily to the risk of being blown away by high winds. There are two distinct types of methods, which may have to be used simultaneously, for doing this: the fallow land must be divided into strips separated by strips of crop, and these strips must either run across the direction of the dangerous winds, if drifting is the sole

[1] *Soil Res. Lab., Swift Current, Sask., Rept.* 1943.   [2] *Canada Dept. Agric., Publ.* 595, 1938.
[3] J. E. Pallesen and H. H. Laude, *U.S. Dept. Agric., Tech. Bull.* 871, 1941.
[4] *Soil Res. Lab., Swift Current, Sask., Rept.* 1943; *Canada Dept. Agric., Publ.* 598, 1938.

trouble, or follow the contours if soil-washing is also troublesome; and the surface of the fallow soil must be kept protected. This can be done in two ways: the soil can be cultivated with ridging ploughs, or listers, the ridges following the contour if heavy rain is likely; or it can be cultivated with disks, duck-foot cultivators and rotary rod weeders in such a way that the previous year's stubble is anchored in the surface soils but sticks up from it.[1] These erosion control problems are, however, discussed in more detail in Chapter XXXV.

When crops are grown in regions of deficient rainfall, the yield is often very dependent on the amount of water in the soil at planting time, as was shown by F. J. Alway[2] many years ago. If there is too little water great risks are run in getting a crop. Thus, in the spring wheat area of the Great Plains in the U.S.A., J. S. Cole and O. R. Mathews[3] have shown that a good estimate of the chance of getting a profitable wheat crop can be made by finding the depth to which the soil is wet at the time of sowing, as can be seen in Table 99. If the soil is wet to 1 foot, or less, a profitable crop, namely, 15 bushels an acre, will only be obtained one year in six; whilst if it is wet to 2 feet it occurs once in three years. The effect of fallowing is to give at least 3 feet of damp soil at sowing-time three years out of four instead of one year out of four. Tables such as these can show immediately the probability of fallowing being valuable: clearly, if the soil was wet to 3 feet at sowing-time there is no point in taking a fallow—the field should be sown; but if the soil is wet to less than 1 foot it will be very unwise to sow, and the field should be fallowed.

TABLE 99

The Effect of Soil Moisture at Sowing Time on the Yield of Spring Wheat (Great Plains, Montana to Texas)

Yield in bushels per acre

Rotation	Depth to which soil is wet at sowing time						Average
	1 ft. or less		2 ft.		3 ft. or more		
	Per cent of years	Mean yield	Per cent of years	Mean yield	Per cent of years	Mean yield	
Continuous wheat . .	33	6·5	41	11·7	26	15·7	11·1
Fallow—wheat . .	5	6·9	21	12·6	74	19·9[4]	17·7

[1] For methods used in the prairie provinces of Canada, see *Canad. Dept. Agric., Bull.* 179, 1935; for the Northern and Southern Great Plains of the U.S.A., see *U.S. Dept. Agric., Farmer's Bull.* 1797, 1938, and 1771, 1937, respectively.   [2] *J. Agric. Sci.*, 1908, **2**, 333.
[3] *U.S. Dept. Agric., Circ.* 563, 1940. For the corresponding figures for milo (a grain sorghum), see O. R. Mathews and B. F. Barnes, *U.S. Dept. Agric., Circ.* 564, 1940.
[4] Soil often wet deeper than in continuous wheat.

The effect of weeds in decreasing the efficiency of fallows can be illustrated by some results for winter wheat in Kansas.[1] This crop is harvested in July and the following crop is sown at the end of September, and part of the annual rainfall comes in the period between harvest and sowing. If the soil contains less than $1\frac{1}{2}$ inches of available water at sowing-time, the crop is likely to be a failure, whilst if it contains more than 3 inches, a yield of over 25 bushels per acre can be expected. If the land is kept fairly free from weeds between harvest and sowing, by ploughing the land as soon after harvest as possible, in only one year out of four is the available water less than $1\frac{1}{2}$ inches, and in every alternate year it has more than 3 inches. On the other hand, if the land is not ploughed until shortly before sowing, so the weeds can grow unchecked till this time, then the land has less than $1\frac{1}{2}$ inches of water at sowing time every alternate year, and it has over 3 inches in only one year in eight. This benefit of early ploughing is, however, only marked in years, and in regions, when the period between harvest and seed-time coincides with a rainy season.

Yields of some crops, in particular sorghums, and possibly maize, can be increased in very dry seasons by increasing the distance between the rows of the crop, through reducing the water demands on the soil during the early part of the growing season, and thus increasing the amount of soil water available later on. Thus, in the drier parts of the western states of the U.S.A., sorghum planted in 80-inch rows will produce a yield of grain in years when those planted in 40-inch rows fail, and in certain regions the 80-inch rows only give 5 to 10 per cent less grain on the average over a run of years than the 40-inch rows.[2] It may even be profitable at times to grow sorghum or maize at 10 feet spacing between the rows, as the field may be able to store enough water to give the effect of a fallow for the succeeding wheat crop.[3]

In conditions of dry farming when water limits the yields, nitrogen fertilisers and farmyard manure are only of benefit if the nitrogen content of the soil is low, otherwise they may harm the crop by encouraging too much early growth. But, in good years, or particularly following fallow when there is reasonable rainfall at the critical times in the growth of the plant, yields can be increased somewhat by them. Thus, A. F. Bracken and G. Stewart,[4] working in Nephi, Utah, which has an average rainfall of 13 inches, found the yield of winter wheat after fallow could be raised by $2\frac{1}{2}$ bushels per acre by dressings of 5 tons, and by 5 bushels by dressings of 10 tons of

[1] A. L. Hallsted and O. R. Mathews, *Kansas Agric. Expt. Sta.*, *Bull.* 273, 1936. See also R. I. Throckmorton and H. E. Myers, ibid., *Bull.* 193, 1941. For the corresponding results for Nebraska, see L. I. Zook and H. E. Weakley, *Nebraska Agric. Expt. Sta.*, *Bull.* 362, 1944.
[2] J. H. Martin, J. S. Cole and A. T. Semple, *U.S. Dept. Agric.*, *Farmers' Bull.* 1764, 1936.
[3] *Kansas Agric. Expt. Sta.*, *Bull.* 293, 1941.   [4] *Utah Agric. Expt. Sta.*, *Bull.* 222, 1930.

farmyard manure applied in the fallow. But on most light soils, or in areas where variations in rainfall cause large variations in yield, adding manure increases the variability of the yield, improving it in good and depressing it in poor years. This result does not apply to soils low in phosphate; unless the phosphate deficiency of these soils is corrected the crop can never begin to form a vigorous root system, hence can never make proper growth; and this may be the explanation of N. V. Kanitkar's[1] observation that $2\frac{1}{2}$ tons per acre of farmyard manure may be beneficial for wheat in some of the dry-farming areas of India. However, a warning must be given that in some areas on the border of dry farming the beneficial effects of a fallow are, in fact, due to the extra nitrates the fallow has accumulated and not, as has often been considered in these areas, to the extra water.[2]

Rotations are of only limited value in really dry areas because so few crops can be profitably grown. The most important crops are grain crops, which can be used for pasture or hay instead of grain, and, under some conditions, a rotation of wheat or barley—fallow—sorghum —fallow is of value in keeping down certain insect pests such as grass-hoppers.[3] Putting land down to native grasses for a few years can be of great value in weed control, and doubtless also in improving the structure of the soil by reducing its liability to blow and increasing its permeability to rain. The value of leguminous crops has not been established. Lucerne, in particular, but sweet clover to a less extent, may be harmful in regions of deficient rainfall, for they can dry out the subsoil to depths of 20 to 30 feet; and it may take several years' fallow,[4] often a very undesirable procedure because of the danger of soil blowing, to replace this water. As an example of the depth of soil dried out by lucerne, V. S. Kosinsky,[5] working in Krasnodar—a region with an annual rainfall of 500 to 700 mm.—found in August that wheat had used all the available water in the top 120 cm. of soil, one year of lucerne had used it to 140 cm., two years of lucerne to 200 cm., and three years of lucerne to 240 cm. As soon as water ceases to become strictly limiting, however, either by an increasing or more certain rainfall, or by the evaporation decreasing, mixed rotations become advantageous, as E. S. Hopkins and A. Leahey[6] have shown in detail for the prairie provinces of Canada.

[1] Dry Farming in India, *Imp. Counc. Agric. Res., Sci. Monog.* 15, 1944.
[2] See, for example, A. E. V. Richardson and H. C. Gurney, *Emp. J. Expt. Agric.*, 1933, 1, 193, 325.
[3] R. I. Throckmorton and H. E. Myers, *Kansas Agric. Expt. Sta.*, Bull. 293, 1941.
[4] For American results, see T. A. Kiesselbach, J. C. Russel and A. Anderson, *J. Amer. Soc. Agron.*, 1929, 21, 241; 1943, 26, 422; H. E. Myers, ibid., 1936, 28, 106; C. O. Grandfield and W. H. Metzger, ibid., 1936, 28, 115. For Australian results, see E. C. Powell, *Agric. Gaz. N.S.W.*, 1941, 52, 65; F. W. Hely, *J. Aust. Inst. Agric. Sci.*, 1942, 8, 93.
[5] *Sovet. Agron.*, 1946, No. 2, 77.
[6] *Canada Dept. Agric.*, Publ. 761 (*Farm. Bull.* 124), 1944.

CHAPTER XXIII

SOIL STRUCTURE AND SOIL TILTH

SOILS IN THEIR natural condition have at least some of their individual particles clustered into aggregates, or clods or crumbs; and the size distribution of these aggregates, or its converse—the size distribution of the pore spaces between them—determines the soil structure and, in part, the soil tilth.

The concept of soil tilth is still vague, and it involves at least two separate factors: the coarseness or fineness of the tilth, which is concerned with the size distribution of the aggregates; and its mellowness or rawness, properties that have been very little studied. Mellow tilths differ from raw tilths in at least two particulars: when dry, their clods are more crumbly, though they do not crumble into dust easily, and when wet they are less sticky. Hence, soils having a mellow tilth can be cultivated at both higher and lower moisture contents than soils having a raw tilth.

The importance of tilth for plant growth or for ease of managing land is still in doubt, for crop development does not seem to be anything like as sensitive to quite wide variations in the tilth as many farmers firmly believe.[1] From the field point of view the following properties of a good tilth are of great importance:

(*a*) There should be a continuous system of wide pores from the soil surface down to the water table or the land drains through which surplus water can move rapidly and which will allow rapid diffusion of carbon dioxide from the subsoil to the atmosphere.

(*b*) These pores should be sufficiently stable to last several years before being filled up.

(*c*) There should be volumes in between these pores that hold as much water as possible against drainage, but which are readily accessible to the plant roots.

(*d*) The surface soil should be crumbly, and the crumbs should be large enough not to blow away, but small enough to allow good germination of the seed, and sufficiently unsticky when moist for them to keep their individuality when tractors or implements move over them.

A soil can fulfil these conditions without its subsoil possessing any structure in the usual sense of the word; yet in general, on the medium

[1] For an example of the apparent insensitivity of malting barley to the tilth of the seed-bed in England, see E. W. Russell, *Proc. Inst. Brit. Agric. Engnr.*, 1945, **3**, 99.

to heavy soils, subsoils only possess these properties if on drying they break down easily to definite clods which are separated from their neighbours by fairly long-lived cracks or planes of weakness. These cracks open as the soil dries and form drainage channels down which water can seep fairly rapidly. Plate XVII illustrates this for the Rotham-sted subsoil—a clay loam having a good natural subsoil structure. A cultivated surface soil usually possesses a crumb or clod structure, that is, the individual silt and clay particles, and usually the sand and gravel particles as well, are aggregated into definite clods that may range from blocks a foot or more across down to dusty crumbs a fraction of a millimeter in size.

The most desirable size for the surface crumbs or clods to have from the point of view of plant growth lies in the range 1–5 mm.,[1] rather towards the smaller limit in dry conditions and the larger in moist. Crumbs smaller than 0·5 mm. merely block the coarser pores down which water can drain and through which air enters the subsoil, without adding to the water-holding power of the soil, whilst crumbs larger than 5 to 6 mm. usually have too large an air space around them for the rootlets of seedlings.

With crumbs of optimum size Kvasnikov showed that cereals made better and earlier growth, gave higher yields and higher values of the grain-straw ratio, and made a more efficient use of the limited water supply than when the crumbs were either larger or smaller. These conclusions have been confirmed by Yoder, using cotton as the test crop.

A desirable structure, or tilth, once obtained should be as stable as possible. A tilth, or a system of wide pores, can break up in the following ways: the cements holding the particles together can be so weak that the dry crumbs can be easily broken down to dust by culti-vation implements, by animals walking over the land, by the wind being able to raise dust storms that can shatter them, and by heavy rain being able to smash them. Or the cements can fail to hold the particles together when wet. This happens in some alkali soils when the surface crumbs fall down to a mud which fills up all the surface cracks, and when the subsoil clods swell and the surfaces of adjacent clods stick together and disappear. But dry clods can break up during wetting for other reasons. In the first place, the clod swells on wetting, and in the process outside bits of the clod often flake off. In the second place, adsorbed air is displaced from the dry internal surfaces of a clod on wetting, and this air has to force space for itself to occupy, and in

---

[1] A. G. Doyarenko, *Russian J. Agric. Sci.*, 1924, **1**, 451, for podsolised soils near Moscow, and V. U. Kvasnikov, ibid., 1928, **5**, 459, for semi-arid soils near Samara. See M. Krause, *Landw. Jahrb.*, 1931, **73**, 603, for a German summary of this work. See also R. E. Yoder, *Proc. Soil Sci. Soc. Amer.*, 1938, **2**, 21, and H. Dittrich, *Bodenk. PflErnähr.*, 1939, **16**, 16, for similar results.

doing so, disrupts the clod. Both these processes may cause the wider drainage pores to become blocked.

The problems of maintaining a stable soil structure usually only concern the surface soil for the subsoil structure is not usually subject to mechanical shattering, although a tractor wheel running on the top of a wet subsoil can destroy its natural structure and hence its permeability very effectively. The structural units of the subsoil are thus mainly subjected to the general tensions and compressions set up as the subsoil is dried or wetted, with the result that the structural units and the spaces between them possess considerable permanence. This permanence can be vividly seen in horizons in which manganese dioxide has been deposited: natural blocks of the soil look black, and, when broken naturally, break into smaller black blocks; but this blackness can easily be seen to be only a very thin film coating the soil crumbs. Very difficult problems arise when the subsoil clods are not stable to a drying and wetting cycle, for example, when the outer surface of the clods flake off on wetting, and such soils are most troublesome to keep well drained. Some of the English silt soils have this very undesirable property.

The properties of the soil structure that have been most commonly picked out for its classification are the size and shape of the structural units[1] and their stability to wetting; but, as has become obvious from the foregoing discussion, a classification can equally well be based on the geometry and stability of the larger pore spaces and cracks in the soil.[2] This is in fact probably the most profitable approach for many silt and clay soils. Pigulevsky, for example, has classified the structure of such soils by the size of the clods between the major cracks, and F. Hardy and L. F. Derraugh[3] have tried to classify the different types of cracks that develop. These latter authors have pointed out the very important role these cracks play in the general economy of impermeable clay soils: they serve as drains and allow the subsoil to remain reasonably well aerated even when the surface soil is water-logged; they form the spaces in which the plant roots and rootlets live and grow; they allow crumbly and fertile surface soil to be transferred to the sub soil; and when the soil at a suitable moisture content is ploughed or cultivated, they form the planes of weakness which allow the large clods to break down into a fine cloddy tilth. All these effects are of great importance for impermeable clays in tropical climates having a wet and

[1] For a discussion of some present-day systems, see G. R. Clarke, *The Study of the Soil in the Field*, 4th ed., Oxford, and *Soil Survey Manual*, Washington, 1951.
[2] M. C. Pigulevsky, *Trans. 2nd Intern. Congr. Soil Sci.*, Leningrad-Moscow, 1932, **1**, 82; *Theory, Construction and Manufacture of Agricultural Machines*, *Part II*, Moscow, 1936. For a summary of his methods, see E. W. Russell, *Imp. Bur. Soil Sci., Tech. Comm.* 37, 1938. C. L. W. Swanson, *Iowa St. Coll. J. Sci.*, 1941, **16**, 137, and with J. B. Peterson, *Soil Sci.*, 1942, **53**, 173, has also developed a similar method. [3] *Trop. Agric. Trin.*, 1947, **24**, 76.

a dry season and in arid areas under irrigation, such as the Gezirah in the Sudan, and parts of the Nile Valley in Egypt.

Great difficulties arise in the classification of soil structure, because both the structural units which compose the soil in the field, and the pores in the soil, have a wide range of size and shape, and there is rarely any particular property of the shapes that is sufficiently characteristic for accurate description. There is not yet any generally accepted terminology for the different shapes met with,[1] but one recently summarised by C. C. Nikiforoff[2] illustrates the kind of division that can be attempted. He recognises the following four type-shapes of structural units:

Plate-like, in which the natural cracking is mainly horizontal. This is often well developed in the A^2 horizon of leached soils or in soils rich in kaolinite.

Prismatic, in which vertical cracking is better displayed than horizontal, resulting in structural units two to five times as long as they are broad. This develops in the B horizon of many heavy soils, especially in semi-arid regions. Two types of prismatic aggregates are illustrated in Plates XIX and XX.

Blocky, in which vertical and horizontal cracking are equally strongly developed so the structural units have roughly equal axes. Their shape is, however, irregular, but like the prismatic structural units, their edges are sharp and their faces smooth. Typically, they range in size from 1 mm. to 5 cm., and Plate XVIII gives two examples of a blockly soil structure.

Granular, which differs from blocky in not having sharp edges or smooth faces, and which is in consequence more rounded. Their typical size lies in the range 1 mm. to 1 cm. and they are found in the surface layer of pasture, chernozem, and other soils high in organic matter. The granular structure also differs from the blocky and prismatic in that, when the soil is wet, there are considerable volumes of air or water between granular units, but only very small volumes between prismatic or blocky.

The actual shape of the structural units often lies intermediate between two or more of these type-shapes, but Nikiforoff suggests that they can be described by the nearest type-shapes to which they approximate, by their size and by how well the typical shape has been developed, for a well-developed structure has units that are relatively strong individually but weakly bound to their neighbours.

The pore size distribution can easily be measured in many soils by

---

[1] For some of these, see E. W. Russell, *Imp. Bur. Soil Sci., Tech. Comm.* 37, 1938.
[2] *Soil Sci.*, 1941, **52**, 193. For an earlier Russian classification, see S. A. Zakharov, *Achievements of Russian Science in Morphology of Soils*, Acad. Sciences, Leningrad, 1927.

determining first the moisture-content-suction curves for the soil,[1] which gives the volume of water in pores smaller than the pore diameter corresponding to each suction, and then plotting the slope of this curve against the suction, which gives the frequency distribution of the sizes of pore present. An example of this is given in Fig. 40 for a sample of Gault clay that was initially in crumbs between 1 and 2 mm. in size.[2] Techniques have also been developed for obtaining the size distribution and the volume of the larger pores by direct measurement using a low-power microscope.[3]

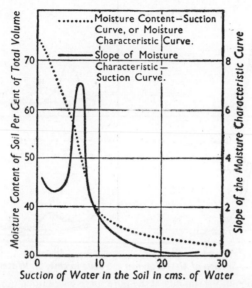

FIG. 40. The moisture content-suction curve, and its differential, for a Gault clay. (Soil initially in crumbs 1-2 mm. size.)

The water stability of the coarse pores can be easily determined by taking these crumbs through several wetting and drying cycles, and constructing slope-suction curves for the sample after each cycle. Fig. 41 shows the stability of the coarse pores in an Upper Lias clay at different depths below the surface when taken through three such wetting and drying cycles.[4] In this soil, the stability of the coarse pores obviously decreases rapidly with depth. Childs has used this method to pick out

[1] For examples of this method, see F. Sekara, *Bodenk. PflErnähr.*, 1938, **6**, 259, 288; E. C. Childs, *Soil Sci.*, 1940, **50**, 239; 1942, **53**, 79; V. C. Jamison, *J. Amer. Soc. Agron.*, 1942, **34**, 307, 393; M. B. Russell, *Proc. Soil Sci. Soc. Amer.*, 1942, **6**, 108; C. L. Feng and G. M. Browning, *Proc. Soil Sci. Soc. Amer.*, 1947, **11**, 67.

[2] Taken from E. C. Childs, *Soil Sci.*, 1940, **50**, 246.

[3] W. Kubiena, *Micropedology*, Ames, 1938; *Entwicklungslehre des Bodens*, Vienna, 1948; G. W. Volk and H. J. Harper, *Soil Sci.*, 1939, **48**, 141; G. C. Redlich, *Soil Sci.*, 1940, **50**, 3. [4] Taken from E. Childs, *Soil Sci.*, 1942, **53**, 84.

soils whose subsoil structure is too unstable for mole drainage to be a practicable method of under-drainage.

The main structural elements present in the field often have a definite structure of their own, particularly in loam and clay soils. Large clods are normally built out of smaller clods, as can be seen by dropping a dry clod on a hard floor when it will break up into smaller clods, usually of characteristic shape; and these in turn are often formed out of still smaller granules binding the sand particles together. This

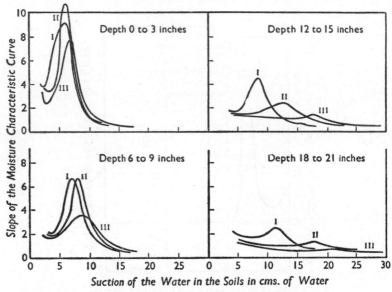

FIG. 41. The variation in the stability of the pore space distribution down the profile of an Upper Lias clay. Curve I is for the first, curve II for the second, and curve III for the third wetting. (Soil initially in crumb 1–2 mm. size.)

can be seen visually by examining the crumb under a low-power microscope, or by scratching its surface with a sharp needle, or by putting a dry crumb in water, all of which will display these granules if they have a definite existence. Crumbs that are built out of such granules are said to have a well-developed micro-structure, and the granules themselves are called the elements of the micro-structure. This concept of the micro-structure of crumbs and clods is very useful, although these micro-structural elements probably have not sufficient persistence and discreteness to be properly regarded as the ultimate basic building units of the crumb structure.

Soils differ greatly in the extent to which their crumbs and clods possess pronounced micro-structure or granularity. Clay soils, particularly when low in organic matter, are liable to dry out into large hard uniform clods, and this tendency is encouraged by working or moulding the clay when it is too wet, or by replacing a proportion of the exchangeable cations by sodium when the concentration of salts in the soil solution is low. Adding calcium carbonate or soluble salts to the clay, by increasing its degree of flocculation, increases the granularity of the clods; but unless the salt content is high, the smallest structural units into which the clods will break down will be several millimetres in size. On the other hand, soils under old pasture are aggregated into crumbs displaying a very pronounced micro-structure, and the granules composing it may be under 0·1 mm. in size.

Direct microscopic examination of crumbs or of thin sections of crumbs usually shows the main cement, or fabric, which holds the particles together. W. Kubiena[1] has given illustrations and has named the main types of cementation between particles, and the arrangements of the different types of particle in crumbs and granules. In the English and other arable soils the author has examined, however, the typical arrangement is for small clusters of particles, which cannot be properly resolved by a low-power microscope, to lie in the spaces between fairly clean sand grains. These clusters presumably hold the sand grains together the more strongly the more they fill the pore space between the sand particles.

The main quantitative methods of structural analysis in use depend on measuring the stability of the structural units to wetting either by determining their size distribution in water, as, for example, by sieving the soil on a bank of sieves in water, or by determining the rate water can percolate into the soil and its decrease with time. The first method, which was introduced by A. T. Tiulin,[2] gives results that are very dependent on the exact technique used, particularly on the dryness of the soil before wetting and on the rate of wetting, due principally to the rate at which water displaces the air from the surface of the soil particles. Thus, a moist soil, or a dry soil wetted under vacuum, breaks up less than a dry soil wetted slowly by capillarity from below, and this in turn breaks up less than a dry soil plunged into water.[3]

The stability of the structure can also be measured by determining the rate at which water penetrates into a soil, or its infiltration rate. The infiltration rate for a soil with a stable structure remains nearly constant with time, except in so far as air bubbles displaced from the dry soil particles block up the coarse pores,[4] but it falls fairly rapidly

[1] *Soil Res.*, 1935, **4**, 380; *Bodenk. PflErnähr.*, 1936, **2**, 1. See also his book, *Micropedology*, Ames, 1938.

[2] *Perm. Agric. Expt. Sta., Dept. Agric. Chem.*, 1928, **2**, 77.

[3] E. W. Russell and R. V. Tamhane, *J. Agric. Sci.*, 1940, **30**, 210.

[4] J. E. Christiansen, *Soil Sci.*, 1944, **58**, 355; A. F. Pillsbury and D. Appleman, ibid., 1945, **59**, 115; R. M. Smith and D. R. Browning, ibid., 1946, **62**, 243.

with time if the structure is unstable so the coarse pores become narrower. The principal soil types in which the wider subsoil pores are unstable to water are some silt and most alkali soils—the cause of instability in the former being that the structural units in these soils are only weak and silt particles are always flaking off the crumbs, so blocking up the pores. In practice the principal cause of a reduction in infiltration rate is not the rate at which the subsoil pores block up, either by the subsoil structure swelling or breaking up, but by the surface structure breaking down and sealing the main drainage channels. No soil structure can be made so stable in farm practice that the bare soil surface can stand up to a heavy rain storm. Once the clods are wet, heavy rain will soon break some up, and the water will become muddy and seal the surface pores. Hence, no bare soil structure can have adequate stability to withstand downpours: the surface must be protected from fast-falling raindrops either by vegetation or by a mulch of straw, manure or compost, for then the percolating water will remain clear, and the pores open, much longer.

The Breakdown of Soil Structure

The soil structure can break down in the field for several reasons. The least important normally is the breakdown of dry crumbs, which can occur if the soil particles are only loosely held together in the clods and if high winds can move an appreciable number of sand grains. Blowing sand grains can break down the surface structure, but they can only be produced in sufficient quantity to be of importance on soils having a high percentage of suitably sized fine sand particles (p. 622).

Disintegration of soil structure only occurs under natural conditions during the process of wetting, though in agricultural practice it can also be brought about by wrongly timed cultivation operations. There are two types of natural breakdown, in one of which the clay and organic matter cease to bind the particles together, and in the other of which they continue to do so.

The first type of instability, when the clay particles cease to bind when wet, has only been recognised in the field with soils having a large proportion of sodium among their exchangeable ions, although a high proportion of exchangeable potassium, or even magnesium, might give the same phenomenon. The cause of the instability is that the clay particles deflocculate on wetting, that is, there is a force of repulsion instead of attraction between them when wet, and this can easily be demonstrated by gently shaking the soil up with water, when the clay will form a stable suspension. The methods for overcoming this trouble, which of itself prevents any agriculture being practised, are discussed in

Chapter XXXIV. There are two principal types of method, one of which is always applicable as it consists in replacing the exchangeable sodium by calcium as far as possible, and the other, only useful in irrigated regions having virtually no rainfall, consists in building up a sufficiently high salt content in the soil by using slightly saline irrigation water, so that the soil solution is always sufficiently concentrated to prevent the clay particles deflocculating.

Dry clods also break up to some extent on wetting for a quite different reason. All clods swell on wetting, some only a little, but some a great deal, and the process of swelling mechanically breaks off pieces from the clod. These pieces may be small micro-aggregates or they may represent appreciable pieces of the original clod. The larger the clod, the greater the amount of break-up due to this cause, because the greater the movement of the outer layers on wetting. This break-up is increased by a second factor, for on wetting a dry clod the adsorbed air is displaced, and in general it is displaced faster than it can diffuse into the atmosphere. Hence, wetting involves a rapid swelling due to this cause also, which is greater the more rapid the displacement of the adsorbed air, that is, the more rapid the wetting. It is an effect of little importance in coarse, sandy soils, or in dry soils wetted very slowly, as, for example, by long-continued gentle rain; but it is much more important than the mere swelling effect for loams and clays when wetted rapidly, as, for example, with flood irrigation.

Clods can also be broken down by mishandling when wet, for pressing wet clods together makes them lose their identity and become a larger plastic mass. This can happen in the field by ploughing or cultivating a soil when it is too wet, or by running a tractor or even farm stock over the land. Puddling the soil is an extreme example of this effect.

Heavy rain can also break up wet soil clods by the mechanical beating the clods receive as they stop large, fast-falling raindrops. This is the primary cause of soil erosion in most parts of the world, and, as will be discussed in Chapter XXXV, the only way to prevent this happening is to ensure the raindrops hit something else, such as a vegetable mulch lying on the surface or the leaves of growing plants above the surface, provided the water can then run down gently into the soil.

The general effect of cultivating a soil is to break up the soil structure, for most cultivation operations, particularly those such as hoeing in dry weather to kill weeds, pulverise the soil and make it more dusty. But cultivations also increase the rate of oxidation of soil organic matter, some fractions of which act as cements binding the soil particles together into crumbs.

The Building up of Soil Structure in the Field

No agricultural system can be permanent that does not maintain an adequate soil structure, and failure to maintain it has been an outstanding characteristic of some unsuccessful farming systems. The methods available for controlling the structure fall into four groups: the proper use of cultivation implements, of climate, of manures, and of growing crops; and structural control must be able to increase as well as decrease the size of the structural units.

THE EFFECTS OF CULTIVATION IMPLEMENTS AND WEATHER

The size of the clods present in a field soil can be altered by the proper use of cultivation implements and by the weather; and the alterations that can be brought about include decreasing and increasing the size of the clods and their stability.

The ability to build up larger from smaller aggregates is of most importance in sandy soils, for crumbs of medium and heavy soils aggregate together naturally on wetting and drying. The principle underlying the method for building up a good stable structure is that the optimum structure is produced when the soil is worked at the minimum moisture content that allows the soil particles to slip over one another and come into closest packing. If the soil is only worked with small pressures, the optimum moisture content for working is about the sticky point, that is, when the soil pores are just full of water, and the stability of the clods so formed falls off fairly rapidly as the moisture content differs from this optimum.[1] As the pressure of working increases, so the optimum moisture content decreases,[2] and the range of moisture contents giving a structure almost as good as the optimum increases.

The breaking down of large clods into smaller ones is easy for light soils, as the dry or nearly dry clods are easily shattered mechanically. Reducing the size of clods of medium to heavy soils, on the other hand, can be a much more difficult process requiring the proper use of weather and machinery, for cutting up wet clods or smashing dry ones —which incidentally produces much dust—requires an extravagant use of power and gives an unsatisfactory tilth.

The art of breaking up large clods of a heavy soil depends on letting the dry clods wet a little before working them. Wetting a large, dry clod has two effects, the relative importance of which depends on the

[1] D. G. Vilensky and V. N. Germanova, *Pedology*, 1934, p. 34; *Trans. 1st Comm. Int. Soc. Soil Sci.*, Versailles, 1934, 17. See also D. G. Vilensky, *Aggregation of Soils*, Acad. Sci. U.S.S.R., 1945. For further examples of this effect, see W. T. McGeorge, *Arizona Agric. Expt. Sta.*, Tech. Bull. 67, 1937; T. F. Buehrer and M. S. Rose, ibid., *Tech. Bull.* 100, 1943.
[2] S. Henin, *Ann. Agron.*, 1936, **6**, 455.

Plate XVII

Profile of the Rothamsted Clay-with-flints soil (0–4½ft.). Note the characteristic rectangular cracking in the subsurface soil and the flat inclined surfaces in the subsoil

(p. 424)

Plate XVIII

Fine blocky soil structure (natural size) (p. 426)

Plate XIX

Fine prismatic soil structure (natural size)
(p. 426)

Plate XX

Rounded and flat tops of prismatic aggregates (half natural size)
(p. 426)

method of wetting: slow wetting, such as that caused by a prolonged drizzle, encourages the clod to break into a number of smaller clods, or at least to develop internal planes of weakness allowing it to be easily broken up by a cultivation implement; whilst rapid wetting, particularly when caused by heavy rain, encourages very small crumbs to flake off the surface of the clod. This flaking off of fine crumbs from a large clod, however, may not result in a finer tilth because if too large a proportion of these fine crumbs have been produced, they will tend to dry into another hard clod, for crumbs of many loam and clay soils finer than a half to a quarter of a millimetre cohere together when wet, particularly if some muddy water is present, and will then dry out into a coherent mass.

A second method of breaking down large clods of a heavy soil is through the action of frost on the wet clod. The effect of frost on a soil depends on its moisture content, the rate of freezing, and the amount of water left unfrozen. Slow freezing tends to cause much of the ice to be formed in relatively thick layers[1] and if the moisture content is not too high, considerable volumes of soil will be left almost ice-free and be subjected to the high pressures due to the expansion of the water on freezing. If these soil volumes have a fairly high content of unfrozen water, that is, if they have a fairly high moisture content at pF values around 4·5 to 5 on the drying curve, so they are relatively plastic in this condition, this pressure will give crumbs of great stability and of a desirable size[2]—between about 30 mm. and 3 mm. for the Rothamsted soil. These crumbs have a smaller pore space than the original clod, owing to the pressure they have been subjected to, so that when the soil is thawed some of the water held by the soil before the frost becomes free water and drains away. Hence, the effect of slowly freezing and then thawing wet clods of a heavy soil is to leave it rather drier than it was before the frost and with a very stable crumb structure of a desirable size distribution.[3]

This desirable frost tilth is only produced under the two conditions of fairly slow freezing of wet clods[4] and reasonable-sized volumes of soil with a moderately high content of unfrozen water between the ice films. Freezing sandy soils tends to destroy the structure, for the pockets of soil between the ice films are too dry to benefit from the pressures set up by freezing. Rapid freezing of heavy soils, or freezing them when wet or at very low temperatures, encourages a more uniform

[1] For the results of Swedish experiments bearing out this point, see S. Eriksson, *LantbrHögsk. Ann.*, 1941, **9**, 80.

[2] G. Torstensson and S. Eriksson, *Kgl. Lantbr. Akad. Tidskr.*, 1942, **81**, 127.

[3] C. S. Slater and H. Hopp (*J. Agric. Res.*, 1949, **78**, 341, 347) have claimed that freezing heavy soils always reduces the water stability of clay clods. The cause of this discrepancy with normal experience was not investigated.

[4] E. Jung, *Ztschr. Pflanz. Düng.*, 1931, A **19**, 326.

distribution of ice throughout the clod, giving smaller volumes of drier soil between the ice films, which, when thawed, fall down to much too fine a tilth.

MODIFYING THE COMPOSITION OF THE SOIL

It has long been known that the structure or tilth of a soil can be modified by adding suitable improvers to it, or growing suitable crops on it. Claying or marling light soils, which has been practised for many centuries in parts of England, helps to bind the sand grains together and improve the water-holding power of the soil. Chalking heavy soils, applying dressings of farmyard manure or composts, ploughing in green manures, and laying land down to long leys or pastures, are all methods used by farmers for improving the tilth of their land.

The way in which lime or chalk added to a soil improves its tilth is not yet understood, for laboratory measurements have not, on the whole, shown up the benefits that practical farmers have always attributed to dressings of chalk. In any discussion on this subject two operative factors must be separated: the effect of replacing the exchangeable aluminium on the exchange complex by exchangeable calcium, and the effect of free calcium carbonate; and these factors may affect the ease with which large clods break down into smaller ones, the water stability of the smaller ones, the mellowness—or lack of stickiness when wet—of the clods, and the type of decomposition suffered by the organic matter in the soil and, in consequence, the types of organic cements being produced. Unfortunately only a few of these effects have been properly investigated.

The great weight of experimental evidence confirms the result that the stability of the crumb structure of an acid soil is not affected by increasing the amount of calcium in the exchange complex,[1] and it is possible that the exceptions to this rule[2] are due to secondary effects, as, for example, on the soil population. The effect of excess calcium carbonate again has not been rigorously established. Its effect seems to be to reduce the size of the clods in a soil[3]—a desirable effect in clays, but undesirable in sands—and at the same time it appears to increase the stability of the clods, for E. C. Childs[4] has noticed that drainage water coming from limed land had fewer suspended silt and clay particles than from unlimed. Chalking a heavy soil may increase the mellowness of its tilth, making it easier to work. This almost certainly

[1] See, for example, L. D. Baver, *Amer. Soil Survey Assoc.*, 1936, **17**, 28; H. E. Myers, *Soil Sci.*, 1937, **44**, 331.
[2] For an example, see H. T. Rogers, *J. Amer. Soc. Agron.*, 1939, **31**, 915.
[3] For an example of this on a sandy soil, see A. Demolon and S. Hénin, *Soil Res.*, 1932, **3**, 1.
[4] *J. Agric. Sci.*, 1943, **33**, 136.

happens on some soils, such as the Rothamsted clay, but it is hard to believe this is a general result, because some of the most difficult English clays to work, such as those on the Gault, may have a high calcium carbonate content.

Adding fertilisers to a bare, uncultivated soil usually reduces the stability of the structure, calcium fertilisers, such as calcium nitrate, having least effect, and sodium fertilisers, such as sodium nitrate, being most harmful, with ammonium fertilisers intermediate.[1] On cropped land, however, these effects are much less striking.[2] On the clay loam soil on Broadbalk, fifty-five annual dressings of 550 lb. of nitrate of soda per acre have had no effect whatever on the structure, though both sodium nitrate and potassium chloride have harmed the structure somewhat on the heavier, less well-drained Barnfield, in continuous mangolds.

The role of organic matter in soil structure depends on the type of organic matter present. Mere organic remains, such as some types of peat, have no effect on soil structure itself—although they may assist the aeration or the water-holding power of the soil—nor is the effect of old stable humic colloidal material very great. Thus, very well-rotted composts have less effect on soil aggregation than less well-rotted ones;[3] and some fen soils, very high in organic matter, can be very poorly aggregated when dry. R. Bradfield[4] also has noted that some prairie soils when badly farmed after being broken up, can have a higher organic matter content, but a much poorer aggregation, than well-farmed neighbouring soils that have been longer in cultivation.

Dressings of farmyard manure or compost, particularly if generous dressings are given regularly, can have very beneficial effects on the soil structure. They cause an increase in the cohesion between sand particles, thus increasing the resistance of the soil surface to wind blowing and to sealing by rain storms, and they also cause an increase in the number of centres around which contraction takes place when a clay is dried. This increases the number of fine cracks that develop as a clod dries, making it more crumbly[5] and perhaps for the same reason also, less sticky.

The effect of long-continued dressings of farmyard manure on the water stability of crumbs can be illustrated on the permanent wheat and mangold fields at Rothamsted, and on other long-term rotation experiments that have been carried out in other parts of the world. At Rothamsted the proportion of water-stable crumbs larger than

[1] For an example, see A. Demolon and S. Hénin, *Soil Res.*, 1932, **3**, 1.
[2] For examples, see D. G. Aldrich *et al.*, *Soil Sci.*, 1945, **59**, 299; R. B. Alderfer, ibid., 1946, **62**, 151.
[3] J. P. Martin, *Proc. Soil Sci. Soc. Amer.*, 1943, **7**, 218.
[4] *Amer. Soil Survey Assoc.*, 1936, **17**, 31.
[5] See, for example, P. V. Vershinin, *Pedology*, 1938, 1278, for some quantitative measurements.

0·5 mm. in the soil was increased from 28 to 55 per cent on the permanent wheat field, and from 54 to 70 per cent on the heavier soil of the permanent mangold field as the result of long-continued annual applications of 14 tons per acre of manure. This result has not, however, been found in all such experiments; thus twenty-eight annual dressings of 16 tons of manure to a loam soil in south-eastern Ohio[1] had little effect on the structure. Very little information is available on the effect of customary dressings of, say, 10 tons of manure once in every four to five years on the tilth; but in the few cases where experiments have been made the effect has been small or negligible.

Soil tilth can sometimes be improved by ploughing in a green catch crop, and indeed F. Y. Geltser,[2] working in Turkestan, and J. J. Kanivitza,[3] in the Ukraine, both claim that ploughing in a green crop is a more efficient way of improving the soil tilth than ploughing in farmyard manure. J. P. Martin and B. A. Craggs[4] have confirmed this result in some recent laboratory experiments, and have also found this to be the typical behaviour of these two types of material decomposing at soil temperatures in the range 10° to 25°C., but that at higher temperatures the opposite result was more typical. However, experience elsewhere has not always borne out the value of green manuring as a tilth improver, possibly because insufficient green matter has been added to effect any appreciable improvement, and possibly because, as in the tropics where green manuring may actually do harm,[5] the soil temperatures are too high to give anything but a very ephemeral improvement.

The improvement of structure brought about by additions of organic matter depends, at least in part, on the speed with which it decomposes.[6] The improvement in structure normally increases with the ease of decomposition of the material, but it mainly occurs after the first flush of decomposition is over.[7] After the maximum improvement in structure has been reached, which may only take one to three weeks if readily decomposable material is added, it may be maintained for several months with little deterioration, though in some cases, for reasons not understood, it may be much shorter-lived. The role of lime in improving soil structure on acid soils may largely lie in its power of increasing the speed of decomposition, for it appears to be more effective as a structure improver on these soils when used in

---

[1] L. Havis, *Ohio Agric. Expt. Sta., Bull.* 640, 1943.
[2] *Trans. 1st Comm. Int. Soc. Soil Sci., Soviet Sect.,* 1934, A2, 73.
[3] Quoted by N. A. Sokolovsky, *Trans. 1st Comm. Int. Soc. Soil Sci.,* Versailles, 1934, 89.
[4] *J. Amer. Soc. Agron.,* 1946, **38**, 332.
[5] W. S. Martin, *E. Afric. Agric. J.,* 1944, **9**, 189. See also J. B. Peterson, *Soil Sci.,* 1943, **55**, 289, for what appears to be another example.
[6] T. C. Peele and O. W. Beale, *Proc. Soil Sci. Soc. Amer.,* 1944, **8**, 254; G. M. Browning and F. M. Milam, *Soil Sci.,* 1944, **57**, 91.
[7] J. R. McHenry and M. B. Russell, *Soil Sci.,* 1944, **57**, 351.

conjunction with farmyard manure or other decomposable organic matter.[1]

Surface mulches of organic matter—of straw, for example—improve the soil structure underneath them very considerably. Part of their action is undoubtedly that they protect the surface structure of the soil from raindrops, and part is also due to them keeping the surface soil moist for a longer period of the year, so allowing the soil fauna, helped by the micro-organisms, a longer season each year in which to build up a good stable structure. R. E. Stephenson and C. E. Schuster[2] have given an extreme example of this effect. A loam soil was kept under a straw mulch on some plots, in volunteer weeds and grasses in another, and kept clear of vegetation by scraping the surface of the soil in a third. After five years the percentage of water-stable aggregates larger than 1 mm. were 34, 17 and 3 respectively. This effect is large enough, however, to be readily noticeable in gardens.

THE EFFECT OF GROWING CROPS ON THE SOIL STRUCTURE

It is common knowledge that an old pasture field, when broken up, gives a soil having a very desirable structure for several years, and this is sometimes true after a grass or lucerne ley of only a few years' duration. The improvement effected by a ley in a given time depends on the ley itself, the soil and the climate.

The type of grass, and perhaps its management, influences the soil structure very strongly. Thus, in Canada, T. Pavlychenko[3] found that crested wheat grass (*Agropyron cristatum*) was an excellent structure improver on the Canadian prairies, a result also found by E. I. Vorobieva[4] in Russia, whilst slender wheat grass (*A. pauciflorum*) had little value. Similarly, W. S. Martin[5] in Uganda, J. R. McHenry *et al.*[6] in Nebraska, L. B. Olmstead[7] in Kansas, and I. P. Sarakhov[8] in the North Caucasian steppes have all demonstrated great differences between the structure-forming powers of different grasses. No comparable experiments have yet been made in England, though almost certainly our grasses differ considerably in this respect.

The cause of the difference between grasses as structural improvers is not fully understood, though the work of Pavlychenko and of T. M. Stevenson and W. J. White[9] in the Canadian prairies has established

[1] See, for example, A. T. Tiulin and E. V. Biriukova, *Khim. Sotsial. Zemled.*, 1933, No. 2, 113; S. I. Ilmenev, ibid., 1938, Nos. 11–12, 153. These results are summarised by E. W. Russell in *Imp. Bur. Soil Sci., Tech. Comm.* 37, 1938.

[2] *Soil Sci.*, 1945, **59**, 219; 1946, **61**, 219.

[3] *Natl. Res. Counc. Canada, Publ.* 1088, 1942. [4] *Pedology*, 1939, No. 11, 81.

[5] *Emp. J. Expt. Agric.*, 1944, **12**, 21; *E. Afric. Agric. J.*, 1944, **9**, 189. Photographs of the soil under various grasses are given in each of these papers.

[6] *Nebraska Agric. Expt. Sta., 59th Rep.*, 1946, p. 11.

[7] *Proc. Soil Sci. Soc. Amer.*, 1947, **11**, 89.

[8] *Pedology*, 1938, 1265. [9] *Sci. Agric.*, 1941, **22**, 108.

the importance of two of the factors responsible: the weight of root material produced and the strength of the roots, measured by the tensile force required to break them. The relative values of several species of prairie and pasture grasses as structure improvers depends on the amount of strong roots in the soil; very fine weak roots, even though they may be in great abundance, appear to be unimportant as soil-binding agents soon after the grassland has been ploughed out. Thus, crested wheat grass produces a greater length of roots over 0·1 mm. in diameter than slender wheat grass, and its roots, at comparable diameters, are stronger.

The only other plants besides grasses that appear to be efficient improvers of the soil structure are lucerne and some clovers; and the clovers in particular,[1] and perhaps under some conditions lucerne also,[2] may only be able to exert their greatest effect if grown with certain grasses enhancing, in fact, the improvement brought about by the grass alone.

Suitable leys left down for three to four years may give a notable improvement in structure on some soils, and a few typical figures, taken from some results of G. I. Pavlov[3] and F. Y. Geltser[4] on irrigated land in Turkestan, are given in Table 100. However, much longer leys

TABLE 100

The Effect of a Ley on the Water-stable Crumbs in Irrigated Grey Desert Soils (Turkestan)

Per cent of water-stable crumbs larger than 1 mm.

Previous cropping	3 years' cotton	2 years' clover 1 year cotton	2 years' cotton 1 year clover	3 years' clover
	9	17	27	35
Previous cropping	Old meadow	6 years' lucerne	3 years' lucerne	Old arable
	79	30	20	4

than this are probably required on semi-arid soils where irrigation is not practised,[5] and also under some English conditions, for at Rothamsted one field that had been under ley for ten years showed no appreciable improvement in structure, though another that had been down for thirteen years had its structure definitely improved.

The effect of arable crops on the soil structure depends mainly on

[1] N. G. Iovenko, Pedology, 1939, No. 6, 37.
[2] E. I. Vorobieva, Pedology, 1939, No. 11, 81,
[3] Proc. 2nd Int. Congr. Soil Sci., Moscow, 1932, I, 179.
[4] Trans. 1st Comm. Int. Soc. Soil Sci., Soviet Sect., 1934, A2, 73.
[5] P. K. Ivanov, Khim. Sotsial. Zemled., 1937, No. 8, 64; N. G. Iovenko, Pedology, 1939, No. 6, 37.

the amount of cultivation the soil receives. Thus, close-spaced crops, such as wheat, barley and oats, have little effect on the structure, whilst wide-spaced crops, such as maize and potatoes, that receive much inter-row cultivation, may cause a deterioration of structure, but this is probably due to the inter-row cultivations and not to the crops themselves. A proportion of the improvement in structure brought about by long leys may, in fact, be a consequence of the absence of cultivation operations during the period the land is under the ley.

The Mechanism of Crumb and Clod Formation

Crumb formation is mainly brought about in the field through the agency of clay particles, of cements such as certain types of organic matter and precipitated films of iron hydroxide,[1] and of living organisms. In normal arable loam soils the clay is the principal aggregating agency, unless there is more than 2 per cent of organic carbon present,[2] and the clay content naturally controls the proportion of smaller water-stable crumbs more closely than that of larger.[3]

The exact way in which clay binds soil particles together is still not known. In most soils the clay forms a continuous network that enmeshes the silt and sand particles, though if the clay is kaolinitic,[4] and in some other circumstances not yet analysed,[5] the clay may actually bind the sand and silt particles together.

Clay particles aggregate together through the interaction of their exchangeable ions and the charges on their surfaces with the water molecules between the surfaces, and the binding forces increase as the relative orientations of neighbouring clay particles assume certain preferred positions. The evidence for the importance of orientation is still partly inferential.[6] Clay crumbs are larger and stronger if derived from deflocculated, or mainly deflocculated, clay pastes than from flocculated ones—conditions which X-ray evidence shows to be conducive to mutual orientation of neighbouring particles as contrasted with the conditions of more nearly random orientation of the neighbouring particles in flocs. Vilensky's result that working a soil at a certain optimum moisture content, which decreases with increasing pressure, and J. R. McHenry and M. B. Russell's[7] result

[1] J. F. Lutz, *Proc. Soil Sci. Soc. Amer.*, 1936, **1**, 43.
[2] L. D. Baver, *Amer. Soil Surv. Assoc.*, 1935, **16**, 55.
[3] For an example, see G. B. Clarke and T. J. Marshall, *Aust. J. Counc. Sci. Indust. Res.*, 1947, **20**, 162.
[4] J. B. Peterson, *Proc. Soil Sci. Soc. Amer.*, 1945, **9**, 37.
[5] For photographs of some of these conditions, see W. Kubiena, *Micropedology*, Ames, 1938.
[6] See, for example, D. I. Sideri, *Soil Sci.*, 1936, **42**, 381, 461; 1938, **46**, 129, 267; S. Hénin, *C.R.*, 1937, **204**, 1498; *Thesis, Univ. Paris*, 1938; E. A. Hauser and D. S. Le Beau, *J. Phys. Chem.*, 1938, **42**, 961; 1939, **43**, 1037.
[7] *Proc. Soil Sci. Soc. Amer.*, 1944, **8**, 71.

that the aggregation of sand-clay mixtures can be increased by taking them through a certain limited number of wetting and drying cycles, are both explicable on this hypothesis, for in both cases conditions are conducive to helping clay particles take up preferred orientations with respect to their neighbours.

The importance of the exchangeable ions and water for aggregation can be seen from E. W. Russell's[1] observations that strong clay crumbs can only be formed by drying clays dispersed either in water or in a few other polar liquids, such as some of the alcohols, and only then if the clay holds an appreciable number of fairly small exchangeable ions. Russell suggested the simplest way of explaining these results is to assume that clay particles are held together by bridges of orientated water molecules between the dissociated cations and the fixed negative charges on the surface of the clay particle, as shown diagrammatically in Fig. 42. This hypothesis, unfortunately, does not explain why clay crumbs when once dried are usually stable when put back in water.

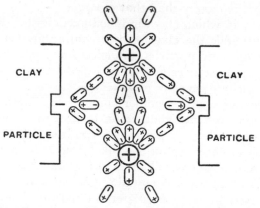

FIG. 42. Diagrammatic representation of two clay micelles held together as in a crumb.

On the other hand, R. K. Schofield has recently shown that the anomalous behaviour of dry crumbs of sodium and potassium clays to disperse water is explicable on the Debye-Hückel theory of electrolytes.

Strong clay crumbs are thus produced by drying clays from gels rather than flocs, for this encourages orientation. Hence, crumbs formed from a deflocculated paste of a sodium-saturated clay are harder than those from a paste of a calcium-saturated clay, as the latter is never so deflocculated; and adding a salt to the paste, by increasing the degree of flocculation, weakens the crumbs and so enables them to be broken up easier when dry, as can be seen from Plate V. Strongly

[1] *Phil. Trans.*, 1934, **233** A, 361.

flocculated pastes not only dry to give weaker crumbs, but the crumbs themselves tend to be built out of micro-crumbs which are probably the individual flocs that were present in the paste.

The relative effects of calcium and aluminium as exchangeable ions on the properties of the dry clay crumbs appear to be that as aluminium ions are more powerful flocculators than the calcium, so the crumbs of acid clays appear to be rather more crumbly, but also rather more water-stable than calcium ones, resulting in acid soils being more permeable and less easily dispersed than calcium soils.[1] But, as already discussed on p. 434, there is still doubt about the general validity of this conclusion.

The effect of the type of clay mineral present in the soil on the soil structure has not yet received much study. Montmorillonitic clays mixed with sand or silt give typical granular structure, and J. B. Peterson[2] has shown that soils rich in kaolinitic clay typically possess a characteristic laminar or platy structure, unless they contain much exchangeable calcium or mobile iron compounds, in which case they also possess a granular structure.

Clay, and possibly silt particles also, can bind certain components of the soil organic matter on their surface, as discussed on pp. 285-8, though what these components are is not known. Crumbs built out of these clay-humus particles are probably weaker, more crumbly or friable, and less sticky when wet than crumbs built out of the uncoated particles. But this important aspect of crumb formation has received little attention from research workers, so cannot be discussed any further.

The mechanisms by which organic matter can cause soil particles to aggregate into crumbs have not all been analysed out. As already pointed out, mere humus does not necessarily possess the power of binding soil particles together, and in fact organic matter often seems to improve the structure more by the process of its decomposition than by its presence. This is still a subject in urgent need of careful research, with few facts really firmly established, so the following discussion must be rather tentative.

Some of the components of the soil organic matter can unquestionably bind silt and clay particles into crumbs, though what these components are cannot yet be specified, as no work with carefully separated organic fractions has yet been done. The theory of humus formation which we have developed in Chapter XV is that it is mainly composed of compounds derived from the oxidation of lignin, and of compounds produced by microbial metabolism. Some of the products of microbial

---

[1] J. F. Lutz, *Missouri Agric. Expt. Sta., Res. Bull.* 212, 1934; L. D. Baver and N. S. Hall. ibid., *Res. Bull.* 267, 1937; H. E. Myers, *Soil Sci.,* 1937, **44**, 331; J. B. Peterson, ibid., 1946, **61**, 247.
[2] *Proc. Soil Sci. Soc. Amer.,* 1945, **9**, 37.

metabolism, particularly polysaccharide gums[1] can be effective aggregators in the laboratory, and so also can some of the fats, waxes, and resins set free during the decomposition. There is still, however, some doubt about the importance of this factor in the field, as the concentration of gum required to produce good aggregation is between 0·1 and 0·5 per cent, which is probably considerably higher than it occurs in the soil. Further, some workers have failed to demonstrate this aggregating effect of gums with the techniques they have used.[2]

It is also fairly certain, although there is little good evidence to prove the statement, that lignin-derived material can be an efficient aggregator. The mechanism through which it functions has not been proved, but metallic ions, such as calcium in neutral soils and aluminium in acid soils, probably play an essential role in linking the organic with the clay particles. If Sideri's views are correct (see p. 287), it is also possible that some organic fractions may help to improve the aggregation brought about by the clay particles through their alleged effect in causing clay particles in their neighbourhood to take up a common orientation.

Earthworms may be an important agent in producing a good soil structure, for their casts have a better structure than the bulk of the soil. The reasons for this better structure have not been worked out: it may simply be due to the clay, humic material and calcium salts all being intimately mixed with each other and with the larger silt and sand particles in the worm's gut, or it may be due to mucilages produced either by the worm or by bacteria in its gut. However, this improvement in structure is only small compared with that brought about by a ley. This is illustrated by the following results of A. K. Dutt,[3] which show the proportion of water-stable crumbs between 4·7 and 2 mm. in size in the top 3 inches of a silt loam soil carrying different crops and in the wormcasts formed on them.

	In top 3 inches of soil	In wormcasts
Arable	7	19
Three-year ley	46	58
Forest	59	68

The wormcasts on the arable soil have a better structure than the soil itself, yet the improvement brought about is much less than that brought about by a three-year ley; and the ley improves the structure of the whole soil whilst the casting-species of worms only improve the structure

---

[1] S. Winogradsky, *Ann. Inst. Pasteur*, 1929, **43**, 549; J. P. Martin, *Soil Sci.*, 1946, **61**, 157; M. J. Geoghegan and R. C. Brian, *Biochem. J.*, 1948, **43**, 5.
[2] See, for example, D. S. Hubbell and J. E. Chapman, *Soil Sci.*, 1946, **62**, 271; R. J. Swaby, *J. Gen. Microbiol.*, 1949, **3**, 236.
[3] *J. Amer. Soc. Agron.*, 1948, **40**, 407.

of a small proportion of the soil in an arable field. R. J. Swaby[1] has confirmed this observation on the Rothamsted soil, for he found that the casts of *A. nocturna*, the most common casting species there, have a good structure if produced on grassland but not if produced on arable.

The living organism itself can certainly hold soil particles on its surface, presumably through the surface containing some of the microbial gums just mentioned. Thus, M. L. Jackson, W. Z. Mackie and R. P. Pennington,[2] using an electron microscope, showed that many soil bacteria had clay particles clustered around them, and that some crumbs are simply aggregates of these tiny granules. Filamentous fungi can also bind soil particles on to their mycelia and so form water-stable clods that are porous and may be fairly strong,[3] but fungi differ very markedly in their power to do this. Thus, some species of *Cladiosporium*,[4] *Penicillium*[5] and *Trichoderma viride*[6] are good aggregators, whilst other species of *Penicillium* and *Rhizopus*[7] are poor. The mechanism of this structure formation is not settled: it may be predominantly a mechanical entanglement of soil particles between the fungal hyphae, or it may be this combined with micro-crumbs of silt and clay adhering to the hyphae. The actinomycetes tested have less power of forming crumbs than the effective fungi. These effects of micro-organisms in producing soil structure are illustrated in the top half of Plate XXI, which shows that the mixed culture of 22 species of soil fungi produced a definite, though weak, water-stable structure when growing in the Rothamsted soil to which a little glucose had been added; the mixed culture of 33 species of soil actinomycetes produced much less effect and the 66 species of soil bacteria still less.

F. Y. Geltser[8] has propounded a theory that the best structure is produced in a soil during the process of the bacterial decomposition of the fungal hyphae. She pictures the process by which the soil structure is improved when one adds decomposable organic matter as follows. The added organic matter is first attacked by fungi, and although this stage is often characterised by the production of dark-coloured gummy or humus-like material, this has little aggregating power. Then the fungal mycelia are attacked by small rod-shaped bacteria, and it is these

[1] *J. Soil Sci.*, 1950, **1**, 195.

[2] *Proc. Soil Sci. Soc. Amer.*, 1947, **11**, 57.

[3] J. P. Martin and S. A. Waksman, *Soil Sci.*, 1940, **50**, 29; T. M. McCalla, *Proc. Soil Sci. Soc. Amer.*, 1947, **11**, 260.

[4] T. C. Peele, *J. Amer. Soc. Agron.*, 1940, **32**, 204.

[5] T. C. Peele and O. W. Beale, *Proc. Soil Sci. Soc. Amer.*, 1941, **5**, 33.

[6] I. I. Kanivets and N. P. Korneeva, *Pedology*, 1937, 1429; *Khim. Sotsial. Zemled.*, 1938, No. 6, 51.

[7] T. L. Martin and D. A. Anderson, *Proc. Soil Sci. Soc. Amer.*, 1943, **7**, 215.

[8] See, for example, her book (in Russian) *The Significance of Micro-organisms in the Formation of Humus*, Moscow, 1940. For an English summary of her views, see *Soils and Fert.*, 1944, **7**, 119.

bacteria that produce the active crumb-forming compounds, which are then excreted into the soil on the autolysis of the bacterial cells. These products are also dark-coloured and gummy, but combine with the clay particles, and it is these clay-humus particles that form the structure.

Some earlier results of J. G. Shrikhande[1] are in accord with Geltser's hypothesis. He was investigating the amount of mucilage produced by various organisms, as measured by the stickiness of the compost, when they were decomposing sterilised oat straw; and he showed that although neither the fungi nor the cellulose decomposing bacteria he used produced any mucilage when in pure culture, yet when the bacteria were inoculated into the straw after the fungi had been decomposing it for forty-eight days, they produced considerable amounts of mucilage, much more so than if they were inoculated into the straw at the same time as the fungi. The production of mucilage, therefore, appeared only when the bacteria began working after extensive fungal development, but the experiment did not show if the bacteria were then decomposing fungal tissue or straw residues. However, the experimental results of R. J. Swaby, illustrated in the bottom half of Plate XXI, do not accord with Geltser's hypothesis, for these show that the weak but water-stable structure produced by fungal hyphae is destroyed if they are attacked by mixed cultures of soil actinomycetes or bacteria.

The products micro-organisms excrete into the soil are not, however, necessarily beneficial. Some by-products, such as gums and mucilages will reduce the size of some of the soil pores, and this could be very undesirable if the soil is fine-textured, so possessing only a few pores down which surplus water can drain, particularly if these pores are near the lower size limit that permits water to move down at a useful rate. In such a soil the aerobic micro-organisms will develop most freely in these few pores, and if such by-products accumulate in them they will be narrowed sufficiently to have their permeability reduced appreciably.[2] There is no evidence that this effect is of any importance in temperate agriculture, though it may play an important role in keeping the permeability of paddy rice fields low. Further, these gums and mucilages may wet with difficulty after they have been dried, so that if they have been produced in abundance, as, for example, through large quantities of sugar or fats having been added to a soil, they will waterproof the crumbs, preventing them from being wetted, and sometimes completely preventing percolation through the soil.

The soil structure formed by grass roots is very characteristic. If a root is carefully removed from the soil it will be seen to have a large

---

[1] *Biochem. J.*, 1933, **27**, 1551.
[2] For examples, see L. E. Allison, *Soil Sci.*, 1947, **63**, 439.

number of small crumbs hanging on to it, as is shown in Plate XXII, and many of these crumbs are clusters of very small crumbs or granules. This characteristic structure thus requires two mechanisms: one for producing the granules and the other for holding them together in clusters. As with so many aspects of soil structure, no adequate examination of these mechanisms has been made; but the root is probably directly responsible for holding the clusters, or at least the larger clusters, together, whilst micro-organisms associated with the roots may be mainly responsible for the granules and for their small clusters.

The evidence for the importance of the root itself is derived from an examination of the rate at which this structure is produced by different types of grasses and the rate at which it decreases after the grassland has been ploughed out; the Canadian work, described on p. 437, illustrates the kind of evidence that is available at the present time. Once the roots holding the clusters together have decomposed, the clusters themselves disintegrate into their constituent granules. But this work does not show how the roots bind the granules together into clusters—it merely shows that the clusters cannot last any longer, and usually last for a shorter time, than the roots.

The evidence for the mechanism holding the fine soil particles together into granules is still meagre, but two, which are not mutually exclusive, have been postulated. One, developed by E. N. Mishushtin[1] in Russia, and D. S. Hubbell and J. E. Chapman[2] in America, is that the granules are formed by the fine soil particles adhering to living root hairs, fungal and actinomycete hyphae or even bacteria, as already discussed. This is a perfectly possible mechanism whilst the grass is growing, for the roots carry a large micro-organic population on and around them, but it is difficult to see on this picture how these granules can survive the ploughing out of the grass with the killing of the root hairs and the micro-organisms associated with the roots. The other mechanism, developed by F. Y. Geltser, is that the fine soil particles are cemented together by organic compounds produced by the micro-organisms living on the grass roots or in their immediate neighbourhood. Geltser considers that the most important cements are the autolytic products of some of the rhizosphere bacteria, and has recently claimed to have increased the speed with which a short-term ley can improve the soil structure by inoculating the seed with a culture of rhizosphere bacteria taken from the roots of leys growing on land having a very good structure.[3]

Our present knowledge about the processes responsible for structure formation in the soil is thus seen to be very limited. Clay is a powerful

[1] *Pedology*, 1945, No. 2, 122.　　　　　　　　[2] *Soil Sci.*, 1946, **62**, 271.
[3] *Pedology*, 1945, No. 8, 421; *Trans. Acad. Agric. Sci.*, 1945, No. 3, 16.

aggregator, but whether it is an acid or a neutral clay seems to make little difference to the stability of the crumbs, though excess calcium carbonate may weaken them mechanically so making them more mellow. Crumbs in which clay is the predominant cement probably possess little granularity: that is, they are usually fairly uniform in internal structure and do not appear to be built out of smaller granules.

Some humic fractions appear to be good aggregators giving weaker, more crumbly clods, that are less sticky when wet than clods held together by clay alone, though whether these clods or crumbs possess a granular structure or not has not been examined in detail. Some workers claim that the ideal cement for a good friable structure is clay particles coated with a suitable humic fraction, but this concept of the clay-humus complex as something more effective than the individual clay and humic particles has not yet been developed in detail.

Crumbs produced by grass rootlets, by some fungi, and possibly by some actinomycetes and bacteria, are very granular. Each granule consists of silt, clay and sometimes fine sand particles clustering around a rootlet or a bit of fungal hypha, and the crumbs are built out of clusters of such granules.

CHAPTER XXIV

THE DEVELOPMENT OF PLANT ROOTS IN SOIL

THE SOIL AFFECTS the plant primarily through its effect on the root system, and these effects should form the basis of this book. Unfortunately, investigations on the root systems of crops growing in the field are difficult to carry out, and in consequence our knowledge of the interaction between the soil, the roots and the aerial parts of the plant and, as important, between neighbouring root systems, is very scanty.[1]

Plant roots can have four separate functions: they absorb nutrients and water from the soil; they transport these from the areas where the absorption takes place to the stems; they may act as food storage organs, as, for example, in the root vegetables; and they may anchor the plant into the soil. The relative importance of these various functions depends on the plant and the local conditions.

Only a restricted part of the plant root takes part in nutrient and water absorption. The growing part of a plant root is usually white, but as it ages it turns brown, due to its outer layers becoming suberised, that is, to a corky material being deposited around them. These unsuberised white roots, except just for the area around their growing points, absorb water and nutrients,[2] but once suberisation begins their absorbing power falls very rapidly. But the absorbing power, both of these roots and the lightly suberised ones, is increased very considerably by the surface epidermal cells in the unsuberised layer, and by some of the lower epidermal cells where suberisation has just started, sending out root hairs into the soil that may be several millimetres long and about a hundredth of a millimetre in diameter.[3] Some results of H. J. Dittmer,[4] given in Table 101, illustrate the great contribution root hairs can make to the absorbing surface. Unfortunately, he only estimated the total surface of the roots; the surface capable of absorbing nutrients is considerably less.

The root hairs have a slimy surface and fine soil particles stick on to them. Thus, the root hair comes into very intimate contact with

---

[1] For accounts of the root system of crops, see J. E. Weaver, *Root Development of Field Crops*, New York, 1926, and other publications of his on this subject; E. C. Miller, *Plant Physiology* (chap. iii), 2nd ed., New York, 1938; and for orchard trees in particular, W. S. Rogers, *J. Pomol.*, 1939, **17**, 67.

[2] P. Prevot and F. C. Stewart, *Plant Physiol.*, 1936, **11**, 509.

[3] For a description of root hair development, see K. Wilson, *Ann. Bot.*, 1936, **50**, 121.

[4] *Science*, 1938, **88**, 482; *Soil Conserv.*, 1940, **6**, 33.

many soil particles. These root hairs and many of the unsuberised roots[1] are often only very short-lived in the soil, as is illustrated in Plate XXIII for some feeding roots of the apple. Hence the plant may be continuously supplying the soil micro-organisms with a fairly readily available food supply in the form of dead and sloughed-off roots and root hairs.

TABLE 101

Surface Area of Roots and Root Hairs of Various Crops

Roots and Root Hairs in a cylinder of soil 3 in. diameter and 6 in. deep

	Roots		Root hairs			
	Length in feet	Surface area, sq. inches	Number in millions	Length in feet	Surface area, sq. inches	Per cent of soil volume occupied by roots and root hairs
Soybeans . .	95	63	6·1	1960	43	0·91
Oats . . .	150	49	6·3	26400	530	0·55
Rye . . .	210	78	12·5	55100	1190	0·85
Bluegrass. .	1260	330	51·6	169500	2450	2·80

These unprotected root hairs and unsuberised roots, which are responsible for the water and nutrient absorption of roots, are easily injured by unfavourable circumstances, such as poor aeration, lack of moisture, high acidity and its consequences of high soluble aluminium or manganese compounds. In so far as roots can grow in such soils, they have few root hairs and the new root tips suberise rapidly;[2] hence roots in such soils only have a very small absorbing system, so that the plants cannot withstand strongly drying conditions. Draining an inadequately drained soil, in fact, increases the drought resistance of the crops it carries, because it allows a greater development of the root area that can absorb water;[3] and water-logging a soil previously well aerated quickly kills all the root hairs and unsuberised roots, and, hence, usually the plant.

The rate of root growth depends on the temperature and the water and air supply in the soil, on the amount of carbohydrates the aerial parts of the plant translocate to the root system, and on the competition they suffer with other roots. Roots only grow in soils in which there are

[1] For method of observing this, and the photographs reproduced in Plate XXIII, see W. S. Rogers, *J. Pomol.*, 1939, **17**, 99.
[2] G. H. Bates, *J. Ecol.*, 1934, **22**, 271.
[3] For illustrations of this effect on the root system of coffee, see F. J. Nutman, *Emp. J. Expt. Agric.*, 1933, **1**, 271, 285.

Plate XXI

| 66 Bacteria | 33 Actinomycetes | Sterile |
| 22 Fungi | All together | Soil inoculum |

The water-stable soil structure built up by mixed populations of different types of micro-organisms (Rothamsted soil and glucose)

| Initial | 10 Fungi | 10 Actinomycetes |
| 7 Bacteria | 15 Bacteria | 30 Bacteria |

The break-up of the water-stable aggregates built up by the mycelia of the fungus *Aspergillus nidulans* (initial), after it had been heat-killed and the soil inoculated with a number of species of other organisms

(p. 443)

Plate XXII

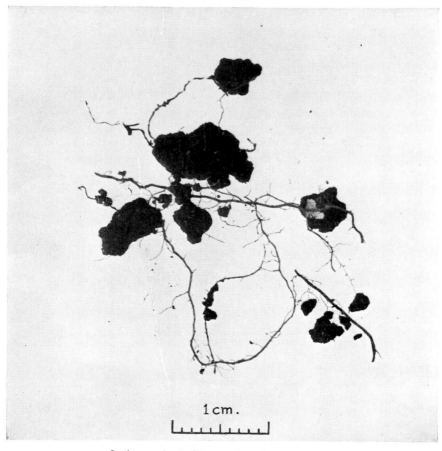

Soil crumbs held together by grass roots
(Ordinary chernozem on clay, 10–20 cm., Khrenovaia Station)
(pp. 445, 580)

an adequate number of channels large enough for the root to penetrate. If the soil is too compact, then root growth is inhibited. Thus roots cannot ramify in hard pans or other subsoil pans, and can only penetrate into them through pre-existing channels or cracks. Again roots cannot ramify throughout the bulk of clay soil but are restricted to the cracks between the clay crumbs and to other channels.

Roots only grow actively in moist soils, although little is known about the maximum suction of soil water that permits root growth. Roots cannot usually grow into soil dried to its wilting-point moisture content, that is, whose water is under a suction of 7 to 10 atm.,[1] and W. S. Rogers[2] found that apple-tree roots will not grow in soils whose water is under a suction about half an atmosphere.

However, under some conditions the roots of some plants can grow in dry soils provided part of the root system is in moist soil.[3] The root system appears to transport water from the wetter regions and excrete it into the drier: the new growth appears, in fact, to take place in the zone wetted by excretion,[4] and under these conditions the roots can take up some nitrogen and perhaps some potassium from the dry soil they have wetted, though their power of taking up phosphates is more doubtful.

The root system of most plants only grows vigorously in well-aerated soils, and in these conditions it develops into a profuse, much-branched system of fine rootlets, many of which are short-lived. As conditions become unfavourable these rootlets are rapidly killed, or unable to develop, leaving a system of thicker, shorter and much less branched roots. Hence plants usually have a finer, more branched root system when growing in a sandy than in a clay soil.

The aeration of the soil affects the roots through three factors: the oxygen content in the soil air, the carbon dioxide content, and the contents of by-products of anaerobic decomposition, such as hydrogen sulphide, methane and hydrogen, which accumulate in the soil. The effects of these three factors have rarely been separated out in the root studies made in the field.

All roots are killed by high CO_2 concentrations, but many appear to tolerate 9 to 10 per cent for short periods. However, for optimum growth, concentrations of under 1 per cent are probably necessary.[5]

[1] See, for example, A. H. Hendrickson and F. J. Veihmeyer, *Plant Physiol.*, 1931, **6**, 567; W. H. Metzger, *J. Amer. Soc. Agron.*, 1938, **30**, 80; A. S. Hunter and O. J. Kelley, *Plant Physiol.*, 1946, **21**, 445.

[2] *J. Pomol.*, 1939, **17**, 99.

[3] J. F. Breazeale, *Arizona Agric. Expt. Sta.*, *Tech. Bull.* 29, 1930; with F. J. Crider, *Tech. Bull.* 53, 1934.

[4] A. S. Hunter and O. J. Kelley, *Plant Physiol.*, 1946, **21**, 445; G. M. Volk, *J. Amer. Soc. Agron.*, 1947, **39**, 93.

[5] J. Stoklasa and A. Ernest, *Zbl. Bakt.* II, 1905, **14**, 723; H. Lundegårdh, *Soil Sci.*, 1927, **23**, 417.

Root development appears to be affected if the oxygen content falls below 9 to 12 per cent, depending on the crop, and to cease if it falls below 5 per cent.[1] The oxygen demands of the root, and its sensitivity to carbon dioxide concentration seem to increase as the temperature increases.[2] These results, however, do not apply equally to all crops. Rice, buckwheat and some willows, for example, grow well with a very restricted air supply around their roots. Tomatoes, and possibly peas and maize, need a very good air supply, and may even only make optimum growth if the air supply around their roots is either artificially improved or enriched with additional oxygen; the cereals and soybeans appear to come intermediate between these classes.[3]

The effect of the by-products of anaerobic conditions on plant roots has not been studied in any great detail. Hydrogen sulphide, even in very low concentrations, is toxic to most plant roots. Methane has been shown by J. Vlamis and A. R. Davis to have little effect on barley and appears to have improved the growth of rice. Hydrogen at low concentrations does not have any pronounced effect on the root development of plants, though it probably inhibits nitrogen fixation by the bacteria in the root nodules of leguminous plants.[4]

There is a close connection between the air conditions around the roots and their uptake of water and nutrients. H. T. Chang and W. E. Loomis[5] grew wheat, maize and rice plants in water solutions in quartz sand, and showed that increasing the carbon dioxide content of the solution reduced the uptake of water and some plant nutrients, particularly potassium and nitrogen, very considerably, whilst reducing the oxygen content of the solution and keeping the carbon dioxide content low, by bubbling through nitrogen gas, had little effect on the plants' uptake of either water or nutrients. On the other hand, L. P. Pepkowitz and J. W. Shive,[6] who grew soybeans and tomato plants in water cultures under conditions where the carbon dioxide concentration was kept low, found that the uptake of nutrients by these plants increased with increasing oxygen tension in the solution to a maximum and then decreased as the tension increased beyond this point.

The temperatures at which active root growth takes place have not been worked out in detail, but the roots of most commercial crops and trees need temperatures well above the freezing-point for active

[1] See, for example, D. Boynton et al., Science, 1938, 88, 569; Proc. Amer. Soc. Hort. Sci., 1943, 42, 53; H. Vine, Trop. Agric. Trin., 1942, 19, 220.
[2] W. A. Cannon, Science, 1923, 58, 331.
[3] E. E. Free, Johns Hopkins Univ. Circ. 198, 1917; W. A. Cannon, Carnegie Inst. Publ. 368, 1925; S. G. Gilbert and J. W. Shive, Soil Sci., 1942, 53, 143; 1945, 59, 453; J. Vlamis and A. R. Davis, Plant Physiol., 1944, 19, 33.
[4] P. W. Wilson and R. H. Burris, J. Bact., 1944, 47, 410.
[5] Plant Physiol., 1945, 20, 221.
[6] Soil Sci., 1944, 57, 143.

growth. Rogers,[1] for example, found that while apple-tree roots could make some growth in soils as cool as 35°F. or about 2°C.,[2] they did not grow actively until the soil had warmed up to 45°F. (7°C.). On the other hand, if the temperature becomes too high, growth again is checked, and this check is more severe the more unfavourable are other soil conditions, such as pH and aeration in particular.

The carbohydrates available for translocation to the roots for their growth appear to be a proportion of those not immediately needed by the aerial parts of the plant. Hence, any factor which allows carbohydrate production to go on but discourages aerial growth encourages active root growth. Thus, root growth does not take place when corn crops are ripening their seed, cotton plants are producing their bolls,[3] or fruit crops their fruit, for then the aerial parts are drawing heavily on the available carbohydrate supplies. An observation of F. J. Nutman[4] affords a good illustration of this effect. He showed that if coffee trees were allowed to overcrop, this so reduced the carbohydrate supply to the roots that insufficient feeding roots were produced to take up enough nutrients to mature the crop without harm to the tree. On the other hand, if a crop is prevented from ripening its seed, by removing its flower heads, for example, it may be encouraged to make extra root growth at this season, and this is the reason for the fruit-grower's practice of preventing newly planted trees from carrying a fruit crop.

The effects of fertilisers on root growth are mainly indirect, as their direct effects are usually on the rate of leaf growth and of carbohydrate production. If a crop is growing in a moderately fertile, moist soil favourable for root growth, and a fertiliser is added which remedies all nutrient deficiencies, the fertiliser may only increase top growth without any great effect on root growth: this is probably the most common effect of fertilisers on normal, reasonably fertile, agricultural soils. On the other hand, if the soil is very poor in a nutrient, all growth may be severely limited if the nutrient is not added. This is illustrated in Plate XXVI, which shows the stunted root system of an eight-year-old gooseberry bush growing on a poor sandy soil without added nutrients and the much deeper and extensive root system of a similar bush given a good dressing of farmyard manure before planting. Soils short of phosphate also illustrate this condition very well. Crops growing on such soils are stunted: they cannot produce much leaf, and hence much carbohydrate, so that the whole plant is starved. Adding phosphates increases leaf growth very considerably, which

[1] *J. Pomol.*, 1939, **17**, 99.
[2] E. B. Earley and J. L. Cartter, *J. Amer. Soc. Agron.*, 1945, **37**, 727, found a similar effect with soybeans.
[3] For an example of this, see F. M. Eaton and H. E. Joham, *Plant Physiol.*, 1944, **19**, 507.
[4] *Emp. J. Expt. Agric.*, 1933, **1**, 271, 285.

can now produce much larger quantities of carbohydrate which, in turn, allows much greater development in the root growth. Phosphates, as such, appear to have no specific effect in increasing root growth, in spite of many earlier statements to the contrary.

This effect of adding a nutrient in short supply on the root development of a plant has the interesting consequence that the fertiliser, by increasing the root range of the plant, increases the amount of nutrients the plant can take up from the soil. Thus, J. W. T. Spinks and S. A. Barber,[1] using radioactive phosphorus P^{32}, showed that wheat plants take up more soil phosphate from a phosphate-deficient soil if they are given superphosphate than if they are not. The authors unfortunately did not examine the effect of the superphosphate on the root development of the crop, but the easiest interpretation of their result is that given above.

The position in the soil where the fertiliser is put, however, affects the root development, for roots will ramify in the fertilised volume. Thus, putting the fertiliser in the subsoil will usually give a greater development of roots there than if it is all put in the surface soil.[2] This practice of deep fertiliser placement can also affect the drought resistance of plants growing on soils having poor subsoils in dry years, and this will be discussed further on pp. 472-4.

The effects of water supply on the root system are also indirect. Plants have usually only a shallow root system if grown in moist, fertile soils, for the aerial parts can use most of the carbohydrates produced. But a drought setting in after the plant has become established encourages a deep root system, for the first effect of water shortage in the soil is to reduce the rate of new aerial growth, hence, is to make more carbohydrates available for root growth. The classical examples of the effect of water supply on the depth of root development come from the American prairies.[3] The deepest root development is found in regions of moderate summer droughts but adequate winter rain, so that at the beginning of each growing season the soil is wet to a considerable depth, and during the summer there is enough rain to keep the prairie plants growing with the help of the water stored in the top few feet of soil. Under these conditions over 65 per cent of the species present will send their roots down to a depth of at least 5 feet, and many will reach 9 feet and a few 20 feet. This is illustrated in Plate XXIV[4] for a prairie at Hays, Kansas, when the root systems were

---

[1] *Sci. Agric.*, 1948, **28**, 79.

[2] For red clover in New Jersey, see N. A. Ferrant and H. B. Sprague, *Soil Sci.*, 1940, **50**, 141; in Ohio, J. Bushnell, *J. Amer. Soc. Agron.*, 1941, **33**, 823. For sweet clover, see D. D. Smith, C. A. Woodruff and D. M. Whitt, *Agric. Engng.*, 1947, **28**, 347.

[3] See, for example, H. L. Shantz, *U.S. Dept. Agric. Bur. Plant Indust.*, Bull. 201, 1911; J. E. Weaver, *Carnegie Inst. Publ.* 286, 1919; 292, 1920.

[4] F. W. Albertson, *Ecol. Monogr.*, 1937, **7**, 481.

examined during a period of years of average rainfall. It shows that a
large proportion of the grass roots extended to 4 to 5 feet and many of
the herbaceous plant roots went down to 6 to 8 feet. But as the rainfall
decreases, so the rain wets the soil to a progressively shallower depth, and
as the root zone is mainly confined to this depth, it becomes shallower.
This is shown in Plate XXV[1] for the same prairie as in XXIV but after
a run of years of low rainfall. It shows clearly that the grass roots are
now confined to the top 1 to 2 feet, and that the depth of rooting of the
herbaceous plants is also much decreased. Weaver has also given an
example from the Great Plains of this effect of amount of rainfall on the

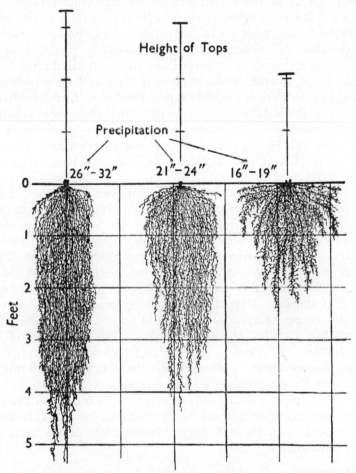

FIG. 43. The effect of the amount of rainfall on the depth of rooting of winter wheat.
(Very fine sandy loam—silt loam in the Great Plains.)

[1] J. E. Weaver and F. W. Albertson, *Ecol. Monogr.*, 1943, **13**, 1.

depth of rooting of wheat, which is shown in Fig. 43.[1] As the rainfall decreases from 26 to 32 inches to 16 to 19 inches, the root system decreases in depth from about 5 feet to 2 feet and the height of the wheat from just over 3 feet to just over 2 feet. On the other hand, as the rainfall increases, so the root system once again becomes more shallow, because the roots can find all the water they need in the superficial layers of the soil to carry the crop through the normal summer droughts. This is probably the principal factor responsible for plants usually being deeper rooted in light sandy than in clay or loam soils in the temperate region,[2] for the former will hold less available water per foot depth of soil than the latter, although the higher carbon dioxide concentration in the subsoil air of the loam or clay may also be in part responsible, in so far as it is not a reflection of the higher water-holding power of the soil.

It is therefore only when conditions favour deep rooting that plants can display their capacity to form deep roots. If conditions are continuously moist, all plants are shallow rooting and their root systems occupy the same layer of the soil. But as conditions increasingly favour deep rooting, the shallow-rooting species have their roots confined to the top layer and the deep rooting have their root system increasingly developed in the lower layers, so that the root systems of different species are increasingly concentrated in their characteristic range of depths.

The dependence of the depth of the root zone on the water supply can be seen very clearly in irrigation work. Frequent light irrigations encourage shallow rooting, and infrequent heavy, deep rooting. Thus, C. A. Thompson and E. L. Burrows[3] found lucerne roots only penetrated 3 to 4 feet when the water was supplied in 2-inch irrigations, but to 5 feet if 5-inch irrigations were used; yet in the semi-arid deep silts of Nebraska they will penetrate 20 to 30 feet, and dry out the soil to that depth.[4] Deeper rooting, and hence heavy, infrequent irrigations are normally desirable in the earlier part of the growing season, mainly to allow the crop to tap as large a volume of soil as possible for nutrients, and to provide an insurance against periods of very high transpiration. These considerations naturally do not apply to market-garden crops grown with large amounts of fertiliser in regions of adequate water supply and only moderately high transpiration rates: here frequent light irrigations are preferable, as all carbohydrate production can then be used for producing more leaves and, hence, usually more saleable vegetables.

[1] *Root Development of Field Crops*, New York, 1926.
[2] K. Linkola and A. Tiirikka, *Ann. Bot. Soc. Vanamo*, 1936, **6**, No. 6; V. J. Kivenheimo, ibid., 1947, **22**, No. 2. [3] *New Mexico Agric. Expt. Sta., Bull.* 123, 1920.
[4] F. L. Duley, *J. Amer. Soc. Agron.*, 1929, **21**, 224; T. A. Kiesselbach *et al.*, ibid., 1929, **21**, 241.

This dependençe of root development on the surplus carbohydrates produced by leaves, as affected by the water supply, becomes of great importance in the correct management of pastures. Hard grazing of pastures reduces surplus carbohydrate production, for then all carbohydrates produced are needed to make good the loss of leaf. Hence, a hard-grazed pasture is typically shallow rooted; and hard grazing is, therefore, a practice only suited to moist climates. As the climate becomes more arid, the herbage must be allowed to grow longer, and hence the grazing must be lighter. Thus, W. R. Hanson and L. A. Stoddart[1] found on the semi-arid ranges of Utah the roots of bunch wheat grass (*Agropyron inerme*) only penetrated to about 30 cm. on over-grazed range and to about 60 cm. on protected range, and E. L. Florey and D. F. Thrussell, working on New Mexico ranges, found the roots of black and blue grama grasses (*Bouteloua eripoda* and *gracilis*) penetrated to about 4 feet on properly grazed range, about 2 feet on over-grazed, and to under 1 foot on badly over-grazed.

The actual type of root system developed by a plant also depends to some extent on the soil conditions. The root system tends to be more branched and more compact in fertile than in poor soil, and if the roots are growing in soils of variable fertility, the habit of the root system varies with the fertility. Thus, if a plant is growing in a rather poor soil recently manured with farmyard manure, each pocket of manure will be filled with short, much-branched roots, and if the soil is stratified with layers of sand and clay, the root system will often be of the fertile type in the clay and the open type in the sand. However, if the clay is rather plastic, the root system will be confined to the spaces and cracks between the clay clods and crumbs, and because of the compression these roots will suffer during wet weather when these cracks seal up as they are often flattened in cross section instead of being rounded.

The root systems of trees often illustrate this dependence of type on soil conditions. Many trees growing in natural forest with an undisturbed floor of litter tend to have an extensive much-branched root system filling the first few inches of the soil and a few deep tap roots. But if these trees are planted in open land where litter cannot accumulate, and particularly if this is done in rather dry regions, many of these trees will develop a root system filling several feet of the soil. F. Hardy[2] has given a good illustration of this with cacao. In humid conditions, or badly drained soils, it has a very superficial root system containing

[1] *J. Amer. Soc. Agron.*, 1940, **32**, 278, and for further examples, see L. A. Stoddart and A. D. Smith, *Range Management*, New York, 1943. For the effect of different grazing methods on the depth of the root zone of pastures in W. European conditions, see E. Klapp, *Pflanzenbau*, 1943, **19**, 221.
[2] *Trop. Agric. Trin.*, 1944, **21**, 184; 1943, **20**, 207.

many mycorrhizas which, with the layer of leaf litter that accumulates, forms a mat on the surface. On well-drained soils, on the other hand, it has a deep root system, carrying no mycorrhiza and forming no surface mat. One of the most difficult problems in tropical agriculture concerns the management of plantation trees that cannot be made to develop a deep root system, for such trees suffer very badly from weed competition, drought and high surface soil temperatures. The principal method of minimising these harmful consequences of shallow rooting is to put a straw or vegetable mulch on the soil surface.[1] As will be explained on p. 638, this encourages favourable conditions for root development to develop under it, and consequently encourages all plants to develop a superficial root system which is of great importance if the principal plant nutrients are all concentrated in the surface layers.[2]

J. Baeyens[3] has summarised much of what has been said in the preceding paragraphs by emphasising two separate properties of the root system—what he calls the root surface and the root volume. The root surface measures the total absorptive area of the root, and the root volume is the volume of soil containing roots. The root system may have the same surface in a fertile well-watered soil as in a rather poor soil subject to drought, but in the first case the root volume would be small, the soil being filled with fine roots and the roots extracting nutrients intensively from this volume, and in the second the roots would be widely distributed throughout a large volume of soil and would only extract small quantities of nutrients from each unit volume of soil. Baeyens further emphasises, what has already been emphasised here, that the root volume is only large if the plant needs water or nutrients. Crops on a fertile moist soil always have a compact root system.

The actual rate of growth of plant roots in the soil varies widely. W. S. Rogers[4] finds 3 mm. a day a common figure for apple roots in the sandy loam soil at East Malling, rising to 9 mm. at times, whilst J. E. Weaver[5] quotes 10 mm. a day being common for grasses and up to 60 mm. a day for maize and squash plants in the silty soils of Nebraska. The total length of a plant's roots can be very large, particularly if it is growing by itself with no competition from other plants. Thus, T. K. Pavlychenko[6] found an isolated plant of wheat, rye or wild oats, growing on the sandy loam soil of Saskatoon, had produced

---

[1] For an account of management of the very shallow-rooting Robusta coffee trees in Uganda, see A. S. Thomas, *Emp. J. Expt. Agric.*, 1944, **12**, 191.
[2] I. W. Wander and J. H. Gourley, *Proc. Amer. Soc. Hort. Sci.*, 1943, **42**, 1.
[3] *Les sols de l'Afrique centrale*, Vol. I, 1938. I.N.E.A.C.
[4] *J. Pomol. Hort. Sci.*, 1939, **17**, 99.
[5] *Root Development of Field Crops*, 1926, New York.
[6] With J. B. Harrington, *Canad. J. Res.*, 1934, **10**, 77; *Sci. Agric.*, 1935, **16**, 151. Also *Ecology*, 1937, **18**, 62, and *Canad. J. Res.*, 1937, **15** C, 33, where the method used is described. For another illustration of the root system of rye, see H. J. Dittmer, *Amer. J. Bot.*, 1937, **24**, 417; for grasses, see T. K. Pavlychenko, *Natl. Res. Counc. Canada, Publ.* 1088, 1942.

40 to 50 miles of roots by the time it came to maturity eighty days after emergence; but if these plants were grown in drills 6 inches apart with eighteen to twenty plants per foot, the root length was reduced about a hundredfold to about half a mile, although the reduction in the dry matter of the aerial parts of the plants was only about 15 per cent. As measured by length, the great preponderance of these roots are very fine, and these roots are reduced far more in proportion than the thicker ones when the root system suffers competition for space. Weeds can still further reduce the length of the root system. Unfortunately, no comparable work is available for normal English soils, and these lengths are probably much higher than would usually be found here, particularly in the moister parts of the country or on the heavier soils.

Plants growing in drills, or close spaced, not only have a shorter but also a more compact root system. A plant grown in isolation will have roots that spread over a very great area laterally, but if grown with neighbours the lateral spread will be very much restricted. On the whole, root systems of neighbouring plants, even of the same species, do not interpenetrate very much through the same volume of soil.

The total length and weight of the roots of different plants in a unit volume of soil depends on many factors, as already explained. But with these limitations in mind, Table 102, taken from some of Pavly-chenko's results,[1] obtained in the central prairie states of the U.S.A. and Canada, is given to show the order of magnitude involved and the difference between grasses and crops. The samples were taken from prairies containing fairly pure stands of the grasses mentioned or from fields of the crops. The table gives some idea of the variation between the amount of roots formed by different grasses, for example, crested and slender wheat grass (*Agropyron cristatum* and *pauciflorum* respectively), and, as was explained on p. 437, this difference is reflected in the relative power of these two grasses for improving the tilth or crumb structure of the soil.

A review of the determinations that have been made on the weight of root residues under European conditions has been given by S. Gericke.[2] He shows that for the cereals the weight of roots left in the soil is about one-eighth the weight of the crop above ground, hence, on a 2-ton crop the root residues would weigh about 5 cwt. per acre, which is about half that given in Table 102, which, however, probably refers to a much lighter crop. The weight of roots produced by clovers and serradella, however, appear to be very variable, ranging from 2 to 50 cwt. per acre, whilst lucerne gives 1 to 1½ tons of roots per year.

[1] *Natl. Res. Counc. Canada, Publ.* 1088, 1942.
[2] *Bodenk. PflErnähr.*, 1945, **35**, 229.

Grasses are like clovers in giving very variable weights of roots, again from 1 to 2 tons per year. The ratio of the weight of roots in a grassland soil to the weight of organic matter in that soil is discussed on p. 578.

TABLE 102

Quantity of Roots Found in Upper 10 cm. of Soil under Different Crops

Numbers and lengths of roots in metres or kilometres per half square metre
Weights of roots in hundredweights per acre

	Prairie grasses			Crops	
	Agropyron cristatum	Agropyron pauciflorum	Poa pratensis	Lucerne	Wheat near harvest
Underground Stems					
Length in m. .	23·0	4·5	28·0	47·0	15·0
Weight per acre . .	24·6	6·7	17·4	16·5	4·2
Main Roots . . .					
Numbers in thousands .	11·7	8·0	16·3	—	1·5
Length in m. . .	935	563	1140	—	179
Average diam. in mm. .	0·4	0·5	0·19	—	0·32
Weight per acre .	9·3	5·1	10·6	—	2·7
Branches, First Order					
Number in millions .	0·65	0·53	1·94	0·0054	0·082
Length in km. .	39·2	21·2	75·5	0·25	4·30
Average diam. in mm. .	0·09	0·1	0·04	—	0·09
Branches, Second Order					
Number in millions .	7·85	2·28	10·57	0·152	1·10
Length in km. .	55·0	16·0	95·1	4·85	15·4
Average diam. in mm. .	0·04	0·03	0·018	—	0·03
Branches, Third Order					
Number in millions .	3·13	1·15	—	0·738	0·83
Length in km. .	9·5	3·1	—	5·16	6·67
Average diam. in mm. .	0·01	0·007	—	—	0·008
All Branches					
Number in millions .	11·6	3·96	12·6	0·895	2·02
Length in km. .	103·4	40·2	170·6	10·3	26·4
Weight per acre . .	14·0	7·5	16·0	—	4·2
All Roots					
Weight per acre . .	47·7	19·4	44·0	19·0	11·1

CHAPTER XXV

THE UPTAKE OF NUTRIENTS FROM THE SOIL

The Absorption of Nutrients and Water by Plant Roots

PLANT ROOTS ABSORB nutrients from the soil in the form of anions and cations. The mechanism by which these are absorbed is still uncertain, but the absorption of the nutrient ions must involve an expenditure of energy, as they are up to a hundred times more concentrated in the cell sap than in the soil solution.[1] On the other hand, there is no theoretical need for energy to be required for the absorption of water, as the osmotic pressure of the cell sap is between 10 and 20 atm. higher than that of the soil solution in most British soils.[2]

The source of the energy expended in nutrient absorption is presumably carbohydrates which are oxidised in the absorbing cells, for these cells require a constant supply of oxygen and removal of carbon dioxide if they are to carry out this process.[3] Water absorption also appears to require a good oxygen supply, and hence to be an energy process, but this may simply be that unless the cells are able to be active they cannot maintain their semi-permeable membranes. Absorption of nutrients and water is thus part of the respiration processes of the root cells, which can therefore only function in a soil that is adequately aerated, and they usually cease to function before they are physically injured by unfavourable conditions. There are, however, a few exceptions to this, as some plants, for example, rice,[4] can allow oxygen from the atmosphere to diffuse through special cells in their stems and roots to the absorbing cells.

The respiration of root cells and their ability to absorb nutrients may, however, be to two aspects of the same process if H. Lundegårdh's theory[5] of these processes is basically correct. This theory pictures the processes involved as follows. Respiration in a living cell involves the

---

[1] For a recent theory, see H. Lundegårdh, *Nature*, 1946, **157**, 575.

[2] D. R. Hoagland and A. R. Davis, *Protoplasma*, 1929, **4**, 610; for further references, see O. C. Magistad, *Bot. Rev.*, 1945, **11**, 181.

[3] V. Iljim, *Jahr. wiss. Bot.*, 1927, **66**, 947; F. M. Eaton, *J. Agric. Res.*, 1942, **64**, 357.

[4] See the work of J. W. Shive and his co-workers, *Soil Sci.*, 1942, **53**, 143; 1944, **57**, 143; D. R. Hoagland and T. C. Broyer, *J. Gen. Physiol.*, 1942, **25**, 865; for review, D. I. Arnon, *Ann. Rev. Biochem.*, 1943, **12**, 493; D. R. Hoagland, *Lectures on the Inorganic Nutrition of Plants*, Waltham, Mass., 1944.

[5] *LantbrHögsk. Ann.*, 1940, **8**, 234; *Ark. Bot.*, 1945, **32** A, No. 12; *Nature*, 1946, **157**, 575; *Ann. Rev. Biochem.*, 1947, **16**, 503. See also R. N. Robertson and M. J. Wilkins, *Aust. J. Sci. Res.*, 1948, **1** B, 332.

transfer of electrons from inside to outside the cell, and the enzyme system that effects their transfer across the living membrane of the cell at the same time effects the transfer of a corresponding number of anions from outside to inside the cell, to maintain electric neutrality. Further, the source of electrons in the cell are hydrogen atoms, which by giving away an electron become hydrogen ions, and the acceptors of the electrons outside the cell are hydrogen ions which become hydrogen atoms. This process is thus equivalent to transferring hydrogen from, say, carbohydrate molecules in the cell, leaving as an end-product carbon dioxide, to, say, oxygen molecules outside the cell with the consequent formation of water, which is another way of considering the process of aerobic respiration. Electron transfers thus increase the hydrogen ion concentration inside the cell and decrease it outside, and this in turn causes some of them to exchange with cations outside the cell across the cell membrane. Thus the process of cation uptake is a base, or cationic exchange—a process which, in fact, is not confined to the excretion of hydrogen ions.

Two consequences follow from the assumption that cation uptake is a base exchange process. In the first place it is not a one-way process. Cells can lose, or excrete, cations other than hydrogen ions, and this has been demonstrated experimentally (see p. 471). In the second place one would expect the root cells to absorb simple small cations in approximately the proportions that they occur outside them. But this does not imply that the cations will be present in this proportion in the plant tissues, for their rate of transfer from the root cells to the plant sap depends considerably on the individual ions. Thus, potassium appears to move more quickly than the other common cations, and incidentally nitrate more so than most other anions, from the soil into the sap,[1] and these are the two ions that appear to be taken up in appreciably higher proportion than their relative abundance in the soil would suggest.[2] On the other hand, aluminium[3] and related ions and some rare earths[4] are taken up by the roots but are hardly translocated at all by most plants.

Plants differ, however, in their power of taking up some cations, or at least in their power of transferring them into their aerial portions. H. Collander[5] found that these differences between plants was most marked for the uptake of sodium and magnesium, some species being able to take up sixty times as much as other species. Thus, halophytes could nearly all take up very large quantities of sodium, whilst buckwheat, maize and sunflower could take up very little. Again, some

[1] H. Lundegårdh, *Nature*, 1946, **157**, 575.
[2] R. H. Bray, *J. Amer. Chem. Soc.*, 1942, **64**, 954; C. E. Marshall, *Missouri Agric. Expt. Sta., Res. Bull.* 385, 1944.   [3] G. E. Hutchinson, *Quart. Rev. Biol.*, 1943, **18**, 1.
[4] L. Jacobson and R. Overstreet, *Soil Sci.*, 1948, **65**, 129.   [5] *Plant Physiol.*, 1941, **16**, 691.

plants, particularly some members of the *Chenopodiaceae*, could absorb large quantities of magnesium. On the other hand, all plants had about the same power of accumulating potassium when growing in potassium-rich conditions.

The distribution within the plant of the different ions taken up by the roots depends on the part of the plant being studied. The mineral composition of the seed or fruit is more a characteristic of the plant than of the abundance of the ions in the soil, whilst that of the root depends more on their abundance in the soil than on the plant; the composition of the leaves and stems is intermediate. Thus, as G. T. Nightingale[1] has shown for pineapples, and D. I. Arnon and D. R. Hoagland[2] for tomatoes, the developing seed or fruit takes just those quantities of mineral from the main reservoir available in the roots and vegetative system needed to give it its characteristic mineral composition. Fruits are in fact relatively high in potassium and low in calcium, perhaps because the plant contains much higher reserves of mobile potassium than calcium in its tissues, for much of the calcium in a plant is relatively immobile.[3]

The fact that the composition of the leaves of a plant reflect to some extent the nutrient conditions in the soil can be used by agricultural advisers to determine, from the analysis of an unhealthy leaf, if the trouble is due to a deficiency of any particular nutrient or to a lack of balance between the nutrients.[4] It has also great agricultural importance, for the leaves of grasses and legumes form the primary food of the world's sheep and cattle. Now the grazing animal requires not only protein and carbohydrate from these leaves, but also its supply of minerals, hence the feeding value of pastures or hay can depend on the soils on which they are grown. The best-known example of this on a world-wide scale is the phosphate content of the herbage, which is usually a fairly good reflection of the available phosphate supply in the soil.[5] There are considerable areas of very phosphate-deficient soils, particularly in South Africa and Australia, which carry a grass or prairie vegetation that has such a low phosphorus content that the animals grazing on them suffer from acute phosphorus-deficiency diseases[6] (Table 103).

The mineral content of plant leaves can thus be affected within

---

[1] *Bot. Gaz.*, 1942, **103**, 409; 1943, **104**, 191; *Soil Sci.*, 1943, **55**, 73.

[2] *Bot. Gaz.*, 1943, **104**, 576.

[3] T. G. Mason and E. J. Maskell, *Ann. Bot.*, 1931, **45**, 125.

[4] For a review of the power and limitations of these methods of leaf analysis, see D. W. Goodall and F. G. Gregory, *Imp. Bur. Hort.*, *Tech. Comm.* 17, 1947.

[5] For an extensive series of soil and plant analyses illustrating this, see G. S. Fraps and J. F. Fudge, *Proc. Soil Sci. Soc. Amer.*, 1938, **2**, 374; *Texas Agric. Expt. Sta.*, *Bull.* 582, 1940.

[6] For corresponding American results, see K. C. Beeson, *Soil Sci.*, 1945, **60**, 9; *Bot. Rev.*, 1946, **12**, 424.

limits by suitable use of fertilisers. Thus, the phosphorus content of grass leaves can be doubled, and at the same time the calcium content increased by 50 per cent by adding superphosphates to a phosphate-deficient pasture,[1] and this may increase the nutritive value of the fodder, as has recently been shown very strikingly in some feeding experiments on differently manured hays by W. A. Albrecht and his co-workers.[2]

TABLE 103

Per cent P in the Dry Matter of Grassland Herbage

	Good soils		Poor soils
Romney Marsh[3] . .	0·26	Transvaal Veld[5] . .	0·04
Scotland[4] . . .	0·32	Bechuanaland[6] . .	0·02
		Victoria[7] . . .	0·04

The dependence of the relative concentrations of the cations in the leaves of a plant on their relative concentrations in the soil as available or exchangeable ions has now been put on a semi-quantitative basis for several crop plants. The following factors are relevant: the crop studied, the relative proportions of these cations in an available form in the soil, the total concentration of these cations in the soil, the type of clay, and the relative contribution of the clay and the organic matter to the base-holding power of the soil.

In the first place plants differ very considerably among themselves in the proportions of potassium, magnesium, calcium and sodium their leaves contain when they are growing in the same soil, in the minimum concentrations of these ions needed for healthy growth, and in the maximum concentrations at which any particular ion can occur. Thus, A. Mehlich and J. F. Reed[8] found that for crops growing in a given soil the relative concentration of calcium to potassium and magnesium in the leaf is lower for oats and timothy than for alsike, red clover and soybeans, and is lower in these than for lucerne, cotton and turnips. This property is not quite that discussed for C. A. Bower and W. H.

[1] W. Godden, *J. Agric. Sci.*, 1926, **16**, 98. Similar results were obtained by G. Paturel in France, *J. Agric. Prat.*, 1911, **21**, 12; also A. E. V. Richardson in Victoria, *J. Dept. Agric. Victoria*, 1924, **22**, 193, 257; in both cases the unmanured herbage contained only 0·1 per cent P, while that receiving phosphatic manuring contained distinctly more.
[2] *Proc. Soil Sci. Soc. Amer.*, 1942, **6**, 252; 1943, **7**, 322; 1944, **8**, 282.
[3] A. D. Hall and E. J. Russell, *J. Agric. Sci.*, 1912, **4**, 339.
[4] J. B. Orr, *Minerals in Pastures*, p. 13, 1929, London.
[5] H. Ingle, *J. Agric. Sci.*, 1908, **3**, 22.
[6] A. Theiler, *Union of South Africa, 11th and 12th Vet. Repts.*, 1927.
[7] H. Kincaid, *Proc. Roy. Soc. Victoria*, 1911, **23**, 363.
[8] *Soil Sci.*, 1948, **66**, 289.

Pierre (see p. 66), as they were interested in the minimum concentrations of these ions needed for optimum growth, but it should be very similar. Unfortunately, the two groups of workers had too few crops in common for a close comparison to be made of the responsiveness of a crop to a potassic fertiliser on a calcareous soil with the relative concentration of potassium to calcium in its leaves.

The effect of altering the concentration of any one cation in the soil whilst keeping the others constant on the cation concentrations in the leaves is that, in general, increasing the calcium in the soil depresses the magnesium in the leaves more than the potassium; increasing the magnesium depresses the calcium more than the potassium; and increasing the potassium may depress the calcium more than the magnesium, or may decrease them about equally. An example of these effects is given in Table 104 for bluegrass (*Poa pratensis*), a plant having a low calcium-potassium ratio in its leaf, and for sweet clover, which has a high ratio.

TABLE 104

The Effect of a Given Increase of a Cation in the Soil on the Composition of the Plant[1]

Milli-equivalents of cation per 100 grams dry matter in the plant

Added to soil	Bluegrass				Sweet clover			
	Ca	Mg	K	Total	Ca	Mg	K	Total
Basal	35	42	54	131	102	62	47	211
+Ca	41	37	53	131	124	57	45	226
+Mg	30	63	50	143	100	97	42	239
+K	23	24	95	142	72	38	102	212

This result can equally well be expressed in the statement that the plant tends to maintain its potassium content more stable than its magnesium, and its magnesium than its calcium, as the concentration of other cations around the plant roots varies.

It is sometimes possible to predict, from a knowledge of the composition of the exchangeable ions in the soil, the proportion of these ions in the leaves of the crop, and on the whole it is found that the ratio of potassium to calcium is much higher in the leaf than in the soil and that of magnesium to calcium somewhat higher; but the factors for converting from the soil ratio to the plant ratio are very dependent on the plant but not very dependent on the soil, or on the actual proportions of the

[1] C. E. Marshall, *Missouri Agric. Exp. Sta.*, *Res. Bull.* 385, 1944. The results given are for the mean of the crops on two soils and at two levels of calcium supply.

exchangeable ions present. However, it is probable that a more accurate prediction can be made if, instead of determining the ratio of the exchangeable ions in the soil, one shakes up the soil with a small amount of hydrochloric acid, enough to supply hydrogen ions for only a small fraction of the exchangeable bases. Then for plants with a moderate calcium demand, the relative concentrations of calcium to magnesium are about the same in the acid extract and in the leaf, but the relative potassium content of the leaf is higher, by a factor of between 2 and 4,[1] than in the acid extract of the soil.

The Soil Solution

The water in the soil contains soluble salts, and hence whenever this aspect of the soil water is relevant, it is usually known as the soil solution. As has often happened in the history of agricultural science, the first investigations on the chemical composition of these dissolved salts was made in France. Th. Schloesing[2] in 1866 devised a method of collecting the soil solution based on displacement by water. He placed 30 to 35 kg. of freshly taken soil containing 19·1 per cent of water in a large inverted tubulated bell jar and poured on it water, coloured with carmine, in such a way as to simulate the action of rain. The added water at once displaced the soil water and caused it to descend so that it could be collected: a sharp horizontal line of demarcation between the added and the original water persisted throughout the experiment, even when eight days were occupied in the descent. A typical analysis of the displaced liquid in milligrams per litre was:

SiO_2	Nitric acid	Carbonic acid	CaO	MgO	K_2O	Na_2O	Sulphuric acid	Chlorine	Organic matter
29·1	305	118	264	13·5	6·9	7·8	57·9	7·4	37·5

The solution, therefore, contained about 850 mgm. of material per litre, that is, its concentration was about 0·08 per cent, or about 160 parts per million of the soil was present in the solution.

Three groups of methods have been in fairly recent use, and all give solutions having reasonably similar compositions. J. S. Burd and J. C. Martin[3] devised a method, still in use to-day, based on forcing water through a tall column of soil, under a pressure of 7 atm. (100 lb.

---

[1] See, for example, R. H. Bray, *J. Amer. Chem. Soc.*, 1942, **64**, 954; T. B. van Itallie, *Soil Sci.*, 1938, **46**, 175; 1948, **65**, 393; A. Mehlich, *Soil Sci.*, 1946, **62**, 393; with J. F. Reed, ibid., 1948, **66**, 289.

[2] *C.R.*, 1866, **63**, 1007; 1870, **70**, 98.   [3] *J. Agric. Sci.*, 1923, **13**, 265.

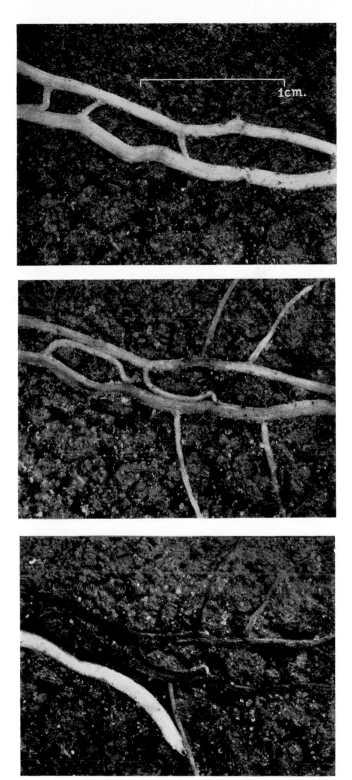

Plate XXIII

1cm.

Apple tree roots growing in a silt loam, photographed on
the 6th, 25th and 35th day after the two thick roots had
first entered the area (about 4 times natural size)
(p. 448)

Plate XXIV

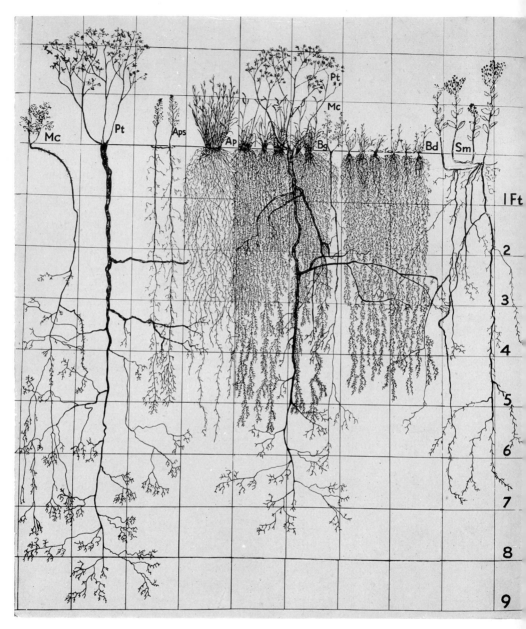

The root systems of plants in a typical short-grass prairie after a run of years with average rainfall (Hays, Kansas)
(p. 452)

Plate XXV

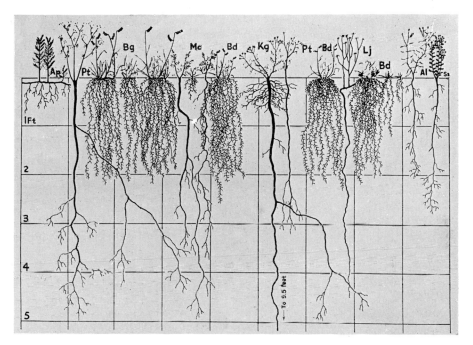

The root systems in the same area after a run of drought years

Al Allionia linearis, Ap Aristida purpurea, Aps Ambrosia psilostachya, Bd Buchloe dactyloides, Bg Bouteloua gracilis, Kg Kuhnia glutinosa, Lj Lygodesmia juncea, Mc Malvastrum coccineum, Pt Psoralia tenuiflora, Sm Solidago mollis, Ss Sideranthus spinulosus

(p. 453)

Plate XXVI

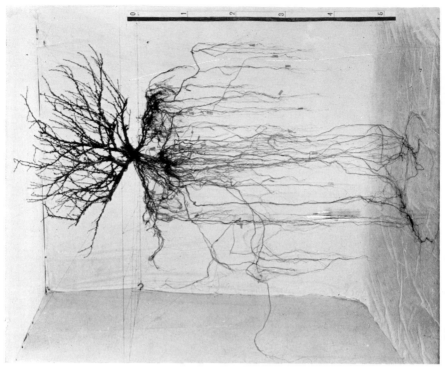

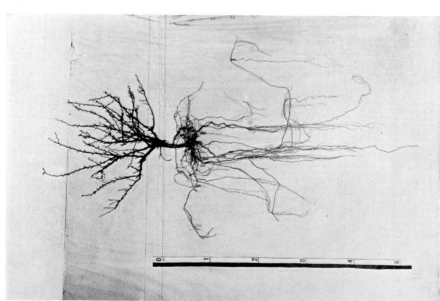

The effect of nutrients on the root development of eight-year-old gooseberry bushes in a sandy soil (Wrotham Heath, Kent) (Left) No manure; (Right) with 45 tons per acre of farmyard manure in the year of planting. The roots of the manured bush, resting on the ground, should continue downwards. The measure is marked in feet per sq. inch) and collecting the effluent in small lots. The first few lots have similar compositions and are taken to represent the soil solution. A second method is based on dispersing the soil solution in a large volume of inert liquid, such as paraffin,[1] and separating out this liquid and analysing the solution it contains. This is based on the assumption that the solution dispersing in the paraffin has the same composition as the soil solution. A modification of this is to use ethyl alcohol or glycol,[2] and to assume that the solution as a whole dissolves and that no extra salts come into solution. A third method, recently introduced by L. A. Richards,[3] is based on putting a thin disk of soil in a pressure cell, sealed at the bottom with a supported cellophane membrane, and forcing the soil water through the membrane by applying a gas pressure of 16 atm. This last method gives a solution from which the phosphate has been removed, for it is held back by the cellophane membrane.

The composition of the soil solution depends on the moisture content of the soil, the growth of the crop in the soil, and the activity of the microbial population. These factors are difficult to separate out in the field, and it is not certain how far results obtained in the artificial conditions of the laboratory apply to the field. The main results, however, are clear enough, and reasonable enough, for their general validity to be accepted.

The effect of the moisture content of the soil on the composition of the soil solution is as follows:[4]

(a) The concentration of nitrate and chloride varies inversely as the moisture content, indicating that all these anions present in the soil are in the soil solution.

(b) The concentration of phosphate, though varying from soil to soil, is independent of the moisture content, being usually about 1 to 3 parts per million. The soil solution is, therefore, presumably saturated with phosphate.

(c) The relative proportions of the cations in the soil solution depend on their concentration. Adding water to it, so diluting it, causes a smaller proportional decrease in the monovalent than divalent ions (see p. 115). Since in most soils calcium is the predominant cation in the soil solution, this means its concentration varies approximately inversely with that of the soil solution, since the total amount of anions in solution remains about constant, and that as the solution becomes more concentrated so the potassium and sodium ion concentrations rise in proportion more slowly than that of the anions or of the calcium.

[1] A. G. Doyarenko, *Versuchsfeld f. allg. Ackerbau. Landw. Akad.*, Moscow, 1924–7, **2**, 1.
[2] A. Kawe, *J. Landw.*, 1932, **80**, 87.
[3] *Soil Sci.*, 1941, **51**, 377; with R. F. Reitemeier, ibid., 1944, **57**, 119.
[4] J. S. Burd and J. C. Martin, *J. Agric. Sci.*, 1923, **13**, 265.

The effect of the growing plant is to deplete the soil solution of much of its nutrient material, particularly its nitrate, as already discussed on p. 307. An example of this depletion, showing how it affects some nutrients much more than others, is given in Table 105, taken from some work of Burd and Martin.[1] It shows the composition of the soil solution before a crop of barley is sown, after harvest, and just before the next crop is put in; the results have been adjusted to the standard moisture content shown in the first column. The large recovery noticeable in the following spring is very dependent on the soil conditions and on the nutrient reserves in the soil.[2]

TABLE 105

The Effect of the Growing Crop on the Composition of the Soil Solution

Solutions displaced by water from cropped soils at beginning (April) and end (September) of growing season (1923) and at the beginning of the next growing season (1924)

Soil	Date	pH	Parts per million of displaced solution								
			NO_3	HCO_3	SO_4	PO_4	Ca	Mg	Na	K	Total solids
No. 7: 12·5 per cent moisture	Apr. 30, 1923	7·4	149	83	561	1·1	242	91	42	21	1190
	Sept. 4, 1923	7·6	58	155	432	0·6	193	47	40	9	935
	Apr. 28, 1924	7·6	252	142	699	0·6	336	76	59	12	1527
No. 11: 12·4 per cent moisture	Apr. 30, 1923	8·2	173	160	671	3·3	222	97	87	41	1454
	Sept. 4, 1923	7·6	16	234	598	1·2	192	64	44	22	1171
	Apr. 28, 1924	8·1	263	259	785	2·9	276	94	78	35	1793

The effect of the micro-organisms is to help bring about this replenishment of the soil solution, particularly the replenishment of the nitrate and sulphate, for, if depleted soils are stored in contact with toluene, so microbiological activity is suppressed, and little or no replenishment takes place.[3]

The soil solution of normal leached agricultural soils under normal conditions of moisture content is found to contain up to 0·05 per cent of soluble matter, and the osmotic pressure of the solution varies from 0·2 to 1 atm., being higher the nearer the moisture content is to the wilting-point. Thus, even at the wilting-point the soil solution is very dilute, and has an osmotic pressure far lower than the 10 to 20 atm. of the root sap. Hence, the transfer of water and nutrients from the

[1] *Soil Sci.*, 1924, **18**, 151. See also *Hilgardia*, 1931, **5**, 455, for a summary of much of their work.
[2] See D. R. Hoagland, *J. Agric. Res.*, 1918, **12**, 369, for a soil showing little recovery.
[3] D. R. Hoagland, *Hilgardia*, 1925, **1**, 227; J. S. Burd, *Soil Sci.*, 1925, **20**, 269.

soil to the root requires a definite expenditure of energy, which the roots of most agricultural plants can only incur if they have access to an adequate supply of oxygen.

The soil solutions of arid and of semi-arid irrigated soils differ from those in leached soils by their higher salt contents; for in these soils calcium and sodium salts, in particular the sulphates and chlorides, accumulate,[1] with the consequence that the osmotic pressure of the soil solution is no longer negligible, but may become high enough to limit crop growth. It has the further consequence that as the soil dries the osmotic pressure of the soil solution rises, so that soils containing so much soluble salts that they are on the margin of profitable cultivation need to be watered frequently (p. 605), for the crop can only extract a small proportion of the water held between field capacity and the direct suction corresponding to pF 4·2 before the osmotic pressure has risen high enough to affect the crop. Thus, as pointed out on p. 403, in such soils only a small amount of the water defined as available on the suction basis is, in fact, readily available; in fact, the concept of available water, based on suction measurements, ceases to be valid once the osmotic pressure of the soil solution at the wilting-point becomes appreciable.

The Sources from which Plant Roots Extract Nutrients

There are three possible sources from which roots can extract their nutrients: the soil solution, the exchangeable ions, and the readily decomposable minerals; and it is very difficult to separate out the relative importance of these three sources for any particular plant. C. G. B. Daubeny, in a classical investigation made over a hundred years ago,[2] showed that only a part of the total supply of plant nutrients was available to the plant. But it was soon found that there was no sharp division between available and unavailable plant foods in the soil, for different species of plants had differing powers of extracting the nutrients. The older investigators attributed the different "feeding powers" of plants to differences in the total acidity of their sap; thus they assumed the reason that leguminous plants could often extract more nutrients from a soil than could the grasses was because they had a more acid root sap,[3] although later work showed that, if anything, they have a less acid sap.[4]

J. von Liebig first introduced the idea that the exchangeable bases in the soil are the primary source of nutrients for the plant, which he

[1] O. C. Magistad and R. F. Reitemeier (*Soil Sci.*, 1943, **55**, 351) give analyses of the soil solution of some saline soils at their field capacity.   [2] *Phil. Trans.*, 1845, 179.
[3] B. Dyer, *Trans. Chem. Soc.*, 1894, **65**, 115; *Phil. Trans.*, 1901, **194** B, 235.
[4] H. Kappen, *Landw. Vers.-Stat.*, 1918, **91**, 1; W. Thomas, *Plant Physiol.*, 1930, **5**, 443.

expressed in the following words: "The power of the soil to nourish cultivated plants is, therefore, in exact proportion to the quantity of nutritive substances which it contains in a state of physical saturation. The quantity of other elements in a state of chemical combination distributed through the ground is also highly important, as serving to restore the state of saturation, when the nutritive substances in physical combination have been withdrawn from the soil by a series of crops reaped from it."[1] This hypothesis that the exchangeable bases are the principal source of these nutrients for the plant was extended by W. Knop[2] in a remarkable investigation of considerable historic interest, and also by O. Kellner.[3] M. Whitney in 1892,[4] and later in collaboration with F. K. Cameron,[5] developed the hypothesis that the plant obtains its nutrients from the soil solution, and hence that a study of the nutrients in the soil solution should lead to an accurate assessment of the fertility of the soil.

Thus, the early investigators had shown that at least some of the nutrients in the soil solution, the exchangeable ions, and readily decomposable minerals are available to the plant roots. Yet these are not three independent sources, for the soil solution is in equilibirum with the exchangeable bases and the phosphate compounds in the soil; and if any nutrient except nitrate is removed from the solution, at least a part of this loss will be made good from the non-soluble nutrient reserves in the soil. The solid material of the soil, in fact, keeps the soil solution well buffered both for pH and for all nutrients except nitrates. But since the power of different plants to extract nutrients from a soil differs, the roots must presumably be able to use at least some proportion of the nutrients contained in the more readily decomposable minerals in the soil.

The mechanism by which roots obtain ions from readily decomposable minerals is principally by excreting carbon dioxide, which forms a solution of carbonic acid on the surface of the mineral, a hypothesis originally due to F. Czapek in 1896[6] and further established by J. Stoklasa.[7] This, however, is not the only mechanism for extracting nutrients that are not dissolved in the soil solution. Direct exchange of hydrogen ions excreted by the roots and root hairs with cations held by the mineral particles, as postulated by H. Jenny and R. Overstreet, is another possible mechanism, and excretion of organic acids is again possible, and is the most likely mechanism by which a few plants, such as lupins, can use difficultly available phosphates (p. 500).

[1] *Natural Laws of Husbandry*, London, 1863.
[2] *Die Bonitie ung der Ackererde*, Leipzig, 1871.   [3] *Landw. Vers.-Stat.*, 1886, **33**, 349.
[4] *U.S. Weather Bur. Bull.* 4, 1892; *U.S. Dept. Agric., Farmers' Bull.* 257, 1906.
[5] *U.S. Dept. Agric. Bur. Soils, Bull.* 22, 1903.
[6] *Jahrb. wiss. Bot.*, 1896, **29**, 321.   [7] *Jahrb. wiss. Bot.*, 1908, **46**, 55.

An example of the soil's power to make good the loss of a particular nutrient from the soil solution is given in Table 106, which shows that the total potassium taken up by a crop is very much greater than the loss of potassium from the soil solution, hence the solid phase of the soil must be continually supplying potassium to make good the loss due to its uptake by the roots.

TABLE 106

Uptake of Potassium by Crops Compared with the Depletion of Potassium in the Soil Solution[1]

Potassium in parts per million of soil

Number of soils used	K in soil solution		After crop harvested	Depletion of K in soil solution	Uptake of K by crop
	Before crop sown				
	Range	Mean	Mean		
14	5–10	8	8	0	104
27	10–15	12	8	4	87
40	15–20	17	12	6	116
29	20–25	22	11	12	133
17	40–45	41	14	28	161
24	45–55	50	16	34	246

A second explanation developed by Jenny and Overstreet[2] of this result is, however, possible. The plant root may be able to obtain exchangeable potassium and calcium directly from the solid particles of the soil, by excreting hydrogen ions from its surface which replace some of the adsorbed cations on the clay, a process Jenny and Overstreet called "contact exchange". These hydrogen ions come in part from the carbonic acid liberated by the roots during respiration, and in part by diffusion through the cell membrane, as in Lundegårdh's theory of nutrient uptake already discussed on p. 459, but they may also come from the organic acids[3] the roots synthesise to neutralise the excess of adsorbed cations[4] over anions. Further, Jenny and Overstreet[5] claim that cations can move fairly readily both over the surface of a clay particle, and also from one clay particle to another, provided their double layers interpenetrate. Hence, roots can draw on a considerable area of contiguous clay surfaces for their ions—they do not need to

[1] G. S. Fraps, *Texas Agric. Expt. Sta.*, *Bull.* 391, 1929.
[2] *Soil Sci.*, 1939, **47**, 257; *Proc. Soil Sci. Soc. Amer.*, 1940, **4**, 125. For a review of the subject, see D. I. Arnon, *Ann. Rev. Biochem.*, 1943, **12**, 499.
[3] *Amer. J. Bot.*, 1942, **29**, 227.   [4] A. Ulrich, *Amer. J. Bot.*, 1941, **28**, 526; 1942, **29**, 220.
[5] *J. Phys. Chem.*, 1939, **43**, 1185.

restrict themselves to the exchangeable ions in their immediate neighbourhood; and, in fact, W. A. Albrecht[1] and his co-workers showed that if contact exchange is the sole means by which a plant growing in the soil obtains its cations, then surface migration must be important. This picture of contact exchange is obviously suited to describe the mode of uptake of nutrients, both anions and cations, when the root system contains many root hairs which have fine soil particles embedded in their surface (see p. 447), or when the anions and cations are both present as exchangeable ions on a mixed anion- and cation-exchange system.[2]

The process of contact exchange does not in fact differ fundamentally from uptake from the solution, for in either case the ion can only be transferred through the water film surrounding the root, and the composition of the soil solution is controlled by the solid phase of the soil as well as by the uptake of nutrients by the crop. The thinner the water film between the surfaces of the root and the solid surface, the more appropriate is the concept of contact exchange. On the other hand, uptake from the soil solution does not mean that the cations must be evenly distributed throughout the solution before they can be taken up: they will, in any case, be more concentrated near the source of the exchangeable ions than farther away.

But the ions present in the soil solution and as exchangeable ions do not form the sole reservoir on which the plant can draw. This is obviously true for calcium, as calcium carbonate is a reservoir of calcium ions. It is also true for potassium, as will be shown in Table 117 on p. 513. Here there must either be a continuous slow transfer of potassium from the non-exchangeable to the exchangeable form, or plant roots must be able to use non-exchangeable potassium by some process not yet discussed, an assumption that need not yet be made.

There is, however, some evidence that plant roots can use cations normally unavailable to them if the soil contains an acid clay. E. R. Graham[3] showed that an acid clay, particularly if it is rich in montmorillonite, is a powerful extractor of cations from mineral particles in the silt range, and he further showed[4] that this acid clay could act as a carrier of calcium from the mineral to the crop. Thus, he found that soybeans could take up more calcium, and make better growth, if they were growing in a mixture of quartz sand, finely ground anorthite and acid bentonite, than if they were growing in the sand and anorthite alone. The soybeans took up 16 mgm. of calcium if grown in the sand alone, 43 mgm. from the sand and anorthite, and 112 mgm. from the sand-anorthite and acid bentonite.

[1] Amer. J. Bot., 1942, **29**, 210.
[2] For examples of plants grown on such substrates, see F. S. Schlenker, Soil Sci., 1942, **54**, 247; H. Jenny, J. Colloid Sci., 1946, **1**, 33.
[3] Soil Sci., 1940, **49**, 277.   [4] Soil Sci., 1941, **51**, 65; Amer. J. Bot., 1942, 29, 210.

The soil solution in most fertile agricultural soils is an adequate source of supply for the phosphate requirements of the plant. The phosphate content of the solution is low, only 0·5 to 2 parts per million of PO_4, but since it remains remarkably constant at this value during the growing season, the solid particles are obviously releasing phosphates into the solution as rapidly as the crop is extracting them. But in soils low in available phosphate the plant roots must possess some means of bringing phosphates into solution, for crops differ considerably in their power of extracting phosphates from difficultly available forms. Their roots increase the soil acidity around their absorbing surfaces, due to the CO_2 they respire, but some roots, such as young lupins, can also excrete organic acids.

Transfer of Nutrients from the Root to the Soil

We have so far been discussing the transfer of nutrients from the soil to the root as if it were a one-way process. Yet roots can only hold their ions against diffusion into the soil if the aeration conditions are adequate, and in particular potassium is often excreted by the roots if the aeration becomes poor.[1] Potassium excretion may also occur towards the end of the growing season, as was discussed on p. 29 and shown in Table 4. Recent analytical work, particularly with radioactive tracer elements, has shown that there is, in fact, a continuous exchange between the nutrient ions in the soil and in the root, though the factors controlling this exchange are unknown. R. Overstreet[2] showed that barley roots put into distilled water or into a sodium chloride solution lost no potassium to either; they lost a little to a calcium chloride solution, but there was a large exchange of potassium from the root to the solution if the roots were in a potassium chloride solution. On the other hand, plant roots lose potassium rapidly if growing in sodium saturated clays, more slowly if in potassium, and still more slowly if in calcium-saturated clays. E. I. Ratner[3] and W. T. McGeorge[4] also found that soils high in exchangeable sodium were able to extract calcium from the plant, and that if the plant had some of its roots growing in a calcium soil and some in a sodium, there was a transfer of calcium through the root system from the high calcium to the high sodium areas, though the experiments did not show if the quantities involved were large enough to have any practical significance. Soils can apparently also remove anions as well as cations from plants, for

[1] H. T. Chang and W. E. Loomis, *Plant Physiol.*, 1945, **20**, 221.
[2] *Soil Sci.*, 1939, **47**, 257; **48**, 9. See also E. I. Ratner, *C.R. Acad. Sci. (U.S.S.R.)*, 1944,
3 313; **43**, 126.
42, *C.R. Acad. Sci. (U.S.S.R.)*, 1945, **48**, 63; *Pedology*, 1944, Nos. 4-5, 205.
[4] *Arizona Agric. Expt. Sta.*, *Tech. Bull.* 94, 1942.

W. A. Albrecht[1] found that soybeans lost some of their phosphates when growing in calcium-deficient soils.

The Need for Fertiliser Placement

Plants can only obtain their main supply of nutrients from damp soil. Hence, if they are to use, during periods of drought, nutrients added to the soil as fertiliser, the mobility of these nutrients in the soil is of great importance. Fertilisers are commonly put in the seed-bed and incorporated with all, or part, of the top few inches of the soil. Of the fertilisers added, only nitrates and chlorides are readily mobile in the soil: they wash down with the percolating water, usually accompanied by an equivalent amount of calcium ions. Potassium is also freely mobile in sandy soils low in organic matter, as they contain no base exchange material capable of holding it. But in land with an appreciable clay content, potassium moves down very slowly if the land is cropped, and only a little faster if it is left fallow, unless such large dressings are given that the surface soil is almost saturated with it,[2] for if the exchange complex in the surface soil has only a small proportion of potassium compared to other exchangeable ions, it will hold additional potassium ions fairly tightly. Phosphates and Calcium carbonate as a neutralising agent move very slowly in the soil. Thus, Rice Williams[3] found that adding basic slag to a pasture for fifteen years barely affected the phosphate content of the soil below 3 inches, and B. W. Doak[4] found little movement below 6 inches after adding phosphate to a pasture for eight years (see also p. 502). However, O. E. Sell and L. C. Olson, working on a pasture on a sandy loam in Georgia,[5] found that dolomitic limestone affected the pH of the soil 6 to 8 inches below the surface five years after the first application, and at 8 to 12 inches after nine years, though little calcium itself had actually moved below 4 inches at this time. They also found that 35 lb. per acre of P, given as a 35 per cent superphosphate in 1936 and again in 1939, increased the available phosphates at the 4- to 8-inch depth in 1944, whilst two dressings, each of 70 lb., increased the available phosphate in the 8- to 12-inch layer at this time. However, if nitrogen and potassium were added with the phosphate so that growth of the pasture was stimulated, penetration of the phosphate was considerably reduced,

[1] *Proc. Soil Sci. Soc. Amer.*, 1940, **5**, 8.

[2] W. H. MacIntire *et al.*, *Soil Sci.*, 1943, **55**, 321.   [3] *Welsh J. Agric.*, 19, **16**, 132.

[4] *New Zealand J. Sci. Tech.*, 1942, **24** A, 141, and 1933, **15**, 155, for a bibliography to earlier work. See also M. Odelien and T. Vidme, *Meld. Norg. Landbr.*, 1945, **25**, 273, for other experiments showing the immobility of potassium and phosphates in soils.

[5] *Proc. Soil Sci. Soc. Amer.*, 1947, **11**, 238; for other American work on this, see L. C. Olson, ibid., 1946, **10**, 443; A. R. Midgley, *J. Amer. Soc. Agron.*, 1931, **23**, 788; P. R. Nelson, *Soil Sci.*, 1929, **27**, 143.

little penetrating below 6 inches. The cause of the discrepancies found in the literature is probably that the phosphate of calcium monophosphate is more mobile in neutral or in limed acid soils than in unlimed acid soils.[1]

Nutrients supplied in fertilisers do not move laterally appreciably in level fields. Thus a grass field at Rothamsted, originally uniform in its herbage, was in 1856 divided into plots, each of which actually touches its neighbours; certain manurial treatments have been given annually to each and continued without change ever since. Marked differences in herbage have resulted, but the edges bounding the plots are fairly sharp; there is no evidence of much lateral diffusion in the period of ninety years.

Phosphates, potassium and calcium carbonate do not, therefore, naturally move easily in a soil, and if one wants to enrich the subsoil in any of these three materials, one should work them into the subsoil direct. This is very necessary for calcium carbonate if the subsoil is acid, for only in this way can the root system of most crops penetrate to a reasonable depth. Experimental evidence is still somewhat incomplete, but it is probably always desirable to plough in lime as deeply as possible if the subsoil is very acid and drought during the growing season probable, for only by neutralising this acidity can the plant roots penetrate into the subsoil and so be able to extract much water from it. It is further probable that at least part of the potassic and phosphatic fertilisers, and in some climates the nitrogen also, should be incorporated with the subsoil in areas subject to summer drought and where the subsoils are poor and the crop needs a good supply of nutrients throughout the summer. Thus, E. W. Russell has found that, in dry summers in England, sugar-beet responds better to potassium and phosphate mixed with the top 9 inches of soil than the top 2 to 3 inches but that wheat and barley do not show this benefit; and D. D. Smith et al.,[2] working on a clay pan soil in Central Missouri, found that maize benefited by deep incorporation of fertilisers but oats and barley did not, for as already stated the small grains take up the bulk of their potassium and phosphate before summer drought has dried out the subsurface soil.

A need for fertiliser placement can arise from another cause besides that for keeping nutrients in damp soil within the root zone for as long as possible. If a soil is very poorly supplied with a particular nutrient, then the crop appears to be able to take up more of this nutrient from

---

[1] W. H. MacIntire et al., Proc. Soil Sci. Soc. Amer., 1948, **12**, 359.

[2] Agric. Engng., 1947, **28**, 347; Proc. Soil Sci. Soc. Amer., 1947, **11**, 539; for confirmatory data for maize only, see J. Pitner (Proc. Natl. Joint. Cttee. Fert. Appl., 1944, **20**, 138), who found the yield of maize was increased 20 to 25 per cent by placing the fertiliser 8 to 10 inches below the seed instead of 2 to 3.

a dressing of fertiliser concentrated in the soil near the plant, than if the same dressing is broadcast over the surface of the soil. This has been shown to be true for potassic and phosphatic fertilisers. The causes of this benefit of fertiliser placement have not been analysed. Part may be due to the fact that when the fertiliser is placed, it is all kept below the soil surface so that none will be in the actual surface layer of the soil. Part may be due to the fact that the plants showing greatest benefit from this placement probably take up the potassium and phosphate they need for good growth early on in the season, before the plant has developed an extensive root system. For potassium on calcareous soils, part may be due to the plant being able to take up potassium easier from a zone containing a high ratio of available potassium to calcium than a low. For phosphatic fertilisers, part may be due to the slower reversion of available phosphate when concentrated in a restricted zone of the soil than when distributed uniformly throughout the soil; and for soils that fix phosphate strongly, it may even be worth while placing pellets of a phosphatic fertiliser under each plant.

The technique of fertiliser placement for cereals is to drill the fertiliser and the seed down the same coulter of the drill. This technique has been extensively used on the phosphate-deficient wheat soils of Australia, where as little as $\frac{1}{2}$ cwt. of superphosphate per acre so drilled enables a crop to grow well in its early stages. It also started to be widely practised in Great Britain during the war on phosphate- and also on potassium-deficient land, for it is only necessary to combine-drill half the dressing of a phosphatic or potassic fertiliser that must be given if it is broadcast, to get a given crop response.[1] There is a second technique of fertiliser placement, that has been widely advocated in America, which is to drill the fertiliser in a band a few inches away from the seed—2 inches to the side and 2 inches below the level of the seed being a common recommendation. G. W. Cooke[2] has tested the value of this technique in England and was only able to show an appreciable benefit for peas; the other crops he tried—potatoes, sugar-beet and swedes—did not benefit by this technically rather difficult method of application. This beneficial effect of placement can be increased still further in some alkaline soils by mixing sulphur with the superphosphate, for the sulphur becomes oxidised and makes the soil and phosphate in its immediate neighbourhood more acid, thus keeping the phosphate in an available form for a longer period.[3]

[1] A. H. Lewis, *J. Agric. Sci.*, 1941, **31**, 295; with A. G. Strickland, ibid., 1944, **34**, 73; E. M. Crowther, *J. Min. Agric.*, 1945, **52**, 170; F. Hanley, *J. Min. Agric.*, 1947, **54**, 354; R. O. Miles, *Jealott's Hill Res. Sta., Bull.* 4, 1947.

[2] *J. Agric. Sci.*, 1949, **39**, 96; *Proc. Fertiliser Soc.*, 1949, No. 6.

[3] W. T. McGeorge, *Proc. Soil Sci. Soc. Amer.*, 1940, **4**, 288.

CHAPTER XXVI

THE SOURCES OF PLANT NUTRIENTS IN THE SOIL

I. PHOSPHORUS

The Phosphates present in the Soil

THESE CAN BE divided into three groups:

(1) Phosphates present in the soil solution. This is always negligible compared with the other forms.
(2) Phosphates present in the soil organic matter.
(3) Inorganic phosphates including both definite phosphate compounds and surface films of phosphate held on inorganic particles.

In general more, and often considerably more, phosphate is present in the inorganic than the organic form, though there are soils, particularly soils on ancient peneplains and some strongly leached tropical soils, where the organic phosphate is the principal reserve of plant available phosphate, although it itself is not available.

ORGANIC PHOSPHATES

There is still considerable doubt on the phosphate compounds present in organic matter (p. 280), but it is almost certain none of them are directly available to the plant. The importance of the organic phosphates is twofold. On soils low in phosphate, put down to grass for example, the rate of build-up of humus may be limited by lack of phosphate, for the C/P ratio in humus is usually between 100 and 200, and inorganic or available phosphate can be converted into unavailable forms by the process. Again in soils low in inorganic phosphate, the phosphate supply to the crop can be very dependent on the relation between the periods when the soil humus is decomposing and releasing phosphate and those when the crop is making demands on the soil phosphates.

More work has been done on the factors controlling the liberation of phosphate by the decomposition of organic matter than its lock up due to humus accumulation. As described on p. 222, one of the important factors which controls the rate of mineralisation of this phosphate is the number of times the soil becomes really dry between re-wettings, and another factor is temperature, for the warmer the soil the more rapid the rate of decomposition can be.[1]

This source of phosphate is naturally the more important the lower the level of available inorganic phosphate, but in fact in the great majority of arable soils it is of minor importance. There are a number of tropical soils, however, where the major part of the potentially plant available phosphate is in the organic matter in the surface soil, so that if the surface gets washed away by rain, or removed by bulldozing or any other cause, the subsurface soil which now becomes the surface is so low in phosphate, and usually in many other elements as well, that crop growth becomes exceedingly slow unless heavy dressings of phosphate are given. Work on organic phosphates in soils is limited by the difficulty of determining this fraction, and none of the methods[2] in use are really satisfactory.

CALCIUM PHOSPHATES

Calcium phosphates exist in several forms, the most important of which for our purposes are:

$Ca(H_2PO_4)_2 . H_2O$, monocalcium phosphate, which is water soluble, and the dominant phosphate of superphosphates.

$CaHPO_4 . 2H_2O$ dicalcium phosphate (hydrated) and about $0·1 H_2O$ (dehydrated). The dihydrate is metastable and goes over to the dehydrated form relatively easily, and both are only slightly soluble in water. Dicalcium phosphate is present in many phosphate fertilisers made by treating monocalcium phosphate with ammonia or calcium hydroxide.

$Ca_4H(PO_4)_3 . 2H_2O$ calcium octaphosphate, probably exists and may be formed by precipitation under suitable conditions.[3]

$Ca_3(PO_4)_2$ tricalcium phosphate, which is certainly formed in high-temperature slags, but there is still doubt if it can be formed by precipitation from aqueous solutions.[4]

$Ca_{10}(PO_4)_6(OH)_2$ hydroxyapatite, which is the phosphatic constituent of bones and teeth.

$Ca_{10}(PO_4)_6F_2$, fluorapatite, the principal phosphatic constituent of mineral phosphates in the great deposits in North Africa, Florida and elsewhere, and which form the principal commercial sources of phosphates.

[1] See, for example, M. T. Eid, C. A. Blake et al., Iowa Agric. Exp. Sta., Res. Bull. 406, 1954.
[2] For these methods, see for example M. L. Jackson, Soil Chemical Analysis. Englewood Cliffs, N.J., 1958.
[3] For a recent discussion on the existence of this phosphate, see N. Bjerrum, Mat. Fys. Medd. Dan. Vid. Selsk., 1958, 31, No. 7, and for its existence in soils J. R. Lehr and co-workers, Proc. Soil Sci. Soc. Amer., 1958, 22, 25, 29, and J. Amer. Chem. Soc., 1957, 79, 5318.
[4] U. Schoen, G. Barbier and S. Henin, Ann. Agron., 1954, 4, 441, claim that a precipitated tricalcium phosphate exists, giving an apatite-like x-ray diagram but on ignition to 900°C. giving β—$Ca_3(PO_4)_2$.

The mono- and dicalcium phosphates do not dissolve congruently in weakly acid, neutral or alkaline solutions, that is, the ratio of phosphorus to calcium dissolved differs from that in the solid phase: relatively more phosphate than calcium comes into solution, so the solid phase becomes more calcium rich. Thus if a pellet of monocalcium phosphate is placed in water or a dilute solution, only a proportion of the pellet dissolves, the residue is a porous pellet of about the same size from which 60 to 80 per cent of the phosphate has gone, leaving an open framework of dicalcium phosphate, which is hydrated if the water is cool and its reaction mildly acid, and anhydrous if hot or alkaline.[1] W. L. Lindsay and H. F. Stephenson[2] showed that, as a consequence of the pellet losing more phosphate than calcium, the saturated solution diffusing out of it is acid, with a pH between 1 and 1·5, and had a composition between 4 and 4·5 M in phosphorus and about 1·3 M in calcium, and it was in equilibrium with the residual dicalcium phosphate, being more acid if the dicalcium phosphate was anhydrous than hydrated. If a granule of dicalcium phosphate is shaken up with water, or with a dilute calcium solution, the ratio of dissolved phosphate to calcium is higher for the anhydrous than for the hydrated form, and the residue is probably hydroxy-apatite if the solution is weakly acid and octaphosphate if neutral or alkaline. But equilibrium between the solution and the solid phase is reached very slowly, particularly if the solution is neutral or alkaline.

An important part of the chemistry of calcium phosphates in soils is that of apatite, and particularly hydroxy-apatite. When a calcium hydroxide solution is added to a monocalcium phosphate solution, or sufficient is added to a phosphoric acid solution to give a precipitate, the precipitate has the crystal structure of hydroxyapatite; but the crystals are so small that their chemical composition may differ appreciably from a calcium-phosphorus ratio of 1·67:1 because the composition of the monolayer on the crystal surface is different from that of the unit crystal cell.[3] Thus apatite crystals in bone are hexagonal tablets about 300 Å across and 25–30 Å thick, that is, three unit cells thick, so only about one-third of the unit cells have the composition of apatite, the other two-thirds have only one face attached to an apatite cell, and the other face is free. Such crystals have a surface area of about 100 sq. m. per gm. Precipitates formed by adding pure lime water to phosphoric acid solutions have the hydroxy-apatite structure

[1] W. E. Brown and J. R. Lehr, *Proc. Soil Sci. Soc. Amer.*, 1958, **22**, 29, and 1959, **23**, 7.
[2] *Proc. Soil Sci. Soc. Amer.*, 1959, **23**, 12, 18.
[3] For the most important papers on this subject see: H. Bassett, *Trans. Chem. Soc.*, 1917, **111**, 620; J. A. Naftel, *J. Amer. Chem. Soc.*, 1936, **28**, 740; P. W. Arnold, *Trans. Faraday Soc.*, 1950, **46**, 1061; and S. B. Hendricks and W. L. Hill, *Proc. Nat. Acad. Sci.* (Washington), 1950, **36**, 731. For a review on phosphates of bone see W. F. and M. W. Neuman, *Chem. Rev.*, 1953, **53**, 1, as well as Hendricks and Hill.

with a surface area between 10 and 20 sq. m. but impurities such as citrate[1] and possibly carbonate ions present in the solution reduce the crystal size.

A consequence of this extremely small crystal size is that these precipitates are not true hydroxy-apatite, for the composition of the surface layer can vary appreciably from that of true apatite, due to the exchange of the hydrion $(H_3O)^+$ for calcium, and possibly of the hydroxyl for phosphate. Thus precipitates giving the hydroxy-apatite structure can have calcium-phosphorus ratios between 1·4 and 1·8.

There is a marked reaction between the apatite surface and carbonate ions in solution. The surface can absorb a monolayer of carbonate ions relatively easily, and the surface of calcite a monolayer of phosphate ions; and the spacing of these ions in the monolayer is such that calcite can build up on the apatite and apatite on the calcite relatively easily.[2] Thus the fine crevices between the apatite crystals in the dentine of teeth are filled with calcium carbonate formed on them, and correspondingly calcium carbonate nodules in soils treated with superphosphates for a long period of years have a film of apatite on their surfaces, as shown by G. Nagelschmidt and H. L. Nixon[3] on Broadbalk field. The presence of this carbonate layer also slows down the rate at which apatite crystals in a solution of calcium, phosphate and carbonate ions reaches equilibrium. Thus J. S. Clark[4] was able to measure the solubility product of hydroxy-apatite quite easily if he worked in CO_2-free solutions, particularly if the precipitate was aged for a few hours at 90° C., but he failed to get an equilibrium value in the presence of CO_2, even after long periods of ageing at high temperatures. This has the consequence that equilibrium between the solid apatites in the soil and calcium and phosphate ions in solution is reached exceedingly slowly; and in such a labile system as the soil solution, the evidence is that a true equilibrium is never in fact reached.

Hydroxy-apatite is not stable in the presence of fluoride ions. Even in very dilute fluoride solutions, the fluoride ion displaces the hydroxyl in the apatite structure, but this displacement goes exceedingly slowly. Thus bones buried in the soil under conditions in which the phosphate does not dissolve pick up fluoride from the soil solution, but the reaction may take thousands of years to come to completion. It is for this reason that the fluorine content of a buried bone can sometimes give a good indication of its age, and that most rock phosphate deposits are fluor-apatites, for they have been formed from phosphates being precipitated in the sea and picking up fluoride ions from it.

[1] D. Patterson, *Nature*, 1954, **173**, 75.
[2] P. Boischot, M. Coppenet and J. Hebert, *Plant and Soil*, 1950, **2**, 311, and C. V. Cole, S. R. Olsen and C. O. Scott, *Proc. Soil Sci. Soc. Amer.*, 1953, **17**, 352.
[3] *Nature*, 1944, **154**, 428.   [4] *Canad. J. Chem.*, 1955, **33**, 1696.

There is also considerable evidence that a small proportion of the phosphate ions on the surface of the fluor-apatite crystals can be replaced by carbonate CO_3^{--}, and that this replacement reduces the small tendency that the fluor-apatite crystals have to grow. Certainly the rock phosphates that are easiest to make superphosphate from, and which are of most use as phosphate fertilisers when simply ground fine, are those which contain the higher amounts of non-calcite carbonate ions, and their presence on the lattices seems to counteract the reduction in the solubility of phosphate one would expect from the replacement of hydroxyl by fluoride.[1]

IRON AND ALUMINIUM PHOSPHATES

In well drained soils the principal crystalline compounds of aluminium and ferric phosphates are probably the variscite—barrandite—strengite group; variscite having the formula $AlPO_4.2H_2O$, strengite $FePO_4.2H_2O$, and barrandite being a mixture of the two in almost any proportions. The only iron phosphate mineral that has been found in crystals which are recognisable in the petrological microscope is vivianite, $Fe_3(PO_4)_2.8H_2O$, a ferrous phosphate that can often be found in water-logged or badly drained soils.

There are also a few minerals found in nature which may occur in soils as crystals too small to have been detected yet, such as sturrettite $3Al(OH).2PO_4.3H_2O$. A number of crystalline phosphates of iron and aluminium have been prepared in the laboratory,[2] and W. L. Lindsay and H. F. Stephenson[3] have shown that when granulated superphosphate is added to a soil, crystals of two of these, a taranakite $H_6K_3Al_5(PO_4)_8.18H_2O$ and one with a composition $H_8K(Al.Fe)_3.(PO_4)_6.6H_2O$ may be formed. Both of these contain potassium and the second has an aluminium-iron ratio of 2 or less.

It is likely that these iron and aluminium phosphates occur in many soils in the form of films, a few molecules thick at the most. These films are probably held on the surface of hydrated ferric and aluminium oxide films, or on ferric and aluminium ions forming part of the surface layer of clay crystals. The properties of these phosphate-hydrous oxide films that are of most importance for the phosphate status of soils concern the ease with which other anions present in the soil can displace this phosphate; and this in turn is usually dependent on their specific interaction with the ferric and aluminium ions in the film.

The principal experimental facts of importance on phosphate

[1] See J. H. Caro and W. L. Hill, *J. Agric. Fd. Chem.*, 1956, **4**, 684, for a discussion of this.
[2] For a discussion on the conditions under which the various crystalline forms of ferric and aluminium phosphates are produced, see J. E. Salmon, *J. Chem. Soc.*, 1952, 2316, and with R. F. Jameson, ibid., 1954, 4013, C. V. Cole and M. L. Jackson, *J. Phys. Coll. Chem.*, 1950, **54**, 128, J. F. Haseman, J. R. Lehr, and J. P. Smith, *Proc. Soil Sci. Soc. Amer.*, 1915, **15**, 76.
[3] *Proc. Soil Sci. Soc. Amer.*, 1959, **23**, 440.

sorption and desorption from hydrous iron and aluminium oxide films are:

(1) Raising the pH of the solution in contact with a film containing sorbed phosphate releases some of the phosphate into solution. This is probably an example of simple exchange with the hydroxyl anion due to the great insolubility of the hydroxides at high pH, but it is probably only of importance at hydroxyl ion concentrations higher than that found in normal soils.

(2) Silicate anions will displace some of the sorbed phosphates from these films, though whether this is simple anion exchange or due to the silicate forming a complex with the iron and aluminium ions has not been properly investigated.

(3) Ions such as oxalate, citrate and tartrate, which form strong chelation compounds with ferric ions and rather weaker ones with aluminium, will displace phosphates from these surfaces, and reduce their power of sorbing phosphates.[1] These hydroxy-acids can be produced by micro-organisms and may be so produced in soils under certain conditions.

(4) Some components of organic matter extracts from soils are strongly sorbed on the surface of these films and these new surfaces only sorb about one half to one third the amount of phosphate that the original surface could. The reason why the coated surface still sorbs phosphate, though the sorbed humic components themselves cannot, is not known.[2]

(5) Iron phosphate films, based on strengite, are more resistant to re-solution than aluminium phosphate films, because the surface of the iron phosphate tends to hydrolyse losing its phosphate ions and leaving a film of ferric hydroxide protecting the ferric phosphate.[3]

The Sorption of Phosphates by Soils

A water-soluble phosphate, such as monocalcium phosphate, added to a soil in the field, is rapidly converted into water insoluble forms. Correspondingly a soil shaken up in the laboratory with a water-soluble phosphate will usually absorb an appreciable amount, depending on the conditions of the experiment; but typically it will not come into equilibrium with this solution—the amount absorbed will continue to increase for periods of weeks.[4] This suggests that no single simple stable compound is formed, at least initially.

[1] See, for example, D. H. Sieling and his co-workers, *Soil Sci.*, 1949, **67**, 3; 1950, **69**, 205, and 1953, **76**, 175.   [2] J. P. Leaver and E. W. Russell, *J. Soil Sci.*, 1957, **8**, 113.
[3] S. C. Chang and M. L. Jackson, *Proc. Soil Sci. Soc. Amer.*, 1957, **21**, 265.
[4] For an example, where precautions were taken to minimise side reactions, see J. P. Leaver and E. W. Russell, *J. Soil Sci.*, 1957, **8**, 113.

Only two mechanisms by which soils hold phosphate in the field have been proved to be of importance, namely, those involving calcium ions and those involving iron and aluminium ions. There is the possibility of a third process, namely, phosphate being held on the edges of clay particles through hydrogen bonding between hydroxyls in the broken edges and the covalently linked oxygens of the H_2PO_4 tetrahedra.[1] This mechanism is consistent with G. W. Cooke's[2] finding that adding selenious acid to the phosphate solution reduces the amount of phosphate sorbed on the iron and aluminium hydroxide surfaces but it does not affect sorption by a clay.

The calcium ions which hold phosphate in a soil may be calcium ions in solution, exchangeable calcium ions forming calcium phosphates on the surface of the clay particles, or calcium ions anchored on the surface of calcium carbonate crystals. This process is of primary importance in inherently neutral or calcareous soils, as can be shown by measuring the amount of phosphate such a soil can hold in equilibrium with a buffered calcium solution at say pH 7 compared with the amount the corresponding sodium-saturated soil can hold in a buffered sodium solution of the same pH and ionic strength. If the pH of the buffer drops below about pH 5·5, there is little difference between the amount of phosphate they hold.[3]

The iron and aluminium ions which can hold phosphate may either be present in films of hydrated oxides, or the aluminium may be present as exchangeable cations if the soil is acid, or a film of aluminium hydroxide if the soil had been acid and has had its pH raised by liming.[4] There is a rough correlation between the free iron and aluminium oxides removed by treatment with mild reducing agents such as hydrogen sulphide or nascent hydrogen, or by acid oxalate solutions, and the amount of phosphate subacid soils can hold. E. G. Williams and his co-workers[5] have been able to separate the effects of iron and aluminium compounds as sites of phosphate sorption for a number of Scottish soils derived from several parent materials. They showed that the phosphate-sorbing power was closely correlated with the amount of aluminium removed by Tamm's acid oxalate treatment, and that the correlation was not improved by allowing for the iron it extracted. The level of aluminium extracted was closely correlated with the level of organic carbon in the soil, an observation whose significance is not yet known (see p. 285). They also showed that when this active aluminium was removed, the phosphate-sorbing power was only about 10 per cent of the original soil, an observation also made by A. C. Chu

[1] W. W. Emerson, *J. Agric. Sci.*, 1956, **47**, 350.   [2] *J. Soil Sci.*, 1951, **2**, 254.
[3] J. P. Leaver and E. W. Russell, *J. Soil Sci.*, 1957, **8**, 113.
[4] For an example, see A. Demolon, P. Boischot and J. Lajon, *Ann. Agron.*, 1953, 291.
[5] *J. Sci. Food Agric.*, 1958, **9**, 551.

and G. D. Sherman.[1] Further, if the soil is pre-treated with say 8-hydroxy-quinoline, or a suitable humic acid extract, both of which are strongly absorbed on the active iron and aluminium ion spots, the phosphate holding power of the soil is reduced, often markedly.[2]

The relative importance of these two mechanisms in any given soil can be roughly assessed in several ways. Thus the phosphate held through calcium ions is released if the pH drops below about pH 5·5; hence solutions of sodium salts buffered at pH 4·5, which are often used to measure the phosphate status of a soil, extract much of this phosphate. Such dilute acid treatment does not remove any of the phosphate held by iron and aluminium ions, and to determine this a solution of sodium hydroxide having a pH above 9, such as a 0·1 N solution, is often used; or a solution containing fluoride ions, which will displace phosphate from alumina films. A simple way of determining if a soil can sorb much phosphate through the iron and aluminium ions it holds is to determine its ability to sorb phosphate from a solution at say pH 5, below that at which the calcium ions will have any influence on the phosphate retention.

Some information about the form of this absorbed phosphate can be obtained from experiments using water-soluble phosphates in which a known proportion of the phosphate ions contain radio-phosphorus, P^{32}. This radio-phosphorus will not only be sorbed with the added phosphate, but it will also undergo isotopic exchange with any phosphate ions which can dissociate from the soil surface. The greater the amount of this phosphate, the more the ratio of P^{32} to P^{31} in the solution will be lowered from its initial value, and the amount of this phosphate can be calculated from this lowering.[3] This isotopically exchangeable soil phosphate is often called the labile phosphate in the soil. It is a reasonably well defined quantity for field soils not recently manured, although it increases slowly with time, particularly with some soils.

This technique can also be used for soils which have recently been allowed to absorb a small amount of a water-soluble phosphate. If the amount absorbed corresponds to the amount of phosphate added to the soil in a light fertiliser dressing, all the sorbed phosphate may contribute to the labile phosphate initially, indicating that it is present either in a mono-molecular layer, or in a thicker layer so loosely formed that all the phosphate ions in it remain easily accessible to the solution. But after a short time a proportion of the sorbed phosphate in the mono-layer, which may be as high as 80 per cent but is usually much less, loses this property of exchangeability. Part of the cause may be that

[1] *Hawaii Agric. Exp. Sta., Tech. Bull.* 16, 1952.
[2] J. P. Leaver and E. W. Russell, *J. Soil Sci.*, 1957, **8**, 113.
[3] For details of this technique see, for example, C. D. McAuliffe, N. S. Hall *et al.*, *Proc. soil Sci. Soc. Amer.*, 1947, **12**, 119.

some of the phosphate migrates into cracks of molecular dimensions and this process is a slow one, part may be due to a slow build-up of thicker or more compact films, part may be due to the phosphate-forming films on surfaces from which iron or aluminium ions dissociate very slowly, and part due to a non-phosphate film forming on top of the phosphate film, as, for example, a film of iron hydroxide or alumina. It is probable that all these processes are taking place in soils, though it is not usually possible to assess the relative importance of each in any particular soil. However, after a time, the level of labile phosphate becomes relatively constant and may remain fairly constant for periods of the order of fifty years[1] and perhaps for millennia.

The Solubility Products of Soil Phosphate

One should be able to prove if the phosphate present in a soil is present as a definite chemical compound or not by determining the apparent solubility product of the soil phosphate. If, for example, one assumes that the concentration of phosphate in a soil solution is due to the solubility of a hydroxy-apatite, one can determine the calcium, hydrogen and phosphate ion activities in the soil solution and test if these are consistent with the solution being saturated for apatite. Now the formula for hydroxy-apatite can be written $Ca_5(PO_4)_3 . OH$, and if it is in equilibrium with the solution, then

$$a_{Ca}^5 \times a_{PO_4}^3 \times a_{OH} = \text{constant}$$

where a_{Ca} is the activity of the calcium ions in solution. If the logarithms of the activities are used, and pCa is written for $-\log a_{Ca}$, this equation can be rewritten in the form[2]

$$7(pH - \tfrac{1}{2}pCa) - 3(pH_2PO_4 + \tfrac{1}{2}pCa) = \text{constant},$$

where the constant is 14·7 at 25°C. for a hydroxy-apatite made in the absence of all carbonates and aged at 90°C., presumably to obtain a fairly stable surface.[3] As already shown on p. 110, the first term $(pH - \tfrac{1}{2}pCa)$ is Schofield's lime potential in the solution, and Schofield has called the second term $(pH_2PO_4 + \tfrac{1}{2}pCa)$ the phosphate potential. It is in fact the negative logarithm of the activity of mono-calcium phosphate in the solution, and is proportional to its negative thermodynamic potential. The larger this term, the lower is the activity of monocalcium phosphate in the solution, so in general the lower the phosphate concentration. This term differs from the lime potential in that the higher the lime potential, as defined above, the

[1] G. E. G. Mattingley, *J. Agric. Sci.*, 1957, **49**, 160; for similar results in America see S. R. Olsen, F. S. Watanabe *et al.*, *Soil Sci.*, 1954, **78**, 141.
[2] For $p(H_2PO_4) = \text{constant} + 2pH + p(PO_4)$ and $p(OH) = \text{constant} - pH$.
[3] J. S. Clark, *Canad. J. Chem.*, 1955, **33**, 1696.

greater is the activity of calcium hydroxide in the solution, because the lime potential is defined as $pH - \frac{1}{2}pCa$ instead of $pOH + \frac{1}{2}pCa$.

If one now determines the lime and phosphate potential in the soil solution, and if they are found to be related by this equation, then one has proved that the most soluble phosphate in the soil is hydroxy-apatite.

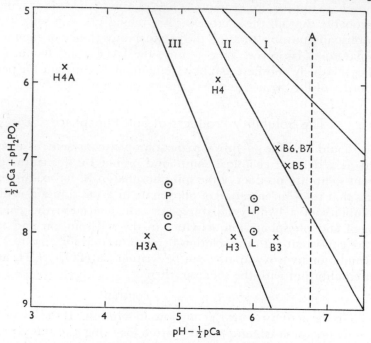

FIG. 44. The relation between the lime and phosphate potential in one Danish and two Rothamsted field experiments.

  I. Solubility curve for dicalcium phosphate dihydrate.
  II. Solubility curve for calcium octophosphate.
III. Solubility curve for apatite.

A. Lime potential for calcium carbonate in equilibrium with air containing 0·03 per cent CO_2.

H. Hoosfield plots Rothamsted: 3 and 3A no superphosphate; 4 and 4A with superphosphate. The A plots receive sulphate of ammonia.

B. Broadbalk plots, Rothamsted: 3 unmanured; 5 with phosphate but no nitrogen; 6 and 7 with phosphate and with sulphate of ammonia.

⊙ Trystofte, Denmark.

C. No phosphate, no lime.

L. Limed 1943.

P. Superphosphate 1943, sampled in 1949.

The corresponding relation between the lime and phosphate potentials for a saturated solution of dicalcium phosphate is

$$(pH - \frac{1}{2}pCa) - (pH_2PO_4 + \frac{1}{2}pCa) = 0·66 \text{ at } 18°C.$$

for a saturated solution of variscite is[1]

J. S. Clark and M. Peech, *Proc. Soil Sci. Soc. Amer.*, 1955, **19**, 171.

$$2(pH - \tfrac{1}{3}pAl) - (pH_2PO_4 + \tfrac{1}{3}pAl) = -2 \cdot 48 \text{ at } 25° \text{ C.}$$
$$\text{or } 3(pH - \tfrac{1}{3}pAl) - (pH + pH_2PO_4) = -2 \cdot 48$$

where one uses the potentials of aluminium hydroxide and aluminium phosphate or phosphoric acid; and for a saturated solution of strengite is[1]

$$2(pH - \tfrac{1}{3}pFe) - (pH_2PO_4 + \tfrac{1}{3}pFe) = \text{constant}$$

when the constant lies between -5 and -7. This constant is not yet well determined, partly because of the difficulty of ensuring equilibrium, and partly because of side reactions which may take place.

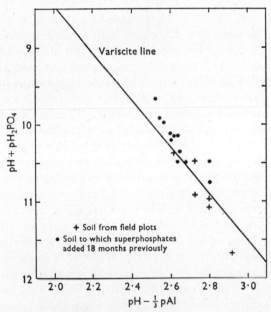

FIG. 45. The relation between the alumina and phosphate potential for Mardin silt loam soils from Mount Pleasant Experimental Farm, New York.

H. C. Aslyng[2] has measured the lime and phosphate potentials for a number of Rothamsted and Danish soils, and J. S. Clark and M. Peech[3] for some New York soils, and some of their results are given in Figs. 44 and 45. Their results can be summarised as follows:

(1) The phosphate in neutral and calcareous soils receiving regular dressings of superphosphate is more soluble than hydroxy-apatite and

[1] S. C. Chang and M. L. Jackson, *Proc. Soil Sci. Soc. Amer.*, 1957, **21**, 265.
[2] *Roy Vet. Agric. Coll. Copenhagen, Yearbook*, 1954, 1.
[3] *Proc. Soil Sci. Soc. Amer.*, 1955, **19**, 171.

less soluble than dicalcium phosphate, but could well approach calcium octaphosphate,[1] although as one would expect for such small crystals, they have no exact composition.

(2) The phosphate in acid soils receiving regular dressings of super-phosphate is less soluble than hydroxy-apatite. Liming the soil raises the lime potential, and making the soil more acid by long continued use of ammonium sulphate lowers the lime potential without affecting the phosphate potential very much.

(3) Variscite, and not a calcium phosphate, is likely to be the dominant phosphate in acid soils. This is shown in Fig. 45 for soils taken from a series of plots on a Mardin silt loam whose pH ranged from 4·2 to 5·5 and which received superphosphate eighteen months previously.

S. C. Chang and M. L. Jackson[2] also found variscite was the domi-nant phosphate in some acid soils, although in some it was strengite and in others a form less soluble than either—a result also found by A. Wild[3] and J. B. Hemwall.[4] It is interesting to note that if variscite is the most soluble form of phosphate present, and the soil solution is saturated with respect to gibbsite, then $pH + p(H_2PO_4) = 10·72$, for $pH - \frac{1}{3}pAl = 2·75$ for a saturated solution of gibbsite. Thus if the pH of such an acid soil is raised one unit by liming, that is, the hydrogen ion concen-tration reduced tenfold, the concentration of the $H_2PO_4^-$ ion should be raised tenfold. No examples of soils with this property have yet been published, though there are a number of examples in the literature of soils on which crops respond either to liming or to phosphate, but on which there is no additional benefit from applying lime and phosphate.

These solubility studies therefore show that only in some soils does the most soluble form of phosphate correspond to a definite compound. In neutral soils the phosphate does not seem to be present in a definite compound, but is usually less soluble than dicalcium phosphate and more soluble than hydroxyapatite; whilst in acid soils, the phosphate may be present either as variscite or as a less soluble compound.

Two other methods have been used to supplement the conclusions drawn from the phosphate potential work. S. R. Olsen and F. S. Watanabe[5] measured the amount of phosphate a soil sorbed from solutions of various concentrations, and they showed that if the soil only sorbed relatively small amounts of phosphate, the sorption followed the Langmuir equation. They were thus able to show that, at equal surface areas as measured by ethylene glycol, an acid soil typically held twice as much phosphate in the monolayer as a calcareous soil, and

---

[1] For independent evidence of the conversion of water-soluble phosphate to the octa-phosphate in calcareous soils, see J. R. Lehr and co-workers, *Proc. Soil Sci. Soc. Amer.*, 1958, **22**, 25, 29.   [2] *Proc. Soil Sci. Soc. Amer.*, 1957, **21**, 265.
[3] *Trans. 5th Int. Congr. Soil Sci.* (Leopoldville), 1954, **2**, 500.
[4] *Soil Sci.*, 1957, **83**, 101.   [5] *Proc. Soil Sci. Soc. Amer.*, 1957, **21**, 144.

that it held the phosphate in this monolayer about five times as strongly. The effective surface area per phosphate ion sorbed was 2200 and 5200 Å². Hence the phosphate is very unevenly distributed over the soil surface. They also found that a soil would sorb very much more phosphate than was needed for a monolayer. Thus a Davidson clay sorbed o·8 millimols P per 100 gm. of soil as a monolayer and 19 millimols from a fairly concentrated solution.

M. Fried and L. A. Dean[1] estimated the relative strength of absorption of phosphate by iron and aluminium hydroxide films by making Fe- and Al-resins, which absorbed phosphate strongly under subacid and neutral conditions. By mixing the Al-resin as small granules and the Fe-resin as large, and vice versa, and shaking the mixture up with a phosphate solution, they found that at low phosphate concentrations, the Fe-resin sorbed three to four times as much phosphate as the Al-resin. However, only about 75 per cent of this sorbed phosphate was isotopically exchangeable, and this sank to about only 20 per cent when very large amounts of phosphate were sorbed.

The Phosphate Reserves in the Soil

Measurements of the thermodynamic potential of the principal phosphate in the soil solution, and of the amount of labile phosphate in the soil, only give information about the composition and extent of the surface films of phosphate. Some of the phosphate in the soil is, however, present either in relatively very thick films or as solid particles, and the amount so present cannot be estimated by the above two methods, yet it may serve as a reservoir to replenish the pool of labile phosphate as the crops growing in the soil slowly deplete it.

Various chemical methods have been devised for determining the properties of the principal inorganic phosphates present in a soil, and these are all based on the following assumptions:[2]

(1) Dilute acids dissolve all the calcium phosphates present except the apatites.

(2) Concentrated solutions of acids dissolve the apatites.

(3) Fluorides displace phosphate from the surface of hydrated aluminium oxides and subsequent treatment with alkali displaces it from the surface of hydrated ferric oxides.[3]

(4) Reducing solutions containing an iron chelating agent will remove phosphate present below the surface of iron oxide films[4] and in particular phosphate present in nodules of hydrated oxide. Typical

[1] *Proc. Soil Sci. Soc. Amer.*, 1955, **19**, 143.
[2] See, for example, L. A. Dean, *J. Agric. Sci.*, 1938, **28**, 234.
[3] R. C. Turner and H. M. Rice, *Soil Sci.*, 1952, **74**, 141.
[4] G. R. Bauwin and E. H. Tyner, *Proc. Soil Sci. Soc. Amer.*, 1957, **21**, 250.

solutions are based on the use of nascent hydrogen as the reducing agent, and tartrates, citrates or oxalates as the chelating agent.

This fractionation is not based on a firm chemical foundation. Thus there is no true distinction in the soil between calcium phosphates and apatites, for dilute acids certainly dissolve some phosphate from ground rock phosphate which has been added to the soil as fertiliser; so this differentiation is probably dependent on the size of the apatite crystals present, but this itself may easily have agricultural significance in acid though probably not in calcareous soils. Again, some of the phosphate which the dilute acid dissolves from a soil may be re-absorbed by iron and aluminium hydroxide films from the acid solution, and this can be marked for acid ferruginous soils. M. O. Ghani[1] and C. H. Williams[2] using dilute (0·5 N) acetic acid as the extractant reduced this re-absorption by adding to the acid 1 per cent of 8-hydroxy-quinoline, which is strongly absorbed on the hydroxide film, so reducing its phosphate sorbing power without, however, neutralising it altogether. G. W. Cooke[3] found that the addition of 0·5 per cent of selenious acid to the acetic acid was more efficient, and finally Ghani and A. Islam[4] have shown that the addition of both these compounds to the acetic acid almost inhibited the absorption of phosphate by iron and aluminium hydroxide films.

Many workers have fractionated the inorganic phosphates in the principal soil groups throughout the world. Whilst the results obtained must vary very widely with local conditions, they are in the main consistent with the generalisation of S. C. Chang and M. L. Jackson,[5] namely, that in calcareous soils, or soils that have not been much weathered, most of the inorganic phosphates are present as calcium phosphates; in moderately weathered soils, the principal form is that sorbed on iron and aluminium oxide films; and as weathering proceeds, an increasing proportion of phosphate occurs inside iron oxide precipitates. In the extreme example of low humic latosols, they showed that all the inorganic phosphate was locked up in these precipitants and concretions.

In soils which are not strongly weathered, as in most British and in fact most temperate soils, E. G. Williams and W. M. H. Saunders'[6] finding for Scottish soils is probably valid, namely, that the apatites tend to be concentrated in the fine sand and silt fractions, and the various sorbed phosphates and organic phosphates in the clay fraction. In strongly weathered soils, such as occur on old land surfaces in the tropics, most of the phosphate may be locked up in concretions, but

[1] *Ind. J. Agric. Sci.*, 1943, **13**, 562.
[2] *J. Agric. Sci.*, 1950, **40**, 233.
[3] *J. Soil Sci.*, 1951, **2**, 254.
[4] *Soil Sci.*, 1957, **84**, 445.
[5] *J. Soil Sci.*, 1958, **9**, 109.
[6] *J. Soil Sci.*, 1956, **7**, 90, 189.

the agriculturally useful form will be in the organic fraction,[1] so it can all be lost relatively easily under unsuitable systems of agriculture.

These methods of fractionation have really been concerned with the natural phosphates in soils; but in the soils of countries with a highly developed agriculture, a large and increasing proportion of the phosphate they contain is derived from past applications of phosphatic fertilisers, usually in the form of superphosphate or of farmyard manure based on imported feeding stuffs. Thus G. W. Cooke[2] has estimated that in 1957, 40 per cent of the phosphates present in the soils of the United Kingdom have been derived from phosphatic manures and fertilisers added to them since 1837. These phosphates have all entered into the labile pool of phosphate in the soil, and a proportion of this phosphate has lost lability. A fractionation that is well adapted to determining these reserves has been developed by O. Talibudeen[3] based on the rate of exchange of added radioactive phosphate with the soil phosphate; and he has put forward a fractionation based on rapidly exchangeable phosphate, namely, that exchanged within twenty-four hours of adding the radioactive phosphate, a slower exchange, namely, that exchanged with 150 hours, and the remainder of the soil phosphate. He found that for Rothamsted soils, the fraction of the phosphate isotopically exchangeable after 150 hours that has exchanged after twenty-four hours, i.e. P_{24}/P_{150}, is higher the more recently the phosphate has been added, being 0·92, 0·76, and 0·49 one, two and five years after superphosphate had been added to the soil.

The Source of Phosphates in the Soil used by Crops

PHOSPHATE DISSOLVED IN THE SOIL SOLUTION

The immediate source of phosphates for crops growing in a soil is probably that of the inorganic phosphate ions in the soil solution. This concentration varies widely for different soils, from below 10^{-7} M to about 10^{-6} M in phosphate in soils known to be deficient in phosphate and above 10^{-5} M and even above 10^{-4} M in soils known to be well supplied.[4] (10^{-5} M corresponds to 0·3 p p m. of P in the soil solution.) Now a soil which has a soil solution 10^{-5} M in P, and which for example holds 2½ inches of available water in the top foot, will have less than 0·04 lb. per acre of P in solution to that depth; and if a crop uses 15 inches of water during its growth, there will only be about 0·2 lb.

[1] See, for example, P. H. Nye and M. H. Bertheux, *J. Agric. Sci.*, 1957, **49**, 141, for examples from Ghana.   [2] *J. Sci. Food Agric.*, 1958, **9**, 761.
[3] *J. Soil Sci.*, 1957, **8**, 86, and 1958, **9**, 120.
[4] See, for example, J. S. Burd and J. C. Martin, *J. Agric. Sci.*, 1923, **13**, 265; W. H. Pierre and F. W. Parker, *Soil Sci.*, 1927, **24**, 119; L. J. H. Teakle, *Soil Sci.*, 1928, **25**, 143, and W. L. Nelson *et al.*, *Agronomy Monog.*, **4**, 1953, 170.

per acre of P dissolved in it, yet it may take up 10 to 20 lb. per acre of P during the growing season. The soil solution can, therefore, only be an adequate source of phosphate if soil phosphate goes from the solid to the solution phase at least as quickly as the crop roots can extract it from the soil solution, and if crop roots can extract phosphate readily from these dilute solutions.

It has been found that the phosphate concentration in the soil solution of many soils does, in fact, remain approximately constant whilst a crop is growing in it; and M. Fried and his co-workers[1] have shown that in a normal soil, moderately well supplied with phosphate, soil phosphate can go into solution at a very much higher rate than roots can possibly take it up.

The soil solution can, however, only be an adequate source of phosphate if the crop can remove phosphate from these dilute solutions at an adequate rate. Experiments to measure the minimum concentration of phosphate needed for good plant growth are technically difficult to carry out, but there seems no doubt that most crops can make adequate and possibly optimum growth if the phosphate concentration around their roots is kept at 10^{-5} M, many crops may be able to make good growth if it is as low at 10^{-6} M, provided the conditions of growth allow good root development,[2] but that for at least some crops 10^{-7} M is much too dilute;[3] and these results are concordant with the observed field behaviour. Thus Aslyng[4] found that at Rothamsted crops growing on soils whose negative phosphate potential was greater than 8, corresponding to a phosphate concentration in the soil solution of 10^{-7} M or less, usually responded very well to phosphate fertilisers; whilst crops on soils with a negative phosphate potential of 6 or less, corresponding to a phosphate concentration of 10^{-5} M or more, rarely responded.

The ability of crops to take up phosphate from these dilute solutions, however, is dependent, to some extent at least, on the absence of some interfering ions. Thus, if the concentration of available ferric ions is too high, the proportion of phosphate taken up by the plant roots that is translocated to the leaves is reduced;[5] and though aluminium ions may sometimes produce this effect, they may also stunt the root system of the crop, so reducing the amount of phosphate the crop can take up from the soil solution.[6]

No very critical work has been done in the field on the relation between the uptake of phosphate and the phosphate concentration in the

[1] *Soil Sci.*, 1957, **84**, 427.
[2] F. T. Bingham, quoted by D. I. Arnon, *Agronomy Monog.*, **4**, 1953.
[3] R. S. Russell and R. P. Martin, *J. Exp. Bot.*, 1953, **4**, 108, 136; 1954, **5**, 327.
[4] *Roy. Vet. Agric. Coll. Copenhagen, Yearbook*, 1954, 1.
[5] W. N. M. Foster and R. S. Russell, *J. Soil Sci.*, 1958, **9**, 280.
[6] K. E. Wright and D. A. Donahue, *Plant Physiol.*, 1953, **28**, 674.

soil solution. R. K. Schofield[1] has suggested on theoretical grounds that the chemical potential of calcium monophosphate, expressed as $\frac{1}{2}pCa + p(H_2PO_4)$ in the soil solution, should control the uptake rather than the phosphate ion concentration, but there is no experimental evidence available to discriminate between these two possibilities. However, some crops can use HPO_4^{--} though usually not as easily as the $H_2PO_4^-$;[2] and above pH 7 the relative concentration of the divalent is greater than that of the monovalent ion. Taking the solubility product of dicalcium phosphate as $pK_2 = 7\cdot2$ at $18°C.$[3] the proportion of the phosphate ions in the solution that are present at HPO_4^{--} are approximately[4] pH 5, 0·6; pH 6, 6; pH 7, 39; pH 8, 86; pH 9, 98·4; and the remainder are almost entirely $H_2PO_4^-$, the proportion of H_3PO_4 and PO_4^{---} being negligible in this pH range. Also in some acid soils low in calcium, the potential of the iron or aluminium phosphates may be much more important than that of the calcium monophosphate.

The advantage of introducing this concept of the phosphate potential in the soils is that it measures the intensity with which the soil is holding its most easily removable phosphate, for the lower this potential the more weakly the phosphate is being held. Thus the phosphate potential describes the phosphate status of the soil in exactly the same way that pF describes its moisture status: there is a pool of soil phosphate whose potential is lowered as more phosphate is added, in the same way that the pF of the soil water is lowered if water is added to the pool of water in the soil, and the potential is raised if phosphate is withdrawn. One should, therefore, be able to plot the amount of phosphate in the pool against its potential, obtaining a curve comparable to the pF-moisture content curve, though this has not yet been done for any soil. This method of measuring the phosphate status of the soil has the theoretical advantage that it is only concerned with the energy needed by the plant to withdraw phosphate from the soil, and not with the mechanisms of absorption; and as with water, so with phosphate, plants differ in their ability to remove phosphate from a high potential pool.[5]

A further complication arises in the field for the concentration of phosphate in the soil solution throughout the soil is not always constant. Some crop roots, and perhaps some rhizosphere bacteria,[6] probably secrete acids into the soil solution which will raise the solubility of phosphates in the solid phase in their immediate neighbourhood, and this affects some forms of phosphate more markedly than others.

[1] Soils and Fert., 1955, 18, 373.
[2] C. E. Hagen and H. T. Hopkins, Plant Physiol., 1955, 30, 193.
[3] R. G. Bates and S. F. Acree, J. Res. Nat. Bur. Stand., 1943, 30, 129.
[4] Taken from S. R. Olsen, Agronomy Monog., 4, 1953.
[5] R. S. Russell, E. W. Russell, and P. G. Marais, J. Soil Sci., 1958, 9, 101.
[6] F. C. Gerretsen, Plant and Soil, 1948, 1, 51, and J. I. Sperber, Nature, 1957, 180, 994.

Again some produce low concentrations of hydrogen sulphide which will increase the phosphate solubility of ferric phosphates in their neighbourhood.[1] Again, soils containing decomposable organic matter which is not intimately and uniformly mixed with the body of the soil, are likely to have a higher phosphate ion concentration in the neighbourhood of pieces of this decomposing matter, which will be higher the more rapidly it is decomposing.

The soil solution often contains more organic than inorganic phosphate compounds; and although the chemical composition of these organic compounds are not known for certain, they are probably bacterial cells. There is no evidence that they are taken up by the roots of the crop.[2]

PLANT-AVAILABLE PHOSPHATE IN THE SOIL

Soil chemists have for a long time been concerned with advising farmers how much fertiliser it is economically justifiable to give to a crop on a particular field. Even if an analysis of the soil solution for phosphate was an adequate method for predicting the need for a phosphate fertiliser, it is one that would be extremely inconvenient and expensive to use in practice. Chemists have, therefore, devoted a very great deal of time, for upwards of a century, to devising easier methods, which in the past have included both the use of chemical extraction agents and of plants or micro-organisms growing in the soil. Since chemical methods are the most convenient to use, far more work has been done with them, and innumerable methods have been devised.

Initially the chemists looked for a chemical that would dissolve the same amount of phosphate from the soil as the plant roots, ignoring the fact that different plants extract different amounts of phosphate from a soil. But they soon realised that any standardised chemical extraction technique which placed the soils in the order of crop responsiveness to phosphate was all that was needed, so recent work has been concerned with determining the correlation coefficient between the responsiveness of a crop to a phosphate fertiliser on various soils (often by pot experiments in a greenhouse rather than in a field trial) and the amount of phosphate extracted by various techniques; and that which gives the best correlation is used for advisory purposes in the region.[3]

One of the earliest methods devised, and still widely used, is that of B. Dyer,[4] based on extracting a soil with 1 per cent citric acid, and the reasons for its limitations are worth discussing to show the chemical problems involved. In the first place, it works reasonably well in practice: Table 107 shows that for as far as sugar-beet in the Eastern

---

[1] J. I. Sperber, *Nature*, 1958, **181**, 934.
[2] A. Kaila, *Valt. Maatalousk. Julk.*, No. 129, 1948.
[3] For an example of this use of correlations, see J. W. Fitts *et al.*, *N.C. Agric. Exp. Sta., Tech. Bull.* 121, 1956.   [4] *Trans. Chem. Soc.*, 1894, **65**, 115, and *Phil. Trans.*, 1901, **194** B, 235.

TABLE 107

Response of Sugar-Beet to Superphosphates on Soils with different contents of citric-soluble Phosphate

English sugar-beet experiments made during 1934–49

Phosphate fertiliser used 6 cwt. per acre of superphosphate (0·44 cwt. per acre P)
1 per cent citric acid used as extractant—all soils contain less than 5 per cent CaCO₃

Citric soluble P in mgm. per 100 gm. soil	Number of fields	Mean response Sugar in cwt. per acre	Per cent of sites giving responses in the range		
			<1·3	1·3–2·5	>2·6
0 –16	57	3·20	35	23	24
16·1–24	69	2·04	39	25	36
24·1–48	131	1·11	54	25	21
>48	55	0·53	60	27	13

counties of England is concerned, it does enable one to predict response to a dressing of superphosphate reasonably well when averaged over a period of years.[1] But it fails on some acid soils for it sometimes dissolves iron phosphates of low availability to the crop, and on some calcareous soils it may dissolve phosphates below the surface of calcium carbonate concretions or lumps of chalk.

Many attempts have been made to overcome these limitations of citric acid, and most of the methods in current use have been devised in the light of our present knowledge of soil phosphates.[2] Thus dilute mineral acids or acetic acid, sometimes buffered at a selected pH have been used, largely to dissolve the readily soluble calcium phosphate in the soil. Again a mixture of dilute hydrochloric acid (either 0·025 N or 0·1 N) and dilute (0·03 N) ammonium fluoride[3] has been used both to dissolve the calcium phosphates and also to displace the phosphate sorbed on the aluminium, and possibly also the iron hydrated oxide surfaces; and dilute (0·1 N) sodium hydroxide[4] has been used for soils in which all the phosphate is expected to be absorbed on these hydroxide surfaces. Again for calcareous, neutral or not very acid soils, a sodium bicarbonate solution,[5] or simply a carbonic acid solution, has been used to displace the phosphate from the surface of the calcium phosphates.

But inherent in the basis of each method is the assumption that crops

[1] D. A. Boyd, H. V. Garner, W. B. Haines, *J. Agric. Sci.*, 1957, **48**, 464.
[2] For reviews see W. D. Brind, *Soils and Fert.*, 1950, **13**, 235, 315, and W. L. Nelson, A. Mehlich and E. Winters, *Agronomy Monog.*, **4**, 1953.
[3] R. H. Bray and L. T. Kurtz, *Soil Sci.*, 1945, **59**, 39.
[4] D. H. Saunder, *Soil Sci.*, 1956, **82**, 457.
[5] S. R. Olsen, C. V. Cole *et al.*, *U.S.D.A. Circ.* 939, 1954, and R. A. Olson, M. B. Rhodes *et al.*, *Agron. J.*, 1954, **46**, 175.

need the same amount of available phosphate for good growth in all soils—an assumption that is certainly incorrect if soils of widely different genetic type are considered, but is reasonably valid for soils of the same general type. Again, these methods would only be expected to be of value if the calcium phosphates soluble in dilute acid and the phosphates sorbed on the sesquioxide surfaces contribute equally easily to the phosphate supply which is taken up by the crop. But general experience in several countries is that naturally neutral soils are more likely to be well supplied with phosphate than either acid or alkaline soils as Table 108 relating to a number of Californian

TABLE 108

Effect of Soil Reaction on the Proportion of Soils likely to Respond to Phosphates

pH of Soil	Number of sites tested	Per cent of soils responding to phosphates
<5·9	105	79
6·0–6·3	91	65
6·4–6·7	89	37
6·8–7·9	116	26
8·0–8·3	27	44
>8·3	20	80

soils indicates.[1] H. F. Birch,[2] working in East Africa, has also found that for certain soils and crops, the lower the pH of the soil, or preferably the lower the percentage saturation of the exchange complex with bases, the greater the probability of a response to phosphate; and on these soils there was no correlation between response and the amount of phosphate extracted by the usual solvents, which was usually quite high.

It is possible that the cause of this greater response on acid or unsaturated soils lies in the control which ferric or aluminium ions in the soil solution may exert on the uptake of phosphate, for Birch found that he could equally well use the amount of water-soluble silica, which was very closely correlated with the base saturation and was presumably inversely proportional to the concentration of these two cations. He found some evidence that the probability of a phosphate response was correlated with the degree of unsaturation of the soil for phosphate, as measured by a standard technique, which could be an indirect measure of the phosphate potential in the soil solution. On the other hand

[1] H. Jenny, J. Vlamis and W. E. Martin, *Hilgardia*, 1950, **20**, 1.
[2] *J. Agric. Sci.*, 1953, **43**, 229, 329.

A. M. Balba and R. H. Bray[1] have produced some evidence that, in some soils at least, the phosphate held on the sesquioxide surfaces may be taken up by the crop more easily than the calcium phosphates. This result was unexpected since it is commonly believed, though on no good evidence, that calcium phosphates are the more available.

The introduction of radio-phosphorus P^{32} into soil research has led to two new methods.[2] One of these is to measure the amount of labile phosphate in the soil; and the second is to add a water-soluble ortho-phosphate tagged with P^{32} to the soil and determine the ratio of P^{31} to P^{32} in plants growing in that soil. If the added phosphate has been converted into the same form as the readily available phosphate in the soil, and if the tagged phosphate has come into isotopic equilibrium with this soil phosphate, then the amount of phosphate in this reservoir of readily available phosphate, a quantity often known as the A value for the soil, can be calculated. For normal agricultural soils, the A value does not depend on the crops grown provided a water-soluble phosphate is used and it has been intimately mixed with the soil,[3] showing that the added phosphate has, in fact, rapidly come into equilibrium with the pool of available phosphate in the soil.

For many normal non-calcareous agricultural soils of the temperate regions it has been found that the amount of labile phosphate, the A-value phosphate, the phosphate extractable on anion exchange resins,[4] and that extractable by solutions such as the Bray and Kurtz solution of $0.025N.HCl + 0.03N.NH_4F$ are approximately the same, indicating that in these soils there is a fairly definite soil phosphate fraction that can reasonably be called available; and it does not matter much if this phosphate is a readily soluble calcium phosphate or is held on the surface of calcium carbonate or on hydrated aluminium, and presumably ferric, oxide surfaces. But in soils very low in phosphate, or in some soils derived from basic igneous rocks and possibly also some types of volcanic ash, these methods may give very different amounts[5] indicating that in these soils, this simple concept of availability is inadequate for understanding the phosphate supplying power of the soil to the crops growing on it.

This assumption that there is a fairly definite pool of available phosphate in the soil fails for soils in which most of the potentially

[1] *Soil Sci.*, 1956, **82**, 365, and 1957, **83**, 131.

[2] For a review of the value of this technique, see G. E. G. Mattingley, *Soils and Fert.*, 1957, **20**, 59.

[3] S. Larsen, *Plant and Soil*, 1952, **4**, 1; M. Fried and L. A. Dean, *Soil Sci.*, 1952, **73**, 263; and M. Fried, *Proc. Soil Sci. Soc. Amer.*, 1953, **17**, 357. For a critical discussion on the interpretation of these A values, see L. A. Dean, *Proc. Soil Sci. Soc. Amer.*, 1954, **18**, 462.

[4] F. Amer, D. R. Bouldin *et al.*, *Plant and Soil*, 1955, **6**, 391.

[5] See, for examples of this, R. S. Russell, E. W. Russell and P. G. Marais, *J. Soil Sci.*, 1957, **8**, 248, and 1958, **9**, 101.

available phosphate is in the soil organic matter, such as exhausted soils very low in available mineral phosphate which have recently been given dressings of farmyard manure, or many tropical soils on old land surfaces. In these soils the organic phosphate is mineralised in flushes, in phase with the flushes of decomposition of the soil's organic matter, as described in p. 222. Simple chemical extraction methods are, therefore, unsuitable for measuring the phosphate supply available to the crop[1] and though an incubation technique is more suitable, the supply depends on the concordance in time between the crop's requirements for the phosphate and its production from the organic matter. It is probable that the amount of organic phosphate mineralised can be estimated from the readily extractable and oxidisable organic matter,[2] and that the proportion actually liberated in the field, or the relative importance of the organic to the inorganic phosphates, is greater the higher the soil temperature during the growing season.[3]

The phosphate status of a soil, as measured in the laboratory or greenhouse, must naturally be used with great caution for predicting field responses, even in the temperate regions; for the amount of phosphate available to a crop not only depends on the amount present per gram of soil, it also depends on the volume of the soil tapped by the root system of the crop. Hence, everything which increases the rate of growth of the root system, such as good husbandry practices, balanced manuring, and even sometimes starter doses of phosphate placed near a seedling, will increase the speed with which the roots will ramify through the soil; and everything which encourages deeper rooting, such as moderate droughts at suitable periods during the growing season[4] (see p. 452) will also increase the volume of soil accessible to the crop.

Phosphate Fertilisers

The principal primary sources of phosphate for fertilisers are certain mineral rock phosphates derived from the phosphate of organisms living in past geological eras, and containing up to 80 per cent of apatite, usually in the form of fluor-apatite. Important commercial sources of supply are the deposits in North Africa, America, certain Pacific islands such as Nauru and Christmas Island, and the Kola Peninsula in U.S.S.R. These mineral phosphates have only a limited use as fertiliser, as the apatite crystal has a very low solubility—it will maintain a

[1] For examples from East Africa see H. F. Birch and M. C. Friend, *J. Agric. Sci.*, 1960, from West Africa see P. H. Nye and M. H. Bertheux, *J. Agric. Sci.*, 1957, **49**, 141, and from Nebraska see R. A. Olson, M. B. Rhodes and A. F. Dreier, *Agron. J.*, 1954, **46**, 175.
[2] A. van Diest and C. A. Black, *Soil Sci.*, 1959, **87**, 145.
[3] M. T. Eid, C. A. Black and O. Kempthorne, *Soil Sci.*, 1951, **71**, 361.
[4] For a possible example of this effect, see K. Simpson, *J. Sci. Food Agric.*, 1956, **7**, 745.

concentration of about 10^{-7} M in phosphate if shaken up with water[1]—
so it is necessary to break up this crystal lattice before they can be used
as a general fertiliser. This is done either by treatment with a mineral
acid or by high temperature sintering processes. Far the most widely
used process is to treat the rock with enough sulphuric acid to convert
the apatite to the water-soluble monocalcium orthophosphate mono-
hydrate, the excess calcium reacting with the sulphuric acid to give
gypsum. This is the superphosphate of commerce, which has been
manufactured since the 1840s and contains between 28 and 32 per cent
of the monophosphate and 50 to 60 per cent gypsum. This fertiliser is
sold in the United Kingdom on a guaranteed content of water-soluble
P_2O_5 which is usually between 16 and 18 per cent, corresponding to
7 to 8 per cent water-soluble P.

Since about 1930 increasing amounts of other phosphate fertilisers
have been coming on to the market. One of these is a much more
concentrated monocalcium phosphate fertiliser known as triple superphosphate. It is made by treating the rock phosphate with phosphoric
acid instead of sulphuric, but this phosphoric acid is usually made by
treating the rock phosphate with sufficient sulphuric acid to remove all
the calcium from the apatite as gypsum. It is not a method for saving
sulphuric acid but for obtaining a more concentrated phosphate
fertiliser, and it contains up to 85 per cent of the monocalcium phosphate or up to 48 per cent water-soluble P_2O_5. Phosphoric acid, however, is increasingly being marketed as a concentrated solution in a few
areas of the world, or it is also converted to the water-soluble mono- and
diammonium phosphates.

A further group of phosphates are derived from monocalcium
phosphate based on the water-insoluble dicalcium phosphate which
will maintain a phosphate concentration of about 10^{-3} M in solution.
The normal reason for their manufacture is to save sulphuric acid, for
if rock phosphate is treated with nitric or hydrochloric acid, the calcium
nitrate or chloride admixed with the monocalcium phosphate is too
hygroscopic to allow the mixture being used as a fertiliser, and the
processes used to remove these involve the conversion of the monocalcium to the dicalcium phosphate.[2]

High-temperature phosphates, all of which are water insoluble, are
also manufactured to a limited extent. Probably the commonest of
these is made by fusing rock phosphate with silica, using soda as a flux,
to give a calcium silicophosphate and calcium silicate, known as silicophosphate, sodaphosphate or Rhenania phosphate. Rock phosphate

[1] K. D. Jacob and W. L. Hill, *Agronomy Monog.*, **4**, 1953.
[2] M. M. R. J. Plusje, *Proc. Fertil. Soc.*, No. 13, 1951, W. D'Leny, ibid., No. 24, 1953, and
F. T. Nielsson, L. D. Yates *et al.*, *J. Agric. Food Chem.*, 1953, **1**, 1050.

is sometimes fused with serpentine or magnesium silicate, and the molten slag rapidly quenched to give a glass, which is then ground. Other high temperature phosphates are tricalcium phosphate and calcium metaphosphate $Ca(PO_3)_2$, which if pure would contain over 70 per cent P_2O_5, or 31 per cent P, and so is one of the most concentrated phosphate fertilisers made. It hydrolyses to orthophosphate in the soil. Most of these will maintain a phosphate concentration of between 10^{-5} and 10^{-4} M in solution.[1]

The commonest high temperature phosphates of commerce are basic slags, which are by-products of the steel industry. They have a variety of compositions, and correspondingly of agricultural value, but the most useful again contain calcium silicophosphate and calcium silicate, and the less useful crystalline fluor-apatites. These are liming materials as well as phosphate fertilisers, for the calcium silicate hydrolyses readily to calcium hydroxide and silica, and the silicophosphate is probably a solid solution of very variable composition.

The relative manurial value of the various phosphate fertilisers is thus largely determined by the tightness with which their calcium ions are bound, for this determines the solubility of their phosphate ions in the soil solution and the rate at which they can enter the soil's pool of labile phosphate. Thus, for comparable soil and plant conditions, these relative values can be assessed fairly accurately by determining the amount of phosphate brought into solution when the fertiliser is treated with a calcium-complexing solution such as neutral or alkaline ammonium citrate or 2 per cent citric acid. This acid solution is extensively used for grading basic slags, as only the citric-soluble fraction has any worthwhile phosphate-fertilising value. Tests have also been developed based on the ability of acid clays and H-saturated cation exchange resins to bring phosphates into solution through their power of extracting calcium from the fertiliser.[2]

The manurial value of a water-insoluble phosphate fertiliser is therefore dependent on the acidity of the soil in which it is used, for in general the more acid the soil the more strongly are calcium ions removed from the soil solution, so the more soluble becomes the phosphate in the fertiliser. Table 109 illustrates this effect of increasing soil acidity increasing the relative fertiliser value of different water-insoluble phosphates for swedes and potatoes.

Dicalcium phosphate, the least insoluble of these fertilisers, is about as effective as superphosphate on most soils if finely ground, particularly if the dehydrate is used, although if incorporated in granular fertilisers

---

[1] Quoted from K. D. Jacob and W. L. Hill, *Agronomy Monog.* 4, 1953, 301.
[2] E. R. Graham, *Proc. Soil Sci. Soc. Amer.*, 1955, 19, 26, and G. Barbier and P. Quillon, *Ann. Agron.*, 1955, 775.

TABLE 109

The Effect of Soil and Crop on the relative values of Phosphate Fertiliser[1]

Field experiments in the United Kingdom 1951–53

Number of lb. of superphosphate needed to give same response
as 100 lb. of fertiliser

Soils	Swedes			Potatoes		
	Very Acid <pH 5·5	Acid pH 5·5–6·5	Neutral >pH 6·5	Very Acid <pH 5·5	Acid pH 5·5–6·5	Neutral >pH 6·5
No. of Expts. .	10	22	3	10	15	9
dicalcium phosphate. .	97	85	95	122	62	84
silicophosphate .	90	84	52	92	56	30
Gafsa rock phosphate. .	91	86	12	34	37	4

it is definitely less effective on neutral and alkaline soils.[2] The next group, including fertilisers such as calcium metaphosphate, silicophosphate or Rhenania phosphate, and basic slag can be as effective as superphosphate on acid soils—the last two can in fact be more effective because of their value as a liming material—but are usually only one half to one third as effective on neutral or calcareous soils, whilst the least soluble, ground rock phosphate, can be quite useful on acid soils but of little or no value on neutral.[3]

The manurial value of water-insoluble compared with water-soluble phosphates, however, depends on the crop grown as well as the soil. Some crops, such as lupins, buckwheat, swedes and turnips, have a very considerable ability to use insoluble phosphates; a number of leguminous crops, such as red and white clovers, lucerne and crotalaria have rather less ability; and many important crops such as the cereals, many grasses, and potatoes have apparently relatively little ability.[4]

In part these differences are due to the phosphate demands of different crops being different at different stages of their growth, if their final yield is not to be limited by lack of phosphate. Potentially fast-growing crops usually need a relatively high concentration of phosphate in the soil solution, or at least in numerous pockets of the soil solution,

[1] From G. W. Cooke, *J. Agric. Sci.*, 1956, **48**, 74.

[2] G. W. Cooke, *Agricultural Value of Phosphate Fertilisers*, O.E.E.C., 1956, and G. W. Cooke, G. E. G. Mattingley and F. V. Widdowson, *J. Agric. Sci.*, 1958, **50**, 253; 1959, **53**, 46.

[3] For American experience, see H. T. Rogers, R. W. Pearson and L. E. Ensminger, *Agronomy Monog.*, **4**, 1953, and for British, see G. W. Cooke, *J. Agric. Sci.*, 1956, **48**, 74.

[4] See, for example, D. N. Prianischnikov, *Phosphorsäure*, 1934, **4**, and M. Fried, *Proc. Soil Sci. Soc. Amer.*, 1953, **17**, 357.

if they are to make rapid growth, and the more soluble the phosphate fertiliser, the better these demands can be met. Other crops may need a relatively high phosphate supply when young so they can start off growing rapidly from the seedling stage, and this demand is best met by placing a water-soluble phosphate close to the seedling. On the other hand the phosphate from the less soluble phosphates takes time to enter the soil's pool of labile phosphate, so that if one compares the phosphate content of a crop manured with a soluble and a less soluble phosphate fertiliser, the two crops may have the same phosphate content at harvest but yet the crop manured with the water-soluble will take up a higher proportion of its phosphate in its early growth. Thus the less soluble phosphates can be as efficient as the water-soluble for crops having a larger demand in the latter than in the early part of their growth. And this relative inefficiency of the less soluble phosphates can be reduced in some circumstances by applying them to the soil several weeks or even months before the crop is planted.[1]

There is also evidence that the root systems of crops may differ in their ability to extract phosphate from the less soluble forms. Thus the root systems of some crops will ramify around particles of these insoluble phosphates, so having a larger absorbing area close to the phosphate surface, although this does not necessarily ensure that the roots will take up any useful amount of phosphate from the fertiliser.[2] But the roots of some plants can almost certainly increase the rate at which the insoluble phosphate is brought into solution,[3] either because they excrete calcium-complexing acids or because they have bacteria in their rhizospheres which can bring this phosphate into solution. Thus oats growing with lupins,[4] or grass growing with white clover, can take up more phosphate from an insoluble phosphate than if growing alone; and a cereal following buckwheat manured with an insoluble phosphate will take up more phosphate than if the preceding crop was another cereal.

THE MOVEMENT OF FERTILISER PHOSPHATE IN THE SOIL

When a pellet of water-soluble phosphate fertiliser, say super-phosphate, is buried in the soil, phosphate starts diffusing out into the soil solution quite quickly, even if the soil is fairly dry, but the diffusion is limited in space because the phosphate ions are quickly removed from the soil solution.[5] But the composition of this solution diffusing out of

[1] S. L. Tisdale and E. Winters, *Agron. J.*, 1953, **45**, 228.
[2] J. R. Lehr and W. E. Brown, *Proc. Soil Sci. Soc. Amer.*, 1958, **22**, 29.
[3] M. Drake and J. E. Steckel, *Proc. Soil Sci. Soc. Amer.*, 1955, **19**, 449.
[4] Domontovitch *et al.*, *Trans. Sov. Sect. Int. Soc. Soil Sci.*, Comm. IV, 1933, **2**, 214.   H. Schander, *Bodenk. PflErnähr.*, 1941, **20**, 129.
[5] K. Lawton and J. A. Vomocil, *Proc. Soil Sci. Soc. Amer.*, 1954, **18**, 26; and 1955, **19**, 315, and J. M. Heslop and C. A. Black, *Soil Sci.*, 1954, **78**, 389.

the pellet may differ appreciably from monocalcium phosphate. As mentioned on p. 477, the solution is likely to be very acid, as it contains more phosphate than calcium, and it can have a composition of between 4·0 and 4·5 M in phosphorus, about 1·3 M in calcium and a pH of 1·0 to 1·5. In acid soils this solution will dissolve aluminium and iron compounds in the immediate neighbourhood of the pellet, and in one such soil Lindsay and Stephenson[1] found the solution became 0·7 M in aluminium and 0·2 M in ferric iron. As the solution diffuses away, its pH rises and most of the phosphate is precipitated in the pH range 2·3 to 3·0. Some of the precipitate is amorphous, but crystalline precipitates of hydrated and dehydrated dicalcium phosphate and potassium taranakite[2] $H_6K_3Al_5(PO_4)_8.18H_2O$ can be determined petrographically, as well as an iron aluminium phosphate $H_8K(Fe.Al)_3(PO_4)_6.6H_2O$ when the precipitation begins at the lower end of the pH range. This is the first piece of evidence that potassium ions are concerned in the precipitation of phosphate ions in soils.

The movement of this phosphate in a soil can be followed relatively easily by incorporating a proportion of P^{32} atoms in it. Thus D. R. Bouldin and C. A. Black[3] have shown that although the phosphate may be precipitated uniformly throughout a spherical shell of soil surrounding the granule, it is sometimes precipitated either in zones which look like Liesegang rings, or in a series of spots.

The American workers[4] who have studied the dissolution of a tablet of superphosphate or triple superphosphate in soils have concluded that a spongy framework of dicalcium phosphate, with or without calcium sulphate, is left behind in the first instance, though normal field experience with granular superphosphate in England indicates that after a time the dicalcium phosphate must itself go, as such granules have been found to consist of a calcium sulphate framework only. They also find that in acid and mildly acid soils the dicalcium phosphate is present as the hydrate if the soil is moist, though in time it goes over to the anhydrous form; but if the soil is fairly dry, or if it is neutral or calcareous, the anhydrous is formed almost immediately.

The consequence of this movement of phosphate from fertiliser particles into the soil by diffusion is that for a period after the phosphate has been added, there is a great variability in the phosphate potential from point to point in the soil, being much lower near each granule than in the bulk of the soil. From this point of view the phosphate potential of a fertilised soil can be pictured as a plateau of fairly

[1] *Proc. Soil Sci. Soc. Amer.*, 1959, **23**, 12, 18.
[2] For a petrographic description, see J. P. Smith and W. E. Brown, *Amer. Min.*, 1959, **44**, 138.
[3] *Proc. Soil Sci. Soc. Amer.*, 1954, **18**, 255.
[4] J. R. Lehr, W. E. and E. N. Brown, *Proc. Soil Sci. Soc. Amer.*, 1959, **23**, 3.

constant potential with troughs of lower potential around each fertiliser particle, and it is from these troughs that the plant roots can most easily take up their phosphate. This extremely patchy distribution lasts a fairly long time in undisturbed soil—how long is not known—and it probably lasts longer around a relatively insoluble phosphate particle than around a soluble one of the same size, though it takes longer to build up; and it lasts longer around a fairly large granule of a granulated superphosphate than around a small particle of a powdered super.

The reason that fertilised soils possess this very uneven distribution of phosphate for a relatively long time is the low solubility of the soil phosphate. As already mentioned, if 12 inches of water drains through a soil a year, and this water has the same concentration of phosphate as the soil solution, only 0·08 lb. per acre of phosphorus, equivalent to about 1 lb. of superphosphate, will be moved, if the solution is 10^{-6} M in phosphate.[1] Thus B. B. Roy and B. Thomas[2] found on Tree Field at Cockle Park, Northumberland, which has been in pasture for a very long time and which had received dressings of phosphate at three-year intervals for nearly fifty years, that none of the phosphate had moved down to more than 8 inches from the surface, as can be seen from Table 110; and they could account for all the phosphate added by the

TABLE 110
Movement of Phosphate down a Pasture Profile

Permanent pasture, Tree Field, Cockle Park
Total P in mgm. per 100 gm. soil
700 lb. P added by equal additions every third year from 1897 to 1945

Depth of soil layer in inches	0–2	2–4	4–6	6–8	8–11
No phosphate	44	39	37	30	27
Basic Slag	96	66	50	40	28
Superphospate	100	65	46	40	29

extra phosphate found in the top soil and that removed by the grazing animals. One naturally cannot say how much of this phosphate moved down in the soil solution and how much was transported through the plant roots or earthworms. Thus if one wants to move phosphate into a subsoil, for example, it is almost essential either to plough it in or to place a distributor behind a deep cultivator or subsoil tine, unless very

[1] For the losses from a Versailles soil, see E. M. Bastisse and S. Henin, *Ann. Agron.*, 1955, 203.
[2] *Emp. J. Exp. Agric.*, 1951, **19**, 175. For a later sampling, see B. Roscoe, *Plant and Soil*, 1960, **12**, 71. For another example, see P. C. Sandal and C. L. Garey, *Agron. J.*, 1955, **47**, 229.

heavy dressings are used,[1] or the soils are very sandy and low in sesquioxides.

This very slow movement of phosphate through a soil profile is reasonably well proven for well drained soils. But for soils which are seasonally water-logged, phosphate may move much more easily down the profile,[2] possibly being carried by ferrous ions.

THE UPTAKE OF FERTILISER PHOSPHATE BY CROPS

In general if one adds a phosphate fertiliser to a soil, even if the crop responds well to it, the additional phosphate the crop has taken up is usually about 5–10 per cent of the phosphate added, and it is often less, though on phosphate-poor soils using a phosphate-demanding crop such as swedes, average recoveries of about 20 per cent for dressings of 0·14 cwt. per acre of P and of about 15 per cent for dressings of 0·28 cwt. have been obtained in a number of Scottish experiments.[3]

Table 111 gives an example, using swedes for phosphate-deficient English soils.[4] Higher recoveries can, however, be found. Thus if a moderate dressing of phosphate is suitably placed relative to the seed of swedes on a phosphate poor soil, the additional phosphate taken up

TABLE III

Uptake of Added Phosphate by Swedes on Phosphate-deficient Soils

Mean of 27 experiments, 1942
Phosphorus added as superphosphate

P added in fertiliser, cwt. per acre	Yield of roots in tons per acre	Increase in yield due to each increment of phosphate	P in roots, cwt. per acre	Uptake of P from each increment	
				In cwt. per acre	as per cent of P added
0	6·1	—	0·025	—	—
0·22	15·4	9·3	0·060	0·035	16
0·44	17·2	1·8	0·080	0·020	9

by the much better crop, may equal 50 per cent of the fertiliser applied. But it is not legitimate in these examples to argue that all the additional phosphate came from the fertiliser, much has certainly come from the soil due to the much more vigorous root system of the manured crop.

[1] See, for example, R. E. Stephenson and M. D. Chapman, *J. Amer. Soc. Agron.*, 1931, **23**, 759.
[2] R. Glentworth and H. G. Dion, *J. Soil Sci.*, 1949, **1**, 35; A. J. McGregor, *J. Soil Sci.*, 1953, **4**, 86, and G. W. Cooke and J. K. R Gasser, *J. Soil Sci.*, 1953, **6**, 248.
[3] A. M. Smith and K. Simpson, *J. Sci. Food Agric.*, 1950, **1**, 208; 1956, **7**, 754.
[4] I am indebted to Drs. Crowther and Cooke for this table.

However, an example from Kericho, Kenya, of the effect of super-phosphate on the response of elephant grass (*Pennisetum purpureum*) to superphosphate shows a recovery as high as 67 per cent, most of which must have come from the fertiliser.[1] The grass was given the equivalent of 13 lb. per acre of phosphorus four years running, eight cuts of the grass were taken, and the total yield of dry matter was increased from 11·2 to 21·8 tons, and the uptake of phosphorus from 26·4 to 61·5 lb per acre.

The use of techniques based on incorporating P^{32} in phosphate fertilisers has led to a clearer understanding of the relative value of the added fertiliser phosphate compared to the soil phosphate as the source of the phosphate taken up by the crop.[2] Thus it can be shown that the young plant will take up nearly all its phosphate from a band of soluble fertiliser suitably placed with respect to the seed, and that crops will take up nearly all their phosphate from the fertiliser if a heavy dressing of a water-soluble fertiliser is used.[3] Correspondingly, if a fertiliser containing a mixture of water-soluble and water-insoluble phosphates is used, the crop will take up a higher proportion of phosphate from the soluble than from the insoluble, and the presence of the soluble phosphate depresses the uptake of phosphate from the insoluble, if it had been used by itself.[4] These results in fact show that the plant roots tend to take up their phosphate from these volumes of the soil where the phosphate potential is low; and the lower the potential in these spots, and the more of them there are, the less phosphate in proportion will be taken up from the high potential volumes.

The conditions which control the uptake by a crop of phosphate from a moderate dressing of a water-soluble phosphate fertiliser added to a soil can now be understood. Low uptake can be a consequence of adding the fertiliser to a soil of high phosphate status, the most usual cause in well farmed land, or of a poor crop whose growth is limited by some factor other than the phosphate supply, or of an inefficient method of applying the phosphate so the roots of the crop cannot take it up when they require it because it is distributed through too large a volume of soil, and finally because the dressings usually given supply far more phosphate than even a good crop can take up.

There has been much discussion on whether liming an acid soil affects the availability of soil phosphates to a crop. One would expect liming a soil, by raising its pH to reduce the availability of the calcium phosphates, but the data, such as exist, suggest that liming most soils

[1] R. Child, N. A. Goodchild and J. R. Todd, *Emp. J. Exp. Agric.*, 1955, **23**, 220.
[2] S. Larsen, *Plant and Soil*, 1952, **4**, 1, and O. Gunnersson and L. Fredrikson, *Bull. Document*, 1952, No. 42; M. Fried, *Proc. Soil Sci. Soc. Amer.*, 1953, **17**, 357.
[3] For example, see J. Mitchell, *J. Soil Sci.*, 1957, **8**, 73.
[4] J. T. Murdock and W. A. Seay, *Proc. Soil Sci. Soc. Amer.*, 1955, **19**, 199.

has little effect on the phosphate potential though it puts down the concentration of phosphate in the soil solution (see Fig. 44, p. 484). Yet the experimental evidence is often that liming does in fact increase the phosphate uptake by a crop and reduce its response to a phosphate fertiliser, just as if it were a phosphate fertiliser in itself.

The full explanations of the experimental results on the effect of lime on phosphate uptake from acid soils are not known. Part of the effect is often that liming the soil encourages the crop to make better root growth, so it can tap a larger volume of soil for phosphates; part may sometimes be due to the consequent increase in the rate of decomposition of organic matter in the soil, resulting in a greater liberation of phosphate; and part may also be due to a consequent decrease in the concentration of iron or aluminium ions or complex ions in the soil solution which may be interfering with the translocation of phosphate from root to tops (see p. 490). But there is probably still no incontrovertible direct field evidence that liming really increases the availability of the soil phosphates.

Uptake of phosphates from fertiliser also seems to be encouraged if ammonium ions are intimately associated with the phosphate, such as if an ammonium phosphate is used.[1] This effect may only be noticeable when the crop is young, and it may explain the very satisfactory results many farmers have had when they have combine-drilled ammonium phosphate with the seed.

THE RESIDUAL EFFECTS OF PHOSPHATIC FERTILISERS

For reasons which have just been given, a crop usually only takes up a small fraction of the phosphate added as fertiliser to the soil, and in many examples the uptake is less in the succeeding year, and by the third or fourth year has become too small to determine by field experiment. Often only 20 to 30 per cent of the added phosphate has been removed by this time, on the assumption that all the extra phosphate taken up from the fertilised soil came from the fertiliser. This is illustrated in Table 112, using the results of seven English grassland hay experiments made between 1930 and 1935.[2]

The old explanation of this type of result was that the phosphate fertiliser added to the soil slowly reverted to unavailable forms, or was fixed by the soil in such forms, and the phenomenon was known as phosphate reversion or fixation. However, if a water-soluble phosphate is added to a soil, it is very rapidly converted to an insoluble form, and

---

[1] R. A. Olson and A. F. Dreier, *Proc. Soil Sci. Soc. Amer.*, 1956, **20**, 509; D. A. Rennie and R. J. Soper, *J. Soil Sci.*, 1958, **9**, 155. For a review, see D. L. Grunes, *Adv. Agron.*, 1959, **11**, 369.

[2] Figures taken from E. J. Russell, *Min. Agric. Bull.* 28, 3rd ed., 1939, and from the Basic Slag Reports to *Min. Agric.*, 1933 and 1934.

TABLE 112

Uptake of Phosphate by Hay and Grass in Successive Years after Phosphate Manuring

Per cent of added P recovered in Hay or Mowings

0·44 cwt. P per acre added as superphosphate

Year	2 neutral soils[1]	3 acid soils[2]	2 soils, grass mown[3]
Application	7·7	8·3	13·7
1 year after	5·7	5·0	9·4
2 years after	1·8	3·3	5·8
3 years after	1·5	2·3	2·1
Total recovery	16·7	18·9	31·0

this phenomenon is also spoken of as phosphate fixation; but there is no necessity for this phosphate to lose its fertilising value just because it has lost its solubility, and much confusion has been caused by these two different uses of the phrase "phosphate fixation".

There is now a much wider appreciation of the confusion in thought that this double use of the phrase "phosphate fixation" has caused. Current farming experience in countries using large amounts of phosphate fertilisers is that it is becoming increasingly difficult to find soils on well managed farms on which one can obtain responses to phosphate fertiliser, other than to the use of starter doses of a water-soluble phosphate to some very phosphate-demanding crops. Thus in Australia, wheat soils which used to be very phosphate-responsive have ceased to be when 15 to 20 cwt. per acre of superphosphate, say about 150 lb. per acre of P, have been applied since the land was first opened up.[4] Again land which received very heavy dressings of phosphate, in the form of dung or household waste, two or more millennia ago, still have a higher level of plant available phosphate than on land immediately adjacent which did not receive such dressings.[5]

Our general understanding of the conditions under which phosphate fertilisers are likely to have a well-marked residual effect has been helped by the concept of a pool of labile phosphate at a definite thermo-dynamic potential. If enough phosphate is added to lower this potential appreciably when it has become incorporated with the soil, the fertiliser

[1] Braintree, and Badminton, Glos.
[2] Northallerton, Chesterfield and Lydbury, Salop.
[3] Dartington Hall, Totnes (acid) and Much Hadham, Herts (neutral).
[4] A. J. Anderson and K. D. McLachlan, *Aust. J. Agric. Res.*, 1951, **2**, 377, K. Woodroffe and C. H. Williams, ibid., 1953, **4**, 1927, and C. H. Williams, *J. Agric. Sci.*, 1950, **40**, 243.
[5] For an example, see K. D. M. Dauncey, *Advanc. Sci.*, 1952, **9**, 33.

will have a long continued residual effect for, as will be demonstrated below, the phosphate potential will rapidly settle down to a reasonably constant value, except in so far as phosphate is removed from the pool by cropping. Thus a heavy dressing of fertiliser will have a more marked residual effect than a light, as it will reduce the phosphate potential more. But if the phosphate potential in the soil is already low, an added phosphate fertiliser will lose most of its fertilising effect as soon as its phosphate has equilibrated with the phosphate pool, for this addition will have little effect on its potential. Correspondingly all phosphate fertilisers in which the phosphate can migrate from the fertiliser to the pool will have the same residual effect at equivalent dressings of phosphate.

Two groups of experiments at Rothamsted are available for demonstrating in detail the application of this principle to farming practice. The first experiment—the Hoosfield Exhaustion Plots—is on a slightly calcareous clay loam. Some plots received forty-five annual dressings of 3 cwt. per acre of superphosphate between 1856 and 1901, and some twenty-six annual dressings of 14 tons per acre of farmyard manure between 1875 and 1901, and since then the plots have received nothing but some nitrogen fertilisers from time to time. Yet in the five years 1949–53, barley took up an extra 4·4 lb. per acre P per year from the phosphate plots and 5·3 lb. per acre from the manured plots compared with the plots which had received no phosphate as can be seen from Table 113. The phosphate plots received about 1,000 lb. per acre P between 1856 and 1901, and they now contain about 360 lb. per acre P

TABLE 113

Mean Yield and Composition of Barley on Hoosfield Exhaustion Plots (1949–53)

Treatment 1856–1901

	No P, No K	P[1]	PK	Farmyard manure[2]
	Mean yield in cwt. per acre			
Grain . . .	10·8	18·4	19·7	20·5
Straw . . .	12·7	19·1	20·6	20·4
	Nutrients in total crop lb. per acre			
P	4·1	8·1	8·6	9·4
K	16·9	26·4	38·0	34·0

[1] PK 1856–75. P 1876–1901.   [2] 1876–1901.

more than the unmanured, so 65 per cent of the phosphate that was added to the land before 1901 has now been taken up by crops, and barley is still taking up about 1·2 per cent of the residual fertiliser phosphate each year.[1]

These plots, together with some other Rothamsted plots, afford some fairly definite evidence on the form of the residual fertiliser phosphate in the soil. G. E. G. Mattingly[2] has shown that on the neighbouring Permanent Barley plots on Hoosfield and Permanent Wheat Plots on Broadbalk which have been receiving annual dressings of super-phosphates for a very long period of years, that between 35 and 45 per cent of the total fertiliser phosphate remaining in the soil contributes to the A value of the soil phosphate. In the Hoosfield Exhaustion Plots, those which received phosphates till 1901 contained in 1956 20 mgm. more phosphorus per 100 gm. soil than the unmanured, and they had an A value 7 mgm. higher, showing that after fifty-five years' cropping without any phosphate fertiliser, 35 per cent of the phosphate in the soil derived from the fertiliser still contributed to the A value. This can only mean that as a crop removes phosphate from the pool of labile phosphate, a proportion of the added phosphate which was converted into a non-labile form goes over into the labile form to maintain the proportion in the pool, even when two-thirds of the added phosphate has been removed by crops.

The second Rothamsted experiment—the Four Course—is on an adjacent area of Hoosfield, and the treatments are closer to normal farming practice. In this experiment 6 cwt. per acre of superphosphate is added once every five years to some plots which are cropped to a 4-course rotation, and other plots receive rock phosphate, which is now known to have virtually no effect, and so can be used as controls. Table 114 illustrates some of the results of this experiment for the twenty-one years ending in 1954.[3] It shows clearly that potatoes, barley and ryegrass respond best to fresh phosphate, and the response to phosphate added any time in the previous four years is almost constant, so there is no evidence for any appreciable slow reversion. Although in this experiment phosphate uptakes have not been determined nor has the response curve, yet G. E. G. Mattingley and F. V. Widdowson[4] were able to show, using a radio-phosphate technique, that if one compares fresh with residual superphosphate on this soil, and harvests the crop at six weeks from sowing, when it is still young, the

[1] R. G. Warren, *Proc. Fertil. Soc.*, 37, 1956.
[2] *Rothamsted Rept.* 1957, 61, and *J. Agric. Sci.*, 1957, **49**, 160. For other examples, see S. R. Olsen, F. S. Watanabe *et al.*, *Soil Sci.*, 1954, **78**, 141, G. Barbier, C. Lesaint and E. Tyszkiewicz, *Ann. Agron.*, 1954, 923, and W. W. Moschler, R. D. Krebs *et al.*, *Proc. Soil Sci. Soc. Amer.*, 1957, **21**, 293.
[3] *Rothamsted Exp. Sta. Ann. Rept.*, 1954, 154.
[4] *Trans. 6th Int. Congr. Soil Sci.* (Paris), 1956 B, 461.

TABLE 114

Residual Effect of Superphosphate on Hoosfield (21 seasons)

	Response in year of application	Response to phosphate added years previously			
		1	2	3	4
Potatoes in tons per acre					
low nitrogen .	2·3	1·2	1·3	1·2	1·0
high nitrogen .	2·9	1·9	1·7	1·5	1·5
Barley grain cwt. per acre .	3·1	1·3	1·9	1·9	1·3
Ryegrass hay dry matter cwt. per acre .	2·6	2·4	1·9	1·1	1·1
Wheat grain cwt. per acre .	0·4	−0·5	0·1	−0·2	0·3

residual phosphate has only one quarter the value of fresh; but if one harvests the crop when it is older it has a value of one half of the fresh, as measured by phosphate uptake.

The conclusions drawn from these two Rothamsted experiments are valid for a wide range of soils, for they are concordant with the results of almost every well designed experiment made anywhere in the world. Table 115 illustrates this result from one of the few published suitable experiments which have been made in the Tropics, and shows that in

TABLE 115

Residual Response of Crops to Phosphate at Kano (N. Nigeria)

220 lb. per acre superphosphate (about 15 lb. per acre P) given in 1937

Yields in lb. per acre

	No Phosphate	Superphosphate given in 1937	Response[1]
1937 millet (manured) . .	381	803	422
1938 sorghum .	617	781	164
1939 groundnuts .	785	973	188
1940 millet . .	363	449	86
1941 sorghum .	356	459	103

[1] All responses significant at 1 per cent level.

general these conclusions are as valid there as in the temperate regions.

There are, however, a few examples of soils in which even massive dressings of phosphate rapidly lose availability. Thus E. G. Williams[1] found on two Aberdeenshire soils, one derived from a basic igneous and the other from a granitic till, that the fertilising effect for turnips of a dressing of 25 cwt. per acre of superphosphates applied to the previous crop was about equivalent to 6 cwt. applied to the turnips, and that in the following year the residues from the two dressings of superphosphate was about proportional to the total amount of phosphate added in the two preceding years, yet in the third and subsequent years the manurial effect had effectively disappeared. The reasons for the difference in behaviour between these soils and most other soils are not known.

There can be no appreciable difference between the residual effects of fertilisers when the phosphate they contain has entered the soil's phosphate pool; and this is concordant with the general conclusion reached from a study of the published experiments. But a word of caution is needed here, because in many experiments in which the residual effects of superphosphate and ground rock phosphate have been compared, about two to three times as much phosphate has been added as rock than as superphosphate, for the additions were made at about equal cost per acre and not at equal phosphate per acre. In a number of these experiments the residual effect of the rock phosphate has been appreciably higher than that of superphosphates, but these experiments can unfortunately give no information about what the residual effects would have been if they had been used at equal phosphate per acre.

The residual manurial effects of ground rock phosphate can appear to be complicated due to the phosphate taking more than a year to enter the phosphate pool. Thus crops may respond better in the second or third year than in the year of application[2] and G. A. Cowie[3] has given an example of it taking even longer. He examined the results of a long term 6-course experiment in Aberdeenshire and showed that potatoes, barley and oats hardly responded to the rock phosphate in the first ten years of the experiment, but in the second ten years they showed a response equivalent to that obtained from half the dressing of phosphate, as superphosphate.

There is one other process which may make a phosphate fertiliser change to a relatively unavailable form, but which nevertheless will let it have a slow long-lasting effect. If a soil low in organic matter and

[1] *J. Sci. Food Agric.*, 1950, **1**, 244.
[2] For an example, see G. H. A. Edwards, *Proc. 6th Int. Congr. Soil Sci.* (Paris), 1956 D, 13,
[3] *J. Agric. Sci.*, 1945, **35**, 197.

in phosphate is put down to grass for a period of years and is manured with a phosphate fertiliser, the organic matter content of the soil may rise very considerably and fairly rapidly, and this organic matter will be locking up phosphate, which in these conditions has been derived from the fertiliser. Thus in New South Wales, C. M. Donald and C. H. Williams[1] found that adding superphosphate to a subterranean clover pasture, about one half of the added phosphate was converted into organic phosphate with a consequent increase of about 76 lb. of soil organic nitrogen per 100 lb. of superphosphate added; and in these examples the ratio of $C:N:S:P$ remained at $155:10:1\cdot4:0\cdot7$, the same as in the soil of the unimproved pastures.

Responsiveness of Crops to Phosphate Fertilisers

Three separate types of relation between crop and phosphate fertiliser can be recognised:

(1) The sensitiveness of a crop to phosphate shortage. Crops such as swedes, potatoes and barley have their yields very seriously reduced by a shortage of phosphate when growing in soils in which wheat and oats may make fair growth and some grasses good growth. This can be seen in part from Table 114. It is also probable that sorghum is more sensitive to low phosphate in a soil than is maize.[2]

(2) The responsiveness of a crop to added phosphate. On the whole this is the same property as the first, for crops which are sensitive to phosphate shortage respond best to a dressing of phosphate. But it includes in addition the ability to continue to respond to phosphate as the fertiliser dressing is increased. Thus maize will respond to a considerably higher dressing of phosphate than will groundnuts.[3]

(3) The ability to use phosphate from relatively insoluble phosphate fertilisers. Crops such as swedes, turnips and mustard amongst the brassica crops; lupins, lucerne and sweet clover amongst the leguminous; and buckwheat all can use phosphate from relatively insoluble forms such as ground North African rock phosphate much more easily than can crops such as potatoes, the cereals and cotton.

---

[1] *Aust. J. Agric. Res.*, 1954, **5**, 664, and 1957, **8**, 179. For an example from New Zealand, see R. H. Jackman, *Soil Sci.*, 1955, **79**, 207.
[2] P. H. Nye, *Emp. J. Exp. Agric.*, 1954, **22**, 101, and L. R. Doughty, *E. Afr. Agric. J.*, 1953, **19**, 30.
[3] P. H. Le Mare, *Emp. J. Exp. Agric.*, 1959, **27**, 197.

CHAPTER XXVII

THE SOURCES OF PLANT NUTRIENTS IN THE SOIL

II. NUTRIENTS OTHER THAN PHOSPHORUS

The Potassium Compounds

THE PRIMARY SOURCES of potassium in the soil are the potassium-bearing minerals. The potash micas, biotite and muscovite, yield up their potassium fairly readily,[1] particularly if finely ground; and some biotites can do this so easily that they have been used as potassic fertilisers in Norway.[2] The potash felspar orthoclase does not weather so easily as the two micas, whilst microcline is very resistant to weathering and releases its potassium very slowly. Clay minerals, particularly those derived from micas, also contain some potassium, which may be released slowly by weathering. A second source of potassium is the exchangeable potassium, and a third source is the exchangeable potassium that has been converted into a non-exchangeable form, as described on p. 113. This is converted back slowly into the exchangeable form when the level of exchangeable potassium in the soil becomes very low.

The primary source of potassium for plants is the exchangeable potassium,[3] and its level in the soil is an important factor in determining the responsiveness of a crop to a potassic fertiliser. This is illustrated in Table 116, which shows the response of sugar-beet to potassic fertilisers in a large number of English experiments.[4] Exchangeable potassium is quite obviously an important, though not the only, factor affecting the responsiveness of the crop to the potassic fertiliser.

Plants remove more potassium from the soil during the growing season than corresponds to the reduction in the exchangeable potassium content, but the amount of non-exchangeable potassium they use from a given soil depends to some extent on the crop. These non-exchangeable sources may be as important when the exchangeable potassium

---

[1] I. A. Dennison, W. H. Fry and P. L. Gile, *U.S. Dept. Agric., Tech. Bull.* 128, 1929.
[2] P. Solberg, *Meld. Norg. LandbrHøgsk.*, 1928, **8**.
[3] R. Stewart, *J. Agric. Sci.*, 1929, **19**, 524 (for some Scottish soils); R. H. Bray, *Soil Sci.*, 1944, **58**, 305 (for some Illinois soils).
[4] E. M. Crowther, *Bath and West Agric. Soc., Pamph.* 13, 1948.

TABLE 116

Mean Response of Sugar-beet to Potassic Fertiliser on Soils with Different Contents of Exchangeable Potassium

English sugar-beet experiments made during 1936–46

Potassic fertiliser—I cwt. K per acre (as 2 cwt. potassium chloride)

Exchangeable potassium determined by 0·5 N acetic acid

Response to potassic fertiliser measured in presence of 4 cwt. per acre ammonium sulphate

Acetic acid soluble potassium in mgm. per 100 gm. soil	Number of fields	Response of sugar-beet to potassic fertiliser. Extra sugar in cwt. per acre
Below 5 . .	63	4·7
5–6·5 .	61	4·4
6·5–9 .	62	2·0
Over 10 . .	62	0·8

is high as when it is low, as is shown in Table 117.[1] Soils differ, however, very considerably in the rate at which they release their non-exchangeable potassium. The rate of release is naturally more important in soils with small amounts of exchangeable potassium.[2] Soils undergoing rapid weathering, as, for example, young soils being derived from basic igneous rocks in humid tropical climates, release very large

TABLE 117

Uptake of Exchangeable and Non-exchangeable Potassium from some Texas Soils

5 kg. soil in large container, crop of maize and of kafir or sorghum taken

Quantities of K in parts per million of soil

Number of soils tested	Amount of K removed by crop		Loss of exchangeable K from soil	Exchangeable K in soil before cropping	Non-exchangeable K released by soils
	between	mean	mean	mean	mean
11	0 and 41	35	17	100	18
20	42 and 83	66	25	110	41
31	81 and 165	120	50	167	70
7	415 and 580	490	216	504	274

[1] G. S. Fraps, *Texas Agric. Expt. Sta., Bull.* 391, 1929. See also for similar results R. F, Chandler *et al., J. Amer. Soc. Agron.,* 1945, **37**, 709, using Ladino white clover.
[2] D. R. Hoagland and J. C. Martin, *Soil Sci.,* 1933, **36**, 1; F. E. Bear *et al.,* ibid., 1944, **58**, 139; E. H. Stewart and N. J. Volk, *Soil Sci.,* 1946, **61**, 125.

amounts of potassium in an available form annually. Thus, H. W. van der Marel[1] finds that sisal can take up 250 kg. per hectare of potassium from soils rich in biotite in Sumatra, and sugar cane up to 200 kg. from soils rich in andesine in Java, apparently indefinitely without the soil becoming impoverished in potassium; and as an extreme example, A. S. Ayres and his co-workers[2] in Hawaii grew sixteen crops of elephant grass (*Pennisetum purpureum*) in four and a half years, and found each removed about 250 lb. of potassium per acre without appreciably affecting the content of exchangeable potassium in the top 3 feet of soil.

The discussion so far has assumed that soil minerals release potassium into the soil and the plant roots then take it up. But this over-simplifies the problem: plant roots can take an active part in helping minerals to release potassium. Very little work has been done on this aspect of the

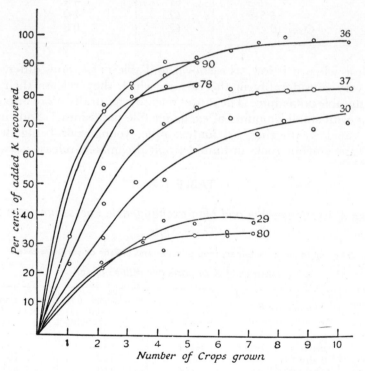

FIG. 46. Recovery of added potassium by a succession of barley and tomato crops grown in different soils.

For soils 30, 36 and 37, crops 1, 2, 4, 7 and 9 were barley, while crops 3, 5, 6, 8 and 10 were tomato; for soils 29, 78, 80 and 90, crops, 1, 3, 5 and 7 were barley, while crops 2, 4 and 6 were tomato. (Recovery calculated on basis of comparison between NP and NPK fertilised soils.)

[1] *Soil Sci.*, 1947, **64**, 445.   [2] *Proc. Soil Sci. Soc. Amer.*, 1947, **11**, 175.

problem, though C. C. Lewis and W. C. Eisenenmger[1] have recently shown that different families of plants have very different abilities to extract potassium from an orthoclase felspar.

Some soils possess considerable power of converting added potassium into forms unavailable to the plant, as is shown in Fig. 46, for some Californian soils.[2] The reason why soils 29 and 80 in this figure fixed so much more potassium than the other soils was not investigated and is not known.

The Calcium Compounds

These fall into four groups:

1. Calcium present in the mineral particles. These calcium-containing minerals are nearly all primary, such as basic plagioclases rich in anorthite, epidote, and some constituents of basic rocks such as gabbros, basalts and diabases. They all weather fairly readily, particularly if finely ground, yielding up their calcium.

2. Calcium carbonate, normally the most important source of calcium in soils.

3. Simple salts. (a) Calcium ions are usually the dominant cation in the soil solution: they cannot be considered as attached to any particular anion, though the two main anions they balance are nitrate and bicarbonate. (b) Calcium phosphate, mainly in the form of apatites, but this is usually only present in small quantities. (c) Calcium sulphate as gypsum, usually only important in arid soils though it occurs in considerable quantities in the lower layers of some English clays, such as the Kimmeridge.

4. Exchangeable calcium.

Calcium differs from phosphorus and potassium in that the calcium of simple compounds added to a soil remains available to plants until it is removed from the soil either by leaching or by being taken up by the plant. Perhaps the only mechanism whereby calcium can become fixed in the soil is in combination with phosphate in mildly acid to alkaline soils.

The exchangeable calcium in a soil is not all equally easily available to the plant. Calcium saturated montmorillonitic clays yield up their calcium with increasing difficulty as they become progressively unsaturated, but this property is displayed less strongly in clays of the illite type and still less by the kaolinitic clays or soil organic matter.[3]

[1] *Soil Sci.*, 1948, **65**, 495.
[2] D. R. Hoagland and J. C. Martin, *Trans. 3rd Int. Congr. Soil Sci.*, Oxford, 1935, **1**, 99.
[3] W. H. Allaway, *Soil Sci.*, 1945, **59**, 207; A. Mehlich and W. E. Colwell, ibid., 1946, **61**, 369.

The Manganese Compounds

Manganese occurs in many primary rocks, particularly in ferro-magnesian rocks rich in iron. It also occurs in many soils as MnO_2, often in a hydrated form, and possibly also as trivalent manganese, though where this is held is not known. Soils also contain divalent manganese, present as an exchangeable cation.

The mechanisms by which soils supply an adequate quantity of manganese to plants are still far from elucidated. Plants can certainly use divalent and almost certainly cannot use tetravalent manganese, though whether they can use trivalent manganese, and if so, whether they take up any appreciable proportion of their manganese in this form is quite unknown. In practice, the problem is to maintain a reasonable, but not excessive, concentration of divalent manganese in the soil.

The factors controlling the proportion of soil manganese in the divalent form appear to be bound up with the form of the organic matter present and the microbiological conditions prevailing. Three processes seem to be important in this connection:

1. Hydrated manganese dioxide is reduced to divalent manganese by bacteria in the presence of a suitable hydrogen donator and carrier, as, for example, sugars and acetates with pyocyanine as carrier.[1] Thus, water-logging a soil and then draining it, a condition that often arises in countries with cool, moist winters, increases the amount of divalent manganese in the soil.[2] It can be reduced in the field by adding hydroquinone or creatinine,[3] and this reduction can take place without the aid of micro-organisms.[4] In fact, phenol in acid soils, polyhydric phenols and sulphydryl compounds, such as cysteine in acid or alkaline soils, and hydroxy-acids, such as citric,[5] can all bring about reduction of the hydrated dioxide to manganous ions.

2. Divalent manganese is oxidised by certain soil bacteria to hydrated manganese dioxide,[6] and this oxidation can be much reduced by certain inhibitors, such as sodium azide or chloretone.[4] V. B. D. Skerman and S. M. Bromfield[7] have made the interesting observation that single species of bacteria, in pure culture, cannot bring about this oxidation; it was necessary to use pairs of suitable species. These bacteria

[1] G. D. Sherman and P. M. Harmer, *Proc. Soil Sci. Soc. Amer.*, 1943, **7**, 398.
[2] G. W. Leeper, *Soil Sci.*, 1947, **63**, 79.
[3] F. Steenbjerg, *Tidskr. Planteavl*, 1934, **40**, 337; G. D. Sherman and P. M. Harmer, *J. Amer. Soc. Agron.*, 1941, **33**, 1080.
[4] P. J. G. Mann and J. H. Quastel, *Nature*, 1946, **158**, 154.
[5] P. J. G. Mann and S. G. Heintze, *J. Agric. Sci.*, 1947, **37**, 23.
[6] F. C. Gerretsen, *Verslag. Landbouwk. Onderzoek.*, 1936, **42** A, 57; G. W. Leeper and R. J. Swaby, *Soil Sci.*, 1940, **49**, 163; J. D. MacLachlan, *Sci. Agric.*, 1941, **22**, 201.
[7] *Nature*, 1949, **163**, 575.

congregate round the roots of some plants, and thus prevent them taking up manganese. This trouble can often be cured by partial sterilisation, which seems to reduce the activity of these bacteria markedly.[1]

3. Certain types of readily soluble soil organic matter can absorb divalent manganese and other metallic ions such as iron and copper, forming insoluble co-ordination compounds. This manganese is not exchangeable nor available to the plant, though it can be extracted both by neutral pyrophosphate and by some hydroxy-acids capable of forming co-ordination compounds with these metals.[2]

C. K. Fujimoto and G. D. Sherman have found that two other factors influence the level of exchangeable divalent manganese in the soil. Steam sterilisation can sometimes increase its level considerably, enough in fact for crop growth to be limited by manganese toxicity,[3] and a surface mulch can reduce it;[4] but the reason for neither of these is known.

The net effect of these processes is that acid mineral soils are usually well supplied, and sometimes over supplied with divalent manganese; that calcareous soils are usually very low in divalent manganese; that many organic soils, in spite of containing considerable quantities of total manganese, are very poor suppliers of manganese to the crop; and that crops suffering from manganese deficiency diseases on either of these types of soil need far less manganese to be given them if it is sprayed on their foliage than if it is applied to the soil. It is possible, however, that adding sufficient sulphur to an organic soil to bring its pH below 7 may be as effective as adding manganese.[5]

The Sulphur Compounds

Sulphur normally occurs in primary rocks as sulphides, and tends to be higher in basic than in acid igneous rocks. These sulphides oxidise fairly readily in well-aerated soils, so that sulphate is the normal form of the inorganic sulphur in well-drained soils. Rain also brings down small amounts of sulphur as sulphur dioxide, but this is only appreciable in the neighbourhood of industrial towns. The main source of new sulphates in most soils is in the superphosphate added, for ordinary superphosphate contains about 60 per cent of calcium sulphate.

The main reservoir of available sulphur in most agricultural soils is, however, in the organic matter, for plants take up sulphates from the soil and use them in the synthesis of the amino acids cystine and

[1] M. I. Timonin, *Proc. Soil Sci. Soc. Amer.*, 1947, **11**, 284.

[2] J. M. Bremner *et al.*, *Nature*, 1946, **158**, 790; S. Mattson, *LantbrHögsk. Ann.*, 1948, **15**, 291.

[3] *J Amer. Soc. Agron.*, 1948, **40**, 527.   [4] *Proc. Soil Sci. Soc. Amer.*, 1947, **11**, 206.

[5] G. D. Sherman and P. M. Harmer, *J. Amer. Soc. Agron.*, 1941, **33**, 1080; J. H. Quastel *et al.*, *J. Agric. Sci.*, 1948, **38**, 315.

cysteine, which form a part of many plant proteins. When the plant residues are returned to the soil and attacked by the soil fauna and micro-organisms, some of the sulphur reappears as sulphate, though much remains as part of the soil humus. The sulphur chemistry during humus formation is quite unknown; but, as was discussed on p. 281, the sulphur contents of some Minnesota soils range from about one-hundredth of the carbon content in the prairie soils to between a half and a quarter of this proportion in the podzolic soils.[1]

Little is known about the processes by which organic sulphur is converted into sulphates in well-drained soils and into sulphides if anaerobic conditions set in, for these are the only two simple sulphur compounds present. The first product is probably hydrogen sulphide, or possibly a mercaptan,[2] which can be produced by many micro-organisms from sulphur-containing proteins, and this is then oxidised to sulphates if the oxygen supply is adequate. Probably also many organisms can reduce sulphates to sulphides whenever the oxygen supply in the soil becomes too restricted.

There is another reaction of great importance in some arid soils, namely, the oxidation of elementary sulphur to sulphates, for adding sulphur to an alkaline soil is one of the standard ways of lowering its pH (see p. 614). The only organisms that have definitely been proved to carry out this oxidation are some autotrophic species of the *Thiobacillus* group of bacteria,[3] which appear to be naturally widespread in alkaline soils.

The Nitrogen Compounds

The nitrogen compounds in the soil are derived mainly from proteins synthesised by the plants growing on the soil or by the soil organisms living in the soil, though very little is known about the actual chemical combinations in which they occur. They can, however, be divided into three groups:

1. Nitrogen present as nitrate or ammonium ions, which rarely account for more than 1 to 2 per cent of the total nitrogen present, but which forms the primary source of nitrogen for the crop.

2. Nitrogen present in compounds that decompose fairly readily to give ammonium or nitrate ions, often known as the nitrifiable nitrogen compounds.

3. Nitrogen present in compounds that are only slowly decomposed by the soil population.

[1] C. A. Evans and C. O. Rost, *Soil Sci.*, 1945, **59**, 125.
[2] H. L. A. Tarr, *Biochem. J.*, 1933, **27**, 1869.
[3] For an account of the chemistry of this oxidation, see K. G. Voglu *et al.*, *J. Gen. Physiol.*, 1942, **26**, 89, 103, 157.

There is naturally no sharp division between the second and third groups, but the division has been found useful, particularly under some conditions.

The amount of nitrogen in the soil that is available to the crop during the growing season depends on the rate of nitrate production in the surface soil during the season, and also on the amount of nitrates produced in the previous season that are stored in the subsoil within the range of the crop roots. The rate of nitrate production in the surface soil depends both on the amount and nitrogen content of the readily oxidisable organic matter present, and on the actual rate of oxidation, and this latter is only rapid in moist, well aerated soils.

The quantity of nitrates that can be stored in the subsoil, and the depth from which plant roots can extract this nitrate, depends very largely on the climate. F. J. Sievers and H. F. Holtz[1] showed that on the heavyish soils in the Palouse area much of the nitrates produced during a summer fallow were washed down by the winter rains to a depth between 2 and 5 feet, though some was held in the sixth foot and doubtless some was washed out by the rains; and they showed that the subsequent wheat crop could use much of these nitrates held in the subsoil.

The reason that heavy soils can hold nitrates in their subsoil against drainage during winter is presumably because the drainage water can only move down through cracks and channels in the soil whilst the nitrates can be held inside the principal structural units in the subsoil, through which the drainage water cannot move. Thus, R. Warington[2] long ago showed that the composition of the water first draining out of Broadbalk field at Rothamsted after a heavy rain had almost the same composition as the rain-water itself: it was only in the last runnings that its composition approached that of the soil solution.

This concept of subsoil storage of nitrates over winter on heavy soils explains a number of observations that are otherwise difficult to understand.[3] In the first place, it is only possible on the heavier soils, for in the lighter the main drainage channels are closer together and more evenly distributed throughout the soil, hence there is a much smaller volume of soil available for holding nitrates against drainage. In consequence, it is only on the heavier lands that rotational fallowing is practised, for it is only these that can hold the nitrates produced in the surface soil by the summer cultivations for the use of a crop in the following year.

The effect of rotational fallowing on the wheat yield on Broadbalk furnishes an excellent example. Table 118 shows that one year's fallow

[1] *Washington Agric. Expt. Sta., Bull.* 166, 1922.
[2] *J. Roy. Agric. Soc. England*, 1882, **18**, 1.
[3] E. M. Crowther, *Trans. 3rd Int. Congr. Soil Sci.*, Oxford, 1935, **3**, 126.

TABLE 118

Response of Wheat to a One-year Fallow: Broadbalk, 1935–45
Yield in dressed grain in bushels per acre

Nitrogen manuring in lb. per acre of nitrogen as sulphate of ammonia per year	Years after fallow			Increase in yield over the third and fourth year	
	First	Second	Third and fourth	In first year	In second year
0	30·8	15·1	14·0	15·8	1·1
43	36·2	24·0	22·7	13·5	1·3
86	38·7	30·1	29·3	9·4	0·8
129	39·5	35·2	32·7	6·8	2·5

adds the equivalent of about 90 lb. per acre of nitrate nitrogen, which, as Fig. 22 on p. 303 shows, is considerably less than the extra nitrate nitrogen found in the top 18 inches of soil during the fallowing, for it corresponds to between 15 and 20 p.p.m. of nitrate nitrogen throughout this depth of soil. Yet, as both this figure shows, and as has been subsequently confirmed by J. B. Marshall in 1935,[1] the nitrate nitrogen content in the top 18 inches of fallow soil during the winter is almost the same as in the cropped soil. Hence, this nitrate is presumably held in the subsoil.

This has not been directly proved at Rothamsted because the soil is a gravelly clay, and hence deep subsoil sampling is difficult, but it can be deduced from the response of the following wheat crop to rainfall. The response of wheat to fallow is independent of the winter rainfall, but it is much reduced if the late spring and early summer are wet, presumably because under these moist conditions the wheat remains shallow rooted, and hence its roots do not reach the nitrates stored in the subsoil. This result can be tested in another way on Broadbalk, for on one plot all the sulphate of ammonia given to the wheat is applied in the autumn whilst on the others one quarter is applied in the autumn and three quarters in the spring. The difference between the responses of the wheat to these two treatments does not depend on the winter rainfall, but the autumn nitrogen becomes increasingly ineffective as the late spring and early summer rainfall increases.[2]

On light sandy soils this subsoil storage of nitrates is not possible during moist winters, such as usually occur in the British Isles. Hence, the ideal way for such a soil to carry a store of available nitrogen over the winter is in a succulent green crop which is ploughed in in the

[1] Unpublished Ph.D. Thesis, London.   [2] "Alumnus", J. Agric. Sci., 1932, 22, 101.

spring just before the main crop is to be sown. This is particularly effective if the crop is well established before the winter rains begin and the climate is sufficiently mild for the crop to grow continuously and hence to take nitrates from the soil, during this season. However, over much of this country catch crops have not made much growth before winter begins and make very little during the winter, and this limits the use of green manuring to a few favoured districts only.

The Organic Matter

It has already been stated (see p. 25) that there is no evidence that any of the organic compounds in the soil organic matter are direct nutrients for the plant, yet in many natural soils high crop yields can only be secured if there is an adequate supply of suitable organic matter.

Experimental evidence for the first part of this statement can be found in the Rothamsted field experiments with cereals. Average yields of wheat, barley and mangolds on land that has received adequate fertiliser dressings but no farmyard manure for eighty to a hundred years are as good as on land that has received generous dressings of farmyard manure every year, although the yields on the fertiliser plots are rather more variable. But this could be due to the better physical condition of the manured plots.

A more detailed comparison of fertilisers with farmyard manure was made over a twenty-year period at Askov, in which amounts of fertiliser strictly comparable to that in the farmyard manure were used. Here the fertilisers proved distinctly superior to the manure: indeed, it took twice as much nutrient in the form of farmyard manure to give the same effect as a given dressing of fertiliser.[1]

There are, however, crops that seem to respond especially well to manure in a way that they do not to fertilisers. An example of this has already been given for potatoes on p. 63, and certain fruit bushes may also show this behaviour. But in these examples the improvement in soil condition brought about by the manure is probably a sufficient explanation of its additional beneficial effect. Beans also have been suspected of responding to farmyard manure over and above that due to the nutrients it contains, but there are not sufficient experiments to decide yet if this is a fact, because in much of the earlier work the need for potassium, which is present in considerable quantities in good farmyard manure, was not realised.

[1] K. Iversen, *Ztschr. Pflanz. Düng.*, 1928, B **7**, 457. Reviews of the older work by O. Lemmermann, ibid., 1932, B **11**, 1; M. Gerlach, ibid., p. 385; A. W. Blair, *J. Amer. Soc. Agron.*, 1933, **25**, 540, lead to the general conclusion that after allowing for ordinary nutritive and physical effects there is little left to account for.

Farmyard manure, and other organic manures, can, however, have another very important function in the soil, for they maintain in it an adequate supply of iron[1] and other trace elements needed by the crop in a form available to the crop. This function is particularly important in soils where these elements are rapidly converted into an unavailable form. The mechanism of this process is probably the slow release of these elements during the decomposition of the organic matter, though the possibility of other mechanisms for preventing these elements from being converted into unavailable forms cannot be ruled out. Farmyard manure can even be a valuable carrier of phosphate, and K. T. Hartley[2] has given an example from Nigeria of the great benefit crops receive from dressings as low as 1 to 2 tons per acre of farmyard manure. Here the manure decomposes and releases its phosphate so rapidly that the crop can take up the bulk of it, for 1 ton of manure only contains the same total amount of phosphate as 64 lb. of superphosphate.

Humic colloids, as distinct from decomposing organic matter, may also maintain some inorganic ions in a form available to plant roots under conditions when they would otherwise be converted into unavailable forms if the organic colloids were not present. Thus, humic colloids will help maintain iron and other trace elements in an available form in alkaline soils, and phosphates in an available form in acid soils containing active aluminium, as, for example, in many tropical soils.[3] Though humic colloids are probably the most important agency in the soil having this power, colloidal silicates can also fulfil the same function. Thus, A. Demolon and E. Bastisse[4] showed that the chlorosis of vines and fruit trees that may develop on calcareous soils can sometimes be cured by adding a silicate solution containing iron protected by colloidal silicates.

[1] J. Bonner, *Bot. Gaz.*, 1946, **108**, 267.
[2] *Emp. J. Expt. Agric.*, 1933, **1**, 113 (with M. Greenwood); 1937, **5**, 254.
[3] R. Chaminade, *Ann. Agron.*, 1944, **14**, 1; 1946, **16**, 229; *C.R. Conf. Pédol. Méditerr.*, 1948, 222.
[4] *C.R. Acad. Agric.*, 1944, **30**, 501; *Ann. Agron.*, 1946, **16**, 434.

CHAPTER XXVIII

THE EFFECT OF SOIL ACIDITY AND ALKALINITY ON PLANT GROWTH

The Effect of Soil Acidity

NATURAL SOILS DIFFER considerably in their reaction, or pH, and these differences are reflected in the vegetation or crops they carry. For a long time it was not clear how far these differences were due to the sensitivity of the plant roots to the hydrogen-ion concentration of the soil or soil solution in which they were growing, and how far to secondary effects brought about by the reaction. Water-culture experiments have now proved conclusively that the harmful effects of acidity are due to secondary causes, except in extreme cases. Thus, D. I. Arnon and his co-workers[1] showed that many crops would grow satisfactorily in solution whose pH ranged from pH 4 to 8, provided precautions are taken to eliminate harmful secondary effects, but that plant roots are definitely injured in solutions as acid as pH 3, and are unable to absorb phosphates at pH 9.

The secondary effects of high acidity, or low pH, in a soil are shortage of available calcium and sometimes phosphate and molybdenum on the one hand, and excess of soluble aluminium, manganese,[2] and perhaps other metallic ions on the other. The relative importance of these factors depends on the composition of the soil, in so far as it affects the level of available calcium, phosphate, aluminium and manganese, and on the susceptibility of the crop to a deficiency of calcium or an excess of aluminium or manganese. Excess manganese accumulates in all tissues and interferes with their proper metabolism. Excess aluminium accumulates in the roots[3] and may reduce very considerably their power of translocating phosphates from the soil to the vascular system [4] Excess aluminium may therefore cause the plant to suffer from a phosphate starvation which cannot be corrected by adding phosphate to the soil.[5]

[1] *Plant Physiol.*, 1942, **17**, 515, 525.
[2] For English figures, see T. Wallace *et al.*, *Nature*, 1945, **156**, 778; J. B. Hale and S. G. Heintze, ibid., 1946, **157**, 554. For American figures, see M. J. Funchess, *Alabama Agric. Exp. Sta.*, *Bull.* 201, 1918; H. G. M. Jacobson and T. R. Swanbank, *J. Amer. Soc. Agron.*, 1932, **24**, 237.
[3] For a summary of the literature, see G. E. Hutchinson, *Quart. Rev. Biol.*, 1943, **18**, 128.
[4] K. E. Wright, *Plant Physiol.*, 1943, **18**, 708; E. J. Hewitt, *Long Ashton Ann. Rep.*, 1948, 58.
[5] I am indebted to Professor T. Wallace for this observation.

Crops differ in their susceptibilities to these consequences of acidity, hence it is impossible to draw up any table showing the critical pH at which a given crop begins to suffer severely from acidity, even if any definite meaning could be given to the pH figure. There is no necessary close connection between the pH of a soil and its suitability for a given crop in the moderately acid range.

The relative importance of the three major consequences of soil acidity—low calcium and high aluminium and manganese—affect different crops differently, and only recently has critical work been started to assess their relative importance. E. J. Hewitt,[1] of Long Ashton, has published some preliminary observations. He finds that sugar-beet

TABLE 119

Soil Reaction and Plant Growth
Survey of about 200 Swedish Farms

The unbroken lines indicate frequent occurrence and good yields, the dotted lines poor yields and less common occurrence

pH	7·5	7	6·5	6	5·5	5	4·5
Lucerne							
Sugar-beet							
Barley							
Wheat							
Red clover							
Turnips							
Oats							
Rye							
Swedes							
Timothy							

and potatoes have a high calcium requirement, but whereas sugar-beet is relatively tolerant to high manganese and susceptible to high aluminium, potatoes tend to be relatively susceptible to manganese but tolerant to aluminium. The brassica crops are like potatoes and barley is like sugar-beet except they have lower calcium requirements, whilst oats is a reliable crop on all acid land as it has a low calcium requirement and is tolerant of high aluminium and high manganese. The legumes also differ among themselves in their tolerance to manganese. Thus, lespedeza and sweet clover are sensitive to a high level of manganese, groundnuts are tolerant and cow-peas and soybeans come intermediate;[2]

[1] *Long Ashton Ann. Rep.*, 1947, 82.
[2] H. D. Morris and W. H. Pierre, *Agron. J.*, 1949, **41**, 107.

yet lespedeza, for example, commonly grows well on very acid soils, which must, therefore, presumably be low in manganese.

Lists can, however, be drawn up showing the crops that generally only do well on slightly acid to neutral soils, and those that will tolerate more acid conditions. Thus, in England, lucerne, barley, sugar-beet and mangolds are only considered suitable for neutral to mildly acid soils; wheat, red clover, peas, beans and vetches will often succeed in rather more acid soils; and white clover, many grasses, oats, rye, lupins and potatoes will grow on soils too acid for the others.[1] Among subtropical crops tolerant of acid conditions are lespedeza, soybeans and some varieties of beans, millets, sorghums, including sudan grass, and sweet potatoes.

Table 119, which gives a summary of a cropping survey on 200 Swedish farms made by O. Arrhenius,[2] illustrates this by showing the actual cropping practised by farmers on soils of different *p*H. But this table must be correctly interpreted: it does not show the optimum value of the *p*H for any crop, but only the tolerance of the crop to acidity. Thus oats, rye, swedes and potatoes[3] can all be grown as successfully in neutral as in acid soils, though true calcifuge plants, such as lupins among agricultural crops, and heaths and rhododendrons among shrubs, will only thrive on acid land, probably because of their intolerance of a high level of calcium, though perhaps in part because they cannot obtain iron from nearly neutral soils.

A point of some importance arises here. If one has an acid soil, should one regard the acidity as inherent, and crop the soil accordingly with acid-tolerant crops, or should one neutralise the acidity and have greater freedom of cropping? The same point arises on low phosphate soils: should one choose crops that can stand low phosphate status, or should one raise the soil's phosphate status? In either case the undesirable condition may be aggravated by continuous cropping with tolerant crops.

Two other points on the effect of soil acidity on the distribution of crops can be made. Liberal dressings of farmyard manure ameliorate the effects of acidity, and for reasons not fully explained, crops are more tolerant of acidity in cool, moist climates than in warm, dry ones. Thus, crops can be successfully grown on more acid soils in parts of Wales, Scotland and Scandinavia than in the southern and eastern parts of England.

The second point is that variations in soil reactions may affect the susceptibility or resistance of the crop to a particular fungus disease.

[1] For a more detailed discussion, see H. W. Gardner and H. V. Garner, *The Use of Lime*, London, 1953.   [2] *Kalkfrage, Bodenreaktion und Pflanzenwachstum.*, Leipzig, 1926.
[3] For example, O. Smith (*Cornell Agric. Expt. Sta.*, *Bull.* 664, 1937) found potatoes grew equally well in soil between *p*H 4·8 and 7·1.

Thus, *Plasmodiophora brassicae*, the fungus that causes finger-and-toe, or club-root in the cultivated brassica crops (swedes, turnips, cabbage, etc.) tolerates soil acidity better than its host crop, and is therefore most likely to be injurious on acid soils. Addition of lime reduces the acidity and either makes the soil less suited to the pathogen or increases the resistance of the crop to the fungus. Table 120 gives some examples of this correlation between the *p*H of the soil and the incidence of

TABLE 120

pH Values for Pairs of Comparable Soils Differing as Habitats for Plants or Micro-organisms[1]

Centre	Crop	Condition	pH	Condition	pH
(1) Rothamsted	Swedes	Finger-and-toe	5·85	No finger-and-toe	7·90
,,	,,	,, ,,	6·05	,, ,,	7·87
(2) Garforth .	,,	,, ,,	5·66	,, ,,	6·13
(3) Aberdeen .	Turnips	Much finger-and-toe	6·21	Little finger-and-toe	7·13
(4) Somerset .	Barley	Failure	4·41	Good	5·77
(5) Ipswich .	Lucerne	,,	6·15	,,	7·86
(6) Carrington[2]	—	Uncultivated	3·01	Cultivated	5·52
Moss .	—	Bad field	4·88	Good field	5·14
(7) Pusey .	Potatoes	Much scab	7·40	Little Scab	6·13
	,,	,,	7·65	,,	6·75

the disease.[3] On the other hand, *Actinomycetes chromogenus* (*Oospora*), potato scab, is less tolerant of acidity than its host, and over a certain range potatoes can be grown well without fear of attack. Even though their soils need lime for other crops, Cheshire farmers do not add it until after the potatoes are lifted, otherwise "scab" may develop. Potatoes need calcium on more acid soils, but care must be exercised in applying lime or "scab" results. Thus, W. L. Nelson and N. C. Brady[4] found that potatoes growing on very acid soil (*p*H 4·2) could get all the calcium they needed if the lime was mixed with the subsoil only, so allowing the tubers themselves to grow in the surface soil that was too acid for the pathogen. The fungus causing "take-all" in wheat (*Ophiobolus graminis*) develops much more readily in slightly alkaline than in acid conditions: it is liable to do damage on calcareous soils, but not on slightly acid sands or heavy loams.

[1] E. M. Crowther, *J. Agric. Sci.*, 1925, **15**, 201.
[2] These soils have been discussed by E. Price Evans, *J. Ecol.*, 1925, **11**, 64.
[3] For further field trials on the control of the disease by liming, see J. Hendrick, *Trans. Highl. Agric. Soc. Scotland*, 1918, **30**, 137.
[4] *Proc. Soil Sci. Soc. Amer.*, 1944, **8**, 313.

The effects of acidity are usually more marked in meadows and pastures than on arable land, for here very many species of plants are growing in competition with each other. Plants which tolerate acidity a little better than their neighbours will tend to spread at their expense, and come to dominate the flora of acid soils, though they do not necessarily thrive best in acid soils in the absence of competition. This effect of pH on the floristic composition of some Danish meadows is

TABLE 121

Average Frequency[1] *of Meadow Species on Soils of Different pH Values*

pH range	3.5–3.9	4–4.4	4.5–4.9	5–5.4	5.5–5.9	6–6.4	6.5–6.9	7–7.4	7.5–7.9	No. of localities
Deschampsia flexuosa . .	86	68	40	—	—	—	—	—	—	13
Calluna vulgaris	20	47	10	20	—	—	—	—	—	13
Gallium hercynicum . .	94	77	40	20	15	—	—	—	—	18
Potentilla erectum	67	99	63	73	48	45	10	20	—	39
Agrostis canina .	—	100	100	73	63	100	—	—	—	12
Festuca ovina .	—	100	47	35	20	20	50	—	—	12
Anthoxanthum odoratum .	33	47	79	80	83	76	27	30	30	46
Deschampsia caespitosa . .	—	—	—	40	67	62	33	52	23	33
Circium oleraceum . .	—	—	—	—	—	—	50	100	80	8
Angelica sylvestris . .	—	—	—	—	—	35	33	48	30	14
Tussilago farfara .	—	—	—	—	—	10	10	55	80	9
Agrostis alba .	—	—	—	—	—	—	30	65	60	7

illustrated in Table 121.[2] It is also well shown in the Rothamsted grass plots, in which the manuring has been unaltered for ninety years in some cases.[3] The effect of high acidity can be indirect, for when the soil becomes too acid, the soil fauna becomes very restricted. Thus earthworms die out, so there is no mechanism for mixing the surface litter with the soil, and the activity of the surface feeding fauna becomes sufficiently low to allow a mat of dead vegetation to form on the surface under which, and in which, the seedlings of most plants cannot germinate. Again, hill pastures in Great Britain can have the feeding value of their herbage greatly increased by liming and phosphating, for this

[1] The frequency is determined on ten trial areas each of 0·1 sq. m. at each centre. If a plant is found on eight of these areas at one centre, the frequency is 80 per cent. The figures in the table are the average of the frequencies at all the centres.
[2] C. Olsen, *C.R. Lab. Carlsberg*, 1923, **15**, 1.
[3] For an account of the floristic compositions of these plots, see W. E. Brenchley, *Manuring of Grassland for Hay*, London, 1924.

causes the coarse *Nardus* and *Agrostis* grasses to be replaced by more nutritious species, such as rye-grass and rough- and smooth-stalked meadow grass.[1] Even on ordinary pastures the herbage depends on the acidity of the soil, and, as W. R. G. Atkins and E. W. Fenton[2] showed, cattle and sheep tend to graze the less acid areas more closely than the more acid ones. Thus they found the animals only reluctantly grazed the pasture where its pH was under 5, and preferred the areas where it was over 6·5.

The Lime Requirement of a Soil

Soil acidity can be corrected by applying chalk or limestone to a soil. This practice is very ancient: Pliny[3] describes the method the Belgae used for chalking their land, and his description held almost exactly for the traditional method in the English Home Counties until the end of the nineteenth century.[4] The amount of chalk applied per acre was very high, and the dressing given at long intervals. But it is possible that these very heavy dressings had some subsidiary benefits in addition to the correction of soil acidity. Thus it is probable that the chalk often contained some available phosphate, and it may have improved the soil structure as well[5] (see p. 434).

Present-day agriculture requires, for financial reasons, much smaller and more frequent dressings; and this is particularly important on some sandy and organic soils in which crop yields can be reduced if too high a dressing of lime is applied (see p. 533). For this reason the early soil chemists sought for methods to estimate the minimum amount of calcium carbonate or lime that must be added to a soil to neutralise its acidity, and this quantity they called its "lime requirement". We now know we can attach no definite meaning to the phrase "to neutralise the acidity of a soil", so correspondingly this is an inadequate definition of the lime requirement. Nor can we define the lime requirements of a soil as the amount of lime needed to give maximum crop yields, for crops vary in their requirements. We can only define it as the amount needed to give maximum economic return from the crop rotation we wish to follow.

Liming an acid soil can have several immediate consequences. Thus it automatically raises the pH and raises the lime potential (see p. 111), and the calcium ion concentration in the soil solution. It will result both in calcium ions displacing aluminium ions from the clay, and in raising

[1] See, for example, W. E. J. Milton, *J. Ecol.*, 1940, **28**, 326; 1947, **35**, 65.
[2] *Sci. Proc. Roy. Dublin Soc.*, 1930, **19**, 533.
[3] *Naturalis Historiae*, Lib. 17, Cap. 4.
[4] E. J. Russell, *J. Bd. Agric.*, 1916, **23**, 625.
[5] For an example, see B. Roscoe, *Plant and Soil*, 1960, **12**, 17.

the pH of the soil solution, so causing the precipitation of some of the aluminium ions it contains as aluminium hydroxide. A. Mehlich[1] has shown, however, that in some soils having a high aluminium ion concentration in the soil solution, manganese may also precipitate out at a lower pH than if only a little aluminium is present, presumably because it is precipitating on the freshly formed aluminium hydroxide. This may be the explanation of the observed fact that liming some very acid soils up to pH 6·5 can induce severe manganese deficiency.

Liming the soil also increases the degree of saturation of the exchange complex with calcium. The older workers assumed it was desirable to saturate the soil to about pH 7, but A. Mehlich and his colleagues[2] have put forward evidence that for many crops it is only necessary to neutralise the permanent negative charge on the clay particles, that is, to have only a small proportion of exchangeable aluminium ions on the clay. The difference between this concept and that of saturating the soil to pH 7 is not very large in practice for soils whose clay fraction is predominantly composed of micaceous minerals, but the difference can be very great for soils whose clays are kaolinitic, for these have a larger pH-dependent charge than permanent negative charge. Certainly in the tropics and sub-tropics where many of the well-drained soils are kaolinitic, liming only improves crop yields on very acid soils, and usually reduces yields on moderately acid soils.

Historically, however, the lime requirement concept in Western Europe has been based on determining the amount of lime needed to raise the soil to a given pH, very often 6·5 or pH 7.[3] One can determine this for a soil sample in the laboratory, but if one then applies this amount of lime to the soil in the field, the field pH does not rise as much as expected. This is illustrated in Fig. 47 for two Danish acid soils,[4] which shows that the soil in the field needs two to three times more lime to bring its pH up to a selected value than is indicated by the laboratory titration curve. This factor is known as the liming factor, and is based on the assumption that the calcium carbonate is uniformly distributed throughout the top 20 cm. of soil, which is assumed to weigh 2·4 million kg. per hectare.

R. L. Mitchell[5] found a similar factor for four out of five Scottish soils, although the fifth soil gave a factor nearer to unity. O. de Vries and P. Bruin[6] found many Dutch soils had a liming factor of 2 and

[1] *Proc. Soil Sci. Soc. Amer.*, 1957, **21**, 625.

[2] For a review of their ideas, see N. T. Coleman, E. J. Kamprath and S. B. Weed, *Adv. Agron.*, 1958, **10**, 475.

[3] For a comparison of several methods in use, see R. F. Innes and H. F. Birch, *J. Agric. Sci.*, 1945, **35**, 236, and S. K. Mukherjee *et al.*, *Ind. J. Agric. Sci.*, 1944, **14**, 74, 203.

[4] From H. R. Christensen and S. Tovborg Jensen, *Trans. 2nd Comm. Int. Soc. Soil Sci.*, Groningen, 1926 A, 94.

[5] *J. Agric. Sci.*, 1936, **26**, 664. See L. A. Whelan, ibid., 1939, **29**, 306, for a continuation of this work. [6] *Emp. J. Expt. Agric.*, 1947, **15**, 260.

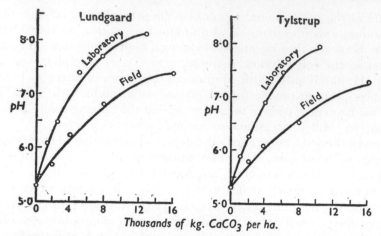

FIG. 47. Influence of successive additions of CaCo³ on the pH values of two acid soils in the laboratory and the field respectively.

about one-third had one of 3, and L. E. Dunn[1] found some medium to heavy soils in western Washington had liming factors under 2.

The full explanation of the cause of this liming factor has not been critically examined. In part it is due to the added calcium carbonate taking several years to achieve its full influence on the pH of the soil, during which time an appreciable amount of the carbonate has been washed out. And in part it may be due to the conditions under which the pH is measured, as it is possible that if all the pH values of the soil were determined in 0·01 M calcium chloride the discrepancy between the laboratory and the field would be much less marked.

Some confusion has been caused by the use of the word "lime" for the material added to the soil to neutralise soil acidity. At the present time, lime usually refers to calcium oxide, also called burnt or quick-lime, or to calcium hydroxide, also called hydrated or slaked lime; but in the past it also included calcium carbonate, as can be seen in the word limestone. There is no accepted word for a material that neutralises soil acidity, which must include not only these compounds but also some slags and other forms of calcium silicate, and the phrase "liming material" must often be used. The question arises whether any particular form of liming material is better than any other, and in particular if there is any object in using fuel to burn limestone or chalk to convert it into the oxide or hydroxide. There used to be an advantage because it was once the easiest way to convert the rock into a powder, but crushing machinery is now available for grinding limestones to any degree of fineness. Finely divided calcium oxide and

[1] *Soil Sci.*, 1943, **56**, 341.

hydroxide when mixed with the soil are rapidly converted into the carbonate and though it is possible that either may neutralise soil acidity rather faster than finely ground carbonate, there seems to be no field evidence that this is of any practical consequence if the liming material is applied one or two months before the crop is planted, and in fact the long-term effect of all liming materials on other soil properties, such as the level of the soil organic matter, appears to be independent of whether calcium oxide or carbonate is used.[1]

The calcium carbonate must, however, be crushed if it is to become available fairly quickly in the soil. If it is chalk, crushing to a fine powder is technically simple, although the chalk may have to be dried beforehand. If the carbonate is a limestone rock, the coarser the material can be ground, the cheaper will be the process. Limestone crushed to pass a 10-mesh screen (aperture 2·0 mm.), but to be retained by a 30-mesh (aperture 0·59 mm.) takes longer to affect the pH of a soil than if it is crushed to pass a 100-mesh sieve (aperture 0·15 mm.), but twelve months after application the effects of the coarse and the fine are about equal, and for the next few years the residual effects of the coarse are rather higher than of the fine, as the fine washes out quicker in the drainage water.[2] Limestone coarser than 2 mm. is, however, an inefficient liming material. Now the process of crushing limestone rock produces fragments of many sizes, from fine dust upwards. Thus limestone crushed to pass a 10-mesh or a 20-mesh sieve may contain 25 per cent or 45 per cent of material that passes a 100-mesh sieve. Hence, this material, which is what the crushing mills naturally produce, is agriculturally preferable to material crushed and screened to a uniform size. Whether passing a 10-mesh or a 20-mesh sieve is the preferable upper limit of size has not been fully investigated, but for many limestones there appears to be little to choose between them; the important thing is to have a considerable variation in particle size in the material to ensure both rapid action initially and a reasonably long residual action.[3]

Now calcium bicarbonate is being continually washed out of the soil at an average annual rate equivalent to 2–4 cwt. of $CaCO_3$ per acre, as can be seen from the table on p. 555, but this rate depends on the amount and the solubility of calcium carbonate in the soil. Thus T. W. Walker[4] found for a sandy soil having a lime requirement of

[1] For the results of the Pennsylvania trials on this point, see J. W. White and F. J. Holben, *Soil Sci.*, 1924, **18**, 201.

[2] For American results, see W. H. Pierre, *Soil Sci.*, 1930, **29**, 137; T. L. Lyon, *Cornell Agric. Expt. Sta.*, Bull. 531, 1931; W. H. MacIntire *et al.*, *J. Amer. Soc. Agron.*, 1933, **25**, 285; R. H. Walker and P. E. Brown, *Iowa Agric. Expt. Sta.*, *Res. Bull.* 178, 1935. For New Zealand results, B. W. Doak, *N.Z. J. Sci. Tech.*, 1941, **23** A, 24.

[3] For an example, see W. A. Albrecht, *Soil Sci.*, 1946, **61**, 265.

[4] *J. Soil Sci.*, 1952, **3**, 261.

40 cwt. per acre of calcium carbonate, that the rate of loss of added calcium carbonate was as follows:

Dressing applied	100	50	25 cwt. per acre CaCO$_3$
	Rate of loss of added CaCO$_3$		in cwt. per annum
During first 5 years	8	5	3
second	4	$2\frac{1}{2}$	$1\frac{1}{2}$
third	2	1	$\frac{1}{2}$
Total loss in 15 years	70	42	25

P. Tuorila[1] has also found from the analyses of many Finnish liming experiments that the average annual loss of calcium carbonate from acid soils was roughly proportional to the dressings of calcium carbonate given, and that the effects of suitable dressings last for about eight to ten years, during which time between one-half and one-third of the calcium added has been lost in the drainage water. The present statutory compensation for the residual value of calcium carbonate allowed to outgoing tenants in England is based on the assumption that one-eighth of the carbonate is lost each year.

This rate of loss of carbonate probably depends on the fineness of grinding the limestone: the coarser the grinding, the smaller will be the loss in the first two to three years. But no figures appear to be available to show the magnitude of this effect.

The Effect of Soil Alkalinity

The harmful effects of high alkalinity are again usually due to consequences of the alkalinity rather than to the hydroxyl ions themselves. The great difficulties experienced by plants growing in alkaline soils are absorbing enough iron, manganese, boron and perhaps other trace elements on the one hand, and phosphates on the other, not because their roots are incapable of absorbing these nutrients from solutions at these pHs, but because the nutrients are in so insoluble a form that the roots cannot bring enough of them into solution for their requirements. These harmful effects can often be seen when acid sandy soils, particularly when high in organic matter, are heavily limed.

Calcareous soils free from sodium salts cannot have a pH exceeding 8·2 to 8·4, for, as explained on p. 108, a moist calcareous soil would have a pH of 8·4 when in equilibrium with air having the same carbon dioxide content as in the atmosphere, and at this pH the concentration of these essential ions is too low for the plant to obtain an adequate supply.

---

[1] *Svenska Vall-o. MosskForën. Tidskr.*, 1945, **7**, 83. For an example from Woburn, see E. J. Russell and J. A. Voelcker, *Fifty Years of Field Experiments at Woburn*, London, 1936.

The maximum pH which a soil can have for these ions to be present in an adequate concentration for the crop has not been worked out, and in fact this particular problem is probably not worth the tackling because of the inherent limitations in the meaning that can be given to the phrase "the pH of the soil". But the pH of the soil solution in a calcareous soil, which is an important factor controlling the availability of these nutrient ions, depends on its carbon dioxide content,[1] hence the problem that probably can be profitably investigated is to find the minimum carbon dioxide content of the soil air that allows the crop to take up enough of these nutrients.

The consequences of the variations of carbon dioxide content on the availability of these nutrients in different types of calcareous soils have not been worked out quantitatively.[2] But the general consequences are clear. Sandy soils are usually better aerated than loams and clays, and nutritional troubles due to over-liming are usually confined to such soils. The carbon dioxide concentration in a soil can be increased by rolling it, and heavy rolling is essential on many of the lighter calcareous soils for good germination and early growth. Pastures have a higher carbon dioxide content than arable, and grassing down miserable orchards on light or thin calcareous soils often increases their health and vigour markedly. This is not to imply that pH or carbon dioxide content of the soil air is the sole factor responsible for the nutrient deficiencies that occur on calcareous or over-limed soils, for some of the factors that increase the carbon dioxide concentration in the soil also increase the amount of potassium taken up by the crop, for some reason not yet explained (see p. 640). Further, as T. Wallace and E. J. Hewitt[3] have pointed out, anything that increases the potassium uptake in calcareous soils is particularly important because potassium deficiency sometimes induces iron deficiency or chlorosis—one of the characteristic troubles of calcareous soils.

A practical consequence of this danger of over-liming is that naturally well aerated soils, such as light sands and many peats, must never be given large dressings of calcium carbonate, for this either causes the whole soil, or very many pockets in the soil to have too high a pH. It is usually desirable to aim at maintaining the pH of such soils at under rather than over 6·5, and they should be given frequent light applications of lime. Very difficult problems may arise, however, when one sets out to reclaim a very acid heath: one must normally apply only

[1] For illustrations of the importance of this for phosphate uptake, see T. F. Buehrer, *Arizona Agric. Exp. Sta., Tech. Bull.* 42, 1932; W. T. McGeorge *et al., J. Amer. Soc. Agron.*, 1935, **27**, 330.

[2] For an example of the effect of the CO_2 content of soil water on the level of available manganese in a soil, see B. D. Bolas, *Nature*, 1948, **162**, 737.

[3] *J. Pomol.*, 1946, **22**, 153.

sufficient lime to allow acid-tolerant crops such as potatoes and rye to be grown and slowly increase the calcium status until the full range of farm crops can be taken.

Soils can only have pHs exceeding 8·4 if they contain appreciable quantities of exchangeable sodium. The maximum recorded pH for a soil is probably 10·0 for an alkali soil at field capacity containing sodium carbonate in the State of Washington:[1] its pH in a 1 : 5 water suspension was 10·75. Soils containing exchangeable sodium but no calcium carbonate can, in fact, have their pHs raised to high values by applying calcium carbonate, for this allows some sodium carbonate to be formed by exchange.

In humid soils the main change of reaction that one wants to bring about is raising the pH, but in arid regions it is often desirable to lower it. One way of doing this is to increase the CO_2 content in the soil air, by, for example, ploughing in manure or green manure. Another way is to apply sulphur to the soil, which is oxidised to sulphuric acid by certain soil bacteria that seem to be widely distributed in alkaline soils. Aluminium sulphate has also been used, for the aluminium is precipitated either as hydroxide or basic sulphate with the liberating of sulphuric acid, but it is not as efficient as sulphur on the basis of equal sulphur contents. These two methods can naturally be combined in the use of sulphur composts, made by adding sulphur to the plant residues when they are put into the compost heap, and this is probably the most satisfactory method for horticultural or orchard crops. These methods are, however, discussed in more detail on p. 614.

W. T. McGeorge[2] has given examples of the value of adding sulphur or other acid materials to fertilisers to improve their effectiveness on alkaline soils. The sulphur, by increasing the soil acidity, helps the crop to take up more iron, manganese and often zinc, as well as phosphate, and, in fact, the use of acid phosphates, or sulphur-phosphate mixtures is strongly recommended for the Arizona conditions. In the same way ammonium fertilisers are usually more effective than nitrates,[3] presumably because they tend to leave the soil more acid.

[1] W. P. Kelley and S. M. Brown, *J. Amer. Soc. Agron.*, 1939, **31**, 41.
[2] *Arizona Agric. Expt. Sta., Tech. Bull.* 101, 1943.
[3] K. Mehring, *Landw. Jahrb.*, 1935, **79**, 481.

CHAPTER XXIX

THE EFFECT OF A GROWING PLANT ON THE SOIL

LIVING PLANT ROOTS can affect the biotic conditions in the soil by their differential absorption of nutrients from it and by their excretions into it.

Plant roots take up their anions and cations preferentially, so do not necessarily take equivalent quantities of each from the soil solution. Hence, the plant may cause a shift in the pH of the soil for this reason. This effect has been known for a long time. Thus, W. Knop[1] found that if plants grew in culture solution containing nitrates the solution became progressively more alkaline until the plants suffered from chlorosis and died. Shortly afterwards F. Rautenberg and G. Kühn[2] found that if the culture solution contained ammonium salts it became progressively more acid. In 1881 A. Mayer,[3] in discussing some of the erratic results obtained with potassic fertilisers, suggested that the preferential uptake of potassium by plants might produce acidity in the same way as with ammonium salts. He introduced a classification of fertilisers into—

(1) Physiologically acid, e.g. ammonium and potassium salts.
(2) Physiologically neutral, e.g. calcium and magnesium sulphates, superphosphates and calcium chloride.
(3) Physiologically alkaline, e.g. Chilean nitrate, calcium carbonate, lime.

These results, based on the results of pot experiments, cannot properly be used to estimate the corresponding effect of the fertiliser in the soil. Thus, in arable soils acidification by ammonium salts is primarily due to nitrification, but the term physiological acidity may be retained if it is extended to include the removal of ammonium by micro-organisms as well as by plants. Nitrates undoubtedly conserve soil bases and reduce soil acidity and may correctly be termed physiologically basic in Mayer's sense. Potassium salts have no appreciable effect on soil reaction and are not physiologically acid in this wider sense, although in culture solutions and in sand the acidity produced by growing plants may be measured and used to increase the availability of relatively insoluble phosphates.[4] Mayer correctly regarded superphosphate as

---

[1] *Landw. Vers.-Stat.*, 1861, **3**, 295.   [2] *Landw. Vers.-Stat.*, 1864, **6**, 358.
[3] *Landw. Vers.-Stat.*, 1881, **26**, 77; *J. Landw.*, 1864, **12**, 107.
[4] D. N. Prianischnikov, *Die Düngerlehre*, Berlin, 1923; *Ztschr. Pflanz. Düng.*, 1933, A **30**, 38.

physiologically neutral in spite of the acidity of its solutions, but many later writers erroneously assumed that superphosphate increased soil acidity. Alkaline materials, such as lime or basic slag, should not be described as "physiologically" basic.

Plants take up different amounts and different proportions of nutrients from a soil according to their species. The exact amounts taken up depend on the soil conditions (see p. 461), but certain broad generalisations can be made. Table 122 shows typical quantities of

TABLE 122

Amounts of Various Substances Absorbed from an Acre of Soil by the Common Agricultural Crops of England

	At harvest lb.*	Dry lb.*	Total pure ash lb.	Nitrogen lb.	Sulphur lb.	Potassium lb.	Sodium lb.	Calcium lb.	Magnesium lb.	Phosphorus lb.	Chlorine lb.	Silicon lb.
Wheat, grain, 30 bush.	1800	1530	30	34	2·7	7·7	0·5	0·7	2·2	6·2	0·1	0·3
straw	3160	2650	142	16	5·1	16·2	1·5	5·9	2·1	3·0	2·4	45·0
Total crop	4960	4180	172	50	7·8	23·9	2·0	6·6	4·3	9·2	2·5	45·3
Oats, grain, 45 bush.	1890	1630	51	34	3·2	7·5	0·6	1·3	2·2	5·7	0·5	9·3
straw	2830	2350	140	18	4·8	30·7	3·4	7·0	3·1	2·8	6·1	30·6
Total crop	4720	3980	191	52	8·0	38·2	4·0	8·3	5·3	8·5	6·6	39·9
Beans, grain, 30 bush.	1920	1610	58	78	4·4	20·2	0·4	2·1	2·5	10·0	1·1	0·2
straw	2240	1850	99	29	4·9	35·5	1·3	18·8	3·4	2·7	4·3	3·2
Total crop	4160	3460	157	107	9·3	55·7	1·7	20·9	5·9	12·7	5·4	3·4
Meadow hay, 1½ tons	3360	2820	203	49	5·7	42·3	6·8	22·9	8·7	5·4	14·6	26·6
Red clover hay, 2 tons	4480	3760	258	98	9·4	69·1	3·8	64·4	17·0	10·9	9·8	3·3
Turnips, roots, 17 tons	38100	3130	218	61	15·2	90·1	12·6	18·2	3·4	9·8	10·9	1·2
leaf	11400	1530	146	49	5·7	33·4	5·6	34·6	2·3	4·7	11·2	2·4
Total crop	49500	4660	364	110	20·9	123·5	18·2	52·8	5·7	14·5	22·1	3·6
Mangolds, roots, 22 tons	49300	5910	426	98	4·9	185·0	51·5	11·3	11·0	15·4	42·5	4·1
leaf	18200	1650	254	51	9·1	64·7	36·6	19·3	14·6	7·6	40·6	4·3
Total crop	67500	7560	680	149	14·0	249·7	88·1	30·6	25·6	23·0	83·1	8·4
Potatoes, tubers, 6 tons	13400	3360	127	46	2·7	63·5	2·8	2·4	3·8	9·4	4·4	1·2

* Weight of crop. The yields quoted are not averages, though they are commonly obtained on farms.

various substances English crops remove from the soil,[1] and E. Wolff[2] and H. Wilfarth and his co-workers[3] have published other tables. They all show that cereals absorb less mineral nutrients per acre than any other crop studied, although they give a large amount of dry matter per acre. The animal fodder crops—grass and clover hay and the root crops—all take up large amounts of nutrients, and hence the need for good conservation of the nutrients in farmyard manure made from these crops, otherwise the soil will rapidly become impoverished. A consequence of this differential absorption of nutrients by crops is that if the nutrient status of the soil is low, crops taking large amounts of

[1] R. Warington, The Chemistry of the Farm, 4th ed., London, 1886.
[2] Aschen Analysen, Berlin, 1871.　　　　　　[3] Landw. Vers.-Stat., 1905, 63, 1.

nutrients from a soil leave it poorer than crops only taking small amounts of nutrients. Thus, on acid soils with low base reserves at the Rhode Island Station[1] crops sensitive to acidity do much worse after mangolds, which take up large amounts of base, than after the grass red top (*Agrostis alba*) which takes up much less.

Roots excrete carbon dioxide, or carbonic acid, into the soil solution, but this will only affect the acidity of the soil, or its base reserves, in so far as the carbonic acid is neutralised by calcium and washed out as calcium bicarbonate during periods of strong leaching. It will normally not affect the soil acidity in so far as the carbon dioxide excreted enters the soil air and is exchanged for atmospheric oxygen by diffusion.

Some plant roots excrete substances that are harmful to young roots of other plants (see p. 546); some varieties of flax excrete prussic acid,[2] HCN, which protects their roots from attack by some pathogenic fungi; some species of lupins apparently excrete acids that can bring relatively insoluble phosphates into solution (see p. 500). Plant roots probably also excrete enzymes such as ureases and phosphatases into the soil, but these may be introduced through the sloughing-off and decomposition of dead tissue and not be an actual excretion, though the separation of these two processes may be very artificial. Plant roots also probably supply the soil micro-organisms with some nutrients and growth factors, for they often carry a large microbial population (see p. 226), but although part of these nutrients may be excreted by the roots, the organisms may also take a proportion from the outer cells of the roots, possibly through the agency of fungi that have part of their mycelia within and part outside the roots.

Plant roots can also affect the organisms living in the soil. This subject has received very little study so far, but some information is available on the relation between the type of crop and wireworms.[3] Wireworms feed on the roots of most farm crops, but they cannot feed on flax or linseed roots. Beans, and perhaps peas, however, appear to excrete something into the soil that actually kills them, for A. C. Evans[4] at Rothamsted, found that a bean crop has a very powerful depressing effect on wireworm number—an effect not shown, for example, by linseed, whose roots are merely inedible to them.

Plants can also excrete inorganic cations and probably anions as well. This has been proved for potassium, calcium and phosphates (see p. 29 and p. 471) and probably ammonium,[5] and has been claimed for other ions, but with less satisfactory experimental evidence.

[1] B. L. Hartwell, *J. Amer. Soc. Agron.*, 1927, **19**, 255, gives a summary of these results.
[2] See, for example, M. I. Timonin (*Soil Sci.*, 1941, **52**, 395).
[3] See, for example, *Min. Agric. Bull.* 128, 1944.   [4] *Ann. Appl. Biol.*, 1944, **31**, 235.
[5] D. N. Prianischnikov, *Trans. 3rd Int. Congr. Soil Sci.*, Oxford, 1935, **1**, 207; *Ztschr. Pflanz. Düng.*, 1934, A **33**, 134.

Plants can therefore affect the pH of the soil in which they are growing by two well-proven means: excretion of carbon dioxide and differential uptake of anions and cations. Claims have been made that by these processes the plant can change the pH of its medium from one unfavourable to one more favourable for its growth,[1] but not enough work has yet been done on this subject to say how far this is a correct generalisation.

Plant roots can also have two physical effects in the soil. Some can bind soil particles together into strong and characteristic crumbs, and this is particularly marked with some grasses, an effect that has already been discussed on p. 445, and some roots are such strong growers that they can penetrate even quite compact subsoils, and hence a succession of such crops can improve the drainage or aeration of the subsoil. Lupins have been used in Germany to penetrate the hard pan underlying some of their sandy soils; lucerne and sweet clover have been used in irrigated regions to improve the drainage through a compact subsoil, and trees are sometimes used in the tropics for the same purpose, so reducing the amount of rain that runs off the soil surface and in consequence its erosive action.[2]

The Effect of a Crop on its Successor

Crops can influence their successors through the amount of water or available nutrients they leave behind in the soil and through their residues, which may be either beneficial or harmful. At one time various workers, such as de Candolle, assumed that plants could excrete toxins from their roots which remained in the soil for some time and which injured other plants of the same species, and that this was the reason why crops grew better in rotation than in continuous cropping. But C. G. B. Daubeny[3] at Oxford showed experimentally that this was not the correct explanation for the practice of crop rotation. He grew eighteen different crops continuously on the same plots, and compared the yields with those obtained when the same crops were shifted from one plot to another, so that no crop ever followed another of the same kind. No manure was supplied. The results showed a gradual decrease in the yield in almost every instance, and the decrease was generally greater when the crop was repeated year after year on the same plot than where it was shifted from one to another. Nevertheless, the difference between the yields in the two cases was not sufficient to justify any assumption of the existence of a toxin, except perhaps in the

[1] See, for example, A. Koslowska, *J. Ecol.*, 1934, **22**, 396; H. Kaserer, *Bodenk. PflErnähr.*, **21–22**, 1941, 697.

[2] For a short bibliography on this subject, see *Imp. Bur. Soil Sci., Tech. Comm.* **22**, 1931.

[3] *Phil. Trans.*, 1845, p. 179.

case of *Euphorbia lathyris*; in the other seventeen cases it was attributed to the more rapid removal from the continuous plots of the mineral nutrients required by the plant. This explanation was supported by analyses of the plant ash and of the soil—analyses which led to the important distinction between "available" and "unavailable" plant food.

Farmers have, however, found by experience that crops grow better in rotation than in continuous succession. It is true that continuous cropping is possible: the Broadbalk wheat field at Rothamsted has already produced more than a hundred crops of wheat in succession with only a few fallows for weed control, and the Woburn Stackyard field produced more than fifty; but it is more difficult to secure good yields on Broadbalk than on Agdell Field, where wheat is grown only once in four-year rotation, other crops being taken in the intervening years (Table 123). But the cause of this benefit of the rotation is not due to the Broadbalk soil becoming "wheat-sick", though a quantitative explanation of the benefits of rotational cropping has not been worked out.

TABLE 123

Wheat Grown in Different Rotations but without Manure at Rothamsted

(1) Grown Continuously (2) in Alternation with Fallow
(3) in Four-course Rotation

Average for the year 1851 and every fourth year thereafter until 1927

Dressed grain in bushels per acre

Continuous wheat (Broadbalk, Plot 3)	Wheat after fallow (Hoosfield)	Rotation wheat (Agdell Field, Plot 5) formerly 21–22
11·3	14·0	24·0

The one group of crops that cannot be long grown continuously on the same piece of land are the legumes, and in particular clover and beans. Land continuously cropped to clover soon becomes clover-sick, and the lower the soil is in organic matter, the sooner clover-sickness sets in. The cause of this clover-sickness is almost certainly due to toxic substances produced by the clover roots: it or they can be destroyed by heating the soil when moist to 70°C., or by air-drying the soil in thin layers, and new clover plants can be protected from its toxic effects if large quantities of farmyard manure are added to the soil, but the toxic substance itself has not yet been isolated.[1]

[1] These remarks apply to clover-sick Woburn soils. I am indebted to H. G. Thornton and H. H. Mann for these unpublished results.

The principal arable crop that affects its successors in English farming is clover: a one-year clover ley can improve the following crop very considerably due to the nitrogen it adds to the soil. This is shown in Table 124,[1] which gives the yield of wheat after fallow and after three different one-year leys from which either two hay cuts were taken or one hay cut and a bastard fallow, that is, the land was ploughed shortly after this cut, and the soil then kept bare and free from weeds until the wheat was sown. It also gives the nitrate nitrogen in the soil in the preceding October just after the second hay cut had been taken and just before the autumn rains had started to wash the nitrate into the subsoil. It shows that for the bastard fallow plots there is a general correlation between the nitrates in the soil surface in the autumn and the yield of wheat the following year.

TABLE 124

Effect of Type of Ley on Yield of Succeeding Wheat Crop
Rothamsted, 1933

Treatment in 1932	Fallow	Clover	Clover and rye-grass	Rye-grass
Yield of wheat, grain in cwt. per acre				
One cut .	30·6	25·5	21·4	18·1
Two cuts .	—	25·1	18·9	13·8
Nitrate nitrogen in p.p.m. in surface 20 cm. of soil: October 1932				
One cut .	22·6	21·3	17·7	13·6
Two cuts .	—	9·3	7·7	5·6

Under some conditions the benefit of a one-year's leguminous crop can be very large. Thus, T. B. Noonan[2] has given an example from New South Wales where the yields of maize and oat hay when grown in a three-course rotation with red clover were 50 per cent higher than in a two-course rotation, as shown in Table 125.

The residual effect of different legumes depends on the legume—a point which has already been discussed on p. 345, and illustrated in Table 76, gives some results obtained by T. L. Lyon in Cornell. These results showed that lucerne and clovers enriched the soil in nitrogen and benefited the succeeding crop markedly, whilst soybeans and beans taken for seed had little effect on the soil nitrogen and much less effect on the succeeding crop. And this result that annual leguminous crops taken for seed, such as beans, peas, soybeans and groundnuts, do not enrich the soil in nitrogen and do not have any appreciable beneficial

[1] E. R. Orchard, unpublished Ph.D. Thesis, London.
[2] Agric. Gaz. N.S.W., 1946, **56**, 527.

TABLE 125

Benefit of Red Clover in Increasing the Yields of Subsequent Crops

	Two-course rotation Maize—oat hay		Three-course rotation Maize—oat hay—red clover	
	Total yield over 12 years, cwt. per acre	Yield per crop, cwt. per acre	Total yield over 12 years, cwt. per acre	Yield per crop, cwt. per acre
Maize . . .	89·5	14·9	94·2	23·5
Oat hay . .	143·3	23·9	156·6	39·1
Red clover . .	—	—	4 grazing swards	18 months at 3 sheep per acre

residual effect on succeeding crops appears to be generally true under many conditions. Thus, A. E. V. Richardson and H. C. Gurney[1] found at the Waite Institute, Adelaide, that 1 cwt. per acre of sulphate of ammonia increased the yield of wheat following a corn crop by 7 bushels per acre, following a pea crop 6 bushels per acre, and it had no effect on wheat following a fallow. This result calls into question the current explanation of the English tradition that beans are an excellent preparation for wheat on heavy land. Most unfortunately no critical examination of the effect of a bean crop on the succeeding wheat crop has been made, and the only English experiment that the author is aware of which can give any information on this subject is an early one at Rothamsted on Agdell Field. This field is in a four-course rotation, three of the courses being wheat, swedes and barley, whilst the fourth is either beans and fallow, each on half of the field, or is clover and fallow, again each on half of the field, the clover coming on the same area as the beans. The design of the experiment is very bad, and the results of the clover-fallow comparisons are not consistent with all recent Rothamsted work, such as Table 124, for, as shown in Table 126, clover appears to be considerably better than fallow, provided enough mineral manures are given to ensure a good clover crop, and this beneficial effect appears to be quite marked three years after the clover has been ploughed in. Beans in this experiment also seem to be rather better than fallow for the succeeding crop, but they have no effect on the next two crops. Obviously these effects are sufficiently important, if they are genuine, to warrant a thorough examination of them, using modern experimental techniques.

The length of time the beneficial effects of clovers last in the land depends on many circumstances. As already mentioned in the previous

[1] *Emp. J. Expt. Agric.*, 1933, **1**, 193, 325.

TABLE 126

Residual Effects of Clover Compared with Beans and Fallow over a Four-course Rotation

Agdell Field, Rothamsted

	Clover[1] hay cwt. per acre	Wheat grain bu. per acre	Swedes roots tons per acre	Barley grain bu. per acre	Beans[2] grain bu. per acre	Wheat grain bu. per acre	Swedes roots tons per acre	Barley grain bu. per acre
			Unmanured					
Crop . .	19	24	0·5	15	15	26	0·9	27
Fallow . .	—	29	1·1	17	—	27	1·6	28
			Mineral fertilisers only given to swedes					
Crop . .	55	37	11	28	20	33	9	28
Fallow . .	—	35	9	19	—	31	9	26
			Mineral fertilisers and nitrogen given to swedes					
Crop . .	65	40	17	36	24	35	18	39
Fallow . .	—	35	18	28	—	33	19	38

paragraph, Rothamsted experiments in Agdell Field seem to imply that a clover crop yielding 3 tons per acre of hay is benefiting the land for at least three years, and the results of some Canadian rotation experiments in the moister regions of Ontario,[3] also suggest a one-year clover ley can benefit the second and possibly the third crop following it. But at the present time it is probably wiser to assume that the second and third year residual effects of even a good one-year clover ley are small. However, as W. B. Goldschmidt and E. R. Orchard[4] have shown, clovers can have an extensive root system which contains about the same concentration of nitrogen, phosphorus, calcium and potassium as the tops, and which can exceed the tops in weight. Hence, since the root system decomposes slowly in the soil, it will be releasing nitrogen and other nutrients over a long period. Clovers and the other pasture legumes differ from the annual seed legumes in having a much more extensive and heavier root system, and hence store in it a much higher proportion of the total nitrogen they fix; this may be the principal reason for the great difference in residual effects between them. Some old experiments at Rothamsted suggest that an old lucerne or clover ley will be benefiting corn crops for more than five years after it has been ploughed out,[5] and a recent ley experiment on the light land at Woburn suggests that a three-year lucerne or grazed rye-grass-

[1] Four courses beginning 1874–82–86–94.
[2] Six courses beginning 1854–62–70–78–90–98.
[3] P. O. Ripley, *Sci. Agric.*, 1941, **21**, 522.
[4] *S. Africa Dept. Agric.*, *Pamph.* 222, 1940.
[5] H. Nicol, *Emp. J. Expt. Agric.*, 1933, **1**, 22.

clover ley may affect the third crop after it has been ploughed out, as is shown in Table 127.

The residual effect of the ley, however, probably depends on the way it is managed, though this has received no investigation, for presumably a ley so grazed that clover is encouraged, particularly in the season

TABLE 127

Residual Effect of Three Years' Ley or Three Years' Arable on the Succeeding Crops

Woburn (1941–56), *Plots receiving no dung*

Previous cropping	3 year ley grazed	3 year lucerne cut for hay	3 year arable	
			including 1 year seeds ley	No seeds ley
First crop: Potatoes, tons per acre, 1941–56				
	12·3	11·2	10·1	9·3
Second crop: Barley, grain in cwt. per acre, 1942–56				
	22·5	23·0	19·4	19·8
Third crop: Potatoes, tons per acre, 1943–56				
	11·2	9·9	9·4	9·4
Fourth crop: Grain in cwt. per acre				
Wheat, 1944–8 .	13·9	12·1	9·0	9·8
Rye, 1949–56 .	32·7	33·0	30·3	29·6
Fifth crop: Sugar-beet, sugar in cwt. per acre, 1945–56				
	38·3	37·9	—	33·9

before it is ploughed out, will leave a larger beneficial residue in the soil than one grazed to encourage the grasses.

In arid countries, different preceding crops can affect the yield of a succeeding one simply through the different amounts of water they leave in the soil. Thus, lucerne, by drying out a soil very thoroughly to a great depth, can affect a succeeding crop adversely compared with maize, which is a crop that cannot dry out a soil as thoroughly. This is illustrated in Table 128,[1] which gives the results of some Canadian

---

[1] P. O. Ripley, *Sci. Agric.*, 1941, **21**, 522. He also gives the results for rotations in the more humid regions of Canada. For further examples of the complexity of predicting the response of wheat to lucerne and various grass leys when the leys affect both the nitrates and the soil moisture available to the succeeding crop, see *Canad. J. Res.*, 1939, **17** C, 212, 256. For results similar to the Alberta ones, but secured in Saskatoon, see M. Champlin and A. Wall, *Sci. Agric.*, 1947, **27**, 593.

experiments on the effect of various preceding crops on the yield of
wheat, when the wheat crop is being limited by lack of water. Here
lucerne is an undesirable, and maize a desirable crop, to precede wheat
simply because their effects on the residual water in the soil are of more
importance than on the nitrates.

Crops can, however, have a harmful effect on a succeeding crop if
they leave residues behind that lock up soil nitrates on decomposition.
A well-known example of this is the depressing effect a crop of sorghum
can have on its successor. Thus, H. E. Myers and A. L. Hallsted[1]
found that in a two-year rotation in Kansas, winter wheat yielded on
the average 17 bushels per acre after maize, but only $11\frac{1}{2}$ bushels per
acre after kafir during the period 1918–41. J. P. Conrad[2] showed that
this effect is due to the high sugar content in the crown roots of the
sorghum; it was equivalent to nearly 2,000 p.p.m. of sucrose in the
top foot of soil just under the plant and fell off to 15 to 20 p.p.m. 9 inches
away. On the other hand, maize roots only returned the equivalent

TABLE 128

Effect of Preceding Crop on Yield of Wheat in Semi-arid Regions

3-year average, Lacombe, Alberta

Preceding Crop	Yield per acre	Yield of wheat in bushels per acre
Fallow	—	38·2
Maize	8·7 tons	34·6
Potatoes	6·0 tons	29·8
Lucerne	1·4 tons	23·6
Wheat	33·7 bushels	22·7
Grass ley	2·0 tons	21·8

of 2 to 3 p.p.m. of sucrose to the soil. This depressing effect of the
sorghum is therefore due both to the locking up of nitrates by the soil
micro-organisms as they decompose this sugar, and also to the unfavourable soil structure that may ensue when these sugars are decomposing.[3]
It can be rectified by adding nitrates to the soil, or, as Myers and Hallsted also showed, by taking a leguminous crop just before the sorghum.
Thus they found that, if oats followed sorghum grown after lucerne or
sweet clover, there was enough nitrogen left in the soil from the lucerne
or clover to provide for both the sorghum residues and the oats, but
if soybeans was used as the leguminous crop, the sorghum residues

[1] Proc. Soil Sci. Soc. Amer., 1943, 7, 316.
[2] J. Amer. Soc. Agron., 1927, 19, 1091; 1937, 29, 1014; 1938, 30, 475.
[3] J. F. Breazeale, J. Amer. Soc. Agron., 1924, 16, 689.

depressed both the nitrate nitrogen content of the soil and the yield of oats to about one-third of their normal values, for soybeans do not enrich the soil appreciably with nitrogen.[1]

Crops can enrich the soil for other reasons than increasing the available nitrogen supply to successor crops. Thus, some crops have considerable power of extracting nutrients from compounds that are relatively unavailable to other crops, and accumulating these nutrients in their leaves. Such crops can be used in place of general or specific fertilisers, and for this reason they may have a very important function in primitive and subsistence agriculture where no money is available for buying fertilisers. Examples of this have already been given. Thus, lupins are very good extractors of phosphate (p. 500), and some plants accumulate minor elements such as zinc in their tissues (p. 51). G. H. Gethin Jones[2] has given an example of the leguminous shrub *Glycina javanica*, which in nine years on a poor soil in Kenya added 130 lb. of nitrogen annually, but also doubled the available phosphates in the top 9 inches of the soil as well as forming a litter very rich in phosphate and potash.

The Interaction between Plants Growing Together

Under natural conditions, plants always grow in association with those of other species: it is only in agriculture, and even then in the arable agriculture of the temperate regions, that the growing of pure stands of a single species of crop is traditional. Forests, prairies and even meadows and pastures more than a few years old always carry associations of many species of plants, and traditional cropping practices of the peasants in subtropical and tropical countries usually involve planting several species of plants on the same ground.[3]

Plants growing together, whether of the same or of different species, compete with one another both for space for their leaves above ground and for their roots below. Agricultural crops have naturally been selected through the ages for ability to withstand competition from other plants of the same species, though this is not true for many non-agricultural plants. Competition for light above ground is not always serious, as the leaves of many plants can synthesise carbohydrates in moderate shade. The factors involved in the competition for root space below ground have barely begun to be worked out yet. They include competition for nutrients and, in periods of drought, for water, but

[1] For further examples which show that soybeans taken as a grain crop do not enrich the soil in nitrogen, see R. E. Uhland, *Missouri Agric. Expt. Sta.*, Bull. 279, 1930. For further references, see H. B. Brown, *Louisiana Agric. Expt. Sta.*, Bull. 265, 1935; F. S. Wilkins and H. D. Hughes, *J. Amer. Soc. Agron.*, 1934, **26**, 901.

[2] *E. Afric. Agric. J.*, 1942, **8**, 48.

[3] See H. Nicol, *Emp. J. Expt. Agric.*, 1935, **3**, 189, for an account of some of these practices.

they may also include the roots of one plant excreting soluble compounds into the soil that inhibit the growth of roots of many other plant species in its neighbourhood.[1] This is probably the mechanism that reduces the interpenetration of the root system of neighbouring plants, for plants growing with neighbours close to them typically have a more compact root system than if their neighbours are more distant. These root-inhibiting substances are often somewhat specific, for in general the root system of a leguminous and a non-leguminous plant growing in a mutually tolerated association may interpenetrate very readily.

S. C. Varma[2] further found that the harmful effects of root excretions were most marked when the plants are in the seedling stage, and this is the probable explanation of the observation so frequently made in the field, that even very small weeds can interfere with a germinating crop more than one would expect from their power of competing for light and nutrients. Hence, the great importance of keeping weeds in control during the early stages of crop growth.

The association of two crops growing together need not be harmful, particularly if their root systems tap different layers of the soil, or if the soil is well supplied with water or nutrients. In general, no annual crop has its yield per acre increased by being grown along with another, although the total yield per acre may be increased. But perennial crops, such as shrubs and trees, may have their yields increased when grown along with a companion crop, if the second crop occupies a different volume of soil and air, as, for example, ground-cover crops under orchards and tall shade trees over shrubs.

The associations of most importance in arable agriculture are those in which a leguminous plant is grown with a non-leguminous and those in which weeds grow with a crop; but two non-leguminous species are also sometimes planted together.

Taking two non-legumes simultaneously on the same piece of ground is an ancient practice, though it can hardly be used where the produce from each crop is to be sold separately. The old English maslin was a mixture of wheat and rye, and dredge corn is one of oats and barley, although peas or beans may be added to either. There is little doubt that this practice often enables higher yields to be obtained. Thus C. A. Zavitz,[3] working in Ontario, showed that provided one chooses varieties of oats and barley that come to maturity at the same time,

[1] See, for example, S. U. Pickering and the Duke of Bedford, *Science and the Fruit Grower*, London, 1919; S. C. Varma, *Ann. Bot.*, 1938, **2**, 203; H. Oswald, *Vaxtodling*, 1947, **2**, 288.
[2] *Ann. Bot.*, 1938, **2**, 203.
[3] *J. Amer. Soc. Agron.*, 1922, **14**, 225; *Ontario Dept. Agric.*, Bull. 332, 1927. R. H. Morrish, *Michigan Agric. Expt. Sta.*, Spec. Bull. 256, 1934, found the same result, but E. L. Worthen, *Cornell Agric. Expt. Sta.*, Bulls. 748, 749, 1941, and E. Knudsen, *Tidsskr. Planteavl*, 1947, **51**, 331, found no advantage in using dredge corn over the higher yielding member of the pair.

the mixed crop of dredge corn gives a higher yield of grain per acre than that of either of the two components, averaging nearly 2 cwt. per acre above the higher yielding member of the pair. This benefit of growing two non-leguminous crops together can sometimes be seen when two legumes are grown together; thus, E. L. Worthen[1] found that a mixture of red clover and alsike gave a higher yield of hay than either separately: over an eleven-year period they gave annual hay crops of 21 and 19 cwt. respectively, compared with 27 cwt. for the mixture. He considered the reason was that the mixed crop covered the ground better than either alone.

The association of weeds with a crop is obviously of fundamental importance for all types of agriculture, and in this country alone weeds are responsible for a very considerable loss of yield on many farms. Weeds harm the crop by competing directly with it for light, water and nutrients, as well as sometimes by specific inhibitory effects on the crop's root system of the type already discussed. Under semi-arid conditions the main harmful effect of weeds is usually competition for water, which is particularly serious when, as often happens with maize, the weeds can extract more water from the soil than the crop. Under English conditions the main competition is for light if the weed is as tall or taller than the crop, and for soil nitrates.[2] In the latter case it is sometimes possible to neutralise any harmful effect of weeds simply by giving the crop a suitable dressing of sulphate of ammonia. Thus, sugar-beet can be grown almost unweeded without loss of yield on the light loam soil at Woburn if an adequate dressing of nitrogen is given, as shown in Table 129.[3] But this method of minimising the harm done by weeds, even if desirable, is not always possible, for it may happen that the weeds will be able to make better use of the added nutrient than the crop. T. Eden[4] has given an example of this in some Ceylon tea estates on phosphate-deficient soils: adding phosphate encourages some undesirable weeds more than the tea bushes, hence only the minimum quantity that will satisfy the requirements of the tea must be added.

These two examples are special cases of the general problem of the dependence of the competitive power of different plants on the soil fertility. This problem is of particular importance in grassland management, for here the principal methods available for controlling the

[1] *Cornell Agric. Expt. Sta., Bulls.* 748, 749, 1941.
[2] G. E. Blackman and W. G. Templeman, *J. Agric. Sci.*, 1936, **26**, 368; 1938, **28**, 247; H. H. Mann and T. W. Barnes, *Ann. Appl. Biol.*, 1945, **32**, 15.
[3] Mean of years 1940, 1941, 1943. Results for the first two are given by E. W. Russell, B. A. Keen and H. H. Mann, *J. Agric. Sci.*, 1942, **32**, 330. F. Crowther (*Emp. J. Expt. Agric.*, 1943, **11**, 1) in the Gezirah found that cotton gave a larger response to nitrogen, derived from the previous year's fallow, when weedy than clean, in conformity with the above results at Woburn.　　　　[4] With T. E. T. Bond, *Emp. J. Expt. Agric.*, 1945, **13**, 141.

TABLE 129

Effect of Weeds and Nitrogen on Yield of Sugar-beet at Woburn
Yield of washed beet in tons per acre

Sulphate of ammonia given in cwt. per acre	Crop kept		Reduction of yield due to weeds
	Weeded	Weedy	
0	11·68	9·45	2·23
4	15·47	15·43	0·04

composition of old pastures depend on manuring and grazing. The Rothamsted Grass Plots provide much information on the former;[1] they show that unmanured poor meadow land carries a very mixed herbage: very many species can grow, but they all grow badly. As soon as fertiliser is added, the extra nutrients encourage some species at the expense of others, so the number of species falls, though the hay yield usually rises.

The simple plant associations most commonly practised both by primitive and modern farmers is that of growing a leguminous and non-leguminous crop together. We have already discussed this association from the point of view of its nitrogen economy in Chapter XVI. It was pointed out there that whilst much of the experimental data was consistent with the hypothesis that the non-legume could utilise nitrogenous compounds synthesised by the legume, yet it could equally well be interpreted as showing that the legume made no demands on the soil nitrates, and hence the reduced number of non-leguminous plants present in the association as compared with the pure crop, had a larger nitrogen supply to draw on.

The outstanding facts of the legume–non-legume association established on p. 349 are that in general the nitrogen content of the non-legume is higher[2] and of the legume lower than it would be if grown as a pure crop, and that neither crop gives as large a yield in mixed culture as when grown alone, although the combined yield may be higher than either. It also appears, as is shown in Table 130, that on the whole, the yield of the legume is usually more depressed in the association compared with the pure stand than is the cereal, but it is possible this is a property of the particular associations that have been studied.

[1] The conclusions to be drawn from this experiment have been discussed by J. B. Lawes and J. H. Gilbert, *Phil. Trans.*, 1880, **171**, 289; 1882, **173**, 1181; 1900, **192** B, 139; W. E. Brenchley, *Manuring Grassland for Hay*, London, 1924.

[2] For examples of grasses growing with clover, see *Mississippi Agric. Expt. Sta.*, Bull. 356, 1941, with Paspalum; D. B. Johnstone Wallace, *J. Amer. Soc. Agron.*, 1937, **29**, 441, and R. E. Wagner and H. L. Wilkins, ibid., 1947, **39**, 141, with temperate grasses.

In the tropics other associations besides grass or cereal are used with legumes. Thus, groundnuts and cotton go well together in Madras and Tanganyika, and several legumes go with the tropical root crops such as cassava. It is, in fact, possible that some of the most striking benefits of mixed cropping may be seen on the poorer soils of the humid tropics, but little exact information is available at present.

One other example of considerable practical importance of growing two crops together comes from orchard management, for under many circumstances it is profitable to have the ground between the trees carrying a crop. The cover crop can have a number of different

TABLE 130

Effect of Mixed Cropping on Yield of Cereal and Legume

Yields of cereal and legume grain

Country and Association	Yield of cereal		Total	Yield of legume	
	Alone	With legume		With cereal	Alone
Ceylon:[1] In bushels per acre: Millet and beans . .	33	28	31	2·8	7·3
Greece[2] In cwt. per acre: Wheat and lentil, 1939 .	11·9	9·8	15·7	5·9	—
1940 .	7·4	6·6	9·3	2·7	7·3
Wheat and lupins, 1940 .	7·4	6·3	13·5	7·2	12·2
Ohio,[3] U.S.A. Maize and soybeans: Grain in cwt. per acre .	28·6	24·2	27·8	3·6	10·9
Cut for silage: Green weight, tons per acre	8·7	7·7	10·1	2·4	8·1
Total digestible nutrients, lb. per acre . .	4380	3770	4620	850	2730
Total digestible proteins, lb. per acre. . .	260	225	410	185	595

[1] W. R. C. Paul and A. W. R. Joachim, *Trop. Agricst.*, 1941, **98**, 257. Crops were *Eleusine coracana* and *Phaseolus mungo*.

[2] J. S. Papadakis, *Ann. Gembloux*, 1939, **45**, 132; 1940, **46**, 1; *J. Amer. Soc. Agron.*, 1941, **33**, 504. The results given are the means for experiments conducted at six experiment stations. Lentil = *Ervum ervilia*.

[3] H. L. Borst and J. B. Park, *Ohio Agric. Expt. Sta., Bull.* 513, 1932. For a further example, giving the same results, see C. A. Mooers, *Tennessee Agric. Expt. Sta., Bull.* 137, 1927.

effects on the tree. If it is leguminous it can maintain the nitrogen supply to the tree. Cover crops also protect the surface of the soil, keeping it more permeable. They also can enrich the surface soil in minor elements such as zinc, for their root system may be deeper than that of the tree, and hence able to tap a larger volume of soil and in consequence collect a larger quantity of any minor element in short supply. They can also increase the carbon dioxide content in the soil air and perhaps for this reason reduce chlorosis troubles on calcareous soils.

They can also reduce the loss of nitrate by leaching from the soil during the dormant season, and can be used to reduce the nitrate content in the soil at any period during the growing season, but for these two purposes in particular, their periods of growth may have to be very carefully chosen, otherwise they may be competing with the trees for water or nutrients. Thus, in England they are particularly liable to compete for nitrogen, and the techniques of cover-cropping and managing leys under trees must ensure that adequate nitrogen is available for the tree.[1]

[1] For a recent examination of the effects of cover-crops on the growth and yield of apple trees in Kent orchards, see W. S. Rogers and Th. Raptopoulos, *J. Pomol.*, 1945, **21**, 120; 1946, **22**, 92, 103; with D. W. P. Greenham, ibid., 1948, **24**, 228, 271.

CHAPTER XXX

THE WEATHERING OF ROCKS

SOILS ARE DERIVED from the decomposition of the mineral particles they contain and from the plant and animal remains added to them. The organic remains are usually being decomposed continuously and relatively rapidly by the soil organisms, and many of the mineral particles are also decomposing, but usually at a very much slower rate. The chemistry of these processes will be discussed in two parts: firstly, when the mineral particles are decomposing in the absence of organic matter, in which case the products of weathering remaining behind will be called a crust of weathering; and, secondly, when they are decomposing in the presence of organic compounds, when the process will be called soil formation.

Rocks and mineral particles can suffer physical disintegration without change of chemical constitution. Solid rock is broken down into smaller particles by many means. It may suffer grinding in or under ice-sheets, and all the particles in boulder clays may have been produced by this action. It can be broken down into boulders by the expansive pressure of water in any cracks freezing into ice, or by plant roots trying to expand in restricted spaces; and these boulders can be made still smaller by being knocked on to other stones on the bottom of rapidly flowing mountain or desert streams. The solid rock surface can lose some of its constituent mineral grains due to their different coefficients of thermal expansion, for they will expand and contract by different amounts during the diurnal temperature changes of the surface, which can be very large in deserts. The rock can also lose mineral grains by water dissolving the cements which bind them together in the rock. The individual mineral grains can be reduced in size by the grinding action of ice and by abrasion in flowing water, as already mentioned, as well as by sand-blasting in the desert.

These finer particles produced by disintegration may then be carried away by wind, water or ice, and redeposited elsewhere as loess, alluvium or boulder clay. Or those on or near the surface of these deposits may be carried into lower layers with the percolating water.

The mineral particles can also suffer chemical decomposition through the solvent action of the water itself, and through the reactions between the dissolved or suspended substances in the water, as, for example, oxygen, carbon dioxide, alkalis and organic acids, and the surfaces of

551

the particles. Some of these reactions can occur at depths of 30 feet or more below the soil surface, so clearly are of importance in forming the crust of weathering, whilst the effect of organic acids, and possibly of alkalis also, is only of importance near the surface and hence in the soil forming processes.

The fate of the products of decomposition depends mainly on the rate of water movement through the soil: the greater the amount of downward leaching the higher the proportion of the products of weathering that are removed from the zone in which they were formed and either redeposited in lower layers of the soil or else carried with the percolating water into the ground-water and thus into the rivers. Water movement is not the only agency causing movement of the products of weathering. Plants growing on the soil counteract some of the downward movement brought about by the percolating water, for their roots absorb some of the products of weathering from the subsoil and transfer them to their leaves and stems, which later fall to the ground and decompose, releasing these products of weathering in the surface soil. Burrowing animals, such as earthworms, termites and some rodents, also affect the distribution of the products of weathering consequent upon the mixing of soil from different layers which they bring about.

The Formation of the Crust of Weathering

As rain-water percolates through the soil it loses some of its dissolved oxygen and becomes enriched in carbon dioxide. This water causes three groups of reactions to take place on the surface of mineral particles over which it moves: hydration, oxidation and hydrolysis. The mineral surface takes up water molecules to form more hydrated minerals; all ferrous and sulphide ions become oxidised; and ions split off from the surface of the crystal lattices under the influence of the carbonic acid. The speed of these decompositions depends on the constitution of the mineral particles concerned, but increases with the temperature and the quantity of the percolating water.

The exact chemistry of these decompositions has not been worked out. Thus, neither the way in which water molecules become added to the ions forming the mineral lattice, nor the actual ions that split off the mineral lattice are always known in detail. Again, an acid clay particle close to a mineral particle appears to be a more powerful extractor of cations from the mineral than is carbonated water itself, so acid clays may act as weak catalysts in the hydrolysis of mineral particles.[1]

Rock particles do not all decompose uniformly easily. Small particles,

[1] E. R. Graham, *Soil Sci.*, 1940, **49**, 277; 1941, **52**, 291.

by virtue of their increased surface area for a given weight of material, decompose more easily than larger ones. Among the common primary minerals, the ferro-magnesian weather comparatively easily, olivine usually weathering more easily than augite or horneblende. The calcium-rich plagioclase felspars weather more easily than the sodium-rich, and both weather easier than the potash felspars. Of these the orthoclase tends to weather quicker than microcline, which is relatively resistant to decomposition. The biotite micas tend to weather more easily, and the muscovite micas more slowly, than orthoclase.[1] Quartz, if not too finely divided, and some heavy minerals, such as zircon, tourmaline and some of the titanium minerals, are very resistant to weathering and decompose only slowly under conditions very favourable for the decomposition of the other minerals.[2]

The process of weathering involves two stages: the hydrolysis of the minerals and the disposal of the products of hydrolysis. Some products are very soluble in the soil water, for example, chlorides and sulphates, and as fast as these are produced by hydrolysis they appear in the soil solution and move with it. Other products, such as the principal cations sodium, potassium, magnesium and calcium, can be held as exchangeable bases on being set free, and they are relatively easily removed if the soil is subject to much leaching. Soluble silica is also produced and may move out of the soil. Finally, certain products, such as hydrated iron and aluminium oxides, tend to accumulate in the crust of weathering as the other elements are removed.[3]

These stages in the process of weathering of rocks can be seen from the analysis of the products of weathering of igneous rocks within the crust of weathering. Table 131 gives the analysis of three similar rocks and of their weathering products for conditions of slow weathering in Massachusetts, of moderate weathering in Virginia and rapid weathering in British Guiana. The table also gives the percentage loss of each constituent on the assumption that no aluminium in two cases, or iron in the third, has been lost from the soil.

This assumption is not quite accurate, as small amounts of iron and aluminium are found in the drainage waters,[4] so that the percentage loss of constituents of the rock given in the last column of the table is certainly an under-estimate. In these examples one can see how the hydration

[1] See, for example, S. S. Goldrich, *J. Geol.*, 1938, **46**, 17; F. J. Pettijohn, *J. Geol.*, 1941, **49**, 610.
[2] See, for example, F. J. Pettijohn and also F. Smithson, *Geol. Mag.*, 1941, **68**, 97.
[3] For a further discussion of this aspect, see B. B. Polynov, *The Cycle of Weathering*, trans. A. Muir, London, 1937.
[4] A. Demolon and E. Bastisse (*C.R.*, 1944, **219**, 293) have given analyses of the aluminium, iron and silicon contents of water that has percolated through 60 cm. of soil. See also J. S. Joffe, *Soil Sci.*, 1940, **50**, 57, and *Proc. Soil Sci. Soc. Amer.*, 1941, **5**, 187 for other examples. C. S. Howard, *Trans. Amer. Geophys. Union*, 1948, **29**, 375, 379, has given the iron and aluminium contents of the Colorado River and rivers in the north-west of the U.S.A.

of the products of weathering increases, how the bases are removed very strongly under moderate weathering, how the silicon is lost more slowly than the bases, and how the loss of iron does not seem to depend very much on the conditions of weathering.

The relative resistance of iron and aluminium to removal during weathering is not always as given in Table 131. Sometimes more

TABLE 131

The Different Rates of Removal of Constituents from Basic Rocks during Weathering

	Diabase from Massachusetts[1]			Diorite from Virginia[1]		
	Fresh rock	Crust of weathering	Per cent loss of constituent	Fresh rock	Crust of weathering	Per cent loss of constituent
Al_2O_3 . . .	20·2	23·2	standard	17·6	25·5	standard
Fe_2O_3 . . .	3·7	12·7	} 18·1	16·8	19·2	21·0
FeO . . .	8·9	0·0				
SiO_2 . . .	47·3	44·4	18·0	46·7	42·4	37·0
MgO . . .	3·2	2·8	21·7	5·1	0·2	97·0
CaO . . .	7·1	6·0	25·9	9·5	0·4	97·0
Na_2O . . .	3·9	3·9	12·8	2·6	0·6	85·0
K_2O . . .	2·2	1·7	29·1	0·5	0·5	39·0
Loss on ignition .	2·7	3·7	—	0·9	10·9	—
Per cent of rock lost . .	—	—	14·9	—	—	37·5

	Dolerite from British Guiana[2]		
	Fresh rock	Crust of weathering	Per cent loss of each constituent
Al_2O_3	15·2	26·9	12·3
Fe_2O_3	3·1	27·9	} standard
FeO	11·2	3·1	
Quartz	1·6	13·2	} 82·0
Combined SiO_2	49·7	7·9	
MgO	5·6	0·7	94·0
CaO	9·6	0·5	97·0
Na_2O	2·1	0·8	82·0
K_2O	0·6	0·3	73·0
Loss on ignition	0·3	17·3	50·6
Per cent of rock lost	—	—	49·5

[1] G. P. Merrill, *Rocks, Rock-Weathering and Soils*, New York, 1897. These are also given in F. W. Clarke, *Data of Geochemistry, U.S. Geol. Surv., Bull.* 770, 1924.
[2] J. B. Harrison, *The Katamorphism of Igneous Rocks Under Humid Tropical Conditions*, Harpenden, 1934.

iron than aluminium is removed from the crust of weathering, and sometimes titanium is the least mobile.[1] Thus, in the weathering of an amphi-
bolite in Georgia, U.S.A., if one assumes the iron has all remained in the
crust of weathering, then 57 per cent of the silicon, 40 per cent of the
aluminium, and 11 per cent of the titanium have been removed.[2]

Some of the products of weathering move with the percolating water
into the ground-water and thus into rivers. Hence, analyses of the
dissolved salts in rivers emerging from catchment areas on a definite
rock type would give valuable information on the rate of weathering
in situ, provided the analyses were made at a number of times during the
year and the river was gauged, that is, its flow measured. Unfortunately, data of this type do not seem to have been collected. However,
F. W. Clarke[3] has tabulated many analyses of the salts in large rivers
and, assuming that these analyses are typical for the average salt
content throughout the year, has calculated the average rate of removal
of the soluble products produced by weathering over large catchment
areas. Thus, European and North American rivers carry away salts
at the rate of 100 tons of soluble inorganic substances per square mile
of their catchment area per year, which corresponds to the solution of
one foot of soil in about 20,000 to 30,000 years, whilst tropical rivers,
owing to the much higher transpiration of the vegetation growing in
their catchment areas, only carry away about 50 tons per square mile
per year. The actual weight of the soluble constituents so removed,
converted into the more convenient units of pounds per acre per year,
are approximately as follows:

	CO_3	SO_4	Cl	NO_3	Ca	Mg	Na	K	Al_2O_3+ Fe_2O_3	Si
N. American and European rivers	130	49	17	3.5	73	12	21	8	5[4]	15
Amazon	57	15	10	1.1	33	4.5	9	4	10	16
Drainage water, Broadbalk, continuous wheat, un-manured plot[5]	—	56	24	152	159	7	10	3	13	12

Thus, in spite of the fact that the Amazon only carries half as much
salts per square mile of catchment area as the temperate rivers, yet it
carries away as much silicon and twice as much iron and aluminium per
square mile. This result is naturally a corollary of the results given in
Table 131, and the previous paragraphs, for the course of decomposition

[1] For an example on the Hawaiian lavas, see G. J. Hough, P. L. Gile and Z. C. Foster, *U.S. Dept. Agric., Tech. Bull.* 752, 1941.
[2] L. T. Alexander, S. B. Hendricks and G. T. Faust, *Proc. Soil Sci. Soc. Amer.*, 1941, 6, 52.
[3] *Data of Geochemistry.*
[4] Iron and aluminium not separately determined. However, C. S. Howard, *Trans. Amer. Geophys. Union*, 1948, 29, 375, finds the iron content of the waters of rivers in the western states of the U.S.A. to be only between 1 and 5 per cent of their silicon contents.
[5] Calculated from the mean of five samples analysed by A. Voelcker, *J. Chem. Soc.*, 1871, 24, 276.

under intense, as compared with mild, weathering. Under humid tropical conditions when basic igneous rocks are being weathered, the rate of decomposition can be much higher than is indicated in this table. Thus, H. W. van der Marel[1] found that biotite and albite-anorthite rich rocks weather rapidly enough to liberate over 200 to 250 lb. per acre of potassium. Under the cool temperate conditions of Versailles broken granite, in a lysimeter only 60 cm. (about 2 ft.) deep, loses silicon at the annual rate of 17 lb. per acre and calcium at 110 lb. per acre.[2]

Not all the soluble products of weathering are immediately transported into the ground-water and the rivers: some are reprecipitated lower down in the soil and some recombine, either where they have been produced, or lower down in the soil, to form secondary minerals, such as clays, that are resistant to weathering. Thus calcium carbonate and sulphate dissolved from the surface soil are often precipitated in the subsoil, particularly when the rainfall is so low that little water penetrates beyond the root range of the plants.

The factors controlling the type of clay mineral synthesised, and its rate of formation, under different field conditions have not yet been studied intensively. The general rule appears to be that montmorillonitic clays are produced in the presence of a good, and kaolinitic of a poor, base supply.[3] Thus montmorillonitic clays are usually found in areas of poor drainage, which ensures a good base supply, and warm climates, which ensures that weathering will be active enough to produce a good supply of silica and hydrated iron and aluminium oxides. Whether or not the ferrous iron, which is also produced under these conditions, plays a fundamental role in this synthesis is still undecided. The montmorillonitic clays so produced become increasingly mixed with illite-like clays as the proportion of aluminium in 4-co-ordination increases, that is, as the clay becomes more beidellite-like. Kaolinite clays are formed under conditions of a low concentration of bases, that is, in well-drained areas, though as the base status at the site of synthesis rises, so illite-like clays tend to be formed along with the kaolinite. The illite clays thus form the intermediate group between the pure kaolinites of strongly leached, low base soils and the pure montmorillonites of the poorly drained, high base soils.

Illitic clays are also produced directly from micas and perhaps felspars as well. D. M. C. MacEwan[4] has been able to follow the transition of a biotite through hydrobiotite or vermiculite into an illite,

[1] *Soil Sci.*, 1947, **64**, 445.   [2] A. Demolon and E. Bastisse, *Soil Sci.*, 1938, **46**, 1.
[3] For examples from Australia, see J. S. Hosking, *Aust. J. Counc. Sci. Indust. Res.*, 1940, **13**, 206; from India, G. Nagelschmidt, A. D. Desai and A. Muir, *J. Agric. Sci.*, 1940, **30**, 639; from Russia, I. D. Sedletsky, *Pedology*, 1942, Nos. 3–4, 61. For a discussion, see G. Nagelschmidt, *Imp. Bur. Soil Sci., Tech. Comm.* 42, 1944; C. S. Ross and S. B. Hendricks, *U.S. Geol. Survey, Prof. Paper* 205 B, 1945.
[4] *Verre et Silic. Indust.*, 1948, **13**, 41. See also G. F. Walker, *Miner. Mag.*, 1949, **28**, 693.

a process in which it is not necessary to assume that the basic lattice has been completely broken up.

The silica and the iron and aluminium hydroxides taking part in the clay synthesis do not need to be produced at the same place, for silica-rich water, leaching through the aluminium hydroxide left behind as a residual product in the crust of weathering, can convert it into kaolinite. Thus, J. B. Harrison,[1] working in British Guiana, F. Hardy and G. Rodrigues[2] in Trinidad, and L. T. Alexander and his co-workers[3] in the south-eastern States of the U.S.A., found that the gibbsite produced in the crust of weathering of basic igneous rocks becomes converted into kaolinite by this means.

The effect of the climate on the rate of formation of clay and on its composition depends on the amount and the temperature of the percolating water. The greater the amount of water leaching through and the higher its temperature the greater is its power of decomposing rock minerals, the more rapid is the formation of clay, and the lower is its silicon content, that is, the higher the ratio of kaolinitic to illitic clay formed.

The quantitative relationships between the rate of clay formation and its composition with such fundamental quantities have not yet been worked out. What has been done is to make very crude estimates of the two primary variables—the absolute amount and the temperature of the percolating water—and to look for correlations between them and the amount and composition of the clay in the soil over areas where the parent material is reasonably similar. The approximations that have usually been made are to replace the temperature of the percolating water by the mean annual temperature, and to estimate the amount of percolating water from some very inexact assumptions connecting it with the mean annual rainfall and either the mean annual temperature or moisture saturation deficit of the air.[4]

H. Jenny[5] has used this type of method to show how the amount of clay in soils derived from granite and gneisses in the United States increases with temperature and percolation. Little clay is formed unless the mean annual temperature is above 5° C., and appreciable amounts are only formed when it exceeds 10° C. Again, E. M. Crowther[6] and others[7] have shown that the silicon-aluminium ratio in clays decreases as the rainfall increases. But the effect of temperature has

[1] *The Katamorphism of Igneous Rocks Under Humid Tropical Conditions.*

[2] *Soil Sci.*, 1939, **48**, 361.

[3] L. T. Alexander, S. B. Hendricks and G. T. Faust, *Proc. Soil Sci. Soc. Amer.*, 1941, **6**, 52.

[4] For a discussion on these methods, see H. Jenny, *Factors of Soil Formation*, New York, 1941.

[5] *Soil Sci.*, 1935, **40**, 111.   [6] *Proc. Roy. Soc.*, 1930, **107** B, 1.

[7] For example, W. O. Robinson and R. S. Holmes, *U.S. Dept. Agric., Bull.* 1311, 1924; I. C. Brown and H. G. Byers, *U.S. Dept. Agric., Tech. Bull.* 609, 1938; H. B. Vanderford and W. A. Albrecht, *Missouri Agric. Expt. Sta., Res. Bull.* 345, 1942; S. P. Raychaudhuri and J. N. Chakravorty, *Indian J. Agric. Sci.*, 1943, **13**, 252.

not yet been unequivocally demonstrated. Thus, using the same data but different methods of computing the amount of rainfall that percolates to the ground-water, Robinson and Holmes concluded that, for constant amount of percolation, the silicon-aluminium ratio of the clay decreases with increasing temperature, whilst Crowther concluded it had no influence—a conclusion difficult to justify on physico-chemical grounds, but probably due to the method of estimating the amount of percolation being unsatisfactory.

B. B. Polynov[1] has pictured the process of the formation of a crust of weathering from parent rock occurring in four stages, each characterised by a typical accumulation product. The first stage involves the loss of all readily soluble products of weathering, such as chlorides and sulphates, and the accumulation of calcium carbonate precipitated some depth below the surface, and often of calcium sulphate, as gypsum, at a greater depth. The second stage involves the washing out of the calcium carbonate and the formation of clay under neutral conditions; that is, the accumulation of beidellitic and illitic clays. The third stage involves the washing out of the exchangeable bases, so the clay becomes acid and weathers to kaolinitic clays which accumulate, whilst the fourth stage involves strong removal of silicon and the accumulation of meta-halloysite,[2] bauxites and haematites. This stage is only developed under conditions of long-continued leaching under tropical conditions, conditions which also give very deep crusts of weathering.

Laterites and Ferrallites

These processes of rock weathering and mineral synthesis are very clearly displayed in the tropics, for these regions contain many old peneplains that have been subjected to weathering for very long periods with little disturbance. Further, weathering proceeds much more vigorously there, for the soil temperatures are much higher than in the temperate zone. Vageler states that in the regions lying between latitudes 20°N. and 20°S. the soil temperature at a depth of 1·5 metres is nearly constant throughout the year at between 25° and 26°C., whilst in England the mean temperature at this depth is about 10°C. Thus, these weathering processes have produced crusts of weathering over 60 feet thick in places from solid rock. Studies of weathering are particularly profitable in many of these regions as the parent rock is primary crystalline rock and not merely residual products of weathering of previous geological periods.

[1] *The Cycle of Weathering*, trans. A. Muir, London, 1937.
[2] I. D. Sedletsky (*Pedology*, 1942, Nos. 3–4, 61) has pointed out that meta-halloysite, and not bauxite, as assumed by Polynov, is the probable product of accumulation from the weathering of kaolinite.

Two different types of primary crusts of weathering are produced from igneous rocks: those giving aluminium hydroxide residual products or bauxites, and those giving kaolinites, the former being characteristic of basic and the latter of acidic igneous rocks. There is no generally accepted evidence that kaolinites ever lose their silicon by weathering leaving aluminium hydroxides behind as their residual products of accumulation. This division between bauxitic and kaolinitic residual products depends on the weathering of the individual mineral particles in the rocks, and as there is an assortment of different minerals, so it is possible to have bauxites and kaolinites being formed from the same rock.

The actual forms of the residual products of weathering appear to be as follows. The kaolinites are probably present as halloysites; free silica recrystallises as quartz, opal or chalcedony; the aluminium is present mainly as gibbsite or hydrargillite, although böhmite γ-AlO(OH) and diaspore α-AlO(OH) may also be present; and the iron is present mainly as limonite FeO(OH) and haematite Fe_2O_3, but some may be present as magnetite remaining from the original minerals, and some combined with titanium as ilmenite. No iron silicates have yet been isolated or recognised in these crusts of weathering, though F. Hardy and G. Rodrigues[1] considered they had evidence for an iron silicate of composition $2Fe_2O_3.SiO_2.2H_2O$, which corresponds to no known mineral. However, a high proportion of the iron present can usually be brought into solution by Truog's or Tamm's method, and it is possible that if the material was thoroughly treated with Tamm's acid oxalate using Schofield's technique (see p. 79), most of the iron would come into solution, but this point has not yet been established.

There are probably all transitions between the two extreme types of crust of weathering—the kaolinitic and the ferruginous bauxite—and they give soil material having colours ranging from almost pure white or very light yellow or brown, through brown to red of varying intensities to almost purple. The individual particles are all small, mainly in the fine silt and clay fractions, as they are all secondary products of weathering, but they are cemented together into larger particles—sometimes called pseudo-sand because they act as sand particles—by iron oxide cements and possibly aluminium and silicon hydroxides also, although this has not yet been definitely proved. Hence, these soils do not show the general properties of clays: they are not plastic, do not swell on wetting, are permeable, have a very low base exchange capacity, and are easy to cultivate. When the material is red the soil is often called a tropical red earth or loam, and when the amount of kaolinite present is low it has been called a laterite, but for reasons to be discussed shortly,

[1] Soil Sci., 1939, 48, 483.

it will be called a ferrallite instead, a name used by G. W. Robinson[1] in the third edition of his book. Ferrallites are only formed from the weathering of basic igneous rocks on well-drained sites, and are only deeply developed on ancient peneplains, which are fairly level and extensive land surfaces. They are not formed if the crust of weathering is subjected to strong ground-water influences, for ground-water nearly always contains water-soluble silica, which reacts with the aluminium hydroxide to form kaolinitic clays, as already described on p. 557.

The word laterite, which has been so extensively used by pedologists, was first coined by F. Buchanan,[2] a geologist, in 1807 for a reddish to yellow material with a typical vermicular structure, which is as soft as cheese when freshly exposed, but which hardens on exposure to air. It is extensively used in India as a building stone, and Buchanan coined the word laterite from the Latin word *Later*—a brick, from this use. In Malabar it is derived from acid igneous rocks such as granites and gneisses; is somewhat similar to what a geologist calls a lithomarge, contains between 30 and 50 per cent of kaolinite with 15 to 40 per cent of iron oxides, sometimes a little free aluminium hydroxides, and some quartz and unweathered felspars; and it may have been formed under an indurated iron pan, but if it was the pan has disappeared. The cause of the hardening on exposure to air has not been established, though it is probably due in some way to the dehydration of some of the hydrated iron oxides present.

The word laterite is, however, used by the geologists in a different sense from Buchanan's.[3] For them it is an indurated ferruginous crust or hard pan, most typically lateritic when it contains mainly bauxite and hydrated iron oxides. Hence in constitution it approaches the ferrallites described above, but it is a hard crust, not a friable earth, having either a pisolitic or vermicular structure. A pisolitic laterite contains spherical masses of soil material cemented together with hydrated iron oxides, formed at approximately equal distances apart, in a porous clay matrix. These special masses grow outwards until they touch each other, but the spaces between the masses never fill up completely, so the whole always remains porous. These particles vary in size between 3 and 10 millimetres, and if these particles are not

[1] *Soils; Their Origin, Constitution and Classification*, 3rd ed., London, 1949. C. E. Kellogg (*Commonw. Bur. Soil Sci., Tech. Comm.* 46, 1949, and *I.N.E.A.C. Ser. Sci., Publ. 46,* 1949) has introduced the name Latosol for leached red and yellow tropical soils.

[2] *A Journey from Madras through the Countries of Mysore, Canara and Malabar*, 3 vols., London, 1807. C. S. Fox revisited Buchanan's original sites in 1933 and published his observations in *Rec. Geol. Surv. India*, 1936, **69**, 389. This publication quotes the relevant entries from Buchanan's book and gives some chemical analyses of the type material, and has been freely drawn upon in the above paragraph.

[3] See, for example, J. M. Campbell, *Mining Mag.*, London, 1917, **17**, 67, 120, 171, 220, and C. S. Fox, *Mem. Geol. Surv. India*, 1923, **48**, 221, who gives an extensive bibliography on the subject.

Plate XXVII

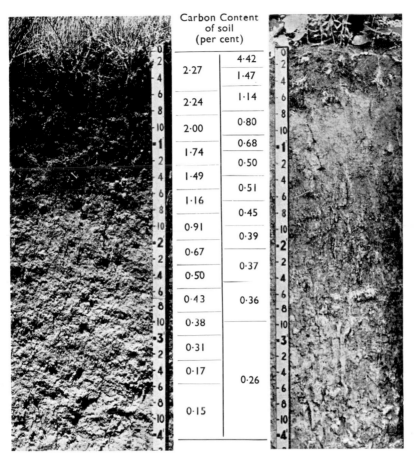

Prairie (Grassland) Soil

Hardwood Forest Soil
(Grey-brown podsolic)

Carbon Content
of soil
(per cent)

Prairie	Forest
2·27	4·42
	1·47
2·24	1·14
2·00	0·80
1·74	0·68
	0·50
1·49	0·51
1·16	0·45
0·91	0·39
0·67	0·37
0·50	
0·43	0·36
0·38	
0·31	
0·17	0·26
0·15	

Weight of Organic Carbon in the top 4 ft. of soil
88 tons per acre   42 tons per acre

The profile and carbon content of a prairie and a hardwood forest
soil on a silty loam in Iowa (Tama and Fayette Series respectively)
(pp. 291, 579)

Plate XXVIII

Nodular or pisolitic laterite with larger cavities, from the South Gate of Pimai, Nakorn Rachasima Province, North-eastern Siam, built in the ninth and tenth centuries A.D.

(p. 561)

Plate XXIX

Part of a quarried block of vesicular laterite from the city wall, built about 150 years ago, Muang Gao, Chantaburi Province, South-eastern Siam

(p. 561)

Plate XXX

Deep   Ordinary   Southern

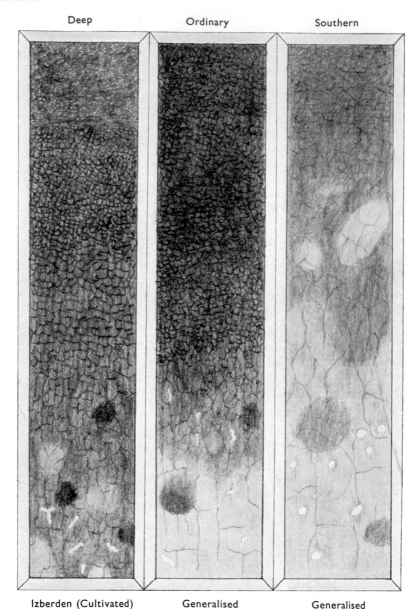

Izberden (Cultivated)   Generalised   Generalised

Typical chernozem profiles

Deep Chernozem (Izberden): granular structure (disturbed by cultivation near surface), becoming pea-like and then nutty below; humus layer over 100 cm. in depth; carbonate as "pseudo-mycelium" below about 90 cm.

Ordinary (Medium) Chernozem: granular structure; humus layer 70–90 cm. deep; carbonate as efflorescence or pseudomycelium below about 70 cm.

Southern Chernozem: structure less well expressed, may be granular or crumb-like near surface; humus layer (often with chocolate-brown tint) 50–80 cm.; carbonate as a characteristic horizon of (soft concretions) "bieloglaska" or "white eyes" below about 70 cm.

(p. 579)

strongly cemented together, the material is often known as pea iron gravel in Africa. The vermicular, or as it is sometimes called, vesicular laterite, is more solidly indurated with iron and perhaps aluminium oxides and hydroxides, but contains many tortuous channels through this ironstone, which are often filled with a light-coloured bauxite, kaolinite or quartz. The reason for these two different types of laterite is not known, but it is possible that the vesicular is brought about in some way by termite activity.[1]

This type of laterite is only found in regions of fluctuating ground-water, and it is formed near the highest level the ground-water reaches. It is for this reason often called a ground-water laterite in soil literature. The zone through which the ground-water level fluctuates may be as thick as 50 feet, as, for example, in parts of India having a high monsoon rainfall, and a proportion of the iron it originally contained has been moved out from it into the laterite horizons above; but this removal and deposition takes place unevenly, for the zone is streaked with red or reddish colours on a white to grey background.

There are several descriptions of laterites in the geological and pedological literature which are considered to be Buchanan laterites. The author unfortunately has not visited Malabar, so has not seen the type area, but he was able to visit a laterite quarry in Malacca in 1949. This laterite has been described by J. B. Scrivenor,[2] who quotes T. J. Newbold's opinion that it was the same material as occurs in Malabar. Yet this laterite appeared to be a pea iron gravel. We could not see what underlay this laterite in the quarry where it was worked, but close by in another quarry was a vermicular laterite, which was being quarried for road metal. Further, the pisolitic and vermicular laterites described by R. L. Pendleton and S. Sharasuvana[3] as used for building stone in Siam, two of whose photographs are reproduced in Plates XXVIII and XXIX, appear to be the laterite of the geologists rather than Buchanan. It is possible therefore that Newbold in Malabar mistook the laterite crust overlying the lithomarge for the Buchanan laterite.

Soil science, therefore, has to deal with three laterites. There is the ground-water laterite, which possesses a horizon indurated with iron, and containing in addition quartz, kaolinite or bauxite, depending on the parent material and drainage conditions. It may be very thick and can be formed on any parent material containing sufficient iron compounds. Then there is the deep red soil, rich in iron and aluminium

[1] I am indebted to Dr. R. L. Pendleton for drawing my attention to this possibility.

[2] J. B. Scrivenor, *The Geology of Malaya*, London, 1931, who quotes a description of this material given by T. J. Newbold, *British Settlements in Malacca*, Vol. I, 1839, who states that this laterite is the same as Buchanan's on the Malabar coast.

[3] *Soil Sci.*, 1942, **54**, 1; 1946, **52**, 423. For a description of what appears to be similar material in Ceylon, locally known as Cabook, see A. W. R. Joachim and S. Kandiah, *Trop. Agricst.*, 1941, **96**, 67.

hydrated oxides and low in kaolinite, and therefore possessing a low silica-sesquioxide ratio, which is only formed on basic igneous rocks under conditions of good to moderately good drainage, and is only deep on old peneplains. But these soils usually occur in regions of high, or seasonally high rainfall, so they nearly always show signs of impeded drainage in their subsoil. This characteristically causes a horizon containing small pea iron gravel concretions, whose concentration increases with increasing amount of impedance in the drainage, which overlies a deep reticulately mottled red to whitish layer becoming whiter with depth due to the increasingly complete removal upwards of the iron initially present in it. The white material is mainly kaolinitic clay formed by the re-silication of the aluminium hydroxides in the ground-water. The reticulately mottled zone is probably Buchanan's laterite, often only weakly developed, for it dries out to hard lumps very resistant to weathering, and for this reason it is most important to prevent the surface of eroded red soils of this type ever being exposed to the sun during dry weather. P. E. Vageler,[1] H. Erhart[2] and E. C. J. Mohr[3] all give coloured plates illustrating this type of soil in their books.

Weathering in the Soil Zone

So far we have only been concerned with the weathering brought about by the percolating water containing dissolved oxygen and carbon dioxide, and this weathering can take place from the surface downwards to considerable depths. But this is not the only process of weathering taking place in the superficial layers of the soil. In the first place, the roots of some plants can hydrolyse some of the minerals they come in contact with, removing more of certain nutrients, such as phosphates and possibly also potassium, from the surface of the particles than can the bicarbonate in the soil solution. In the second place, organic matter derived from the vegetation is being decomposed by the soil organisms, and both the process itself, and the products of the decomposition, will affect the weathering. In the third place, plant roots are continually removing nutrients and other products of weathering from the root zone and incorporating them in their aerial tissues, which fall on to the soil surface at death. Thus, natural vegetation produces a continuous circulation of certain substances in the surface soil and so counter-acts to some extent their washing out in the downward percolating water.

There are not a great many reliable figures to indicate the magnitude

[1] *Grundriss der tropischen und subtropischen Boden*, 2nd ed., Berlin, 1938, 1st ed. translated by H. Greene, *An Introduction to Tropical Soils*, London, 1933.
[2] *Traité der Pédologie*, 2 vols., Strasbourg, 1935 and 1937.
[3] *De Bodem der Tropen in het Algemeen*, Vol. I, Part 2, Amsterdam, 1933.

of this annual return of nutrients under natural conditions. One can, however, make some estimates that must be treated with caution. Thus, in Table 122, on p. 536, meadow hay, giving $1\frac{1}{2}$-ton crop per acre, which is not a heavy crop, has an ash content of 200 lb. per acre, and this contains about 27 lb. of silicon, about 80 lb. of cations, and probably only a few pounds of iron and aluminium. Natural prairies would probably return at least this quantity of minerals every year whenever the rainfall permitted reasonable growth. Forests also seem to return about 200 to 300 lb. per acre of minerals to the soil each year in their leaf fall,[1] but the proportion of cations to silicon in the dead leaves appears to vary between wide limits. E. Wolff,[2] in 1871 and 1880, collected together many ash analyses of forest leaves and litter and found silicon contents varying from 5 to 35 per cent, corresponding to silica content about double this, with 10 to 20 per cent being a common range. The few more recent determinations available all indicate great variability in silicon content, the causes of which have not been analysed out. Returns of up to 50 lb. per acre of silicon, and 55 lb. per acre of calcium are probably not uncommon under hardwood forests, whilst under coniferous forest the annual return of calcium may be under 25 lb. per acre, and probably considerably less than this on very acid soils. The annual silicon return under these conditions is very variable. The amount of iron and aluminium returned is probably under 2 per cent of the total minerals, but these figures are again uncertain, particularly those for aluminium.

It is interesting to compare these figures of annual circulation of calcium and silicon with the amounts carried away by rivers, given on p. 555. Over catchment areas as a whole it appears that the average loss of calcium per year into rivers is of the same order of magnitude as the amount in circulation, but the loss of silicon is probably only about a half of that in annual circulation.

Living organisms have two direct effects on the weathering of the mineral particles in the soil zone. In the first place, they respire carbon dioxide and take up bases, and hence by acting as centres of powerful base extraction, cause the residual mineral to weather more easily. Secondly, they may excrete acids capable of bringing into solution compounds which are relatively insoluble in carbonic acid solutions. Thus, as will be discussed in more detail on p. 574, organic acids such as oxalic, tartaric and citric, which can disperse iron and aluminium

---

[1] The figures quoted here and lower down here have been derived in part from the following papers: R. R. McKibbin and L. I. Pugsley, *McGill Univ., Tech. Bull.* 6, 1930; F. J. Alway et al., *Soil Sci.,* 1933, **36,** 399; H. A. Lunt, *Connecticut Agric. Expt. Sta., Bull.* 394, 1937; *Bull.* 449, 1941; R. F. Chandler, *J. Amer. Soc. Agron.,* 1941, **33,** 859; *Proc. Soil Sci. Soc. Amer.,* 1944, **8,** 409; *Cornell Agric. Expt. Sta., Mem.* 228, 1939; S. Lindberg and H. Nonming, *Svenska SkogsvFören. Tidskr.,* 1943, **41,** 353.
[2] *Aschen Analysen,* Berlin, Vol. I, 1871, and II, 1880.

hydroxides relatively easily, may sometimes be produced by micro-organisms in the soil.

The decomposition of the organic matter can also influence the products of weathering formed, for as it decomposes so the minerals it contains, such as the bases and silica, are released in soluble, and hence in mobile and reactive forms. In particular, the continuous release of mobile silica will encourage clay formation in the lower parts of the soil zone. Thus the root zone of a soil is a zone in which soluble products of weathering are in circulation on the one hand, but in which the weathering processes are proceeding more actively than in the deeper subsoil.

The plant remains can be given back to the soil in three ways. They can be returned to the surface of the soil and only the soluble products of decomposition wash down into it; they can be returned to the surface, but mixed with the superficial layer of the soil by earthworms and other animals; and they can be returned to the soil in the root system of the plant. In so far as any one of these methods is much more impor-tant at a particular site than the other two, so the type of soil that develops there is characteristic of this method of plant debris return. But since all three methods are usually operative to a greater or less extent at every site, these characteristic soil types tend to be models which any particular soil can be compared with. In fact the first method of return is often dominant under coniferous forest, the second under deciduous or broad-leaved forest, and the third under steppe and prairie. This third method, when modified to include the incorporation of plant remains throughout an appreciable depth of soil, is that used by farmers when they plough in farmyard manure or green crops, or when they put the land down to temporary leys.

The type of soil formed in a given region depends not only on the climate and the vegetation, but also on the topography of the land, the goodness of drainage and the parent material from which the soil is being formed. The effect of topography is mainly through the direction in which the products of weathering move on the one hand and the goodness of drainage on the other. The effect of drainage is both through the rate at which products of weathering are removed or accumulate within the root zone, and also on the oxygen content of the soil air. For poor drainage typically has the consequence that no oxygen can reach the lower layers of the soil, hence reducing condi-tions set in. The parent material affects both the vegetation and the products of weathering and of accumulation, for the various minerals composing it have different rates of weathering and release different proportions of plant nutrients and of decomposition products during the process of weathering.

The effects of these soil-forming agents will be illustrated by examples in the following chapters. A detailed description of the various soil types that have been recognised, and of the various schemes of soil classification that have been suggested will not be given here, as several books devoted to these subjects are available.[1] It has become customary to classify soils into three divisions: the zonal, intrazonal and azonal soils. Azonal soils have not been under the influence of soil-forming processes long enough for their parent material to be appreciably affected, and alluvial soils in the temperate regions are typical examples of this group. In the zonal and intrazonal soils the parent material in the superficial layers has been appreciably affected by the soil-forming processes, the zonal soils being those formed on well-drained sites. Thus soils with impeded or transverse drainage, and swamp, marsh and salt soils, are examples of intrazonal soils. Soils in which the parent material has a pronounced but temporary effect on the soil-forming processes are also usually regarded as intrazonal, but this is normally restricted to soils forming on parent material rich in calcium carbonate. Thus, soils developing on chalk and limestone are considered intrazonal as long as any influence that the chalk or limestone may have had on the process of soil formation persists.

It is, however, very difficult to give any precise definition of the terms zonal, intrazonal and azonal. The concept of zonal soils was first introduced by the Russian pedologists when they were developing the theory that soil type was fundamentally determined by the climate, that is, that each climatic zone had its characteristic zonal soil type. But the concept has become progressively less precise as the deficiencies of this simple theory have been recognised.

[1] See, for example, G. W. Robinson, *Soils: Their Origin, Constitution and Classification*, 3rd ed., London, 1949; A. A. J. de Sigmond, *Principles of Soil Science*, London, 1938; J. S. Joffe, *Pedology*, 2nd ed., New Brunswick, 1949; S. A. Wilde, *Forest Soils and Forest Growth*, Waltham, Mass., 1946. For a symposium on Soil Classification, see *Soil Sci.*, 1949, **67**, 77.

CHAPTER XXXI

SOIL FORMATION ON WELL-DRAINED SITES

The Humus of the Forest Floor

TWO CHARACTERISTIC TYPES of humus can be formed on the forest floor of well-drained sites known as mor and mull respectively. Mor formation typically occurs when the leaf litter and the humus produced by its decomposition lie on the surface of the mineral soil, and mull formation when the litter is rapidly mixed with the mineral soil particles, so the decomposition occurs in the superficial layers of the soil instead of on its surface. P. E. Müller, a famous Danish forester, first recognised and named these two types of humus in 1878,[1] and although foresters were at first slow to see the value of this separation, it is now recognised as being of considerable importance for forestry practice in the temperate regions. But well developed typical mor and mull are really two extreme types of humus, although they are developed over wide areas: there are also a whole range of transitional types formed where there is some mixing of plant debris with the mineral matter of the soil, but where this mixing goes on at too slow a rate to give a typical mull. Further, there are considerable variations in the types of humus present in typical mor and mull, as defined above.[2] There is much that is not yet understood about mor and mull formation, and in particular it is not always possible to predict if a change in forestry practice will cause an appreciable effect on the type of humus being formed,[3] though this is not necessarily of great practical importance for many trees will grow equally well on a soil whether the humus is present as a mor or a mull.

Mor formation typically occurs under coniferous forests and heaths growing on very well-drained soils low in available calcium, and which are in consequence very acid; but it can also occur on rather badly drained soils, under deciduous forest, and on only mildly acid soils. The organic layer is often matted, lies like a carpet on the mineral soil, and has a low ash content. It shows a gradual transition from the undecomposed litter on the surface through layers in which it is

---

[1] *Tidsskr. f. Skovbrug*, 1878, **3**, 1; 1884, **7**, 1; *Studien über die natürlichen Humusformen*, 1887, Berlin; *Ann. Sci. Agron.*, 1889, **1**, 85.

[2] See, for example, H. Hesselman, *Medd. Skogsförsöksanst.*, 1926, **22**, 169; 1927, **23**, 337; L. G. Romell and S. O. Heiberg, *Ecology*, 1931, **12**, 567; S. O. Heiberg and R. F. Chandler, *Soil Sci.*, 1941, **52**, 87.

[3] For a discussion of this, see L. G. Romell, *Cornell Agric. Expt. Sta.*, Mem. 170, 1935.

decomposing but in which some of the original leaf structure remains recognisable—Hesselman's F-layer[1]—to a layer of dark, structureless humus below, Hesselman's H-layer.

Mull formation typically occurs under deciduous or mixed forests growing on moderately well-drained soils reasonably supplied with calcium, but it can occur under coniferous forests, particularly if they contain cedars or certain species of spruce whose litter has a high calcium content.[2] Thus, mulls are usually less acid than mors, but are not necessarily so. Their acidity does not fall below pH 4·5 and may be as high as pH 8, whilst that of a mor may fall to pH 3, and be as high as 6·5. The organic layer is crumbly and most of it is mixed with a high proportion of soil particles, so it may only contain as little as 10 per cent of organic matter, and there is a gradual transition from the surface mull to the mineral soil. The mull layer is what the gardener calls leaf or vegetable mould, and if it were not that the sound of the word would lead to confusion with certain types of fungi, this type of humus should have been called mould and not mull in English. Mull soils typically contain many earthworms and often harbour many moles, voles and mice, which burrow extensively under the surface, keeping the surface layers very loose and helping in the mixing of the litter with the soil.

Unfortunately, the number of firmly established facts about the process of mull and mor formation are scanty, so that even the cause of their formation is not agreed. It is probable, however, that the principal agents directly controlling which type of humus is formed are the predominant groups of soil animals present in it. Mull appears to be the characteristic humus formed when earthworms are the predominant group, transitional types of humus when the dominant soil fauna are millepedes, woodlice or larvae of the larger insects or termites, and typical mor when they are mites and springtails. This transitional type of humus in Europe, where termites are of no importance, was called "insect mull" by Müller, and is a mor, in that there is a fairly sharp boundary between the humus and the soil, but the F-layer is weakly developed and the H-layer is usually crumbly, shows little trace of the original structure of the dead litter, and is mainly composed of the excreta of the soil fauna by which it has been produced. Thus, mull types of humus seem to be characteristic of decomposed organic matter that has passed at least once through the alimentary canal of one of the larger soil animals, whilst typical mor humus has not. There is no reason to believe that the decomposed organic matter

---

[1] "F" is short for Förmultningskikt, or fermentation layer, and "H" for Humusämneskikt, or humus layer.

[2] See, for example, M. J. Plice, *Cornell Agric. Expt. Sta.*, Mem. 166, 1934; R. F. Chandler, ibid., *Mem.* 228, 1939.

suffers a different type of change in passing through a mite than a mille-pede or insect larva: it is in the proportion of the organic matter which has passed through that the typical mor differs from the typical mull.[1]

On this concept, the factors controlling mull or mor formation are effective through their control of the animal population. Thus, in north-west Europe, earthworms only occur in soils that are adequately supplied with available calcium, reasonably deep and reasonably well-drained. Earthworms need an adequate depth of soil for hibernation and aestivation, and they also need a soil with a reasonable moisture holding capacity, for they do not flourish in very dry soils such as coarse sands and gravels. Thus, heath soils and thin soils over rock typically have mor humus developing on them. The conditions under which millepedes, woodlice and the larvae of the larger insects become dominant in temperate regions are not yet known, though W. Kubiena,[2] working in some mountain limestone soils of Austria, found that this occurred after a certain depth of soil had accumulated, but before it was deep enough for earthworms to flourish; so it is possible that they only form the dominant soil fauna when all circumstances except depth of soil are suited to earthworms.

On this concept one of the roles of soil micro-organisms in the produc-tion of humus is to prepare the leaf litter for use by the larger soil animals. In typical mor, the fungi are often considered to be the pre-dominant group of micro-organism, and they convert much of the leaf litter into their own protoplasm which is a form that the mites in par-ticular can digest. However, although fungal mycelia and fungal-eating mites are very common in many such mors, no quantitative proof has yet been given that the fungi are, in fact, the most important group of micro-organisms in decomposing the leaf litter. The conditions in a mor are, however, usually too acid for many groups of bacteria to develop. Thus, nitrifying bacteria are typically either absent or present in very small numbers, so mor soils do not contain detectable amounts of nitrates in the field, though they may yield some nitrate when incubated in the laboratory. However, mor soils are also characterised by only contain-ing very small amounts of ammonium nitrogen, probably because of the intense demands of the micro-organisms for available nitrogen, as the litter has usually a low nitrogen content. Further, the roots of trees growing on mor are usually concentrated in the humus layer and covered with mycorrhiza, so the plants are also strongly competing for the available nitrogen there.

No complete fractionation of mor humus has yet been made, but its

[1] See, for example, T. H. Eaton and R. F. Chandler, *Cornell Agric. Expt. Sta.*, Mem. 247, 1942.

[2] *Bodenk. PflErnähr.*, 1942, **29**, 108; 1944, **35**, 22; *Entwicklungslehre des Bodens*, Vienna, 1948.

fulvic acid fraction appears to contain a relatively high proportion of readily dispersible nitrogen compounds. The humus in the mor rapidly releases ammonium nitrogen when the trees have been felled or sufficiently heavily lopped to kill the mycorrhizal fungi, or when it is brought into the laboratory. This ammonia is probably derived from the decomposition of the fungal mycelia in the humus layer but this has not yet been proved.

Bacteria are probably the most important microbial agents of decomposition in mull, and aerobic cellulose decomposers are usually abundant. The soils always nitrify well and differ from mors in having a higher content of ammonium and nitrate nitrogen in the natural state, but in not forming these compounds so quickly when samples are incubated in the laboratory. On the other hand, the roots of the trees and the undergrowth are not concentrated in the mull layer, but extend through a considerable depth of soil, and the roots usually only carry few mycorrhiza. The humus has a lower proportion of the fulvic acid fraction, is less easily mobile and more saturated with calcium than that in a mor, and its humic acid fraction has probably a higher nitrogen content and a higher base exchange capacity.

The fact that the organic matter in the bulk of the mull layer is structureless does not mean that decomposition takes place more rapidly in the mull than in the mor, for the opposite is probably more often true. It is simply a reflection of the fact that earthworms not only mix the leaf litter with the soil, but so macerate it in their gut that all trace of its original structure has been lost in the excrement.

An example of the effect of the absence of earthworms and of extreme shallow rooting habit in encouraging mor formation is well illustrated on the Rothamsted Grass Plots, which are part of an old meadow cut annually for hay. Where the soil has been rendered very acid by repeated high dressings of sulphate of ammonia, a layer of dead grass litter has been converted into a definite mor. There are no earthworms in the soil, and the grasses are very shallow rooting and suffer quickly in droughts, but if the litter is mixed with the soil in the laboratory, decomposition of the mor rapidly takes place.

Well-drained Soils under Mor: the Podsol

The soil developed under well-drained mor is the podsol, which is characterised by having a band of light-coloured soil fairly sharply separated from a darker layer of soil above and below it. It is this band of light soil which has given the podsol its name, for the word signifies in Russian ash-coloured soil. The podsol profile can be divided into several clearly defined layers or horizons. The upper is the mor and is commonly called the A_0 horizon, and is brown to black in colour. Below this comes the top layer of mineral soil, which is also dark in colour, the A_1 horizon, but on many sites this is not developed, and below the A_1 comes the light-coloured bleached layer, or A_2. The next layer, called the B, is dark coloured and usually lightens gradually with depth until it becomes indistinguishable from the parent material or the C horizon. Since the surface humus is a mor, the division between the A_0 and A_1, or A_2 if there is no A_1, is sharp, and the divisions between the A_1 and A_2 and between the A_2 and B are sharp, but the divisions in the B horizon itself, and between the B and C horizons are gradual.

The relative thickness of these layers is very variable, but the cause of the variability cannot always be given. The A_0 can be very thin and the A_1 well developed, as on heaths and some forests with suitable under growth, or the A_0 can be well developed and the A_1 thin or lacking. Thus, in well-developed podsols under coniferous forest on sandy soils there is no A_1 horizon—the mor lies directly on the A_2—and this is probably the profile originally defined as the podsol by the Russians. Similarly, the thickness of the A_2 and of the B varies very considerably, often in quite small areas; and in particular the boundary between the A_2 and the top of the B is often extremely irregular, varying by over 6 inches in very short distances. The total depth of the profile, that is, from the top of the A_0 to the bottom of the B, can vary from a few centimetres to over a metre.

This profile is most clearly developed on coarse, sandy soils rich in quartz grains, for these resistant grains give a large visible surface that can suffer bleaching. As the soil becomes heavier, the separation between the horizons becomes less distinct, until the B may only appear as darker coloured spots or streaks in a uniform bed of parent material. In northern Europe, podsols are extensively developed over the great area of sands left behind by the ice-sheets in the glacial period.

The chemical characteristics of the podsol profile are:

1. The pH is usually lowest in the A_0 horizon and increases down the profile, though in some profiles the A_1 may be the most acid.

2. The A_0 and A_1 horizons have a high base exchange capacity, but are very unsaturated. The percentage saturation usually increases down the profile, but because of the low exchange capacity of the A_2 and below, the actual number of milli-equivalents of base, chiefly calcium, may be highest in the A_0 or A_1.

3. The A_2 horizon is subjected to intense weathering, as can be seen from an examination of the fine sand grains. All those of easily weatherable minerals have either disappeared or are obviously being heavily

attacked. Thus, minerals very resistant to weathering, such as quartz, tend to accumulate in it. There is no evidence that any secondary minerals are formed in this layer.

4. The B horizon is enriched with material that has been washed out of the A horizons, and it is therefore often called an illuvial horizon in contrast to the A's which are known as eluvial. It is enriched with organic matter, clay, and iron and aluminium hydroxides, and often the zone of their maximum accumulation occurs at its top. But, whilst this is probably always true for the organic matter, the maximum for the clay may be in the bottom part of the A_2, and for the iron and aluminium hydroxides below the top of the B. It is very common in Great Britain to find a thin hard pan, often only a few millimetres thick, on top of the B horizon, which is sometimes referred to as the "walnut shell layer" and which is the zone of maximum iron, and possibly of organic matter, accumulation. Table 132[1] illustrates many of these points for a podsol developed under forest in Morayshire, Scotland.

Much of the iron and aluminium deposited in the B horizon is present as hydroxides or hydrated oxides, as can be shown both by the solubility of the iron and aluminium compounds in such solvent as Tamm's acid oxalate and by the power of the soil in the B horizon to absorb acidic dyes. Fig. 48[2] shows the amount of iron and aluminium extracted by Tamm's acid oxalate from a typical podsol of the type being discussed, called an iron podsol in the figure (the iron-humus podsol will be discussed on p. 590): it is greatest at the top of the B horizon and decreases downwards until it falls to a low level in the C. Acidic dye absorption, which can probably only take place on the iron and aluminium hydrated oxides and hydroxides in this layer, follows the acid extract curves very closely.[3]

It is possible, but not yet proven, that some of the aluminium entering the B horizon reacts with soluble silica there to give kaolinitic, or possibly illitic, clays. The B horizon certainly contains these clays,[4] and it is very probable they are being formed there, but this has not yet been proved. On the other hand, D. M. C. MacEwan[5] has shown that in the B horizon of some Scottish podsols, biotites appear to be converted into hydrobiotites and vermiculites and thence into illites, a conversion that does not necessitate the complete disruption of the original biotite lattice.

Much still remains obscure about the chemistry of the podsolisation process, and the two problems that are still unsolved concern the agent

[1] A. Muir, *Forestry*, 1934, 8, 25. [2] Taken from K. Lundblad, *Soil Sci.*, 1934, 37, 137.
[3] K. Lundblad, *Soil Sci.*, 1936, 41, 383.
[4] L. T. Alexander, S. B. Hendricks and R. A. Nelson, *Soil Sci.*, 1939, 48, 273.
[5] *Verre et Silic. Indust.*, 1948, 13, 41.

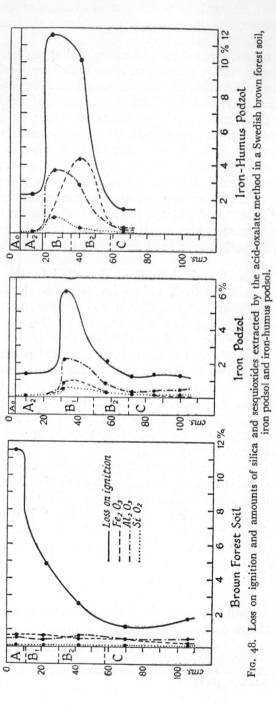

FIG. 48. Loss on ignition and amounts of silica and sesquioxides extracted by the acid-oxalate method in a Swedish brown forest soil, iron podsol and iron-humus podsol.

TABLE 132

Analysis of the Various Horizons of a Podsol Profile in Teindland State Forest, Morayshire

(A) Ultimate analysis as percentage of ignited fine earth (< 2 mm.)

Horizon	A_1 5–7 cm.	A_2 7–14 cm.	B_1 14–16 cm.	B_2 16–26 cm.	B_3 26–50 cm.	C 60–70 cm.
SiO_2 . . .	89·43	91·05	82·49	78·86	76·40	83·12
TiO_2 . . .	0·14	0·12	0·24	0·21	0·21	0·11
Al_2O_3 . . .	6·11	5·81	10·10	10·30	11·08	8·56
Fe_2O_3 . . .	0·89	0·55	2·71	3·59	3·32	2·19
CaO . . .	0·63	0·45	0·52	0·68	0·94	0·59
MgO . . .	0·30	0·54	0·40	0·22	0·71	0·46
Undetermined residue[1] . .	2·50	1·78	3·54	6·14	7·34	4·87
Total . . .	100·00	100·00	100·00	100·00	100·00	100·00
Loss on ignition .	38·73	1·77	7·87	5·66	3·92	1·63
Moisture (105°) .	12·02	0·65	5·41	4·72	4·12	1·46
Clay content .	—	4·75	12·32	10·12	9·25	4·58

(B) Analysis of clay fraction: as percentage of ignited clay

Horizon	A_2 7–14 cm.	B_1 14–16 cm.	B_2 16–26 cm.	B_3 30–40 cm.	C 60–70 cm.
SiO_2 . . .	59·02	46·28	31·73	33·80	35·20
TiO_2 . . .	3·59	1·19	1·82	1·50	1·00
Al_2O_3 . . .	24·20	29·92	38·36	31·62	24·56
Fe_2O_3 . . .	4·18	14·36	20·42	21·71	18·80
SiO_2/R_2O_3 . .	3·71	2·00	0·95	1·26	1·63
SiO_2/Al_2O_3 . .	4·12	2·61	1·03	1·80	1·92
Al_2O_3/Fe_2O_3 .	9·09	3·28	4·01	2·30	2·59

(C) Absorbed bases per 100 gm. of oven-dry soil, and pH value

Horizon	A_0	A_1	A_2	B_1	B_2	B_3	C
m.-eq. Calcium . .	7·0	3·0	0·8	1·1	0·5	0·8	0·8
m.-eq. Magnesium .	n.d.	2·6	1·0	1·0	0·9	0·8	0·8
m.-eq. Hydrogen . .	n.d.	46·2	1·6	23·1	17·7	6·9	2·9
pH . . .	3·7	3·9	4·3	4·5	4·5	4·8	5·1

that mobilises the iron and aluminium in the A layers and carries them down into the B, and the agent that causes the iron and aluminium to be precipitated in the B.

It has long been suspected that there was a connection between the movement of organic matter from the A_0 and A_1 horizons into the B and the solution and transport of the iron and aluminium. The crux of

[1] Probably chiefly K_2O and Na_2O.

this problem hinges on the fraction of the organic matter responsible. There are two different processes, both of which are possible on our present knowledge. Finely dispersed acid humus particles can mobilise the hydrated ferric oxide formed during the weathering process, and carry it down into the subsoil. This process is the one that has been most commonly assumed to be operative, and B. C. Deb[1] has shown that under conditions which may very likely prevail in the surface layers of a podsol, this finely dispersed humus can carry down from three to ten times its weight of iron oxide.

The second possible process is that polybasic carboxylic acids are the principal agents for carrying down the iron oxide. It is known that acids such as oxalic, citric and tartaric are all capable, even in weak solutions, of bringing into solution iron and aluminium in the form of co-ordination compounds,[2] that the free acid is not necessary but only the free anion,[3] and that these acids are typical metabolic by-products of the fungi in the mor layer. But their presence has only been assumed and not actually demonstrated in the downward moving water.[4] It is just possible that the mechanism by which finely dispersed acid humic particles mobilise the iron is through the iron forming co-ordination compounds with its carboxylic acids, in which case the two processes described would both operate through the same mechanism.

The second problem concerns the cause of the deposition of the iron and aluminium in the B horizons. The problem is complicated by the probable fact, to be discussed on p. 575, that only a part, and perhaps a small part, of the iron and aluminium removed from the A layers is deposited in the B, although the current theories on the cause of this deposition all assume that it is complete. The principal theories at present advocated assume that the primary cause of the precipitation is the increased pH in the B horizon. Colloidal particles of iron and aluminium, probably as hydroxides, are assumed to acquire a positive charge under the highly acid conditions in the A layers which is sufficiently great for the colloidal particles to disperse in the downward-moving water, but the charge falls rapidly as the pH increases at the base of the A_2 and the top of the B horizons so that the particles cease to be dispersed in the water and precipitate out. This theory naturally assumes that the iron and aluminium are not in co-ordination compounds with simple organic acids, for these compounds would reduce the positive charge the colloids could acquire in the A horizon.

[1] *J. Soil Sci.*, 1949, **1**, 112.
[2] H. T. Jones and J. S. Willcox, *J. Soc. Chem. Indust.*, 1929, **48**, 304 T.
[3] For the kind of experimental justification available for theories of this type, see P. H. Gallagher, *Proc. Roy. Irish Acad.*, 1942, **48** B, 213. W. J. Dyer and W. D. McFarlane (*Canad. J. Res.*, 1938, **16** B, 91) considered they had evidence that some of the iron in the B layer was in co-ordination compounds of this type.
[4] P. H. Gallagher and T. Walsh, *Proc. Roy. Irish Acad.*, 1943, **49** B, 1.

An alternative theory can probably be based on a mechanism similar to that postulated by H. Jenny and G. D. Smith, to be discussed on p. 593, for the formation of clay pans. Silicic and humic acids could be deposited on the mineral particles on the B horizon during summer droughts, which would give them a negatively charged surface on which, later in the year, the iron and aluminium co-ordination compounds in the downward-moving water would be precipitated as the organic acids mobilising them became attacked by the micro-organisms in this layer. This hydroxide layer would then cause silicic or humic acid, moving in the percolating water, to precipitate on it to neutralise its positive charge. Such a theory may probably come fairly close in many ways to S. Mattson's theory of isoelectric weathering,[1] for he postulates that the cause of material being precipitated in the B horizon is that it is isoelectric at the pH prevailing there. The precipitates are pictured as being built continuously by their removing the requisite proportions of aluminium, iron, silicic and humic acids from the compounds dissolved in the percolating water to give new precipitates that are isoelectric, that is, carry no net electric charge, in the percolating solution.

However, before much further headway can be made in the theory of podsolisation, more factual information is required. Thus, more knowledge is required of the forms of organic matter that actually move down through the A_2 horizon. The newer methods of humus analysis should be able to give a more accurate description of the organic materials that move from the A_0 into the top of B horizon,[2] although they would miss any ephemeral components such as oxalic or tartaric acids, supposing them to be present in low concentrations in the downward-percolating water. Again, not enough is known of the fate of the products of weathering mobilised in the A layers, for not all of them are precipitated in the B. Thus, analyses of the water from springs and rivers show that some of the silicon is washed out of the profile altogether, and this appears to be true for the iron and aluminium also. Thus, A. A. Rode[3] has calculated the loss of constituents from a podsol profile in Russia by assuming that the quartz in the original deposit was uniformly distributed throughout the profile and that none of it had weathered. These results are given in Table 133, which shows that the loss of iron and aluminium together from the whole profile is comparable with the loss of silicon, and though the losses are greatest in the A_2 horizon, yet they are appreciable in the B.

[1] *Soil Sci.*, 1932, **34**, 209, and a series of papers in *LantbrHögsk. Ann.*, beginning 1934, but particularly 1935, **2**, 115; 1937, **4**, 1; 1942, **10**, 241.
[2] For some publications on this, see P. H. Gallagher, *Proc. Roy. Irish Acad.*, 1942, **48** B, 213; I. V. Tiurin, *Pedology*, 1944, No. 10, 441.
[3] *The Soils of the U.S.S.R.*, Vol. I, p. 181, ed. L. I. Prasolov, Moscow, 1939.

TABLE 133

Weight of Soil Constituents Lost during Podsolisation

In tons per acre

Horizon	Si	Al	Fe	Mg	K	Ca	Na
A_1, 0–9 cm. . .	74	44	25	7	10	4	4
A_2, 9–26 cm. . .	138	88	48	14	19	9	7
A_2B, 26–35 cm. . .	43	30	16	5	6	4	3
B_2, 35–50 cm. . .	18	11	4	2	1	4	2
B, 50–63 cm. . .	8	4	2	1	—	—	1
Total, 0–63 cm. . .	281	177	95	29	36	21	17

Average annual loss, assuming soil 10,000 years old, in pounds per acre

	Si	Al	Fe	Mg	K	Ca	Na
A_1 and A_2 . . .	48	30	16	5	7	3	2
Total . . .	63	40	21	7	8	5	4

Tamm's estimate for young Swedish Podsols

	Si	Al	Fe	Mg	K	Ca	Na
A	25	10	7	3	4	2	2

O. Tamm[1] has also found that there is a net loss of iron and aluminium from the B horizon, and R. P. Matelski and L. M. Turk[2] have shown from an optical examination of the minerals in the fine sand fraction of a Michigan podsol that weathering proceeds actively in this zone. In fact, they claim that horneblende weathers more easily in the B than in the A horizons.

Rode also calculated the average rate of loss of constituents from the Russian profile, assuming it has taken 10,000 years to develop. The figures so found, which are also given in Table 133, imply a higher rate of weathering than for Europe as a whole, as deduced from the analyses of river waters given on p. 555, but unfortunately Rode does not say what were the parent mineral particles in the deposit. His results are also rather higher than some previously obtained by O. Tamm,[3] also given in Table 133, and obtained by a similar method, for the rate of removal of constituents from the A horizons of some young Swedish podsols developed on river sand.

The time taken for a podsol to develop its typical profile depends on many conditions, but on sandy soils under coniferous forest between 1,000 and 1,500 years is adequate,[4] though Tamm also finds that an A_2 horizon 1 cm. thick can be formed in 100 years, and A. Muir[5] gives an example of an A_2 horizon 0·5 cm. thick being formed in twenty years in Kincardineshire.

[1] *Medd. Skogsförsöksanst.*, 1932, **26**, 163.   [2] *Soil Sci.*, 1947, **64**, 469.
[3] *Medd. Skogsförsöksanst.*, 1920, **17**, 49.
[4] O. Tamm, *Medd. Skogsförsöksanst.*, 1920, **17**, 49; R. F. Chandler, *Proc. Soil Sci. Soc. Amer.*, 1943, **7**, 454 (for an example from Alaska).
[5] *Forestry*, 1934, **8**, 25.

The podsol profile can be altered very considerably if the drainage becomes impeded, but these alterations will be discussed in the next chapter, in which the general problem of the effect of impeded drainage on soil formation will be discussed.

Well-drained Soils under Mull: the Brown Earths

The typical brown earth differs from the true podsol in three respects: it is found on loams and clays rather than on sands, hence it has a lower air content during wet weather and may even be subject to slight reducing conditions during part of the year; it has a higher content of exchangeable calcium though it is typically acid; and there are no sharp horizons between the different layers in the profile.

The typical forest soil profile under mull begins with a layer of undecomposed litter, then comes a fairly deep layer of crumbly soil whose organic matter content decreases slowly downwards until it gradually grades into the unweathered subsoil. The name brown earth describes the colour of this layer. Since the soils are typically formed under forest, they are often referred to as brown forest soils when in this situation.

The chemical analysis of the profile shows the following characteristics. The pH and the proportion of exchangeable calcium usually increases gradually down the profile. The organic matter content decreases gradually down the profile, and there is no zone in the subsoil of organic matter accumulation. The profile shows the typical effects of weathering, namely, the mineral particles are attacked and the bases and silicon tend to wash out and the aluminium and iron to remain behind, though the intensity of weathering is much less severe than in the A horizon of podsols. There is little free iron and aluminium hydroxides in the profile, as shown by the small amount of these dissolved out by Tamm's acid oxalate, as can be seen in Fig. 48 on p. 572.

The outstanding product of accumulation is kaolinitic and illitic clay, which is formed all through the profile. On mature soils there is often a layer enriched in clay[1] due either to it being a layer of active clay synthesis or to it being a layer of accumulation of clay synthesised nearer the surface and washed down and held either mechanically in the fine pores or else by coagulation and drying on other particles.[2] This process can proceed so far that the layer has become almost impermeable, giving the planosol soil which is characteristic of very

[1] Soils with this layer of enrichment are known as grey-brown podsolic in America, for descriptions of which see M. Baldwin, *Proc. 1st Int. Congr. Soil Sci.*, Washington, 1927, **5**, 276; M. G. Cline, *Soil Sci.*, 1949, **68**, 259.
[2] H. Pallmann, E. Frei and H. Hamdi, *Ber. Schweiz. Bot. Ges.*, 1943, **53** A, 175; *Kolloid-Ztschr.*, 1943, **103**, 111.

level topography under these conditions in America. The chemical analysis of the profile also often shows a zone of relative enrichment with aluminium, that corresponds with the zone of clay enrichment. This may simply be a reflection of the fact that kaolinite clay has a high aluminium content compared with most rock minerals, but no suitable field results seem to be available to test if this is the whole cause of the apparent aluminium enrichment in the B horizon.

Natural brown earths under forest are rare in England and much of Europe because these soils have been cultivated for many centuries, as they are naturally more suitable than the podsols for agricultural crops. Brown earths also occur on hill slopes, but these will be discussed in the next chapter, as they form an example of the effect of topography on soil formation.

It must again be emphasised that there is a whole range of soils between the true podsol and the typical brown earth, for there are all transitions between mull and mor on the one hand and between very free draining sands and slow draining clays on the other. Hence there are soils showing all gradations in such properties as the amount of dispersed humic, iron and aluminium compounds that move into the subsoil and the quantity of clay that is synthesised. Soils in this transitional range are usually known as podsolic—a type that is extensively developed in America.

The Grassland Soils: the Prairie Soils and Chernozems

Grasses differ from forests in that they translocate much of the organic matter they synthesise into the soil as root system. As already mentioned on p. 458, grasses can add over a ton of dry matter to the soil per year as roots, and natural grassland soils may contain over 5 tons per acre of roots below ground compared with only 1 to 2 tons of above-ground material. Thus, J. E. Weaver, V. H. Hougen and M. D. Weldon[1] give the following weights of organic matter and roots in a Nebraska prairie, in tons per acre:

Depth	0–6 in.	6–12 in.	1–2 ft.	2–3 ft.	3–4 ft.
Weight of roots . .	2·6	0·72	0·63	0·30	0·04
Weight of organic matter .	31·0[2]	26·0	26·0	8·1	4·0
Weight of roots as per cent of organic matter . .	8·5	2·8	2·3	3·6	1·1

[1] *Bot. Gaz.*, 1935, **96**, 389. J. E. Weaver and E. Zink (*Ecol.*, 1946, **27**, 115) give further figures for the annual rate of production of roots by three prairie grasses at different depths in the soil.

[2] This figure includes the rhizomes of grasses which occurred in the top 6 inches.

This difference between grassland and forest is also illustrated in Plate XXVII, which shows the profiles, with the distribution of organic carbon down the profile, of a prairie and a deciduous forest soil both on the same parent material, and both from Iowa. Although the prairie soil only contains 50 per cent more organic matter than the forest, yet it is distributed through a considerably greater depth of soil.

The grass roots themselves are extensive and fine, hence, as shown in Table 102, on p. 458, they may have a very great length in the soil and many of the finer roots will decompose quickly. These soils also typically have a large population of earthworms, and also of rodents, which may make extensive burrows and nests in the soil well below the soil surface. Hence, little litter accumulates on the surface, most of it being worked into the top layers of the soil, as in the brown forest soils.

Grassland soils occur naturally in climates that are too dry for forests, although they can also be found on limestones and chalks in the more humid regions. Thus, as both E. M. Crowther and H. Erhart[1] have pointed out, they are characteristic of regions subject to summer droughts sufficiently severe for the available water in the root zone of the soil to be exhausted before the drought breaks. Grasses can withstand these conditions far better than deciduous forest, hence their dominance.

Grassland soils can be roughly divided into three types: the prairie, the chernozem and the chestnut. The typical prairie soils are formed where the summer rainfall is only just too little for deciduous forest, but where there is sufficient rainfall during the rest of the year for considerable leaching to take place. The chernozem soils are developed under rather more arid conditions where little water leaches out of the root zone, and the chestnut under still more arid conditions when the rain-water rarely if ever leaches through the profile. Thus, the prairie soil typically has a weakly leached profile so that the soil may be slightly acid all the way down, the chenozem has a weakly leached surface soil, which may be slightly acid, but has a zone of precipitation of calcium carbonate at the base of a deep root zone, whilst the chestnut soil has a neutral surface soil and its zone of calcium carbonate accumulation comes nearer the surface as the depth to which the rain normally penetrates becomes shallower. The leaching in the chestnut soil is so restricted that at the base of the layer of calcium carbonate accumulation comes a layer of calcium sulphate accumulation. These grassland soils have a very characteristic soil structure. The crumbs are small and friable, sometimes breaking down almost to a dust in the surface and become larger, angular and stronger in the deeper layers of the profile, and have considerable water stability. Plate XXX

[1] *Traité de Pédologie*, Strasbourg, 1935.

gives an illustration, in semi-diagrammatic form, of this structure in a well-developed chernozem, and Plate XXII gives a photograph of actual soil crumbs in a chernozem soil adhering to grass roots.

The prairie soils are similar in many respects to the brown forest soils. The surface layers are often somewhat acid, due to leaching, there is a washing down of organic matter and clay, and clay formation takes place in the profile. But there is probably a greater annual circulation, and hence a greater movement, of silica in prairie than in forest soils, for grasses have a much higher silicon content than tree leaves. As in the brown forest soils, a pronounced clay pan may be formed both by clay being actively formed in this layer and also by clay formed higher up the profile being washed down into it. Otherwise weathering is not very severe. Thus, J. F. Haseman and C. E. Marshall[1] showed that in the Grundy silt loam, a typical prairie soil developed on loess in Missouri, the sand grains larger than 0·046 mm. have barely been weathered at all, the silt particles between 0·025 and 0·002 mm. have been washed down from the top foot into the third and fourth foot, the easily weatherable minerals in the top 2 feet have been attacked, and clay accumulation has taken place in the layer $1\frac{1}{2}$ to $4\frac{1}{2}$ feet below the surface. The clay may be mainly illite or it may be an illite-beidellite mixture with the illite more in the larger and the beidellite or montmorillonite more in the finest fraction.[2]

These soils are well developed in the corn belt of the Middle Western states of America. They are fertile, or can be made so by adding fertilisers, and the rainfall is adequate for excellent crops of maize and soybeans if the land is properly farmed. It is to this soil type that the Western European farmer tries to convert his soil by using leys and farmyard manure.

The chernozems, or black earths, to give the English translation of the Russian word, are so called because of their black colour, which may extend down to a depth of 3 to 6 feet, though the colour lightens with depth. The fundamental climatic characteristic of these soils is that there should be sufficient rainfall for the natural grasses to make good top and root growth, but not sufficient to allow any appreciable leaching. Thus, very little of the rain percolating into the soil ever reaches the ground-water or the rivers. As the amount of rain-water penetrating into the ground-water increases, so the soil type goes over into the prairie, and as the deficiency of the rainfall increases, so the maximum depth to which the soil is wetted each year decreases, and it goes over to the chestnut. The true Russian chernozem occurs in a climate with hot summers and cold winters. In the winter the soil is

---

[1] *Missouri Agric. Expt. Sta., Res. Bull.* 387, 1945.
[2] See also W. E. Larson *et al., Proc. Soil Sci. Soc. Amer.,* 1948, **12,** 420.

frozen for prolonged periods and much of the snow that falls runs off the frozen soil when it thaws in spring.

The soil of the chernozem is neutral or nearly neutral all down the profile, the exchange complex is typically saturated mainly with calcium, and soil organic matter is probably leached down the profile, though to what depth is not known. As shown on p. 578, the roots only account for 2 to 4 per cent of the organic matter in the deeper layers of the profile, so if no leaching takes place it would mean that it takes twenty-five to thirty years, on the average, for the organic matter in the roots to be oxidised away. The organic matter has a relatively high nitrogen content compared with that in most forest soils, its C/N ratio being about 10, and the type of humus is Springer's grey humic acid which, according to Mattson (p. 274), is fully autoxidised and so has a high nitrogen content and a high base exchange capacity. Clay formation, predominantly of the beidellite type, occurs; but the rate of clay formation is much slower than in the prairie soils, and its chemical composition is nearly constant down the profile. There appears to be little translocation of silt or clay particles,[1] and clay pans, which are so characteristic of prairie soils, are less common in the chernozems.

However, under tropical conditions, where weathering can go on during the period the soil is wet because of the high temperature, but in regions where there is not enough rainfall for water to leach out of the root zone, so much beidellite or montmorillonite clay may be formed that the whole soil becomes an extremely heavy black clay carrying grass, or grass and scrub. In spite of the black colour the humus content may be fairly low, presumably again because of the high temperatures, and the only way water can move into the soil is through the large cracks that develop every dry season. They do not have a granular structure like a chernozem, but their subsoils have a very well pronounced columnar structure. These soils are typically formed from basic igneous rocks, probably because they contain a high proportion of minerals that weather easily and which release a high proportion of bases; they are found in many parts of Africa, and in the Dutch East Indies.

The chernozem is characterised also by having a zone of accumulation of calcium carbonate at a depth of about 6 feet. It is present as thin threads and films if the climate is only just arid enough for it to form, but as the climate becomes more arid, soft, white concretions appear. The three chernozem profiles, illustrated in Plate XXX, show this in semi-diagrammatic form. The deep chernozem is formed under the highest rainfall and the southern under the lowest, and the figure

[1] For a discussion of the characteristics of Russian chernozems, see L. I. Prasolov, *Dokuchaev Inst. Soils*, 1939, 1, 225.

shows how the depth at which calcium carbonate is first deposited decreases as the climate becomes more arid. These profiles also show the characteristic burrows of steppe rodents filled in with dark-coloured surface soils. Below the layer of calcium carbonate accumulation in the more arid chernozems comes a zone in which calcium sulphate is precipitated as gypsum.

The chernozems are well developed on the calcareous loess soils that extend from Central Europe through Russia into Central Asia, forming the great belt of the Eurasian steppe. They form the tall grass prairies of America and are probably developed in parts of South America as well. Their main agricultural use is for wheat growing, and they form the wheat soils of the world. The climate is too dry for crops other than wheat and some sorghums to be grown profitably, and their management has already been discussed in the section on dry farming in Chapter XXII.

The chestnut soils are developed under still more arid conditions than the black earths. Their name describes their colour, the colour of the skin of the edible chestnut, *Castanea sativa*, not the horse-chestnut, *Aesculus hippocastanum*. They are formed under conditions where the potential transpiration exceeds the rainfall, so at no time in the year does water leach out of the profile. The effect of the increasing lack of water is to give a grass vegetation with a shorter root system and a smaller annual production of organic matter,[1] so that both the depth to which the organic matter reaches, and its content at each depth, decreases. At the same time the layers in which the calcium carbonate and gypsum are deposited come closer to the surface.

As the climate becomes still more arid, shrubs begin to form an important part of the vegetation, but the production of organic matter both above and below ground becomes small, so that the organic matter content of the soil rapidly decreases, and what is there becomes increasingly concentrated in the superficial layers. The colour of the soil also lightens, becoming first brown and then grey, giving the sierozem or grey desert soils of the Russians.

The effect of increasing temperature on these grassland soils is threefold. In the first place, the colour of the soil reddens, and this is true for the prairie, chernozem and chestnut soils.[2] In the second place the horizon of calcium carbonate deposition may both thicken and harden, becoming a band up to several feet thick. This is known as caliche in parts of America, and *kankar* in parts of India and is also well seen in many parts of the Mediterranean.[3] If these desert soils are

[1] H. L. Shantz, *Ann. Assoc. Amer. Geog.*, 1923, **8**, 81.
[2] J. Thorp and M. Baldwin, *Ann. Assoc. Amer. Geog.*, 1940, **30**, 163.
[3] For a description of this in the black cotton soil area in India, see D. Singh and G. Lal, *Ind. J. Agric. Sci.*, 1946, **16**, 328; in the Mediterranean, G. Gaucher, *C.R.*, 1948, **227**, 154; G. Aubert, *C.R. Conf. Pédol. Méditerr.*, 1948, 330; in New Mexico, J. H. Bretz and L. Horberg. *J. Geol.*, 1949, **57**, 491.

over-grazed, so erosion takes place, these bands become exposed on the surface of the desert, giving a hard pavement. In the third place the organic matter decreases, presumably because of the higher temperature giving a high rate of decomposition. Conversely, when chernozem soils extend into cooler regions their organic matter content increases.

Leached Soils of the Humid Tropics[1]

Weathering in the tropics is relatively a much more corrosive process than in the temperate regions, and the rain when it comes tends to fall in heavy storms, so that such factors as slight changes in topography or in permeability of the soil will cause much greater differences in the type of soil being formed than in the temperate regions. This has the consequence that the land surface in the tropics tends to be a mosaic of very different soil types and this is most pronounced in regions of relatively moderate rainfall.[2]

The parent material from which the soil is being derived is also of great importance, for if the land surface is relatively recent, or if for any reason unweathered rock particles are in the root zone of the vegetation, appreciable amounts of mineral nutrients will be released by the weathering of these particles with a consequent effect on the luxuriance of crops being grown on the land (see p. 556 for example). And this effect again is much more noticeable in the tropics because of the much greater intensity of weathering. On the other hand, if the soil is formed on a crust of weathering on an old land surface, which commonly occurs over much of the tropics, the crust will only contain secondary minerals, which are present there because they are extremely resistant to weathering by downward moving water. Hence soil forming processes can have little effect on the minerals in the crust.

A characteristic of the humid tropics, and the tropics with a fairly long rainy season each year is the enormous rate of growth, and in natural conditions of decomposition, of the vegetation. Thus P. E. Vageler estimates that tropical rain forests may produce over 100 tons per acre of vegetable matter, a figure comparable to G. ap. Griffith's finding that in parts of Uganda elephant grass (*Pennisetum purpureum*), which requires a moderately well distributed rainfall, may produce 60 to 100 tons per acre of vegetable matter, containing 10 to 16 tons of

---

[1] For more detailed discussion on these soils, see P. E. Vageler, *Grundriss der tropischen und subtropischen Bodenkunde*, 2nd ed., Berlin, 1938, and *An Introduction to Tropical Soils*, London, 1933; H. Erhart, *Traité de Pédologie*, 2 vols., Strasbourg, 1935, and 1937; E. C. J. Mohr and F. A. van Baren, *Tropical Soils*, The Hague, 1954; J. Thorp and M. Baldwin, *Ann. Assoc. Amer. Geog.*, 1940, **30**, 163; H. Jenny, *Soil Sci.*, 1948, **66**, 5, 173; *Proceedings of the First Commonwealth Conference on Tropical and Subtropical Soils* (1948), issued as *Tech. Comm.* 46 of *Commonw. Bur. Soil Sci.*, 1949; C. E. Kellogg and F. D. Davol, *I.N.E.A.C. Ser. Sci., Publ.* 46, 1949.

[2] C. G. T. Morison *et al.*, *J. Ecol.*, 1948, **36**, 1.

dry matter and 600 to 1,000 lb. of nitrogen. Yet in well-drained tropical rain forests there may only be a thin layer of dead and rotting but unhumified vegetation lying on the soil surface that may not be thick enough to cover the surface of the soil. In fact H. Jenny[1] found in such forests in Colombia that the weight of the forest floor lying on the soil was only about 2 tons per acre, although as the rainfall decreased so the weight of litter increased.

This dead vegetation is rapidly attacked by saprophytic organisms and though no quantitative estimates are available, it is probable that the soil animals play a relatively more important role here than in the temperate regions. Further, the organisms decomposing this dead vegetation do not produce humus, in the temperate sense of the word. The soil may contain very high amounts of carbon and nitrogen, but this organic matter has a much lighter colour, or may be almost colourless under natural conditions. Nothing is known about the composition of this material. Vageler states that it darkens on oxidation and drying; that it is probably water-soluble, and that it contains acidic groups. Thus the soil just below the forest floor may be very light in colour, a light yellow to brown, or may have a bright red colour, yet contain several per cent of organic matter. It seems to be generally true that the humus in all well-drained tropical soils is lighter in colour than in the temperate regions, and that many tropical soils with impeded drainage have an intense black colour although they may only contain small amounts of organic matter. Hence it is almost impossible to judge the organic matter content of the soils in these regions from their colour.

Another characteristic of many well-drained tropical soils on old land surfaces is their extreme poverty in plant nutrients. Such soils may carry luxuriant virgin forest but yet have almost all their supply of plant nutrients present in the living or dead plants and animals or their ephemeral decomposition products. Hence, once such land has been cleared of vegetation and a few crops taken and removed, all the plant nutrients will also have been removed and the soil left in a condition of extremely low productivity.

The outstanding feature of most chemical analyses that have been made on undisturbed well-drained soils in the humid tropics has been the uniformity in the chemical composition of the soil, the clay and the free sesquioxides down the soil profile.[2] In so far as the soil weathers it must dissolve away completely, leaving virtually no residue behind. The colour of the soils can be either red or yellow to brown. The red

[1] *Soil Sci.*, 1948, **66**, 173.
[2] See, for example, F. Hardy and G. Rodrigues, *Soil Sci.*, 1939, **48**, 361, 483; F. T. Seelye *et al.*, ibid., 1938, **46**, 23 (for Samoa); J. A. Bonnet, ibid., 1939, **48**, 25 (for Puerto Rico); G. J. Hough, *U.S. Dept. Agric., Tech. Bull.* 548, 1937 (for Hawaii).

colour is probably developed under a climate having a hot annual dry season, whereas the yellow is more common either under a hot uniformly wet climate or under a hot climate in which the hot weather coincides with the rains and the cooler weather with the dry season. However, soils devoid of iron have a white to pale yellow or brown colour. The difference in colour is presumably due to the iron being present, limonite, hydrated $FeO(OH)$, under normal humid conditions but being converted to haematite, Fe_2O_3, under hot dry conditions. But whenever the drainage is impeded, the yellow-brown colour is usually dominant.

There is evidence that typical podsols can be found in the hot, humid tropics. They have been described as occurring in permeable quartz sand carrying a heath vegetation with a thin layer of acid mor on the surface of the sand. There is usually up to 10 to 20 cm. of A_1 horizon, from 20 to 100 cm. of bleached A_2 sand, followed by a B horizon that is enriched with iron and aluminium and may be indurated. Table 134, taken from some work of H. J. Hardon,[1] refers to such a soil in the lowlands of Borneo. P. W. Richards[2] has given other examples of podsols under tropical heaths from other equatorial regions.

Podsols also occur in the uplands of tropical regions, at elevations of 6,000 feet or over, when the climate is no longer tropical and the mean annual temperature will be about $15°C.$ instead of $25°C.$ Under some forest conditions the various layers in the profile can be very thick, and both Jenny and also Thorp and Baldwin have noted light coloured A_2 layers up to 3 feet thick.

TABLE 134

The Composition of a Lowland Tropical Podsol from Bangka, Borneo

Horizon	A_0	A_1	A_2	B_1	B_2
Depth in cm.	0–10	10–25	25–40	40–70	70–100
Colour	black	greyish black	greyish white	dark brown	light brown
pH	2·7	3·9	6·1	3·9	4·6
Per cent clay	—	1·6	0·6	7·2	4·6
Analysis of Clay Fraction:					
SiO_2	48·9	60·6	65·2	18·2	14·0
Al_2O_3	18·8	12·3	10·1	70·7	73·2
Fe_2O_3	6·4	3·1	4·2	4·4	6·5
TiO_2	10·1	14·2	8·6	2·7	2·7
$\dfrac{SiO_2}{Al_2O_3 + Fe_2O_3}$	3·62	7·17	8·64	0·42	0·31

[1] *Pedology*, 1938, 325. Note the profile described by him in *Natuurwet. Tijdsche Ned. Ind.*, 1936, **36**, 25, and quoted in the seventh edition of *Soil Conditions* as an example of a tropical podsol, refers to a profile at an elevation of 2,000 m. where the average daily and annual temperature is 14° to 15°C. The mean annual temperature at Bangka is about 26°C.
[2] *Nature*, 1941, **148**, 129; *J. Ecol.*, 1936, **24**, 1.

CHAPTER XXXII

THE INFLUENCE OF TOPOGRAPHY ON SOIL FORMATION

Effect of Impeded Drainage and Ground-water on the Soil

WELL-DRAINED SOILS are characterised by downward leaching of oxygenated water, hence oxidising conditions occur throughout the profile for at least the greater part of the year. But once the downward movement of water becomes impeded, so the micro-organisms and plant roots in the soil use all the oxygen in the water as fast as it is renewed, then reducing conditions set in. It is not that impeded drainage or high ground-water necessarily give reducing conditions; there must also be an agent in the layer of water-logging that not only removes oxygen from the water, but actually creates an oxygen deficit; and micro-organisms decomposing organic matter in this layer are the normal agents creating this deficit.

The effect of reducing conditions in the soil is for the accessible trivalent iron and tetravalent manganese among the metals to be reduced to the divalent condition, and for sulphates and nitrates to be converted to sulphides and ammonia. The effect of lowering the valency of the iron and manganese is to increase their solubility in the soil solution, for divalent iron can have a higher ionic concentration in the soil solution than trivalent, and divalent manganese is a simple cation whilst the tetravalent forms part of the very insoluble manganese dioxide. The effect of reducing sulphates to sulphides is to limit very sharply the amount of microbial and plant root activity in the layer, for sulphides are very toxic to most plant roots and only a restricted number of anaerobic micro-organisms can flourish in their presence.

Soils with impeded drainage are characterised by much of the iron and manganese being mobile, as well as some of the silicon, but the aluminium remains immobile,[1] as it cannot be converted to a soluble form by reduction. Movement of aluminium is therefore more characteristic of well-drained than badly-drained soils, and differs markedly from iron and manganese in this respect.

Impeded drainage and ground-water have another effect on the soil, for impeded drainage reduces the loss of the products of weathering

[1] R. S. Holmes *et al.*, *U.S. Dept. Agric.*, *Tech. Bull.* 594, 1938; I. C. Brown and J. Thorp, ibid., 834, 1942.

from the soil, and both impeded drainage and high ground-water may actually allow products of weathering produced higher up in the soil profile, or from the soil or crust of weathering on higher ground, to accumulate. Hence, soil layers subject to high ground-water or impeded drainage are typically only slightly acid or neutral, and the exchange complex mainly contains either calcium alone or mixed with a considerable proportion of magnesium. These soils also often have the same content of exchangeable bases down the profile, whilst well-drained soils usually have a higher content in the surface layer, which is enriched with organic matter, than in the lower layers. Soluble silica also collects in this layer, particularly if ground-water is entering the area, so that if any clay is formed it is of the montmorillonite type. This can be particularly well seen in some tropical areas having a pronounced wet and dry season, where the soil has only a limited permeability. The soil in all the small depressions is black and some of its clay is beidellite or montmorillonite, and the soil on all the small hillocks is red and the clay mainly kaolinitic;[1] though this simple picture does not apply in all such situations in the tropics.

Impeded drainage or high ground-water can have another consequence in arid basins draining more humid hill or mountain land, for the ground-water is enriched in the products of weathering of the uplands, and as it evaporates it leaves behind the soluble salts it contained when it entered the basin. In this way soils can become so enriched in salts that most plants cease to grow. But salt soils and problems connected with the control of saline ground-water are so important in irrigation practice that they will be dealt with in Chapters XXXIII–XXXIV.

The outstanding visual characteristic of soil layers in which strong reducing conditions prevail is the colour of the soil, for it is a light grey colour tinged with blue or green, presumably due to the ferrous iron present, though what these compounds are is not known, for the colour does not readily become brown on drying or when exposed to the air, and it persists for a long time after the field has been drained. It is soil layers with this colour that are called glei, or gley, a Russian peasant word for this soil. The chemical characteristics of gley horizons[2] are, as already mentioned, that they are neutral or only mildly acid, they contain ferrous iron, much of it as exchangeable ions,[3] but some in other combinations that have not been identified, and they are usually low in phosphates.[4] The cause of the disappearance of phosphates

[1] G. Nagelschmidt, A. D. Desai and A. Muir, *J. Agric. Sci.*, 1940, **30**, 639.
[2] For a full account of these, see A. A. Zavalishin, *Glinka Mem. Vol.*, Leningrad, 1928; for an English summary of this paper, see J. S. Joffe, *Soil Sci.*, 1935, **39**, 391.
[3] V. Ignatieff, *Soil Sci.*, 1941, **51**, 249; A. A. Zavalishin *et al.*, *Probl. Sovet. Pochvoved.*, 1940, **11**, 189.   [4] R. Glentworth, *Nature*, 1947, **159**, 441.

from these layers is not understood, but it is probably connected with the reduction of iron from the tri- to the divalent state; for ferrous phosphate appears to be relatively mobile in the soil profile.

But soils having impeded drainage, or subject to the influence of ground-water, usually have a zone that is only subject to reducing conditions for part of the year, and to normal oxidising conditions for the remainder. Thus, in many parts of the temperate regions, reducing conditions occur nearer the soil surface in the winter six months, when plant growth is very limited, than in the summer six months, when transpiration is active. These conditions of alternating oxidation and reduction have a great influence on the distribution of iron and manganese in the soil, for they tend to accumulate in this layer. During periods of reduction, divalent iron and manganese tend to move into this layer, usually from below, and then be oxidised in the subsequent period of oxidation; and the tendency is for more iron and manganese to move into this layer than out of it. The first effect of this is for the soil in this layer to become mottled or flecked with grey and yellow, the grey being the areas where reducing conditions still prevail, and the yellow being the deposits of ferric hydroxides.

As this process of iron and manganese accumulation proceeds, the pore space between the soil particles becomes increasingly filled with the iron and manganese deposits, and a definite indurated layer is formed which may become a continuous hard pan and which restricts drainage even more. On the whole, this pan formation is more pronounced the more permeable the soil, probably both because oxidising conditions can set in more quickly in summer and also because organic matter can wash down more easily, so that stronger reducing conditions can be set up during its decomposition. As the temperature increases, so the pan tends to become harder, although there also appears a tendency for it to develop more as concretions than as a uniform pan. These concretions are black to brownish black in colour, high in iron and often in manganese, and containing soil particles embedded in this cement.[1] Further, as the iron pan thickens, so usually does the material below the pan lose so much iron that its colour lightens. These pans, when well developed in the tropics, form the ground-water laterites discussed on p. 561.

Impeded drainage and ground-water have a marked effect on vegetation as soon as they cause reducing conditions in the root zone of the plants, for reducing conditions are very inimical to root development, and they also slow up the rate of decomposition of the organic matter. Hence, they encourage shallow rooting and peat formation. Peat, like

---

[1] For analyses of concretions from Illinois podsols, see E. Winters, *Soil Sci.*, 1938, **46**, 33 or Oregon podsolic soils, C. C. Nikiforoff and M. Drosdoff, ibid., 1943, **55**, 459.

mor, accumulates on the surface of the mineral soil, but differs from it in the greater accumulation of certain of the organic fractions. There is, however, no sharp transition between peat and mor: as reducing conditions set in, so the number of species of organisms in the organic layer decreases, and so does the rate at which they decompose the more resistant fractions of the litter. Organic matter rich in lignin-like

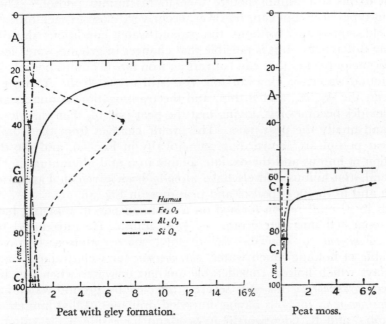

Peat with gley formation.　　　　　　　Peat moss.

FIG. 49. Humus content and amounts of silica and sesquioxides extracted by the acid-oxalate method from two peat profiles.

The A layer in each profile represents the peat layer.

material and in hemicelluloses thus begins to accumulate, and the more prolonged the reducing conditions, the greater the thickness of the peat. If the peat layer is not too thick, so the ground-water level can fluctuate in the soil, a gley horizon develops under the peat in which iron accumulates, as shown in Fig 49,[1] and this may become hardened to give the iron-ore concretions typical of many of these bogs. If, however, the peat thickens too much, because the soil underneath remains permanently water-logged, there is no means for the iron to move and no such accumulation takes place, as is also shown in Fig. 49. These effects can be illustrated by the transitional soils between the well-drained podsol under mor and the peat moss that develop as the ground-water level rises. The A_1 horizon begins to deepen at the expense

[1] From O. Tamm, *Medd. Skogsförsöksanst.*, 1932, **26**, 163.

of the A_0 or mor, due perhaps to grasses and herbs replacing the trees and returning more organic matter into the soil itself, in the form of fine extensive root systems, than the trees.[1] At the same time the amount of organic matter deposited at the top of the B_1 horizon increases and gleying becomes noticeable a little distance below the base of B horizon. These changes convert the well-drained podsol—Frosterus' iron podsol —first to his iron-humus podsol then to his humus podsol.[2] These various types of podsol can, however, occur very close to each other in the field, apparently without the ground-water conditions showing striking differences, so it is possible that changes in ground-water level are not the only ones that can convert an iron into a humus podsol. As the ground-water, or gley horizon, rises still more, so the A_0 horizon thickens, the A_1, A_2, and B thin, and the translocation of humus and sesquioxides becomes less, giving first the peat podsol, then the gleyed peat and finally the peat moss. The profile changes from the iron to the peat podsol are shown diagrammatically in Fig. 50, and the distribution of humus and the oxalate soluble iron and aluminium in the iron and iron-humus podsols have already been given in Fig. 48 on p. 572 and in the peat podsol and peat moss in Fig. 49.

Soils in a small region formed on a common parent material have been separated into four groups by J. H. Ellis.[3] He introduced the words *oromorphic* to describe well-drained coarse sands and gravels incapable of holding much water, *phytomorphic* for well-drained loams and clays which hold a considerable amount of water when wet but drained, *hydromorphic* for soils severely affected by ground-water and *phyto-hydromorphic* for soils having impeded drainage. Ellis[4] himself, in Manitoba, and R. Glentworth[5] in Scotland have shown the value of terminology in classifying and mapping soils in regions where the drainage conditions are more variable than the parent material.

Pan Formation in Soils

Many types of pan can develop in the soil: the iron-humus hard pan, or indurated horizon, that sometimes develops in well-drained podsols, the iron-manganese hard pan that develops under conditions of fluctuating water table, and the clay pan can all be found in humid or semiarid climates. In hot arid climates pans due to calcium carbonate (p. 582) and gypsum can occur, and in some hot climates with a

---

[1] H. Pallmann, A. Hasler and A. Schmuziger, *Bodenk. PflErnähr.*, 1938, **9**, 94.
[2] For an early discussion of these types of podsol, see B. Frosterus, *Geol. Komm. Finland, Geoteck. Medd.*, 14, 1914.
[3] *Sci. Agric.*, 1932, **12**, 338.
[4] *The Soils of Manitoba.*
[5] *Trans. Roy. Soc. Edinb.*, 1944, **61**, 149.

pronounced dry season, pans may also be due to silica cementing soil particles together. C. C. Nikiforoff and L. T. Alexander[1] have given an example of such a silica pan from California, and E. Winters[2] of one from Tennessee. They are presumably due to some of the mobile silica in the soil solution, which has been produced by weathering during the wet period, being precipitated as a cement, instead of as secondary quartz, during the dry. However, A. K. Dutt[3] considers that this silica cementation only occurs when the clay is of the non-swelling kaolinite type and not of the swelling beidellite or montmorillonite type.

The clay-pan soils develop on level plateaux that have been subjected to weathering for a sufficiently long time, and they are known as planosols in America. The mechanism of the formation of clay pans has not yet been agreed. The first problem that needs an answer is the proportion of clay forming the pan that has been synthesised *in situ* to the proportion that has been washed into it from above. There seems little doubt that much of the clay in a clay-pan profile has been formed in the profile, because there is more clay in the profile in proportion to the sand fraction than in the parent material, but there is little conclusive evidence of the proportion of the clay that has been formed in the pan to that translocated into it from above. Some recent results of C. E. Marshall[4] and his co-workers illustrate the present state of our knowledge. They worked with Missouri prairie soils developed on a silty loam loess. They found that in one soil profile a column of soil 1 sq. cm. in cross-section and 1·6 m. deep contained 68 gm. of clay, and they estimate that before weathering it would have contained only 57 gm., so that 11 gm. of clay have been formed during the weathering process. In addition, they estimate that 11 gm. of clay were washed out of the top 45 cm. of soil and 22 gm. were gained in the next 65 cm. There is no means of estimating how much of this extra 22 gm. is represented by the 11 gm. lost by the upper layer, how much represents clay formed in the upper layer and translocated into the clay pan, and how much was formed in the clay pan itself. Translocation was probably responsible for most of the 11 gm. lost by the upper layer because it also lost 11 gm. of silt, all of which appeared in the clay pan. But they further showed that the clay in the clay pan does not merely fill the interstices between the silt and sand particles, it increases the average distance between neighbouring sand and silt particles, and in fact they found that the soil volume containing a sand

[1] *Soil Sci.*, 1942, **53**, 157.
[2] *Proc. Soil Sci. Soc. Amer.*, 1943, **7**, 437.
[3] *Soil Sci.*, 1948, **65**, 309.
[4] With E. P. Whiteside, *Missouri Agric. Expt. Sta., Res. Bull.* 386, 1944; with J. F. Haseman, ibid., 387, 1945.

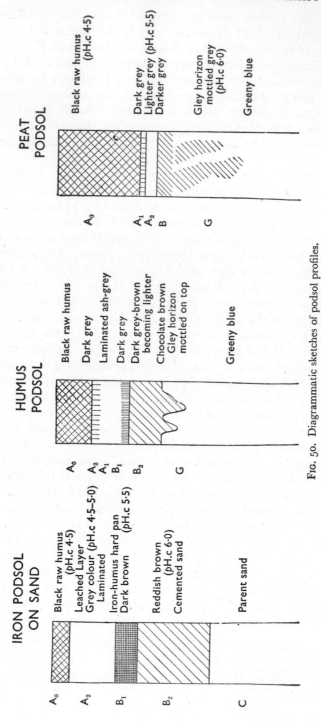

FIG. 50. Diagrammatic sketches of podsol profiles.

Plate XXXI

Salt soils in the Karun delta, Iran. Note the way the salt efflorescences
occur in separate patches
(pp. 386, 597)

Plate XXXII

Alternate strips of wheat and fallow near Monarch, Alberta
(*p. 624*)

Plate XXXIII

Wheat stubble after being cultivated with the Noble cultivator

Noble cultivator used for stubble mulch cultivation
(*pp. 626, 634*)

Plate XXXIV

Coffee bushes shaded by *Grevillia robusta* at Fort Ternan, Nyanza Province, Kenya
(*p. 641*)

particle increased by 50 per cent in the centre of the pan compared with that in the undisturbed soil. In another two profiles, they fractionated the clay at the various levels and showed that the principal gain in clay in the pan was in particles smaller than 0.5μ, which were principally composed of a beidellite type of mineral. There was some translocation, but little formation of coarse clay particles, which were composed of quartz, felspar, kaolinite, illite and beidellite.

The second problem in clay-pan formation is the mechanism which causes the precipitation of the clay in what is to become the clay pan if translocation of clay from the upper layers is important. It is possible that if clay-pan formation starts with clay forming in the interstices in the pan, then clay particles that are being translocated downwards are only stopped in this layer when it is sufficiently dense to filter them out of the downward-percolating water. But if the clay is precipitated in this layer it is probable that the mechanism is somewhat as postulated by H. Jenny and G. D. Smith,[1] who showed that clay pans could be built up in a coarse grained system such as sand or glass beads if an electropositive iron sol and a clay suspension were alternately allowed to percolate through the system. They also showed that if humic colloids were mixed with the clay, no pan was formed.

The formation of the iron-manganese concretions and the iron pan under fluctuating ground-water is again not fully understood. Under many conditions the precipitation of the iron and manganese takes place on concretions already existing, so that the most favoured sites for iron and manganese precipitation is on iron and manganese oxide or hydroxide surfaces. The concretions have been analysed by E. Winters[2] and by M. Drosdoff and C. C. Nikiforoff,[3] who showed that the smaller the concretion the higher its iron content, provided the concretion was above a certain minimum size, and the larger the concretion the higher its manganese content. The iron was nearly all soluble in Truog's iron solvent, so was present probably mainly as limonite $Fe(OH)_3$, with perhaps some Fe_2O_3, but the form of the manganese was not determined. The concretions contained between 5 and 17 per cent of iron and 0.5 to 8 per cent of manganese, which for manganese might be a hundred times higher than in the soil itself. The cause of the mobility of the iron and manganese is, as already pointed out, the alternations of reducing and oxidising conditions, causing the metals to be present as simple divalent cations during the reducing periods and in insoluble unionised compounds during the oxidising.

[1] *Soil Sci.*, 1935, **39**, 377; *Missouri Agric. Expt. Sta., Res. Bull.* 210, 1934.
[2] *Soil Sci.*, 1938, **46**, 33.
[3] *Soil Sci.*, 1940, **49**, 333.

TABLE 135

Analytical Data for a Brown Earth Profile

Depth in cm.	0–10	20–30	30–40	90–100
pH	5·26	5·35	5·24	5·36
Clay, per cent	16·25	14·87	8·87	5·85
Exchangeable Ca (m.-eq.) . .	3·2	2·4	1·2	0·6
Exchangeable H (m.-eq.) . . .	9·7	5·9	3·6	2·4
Composition of clay fraction—				
SiO_2/R_2O_3	1·51	1·45	1·03	0·86
SiO_2/Al_2O_3	1·93	1·92	1·59	1·16
Al_2O_3/Fe_2O_3	3·64	3·08	2·70	2·86
Acid oxalate Fe_2O_3, per cent . .	0·64	3·00	0·69	0·43
Acid oxalate Al_2O_3, per cent . .	0·55	1·75	0·64	0·44
Organic carbon, per cent . .	2·93	1·88	0·85	0·31
Organic nitrogen, per cent . .	0·119	0·097	0·05	—
C/N	24·6	19·4	17·0	—

Soil Formation on Hill Slopes

Soils on hill slopes differ from those on level ground both because the percolating water will tend to move laterally across the profile instead of merely downwards, particularly if there is any layer of low permeability in the profile, and also because the surface soil will be subject to erosion. The soil profile will therefore lose less bases than that on level ground, as the percolating water will be enriched in bases from the higher ground, and the soils will correspondingly be less acid. Thus, in areas where podsols under mor develop on the flat, brown forest soils under mull tend to develop on the slopes. Table 135[1] gives the analysis of such a soil developed on a 20° slope in a podsol region. The only indication of podsolisation is that the acid oxalate extract showed that iron and aluminium are being precipitated in the 20 to 30 cm. layer, although this was not apparent either in the amount of clay present or its sesquioxide content.

Soils on slopes are also liable to erosion, and this movement of soil down the slope may be of considerable importance even for slopes between 5° and 10°, for it will prevent the development of a strongly leached surface soil.[2] When the slope exceeds about 10°, actual creep of the whole soil down the slope may become sufficiently important to mask any effect of weathering due to the percolating water.

[1] A. Muir, *Forestry*, 1935, **9**, 116.
[2] G. W. Robinson, *Nature*, 1936, **137**, 950; G. Milne, ibid., 1936, **138**, 548.

The Soil Catena

The separate effects of topography just discussed cause soil formation to follow a fairly definite pattern according to the topography of the site, whenever the parent material and the climate do not change appreciably over the area. On extensive plateaux and peneplains, where percolation is downward and erosion abnormally slow, clay-pan formation, or planosol soils are characteristic, and since this causes impeded drainage, hard pans may also develop. On the top of hillocks and on the edge of plateaux, where percolation is good and normal erosion takes place, the well-leached soils are developed, and clay-pan and hard-pan formation is usually restricted. On the slopes percolation water enriched in bases and soluble products of weathering leaches across the profile, preventing the formation of profiles characteristic of purely vertical drainage, and pan formation is again rare. At the base of the slopes the products of weathering tend to collect, the soils are neutral, a montmorillonitic type of clay forms, and drainage may become impeded. Further, hard pans may also develop due to a fluctuating ground-water table.

This succession of soil type is so characteristic of land forms with only moderate relief that G. Milne[1] used the word catena to include the whole sequence of soil types that are developed from the water divide to the valley. He initially introduced this concept as a reconnaissance mapping unit, but it was soon found to be very valuable for grouping together in systematic form the individual soil series, recognised by the soil surveyors in the field, that were related to each other in this way. It therefore includes the method introduced by J. H. Ellis (p. 590) for grouping together the soils of a small region that differ mainly in their goodness of drainage. Milne himself has given examples of these catenas in Tanganyika,[2] H. Greene[3] and C. G. T. Morison et al.[4] in the Anglo-Egyptian Sudan, R. S. Holmes et al.[5] in the south-east, and I. C. Brown and J. Thorp[6] in the north of the United States. In hot, humid or semi-humid regions the leached soils are red, particularly in the subsoil, and as drainage becomes impeded so the colour changes through yellow to grey [7]

Tropical and subtropical catenary soil sequences differ from those in temperate regions in that the pH of the soil on the plateau decreases as the drainage becomes poorer in the warmer, but increases in the cooler regions. The reason for this difference is that weathering goes on

[1] Soil Res., 1935, **4**, 183; Trans. 3rd Int. Congr. Soil Sci., Oxford, 1935, **1**, 345.
[2] J. Ecol., 1947, **35**, 192. [3] Soil Res., 1939, **6**, 325. [4] J. Ecol., 1948, **36**, 1.
[5] U.S. Dept. Agric., Tech. Bull. 594, 1938.
[6] U.S. Dept. Agric., Tech. Bull. 834, 1942.
[7] The bulletin of Holmes et al., gives a colour plate of these colour changes in the profiles of the Norfolk catena.

faster in the warmer climate, so that a montmorillonitic type of clay is formed having, in consequence, a high base exchange capacity, and therefore a low pH when unsaturated, whilst in the cooler climate much less of this is formed and more of the kaolinite and illite types, which have a lower base exchange capacity and hence a higher pH when unsaturated.

The effect of drainage on clay type and soil colour can be seen all over the tropics wherever the rainfall is high enough to ensure some leaching. Even quite small changes of relief are enough to give the change from red soils with kaolinitic clay in the better-drained areas to the black soil with montmorillonitic in the less well-drained depressions.[1]

Topography can have another effect on the soil and vegetation, for if changes of relief are sufficiently large, the climate becomes increasingly cool and humid as the land level rises. Hence, in the tropics and subtropics, mountain uplands have a climate, vegetation and soil more similar to the temperate than to the true tropical regions, but as one goes down to lower levels the climate becomes increasingly hotter, and usually increasingly drier also. Hence, the podsols and brown earths of the tropical highland give place first to the prairie, then the chernozem, then the desert and semi-desert soils of the arid lowlands on the one hand,[2] or, if the rainfall does not decrease, to the yellow, then red, and finally the black soils of the humid lowlands.

---

[1] See G. Nagelschmidt, A. D. Desai and A. Muir, *J. Agric. Sci.*, 1940, **30**, 639, for an example of this from Hyderabad.

[2] For examples of these changes, see J. Thorp, *Soil Sci.*, 1931, **32**, 283, for Wyoming; W. P. Martin and J. E. Fletcher, *Arizona Agric. Expt. Sta., Tech. Bull.* 99, 1943, for Arizona; R. H. Spilsbury and E. W. Tisdale, *Sci. Agric.*, 1944, **24**, 395, for British Columbia.

CHAPTER XXXIII

SALINE AND ALKALI SOILS

Saline Soils or Solonchaks

UNDER HOT, ARID conditions soluble salts accumulate in the surface of soils whenever the ground-water comes within a few feet of the surface, as may happen, under natural conditions, in the flood plains of rivers, the low-lying shores of lakes, and in depressions in which drainage water accumulates—in fact, in any region where marsh, swamp or other ill-drained soil would be found in humid regions. During dry periods the surface of these soils is covered with an efflorescence, or salt crust, which is dissolved in the soil water each time the soil is wetted.

Saline soils typically have an uneven surface, being covered with small puffed up spots a few inches high that are enriched in salts, for, as explained on p. 386 and as illustrated in Plate XXXI, salts congregate in the most salty areas because these areas remain moist longest after the onset of drought.

Saline soils normally show no change of structure down the profile, implying that the soil is barely affected by soil weathering and soil-forming processes; and such soils are known as solonchaks by the Russians and were called white alkali by E. W. Hilgard,[1] but are now usually called saline. Usually they are low in humus, because the natural vegetation cannot make much annual growth on them. The salts usually present in the soil are the sulphates and chlorides of sodium and calcium, though nitrates occur in a few places, and magnesium sometimes constitutes an appreciable proportion of the cations. Under these conditions, the pH of the soil is below 8·5 and the colour of the soil surface is light. However, under some conditions an appreciable proportion of the salts present may be sodium carbonate which will raise the pH of the soil to 9 or even up to 10. If other salts are only present in small concentrations, this sodium carbonate may cause the humic matter in the soil to disperse and take on a black colour, giving the black alkali soil of Hilgard, which will be discussed in the next section under the heading Alkali Soils.

Saline soils may contain over 100 tons per acre of salt in the top four feet of soil, that is, the salts may constitute over 1 per cent by weight of the soil, though many saline soils contain less than this. The natural vegetation on such soils has a very high ash content, up to one-quarter of

[1] *Soils*, New York, 1906.

the air-dry plant may be ash, and the greater proportion of the ash may be soluble salts, typically sodium chloride. Hence, the vegetation will also bring salts to the soil surface, but its effect is probably small, amounting to under 200 lb. per acre annually,[1] owing to the small amount of total growth made per year.

The source of the salts in natural saline soils is usually the ground-water, which is enriched with salts from two sources. Part, sometimes all, is derived from the weathering of rocks in the upper reaches of the river, and part is sometimes derived from salt deposits laid down in early geological periods in strata through which the ground-water moves. Saline soils have also been produced artificially by faulty irrigation, for irrigation always involves putting salts on the land as well as water. Hence, salt control is a fundamental part of irrigation and will be discussed in detail in the next chapter.

Alkali Soils: the Solonetz and Solod

When the water table in a natural saline soil falls, so that salts no longer accumulate in its surface, the rain-water washes the salts that were there down the profile, and this process sometimes causes considerable chemical changes to take place in the profile. If the salts are predominantly calcium, or if during the process of washing out over 90 per cent of the exchangeable ions remain calcium, then the saline soil is converted into the steppe or semi-desert soil appropriate to its region.

Much more radical changes in the surface soil take place if the calcium reserves in the soil are so low that, during the washing out of the salts, an appreciable proportion of the exchangeable calcium ions are replaced by sodium. Sodium ions only need to constitute 12 to 15 per cent of the exchangeable ions to reduce the water stability of the soil structure sufficiently for the clay and humic particles to disperse. This harmful effect is accentuated by sodium carbonate being formed in the soil solution during the final stages of the washing out of the salts, causing the pH of the soil solution to rise, often above 9, and consequently increasing the ease of dispersion of the fine particles.

For a long time the source of the sodium carbonate produced during this washing out was not understood, although P. de Mondésir[2] in 1888, and K. K. Gedroiz[3] in 1912, gave essentially the correct explanation. Carbonate and bicarbonate anions are being continually produced in the soil by the carbon dioxide given off by the plant roots

---

[1] V. A. Kovda, *Pedology*, 1944, Nos. 4–5, 144.
[2] *C.R.*, 1888, **106**, 459.
[3] *J. Expt. Agron. (Russian)*, 1912, **13**, 363.

and soil organisms, and these anions must be neutralised by cations or hydrogen ions. These cations will be obtained from the exchangeable cations in the exchange complex unless there are reserves of calcium carbonate in the soil. Hence, if there is an appreciable proportion of exchangeable sodium ions in the soil, enough will come into the soil solution to give what is in effect a solution of sodium carbonate strong enough to raise the pH of the soil to 9 or over.

These conditions of high alkalinity and low salt content lead to the clay and organic matter particles becoming deflocculated and the soil structure water-unstable. The soil surface becomes dark-coloured, often black, due to the dispersed humic particles; the surface typically dries into large, very hard, prismatic units having well-defined edges and smooth surfaces; and clay particles tend to wash down the profile, giving an incipient clay pan. Soils in this condition were called black alkali by Hilgard—he used this name without regard to the amount of other salts present—and they are extremely difficult soils to handle, for they are very plastic and sticky when wet and form hard compact clods when dry.

The second stage in the washing out of salts, when there is an appreciable proportion of exchangeable sodium in the exchange complex, is for clay and organic matter to move down the profile into the developing clay pan, with the consequence that the profile becomes banded rather like a podsol. The surface soil is dark grey, owing to the deflocculated humus, then comes a pale layer, and then another dark, very compact layer having a very sharply defined upper surface and merging gradually into the subsoil with increasing depth. The darker colour of the compact layer compared with the layer above it may be due to its higher clay content, for it does not always have a higher content of organic matter.[1] The top two layers have lost much of their clay, and have a loose, porous, laminar structure, whose upper surfaces may be paler than their lower, possibly because of silica being deposited on them. The clay pan cracks on drying into well-defined vertical columns having a rounded top and smooth, shiny, well-defined sides which can be broken into units about 10 cm. high and 5 cm. across with a flat base. Below this the columns break into rather smaller units with a flat top and bottom which on light crushing break up into angular fragments.

As the leaching of these desalinised soils proceeds, the upper two horizons deepen, and often become slightly acid in reaction. Gedroiz, who was one of the first to give a plausible account of the chemical consequences of the process, noticed that the content of amorphous

---

[1] A. L. Brown and A. C. Caldwell, *Soil Sci.*, 1947, **63**, 183, give an illustration of this for well-leached Minnesota soils.

silica in these horizons, and particularly in the top darker horizon, increased. The further development of these soils has not been worked out in detail, though some of B. B. Polynov's work suggested that the very characteristic clay pan becomes less pronounced, possibly because of sandy material from the A horizon washing down in the cracks between the structural units.

These soils are called solonetz in the early stages and solod in the later stages of their development by the Russians, and they have been extensively studied on the river terraces of southern Russia and Central Asia.[1] Gedroiz assumed that they formed under the influence of exchangeable sodium, as given in the account above, and this assumption has been accepted by many other workers. But there are large areas in western Canada and the United States[2] where soils having the morphology of these solonetz and solods are found, yet where sodium forms a very minor proportion of the exchangeable ions. It is possible that they originally contained over 12 per cent of exchangeable sodium, but that nearly all of this has now been lost by leaching. However, most of these soils that are now low in exchangeable sodium contain over 40 per cent, or even over 50 per cent, of exchangeable magnesium. It is, therefore, possible that if during the leaching out of soluble salts the exchange complex acquires a high proportion of exchangeable magnesium, the soils will partially deflocculate and undergo the same type of profile development as soils with a high proportion of exchangeable sodium. Hence, much more critical work must be done before one can decide just what changes can only be brought about by exchangeable sodium, and what by either exchangeable magnesium or other causes.

Unfortunately, the processes at work during the formation of solonetz and solod soils have not been critically examined by present-day techniques. Thus little is known about the weathering that takes place in the A horizons of these soils, or the source of the silica that can be dissolved by treating the soil with 5 per cent KOH—the method used to determine amorphous silica—or the movement of iron and aluminium hydroxides, if it takes place. Similarly, little is known about the clay in the B horizon, whether it was mainly leached down from the A, or whether it was mainly synthesised *in situ*. Even the type of clay in this horizon has not been investigated in detail. I. D.

---

[1] For some detailed Russian work, see K. K. Gedroiz, *Nosovka Agric. Expt. Sta.*, *Bulls.* 38, 1925; 44, 1926; 46, 1928; D. G. Vilensky, *Salinised Soils*, Moscow, 1924; V. A. Kovda, *Solonchaks and Solonetz*, Moscow, 1937. J. S. Joffe, in his book *Pedology*, New Brunswick, 1938, has given a long summary of Gedroiz's and Vilensky's work.

[2] See, for example, W. P. Kelley, *Amer. Soil Survey Assoc.*, 1934, 15, 45 (California); C. E. Kellogg, *Soil Sci.*, 1934, 38, 483 (N. Dakota); C. O. Rost and K. A. Maehl, ibid., 1943 55, 301 (Minnesota); J. M. MacGregor and F. A. Wyatt, ibid., 1945, 59, 419 (Alberta); C. F. Bentley and C. O. Rost, *Sci. Agric.*, 1947, 27, 293 (Saskatchewan).

Sedletsky,[1] for example, claims to have isolated from Russian solonetz a clay mineral characteristic of these soils which he called Gedroizite, and which he considers to be a vermiculite in which the magnesium is replaced by sodium and potassium. W. P. Kelley and his co-workers,[2] on the other hand, could only find an illite in the B horizon of the Californian solonetz-type soils they worked with, whilst A. L. Brown and A. C. Caldwell[3] found montmorillonite was the principal clay constituent in a number of acid solod soils, although some illitic clay was also found, particularly in the A layer.

It is interesting to guess at the minimum number of processes needed to obtain the solonetz-solod profile. Its characteristics appear to be a darker A_1 and B and a lighter A_2 horizon, a porous A and a compact B, and a clay pan breaking into columns having rounded tops. Most clay pans containing montmorillonite-beidellite type or illite type clays naturally crack into these columns on drying, except they usually have all their sides sharp. The rounded top is presumably due to the original sharp edges breaking away at the top, perhaps due to their water-instability, which in turn would be caused by them having much exchangeable sodium or magnesium in their complex. The B structure is, therefore, probably more characteristic of the clay mineral than of the exchangeable sodium or magnesium. The dispersion of clay in the A horizon and precipitation in an already formed clay pan below probably merely indicates the absence of salts and perhaps also requires low calcium. The formation of the A_2 horizon may only mean that the pores are wide enough to let humic matter pass, and the darker B due to them being so fine that it collects there. The process that seems to be characteristic of these soils, and needs detailed investigation before any specific theories can be formulated, is the formation of amorphous silica.

Under natural conditions, areas of saline and alkali soils usually contain a mixture of solonchak and solonetz, or solonetz and solod, or even all three together, depending on the relief of the area. The low-lying spots may be solonchak, those on moderate relief solonetz, and on higher ground solod; and differences in level of as little as 1 to 2 feet can have a great influence on the stage in the solonchak-solonetz-solod chain that the soil has reached.

Areas containing much solonetz soils may be very misleading to the inexperienced, for in some stages of development the dry soil is black and powdery and looks as if it ought to be fertile. It is only when wet, and particularly after heavy rain or irrigation, when water is held on

---

[1] *C.R. Acad. Sci. (U.S.S.R.)*, 1944, **33**, 308; 1937, **17**, 251.
[2] *Soil Sci.*, 1941, **51**, 101.
[3] *Proc. Soil Sci. Soc. Amer.*, 1947, **11**, 213.

the soil surface because of the impermeable B horizon that one realises how intractable they are. Some solonetz landscapes, however, are characterised by the surface being covered with shallow depressions from which the loose soil appears to have been removed, leaving the top of the B horizon uncovered. These depressions, known as slick spots or burn-outs in the western United States and Canada, are naturally extremely unfavourable for agriculture,[1] for the compacted clay pan is relatively rich in the montmorillonitic type of clay and has an appreciable proportion of exchangeable sodium or magnesium, hence is impermeable, plastic and sticky when wet, and hard when dry, never having a crumbly, mellow tilth.

[1] See, for example, R. Gardner *et al.*, *Colorado Agric. Expt. Sta.*, *Tech. Bull.* **20**, 1937; W. Fitts *et al.*, *J. Amer. Soc. Agron.*, 1939, **31**, 823.

CHAPTER XXXIV

THE MANAGEMENT OF IRRIGATED SALINE
AND ALKALI SOILS

The Effect of Soluble Salts on Plant Growth

SOLUBLE SALTS CAN have two types of effect on the growing plant: specific effects due to particular ions they contain being harmful to the crop, and a general effect due to them raising the osmotic pressure of the solution around the roots of the crop.

Specific effects fall into two classes: those operative at low and those at high concentrations. Of the former only two salts are normally of importance—sodium carbonate and soluble borates. The former may be harmful in itself, but its harmful effect is more likely to be due to the consequences of the high pH it brings about. Thus, many nutrients, such as phosphates, iron, zinc and manganese, become unavailable to the plant at these high pHs on the one hand, and the soil structure tends to become water-unstable on the other, thus bringing about conditions of low water permeability, poor aeration and an unkind, almost unworkable tilth. Borates are directly toxic to the crop, and water containing as much as 1 part per million of boron, present as borate, depresses the growth of borate-sensitive crops, whilst water containing over 2 parts per million is unsuited for irrigation.[1]

Some ions may also have a toxic effect at high concentrations which enhances the harmful effect of mere concentration. Thus, some crops, such as peaches and beans, are damaged by chlorides in the soil solution at osmotic pressures at which sulphates do not harm them, whilst others, such as flax and some grasses, are more tolerant of chlorides than sulphates at equal osmotic pressures. Again, at equal fairly high osmotic pressures, magnesium ions are more toxic than calcium, and calcium may be more toxic than sodium, though these harmful effects have not been recognised in practice because in general sodium is a dominant ion in very saline soils. High contents of sodium ions sometimes appear to have a secondary harmful effect when they occur in soils very low in calcium, for then the crop will suffer from calcium deficiency.

The general effects of a high salt content in the soil is to give a

[1] For a discussion of this subject, with lists of boron-tolerant and boron-sensitive plants, see F. M. Eaton, *J. Agric. Res.*, 1944, **69**, 237; *U.S. Dept. Agric., Tech. Bull.* 746, 1941.

dwarfed, stunted plant, but this is often not apparent in the field if there are no patches of low-salt soil to act as controls; and losses of 20 per cent or more of yield of the crop can be due to salts without salt damage being apparent to the farmer. As the salt content becomes higher the stunting becomes more noticeable, the leaves of the crop become dull-coloured and often bluish-green, and they become coated with a waxy deposit. Further, many crops growing in very saline soils do not display the symptoms of wilting very clearly, so they can be severely set back by lack of water before the farmer is fully aware of their suffering.

A high salt content around the roots of the plant markedly reduces their power of absorbing water. Thus, J. D. Newton,[1] as long ago as 1925, showed that the energy barley plants must expend to absorb water increases as the osmotic pressure of the solution in which they are growing increases, and H. E. Hayward and W. B. Spurr[2] have shown that maize roots absorb water at only one-third the rate from a solution of osmotic pressure 4·8 atm. as from one at 0·8 atm. Further, as already discussed on p. 400, the effective lowering of the free energy of the water in the soil is the sum of that due to the osmotic pressure of the soil solution and to the curved air-water menisci bounding its free surface, and the ease with which the plant root can extract water from the soil decreases as the free energy of the water in the soil decreases. Hence, raising the osmotic pressure of the soil solution is equivalent to raising the suction of the water held by the soil, but whether this is the sole cause, or only an important one, of the osmotic pressure reducing the rate of intake of water by the root needs further investigation, although the results given in Fig. 37 on p. 401 suggest that it must be the predominant factor.

O. C. Magistad and his co-workers at the Regional Salinity Laboratory at Riverside have recently published much work[3] on the relation between the osmotic pressure of the solution around the plant roots and the amount of growth the crop makes, and they concluded that, on the whole, there is a linear relation between the reduction in yield and the osmotic pressure of the solution, though, as shown in Fig. 36, the linear relation does not necessarily hold for crops sensitive to salts. Thus, H. G. Gauch and O. C. Magistad[4] showed that the yield of lucerne was reduced about 10 per cent for each increase of 1 atm. in the osmotic pressure. This factor naturally depends on the plant, for some are more tolerant of high osmotic pressure than others. Thus, beans growing in a solution of osmotic pressure 4·4 atm. only give

[1] *Sci. Agric.*, 1925, **5**, 318.   [2] *Bot. Gaz.*, 1947, **105**, 152.
[3] See, for example, *Plant Physiol.*, 1943, **18**, 151, 556.
[4] *J. Amer. Soc. Agron.*, 1943, **35**, 871.

20 per cent, whilst cotton and sugar-beet give 70 per cent of their yields when growing in a 0·4-atm. solution.[1] Further increasing the osmotic pressure reduces the amount of water transpired by the crop. F. M. Eaton,[2] for example, found that for a variety of salt-tolerant crops growing in sand culture at Riverside in solutions of increasing content of sodium sulphate, that the amount of growth made and of water transpired during a season were:

Osmotic pressure of solution in atm. .	0·7	1·8	3·5	5·1
Dry matter produced, kg. per 18 sq. ft.	11·4	8·9	6·3	3·7
Water transpired, thousand litres .	6·4	4·8	3·5	2·4

Eaton also showed that the cell sap of the plants maintained an osmotic pressure about 10 atm. higher than that in the culture solution, presumably due to the extra amount of salt taken up.

It is only since about 1940 that research workers have fully appreciated the significance of this effect of salts in increasing the effective suction of the water in the soil, and its consequences on the irrigated farm; for the greater the salt content of the soil, the less water the crop can remove from it before it begins to suffer from water shortage. Soils with a high salt content require therefore more frequent irrigation than similar soils of low salt content, and, as already noted, the crops growing on them do not wilt so plainly, so that it is more difficult for the farmer to see when an irrigation ought to be given. These two very important practical points have only recently been properly appreciated by agricultural advisers.

Plants differ in their powers in being able to withstand the harmful effect of salinity, or its consequences in the field. In the first place, as L. J. Briggs and H. L. Shantz[3] showed in 1912, plants have different abilities to extract water from soils in the wilting range, and the plants that are natural inhabitants of saline soils tend to have greater ability to extract water from soils at the drier end of this range. But no statement can yet be made about the existence of any correlation between tolerance to salts and ability to use water held at free energy depressions of, say, 15 atm. But not only must the crop be able to take water from the saline solution, it must also be able to take it quickly enough to maintain a proper transpiration rate if it is to make growth; and since one of the effects of the salt solution is to slow down the absorption of water by the roots, one would expect that plants would be more affected by a given salt concentration under conditions of high transpiration rates, that is, in hot deserts, than of low rates in

[1] O. C. Magistad and R. F. Reitemeir, *Soil Sci.*, 1943, **55**, 351.
[2] *J. Agric. Res.*, 1942, **64**, 357.
[3] *Bot. Gaz.*, 1912, **53**, 229.

cooler regions. This may be a valid deduction, but its field importance has not yet been established.[1]

In practice, salt tolerance is a very complex concept. The tolerance of a plant may be low when it is young but high when established—lucerne is an example of this. The plant may be able to keep alive at high salt contents, but will make very little growth under these conditions and only grow slowly under moderate salt contents, and hence be of little commercial value—some of the alkali grasses are examples. Again, though the plant may be able to grow in fairly saline soils, the quality of the part harvested may be affected. Thus, cereals will grow and produce much green matter in soils too saline for them to produce any grain; sugar-beet growing in saline soils produces a root low in sugar which is difficult to refine; and forage crops may contain so much salts that they are unpalatable or injurious to livestock. Again, in practice, salt tolerance is often bound up with tolerance of alkali, high pHs and low calcium on the one hand, and ability to withstand prolonged water-logging during irrigation, which is a common consequence of alkali, on the other. The effects of these various factors on the development of different crops are only now being examined. Hence, lists of salt-tolerant crops are still largely based on practical field experience in which these factors have not been properly separated out.

Recent American experience has graded crops into three categories: tolerant, moderately tolerant, and sensitive to salts, and an example of such grading is given in Table 136,[2] where plants are arranged approximately in order of salt tolerance in the fruit, arable and ley classes. Dates, sugar-beet, cotton and some grasses fall into the tolerant group, and some of these are very tolerant of salts, whilst peas, beans and most clovers are in the sensitive group. But different varieties of a plant, particularly cottons and strawberry clovers, have been found to have different salt tolerances, so there is a possibility that plant breeders will be able to increase the salt tolerance of any particularly desirable crop.

Some information is now available about the amount of salt a soil can hold before the crops on it begin to suffer appreciably. O. C. Magistad and R. F. Reitemeier[3] showed that if the soil solution held at 15 atm. suction has an osmotic pressure less than 2 atm., that is, if it contains less than 0·4 per cent of dissolved salts, no crops suffer from salt trouble, but if the osmotic pressure at this suction is 10 atm. most crops suffer severely; and provided the soil solution does not contain appreciable amounts of sodium carbonate or borate, the composition of the salts is relatively unimportant compared with their effect on the osmotic

---

[1] For examples of its validity, see O. C. Magistad *et al.*, *Plant Physiol.*, 1943, **18**, 151.
[2] *Diagnosis and Improvement of Saline and Alakali Soils*, U.S. Regional Salinity Laboratory, 1954. See also *U.S. Dept. Agric. Yearbook*, 1943–7, and *Circ.* 707, 1944, for other similar lists.
[3] *Soil Sci.*, 1943, **55**, 351.

TABLE 136

The Relative Tolerance of Crops to Salts in the Western States of America

Good tolerance	Moderate tolerance	Sensitive
Date	Pomegranate Fig, olive, grape	Pear, apple, orange, grapefruit, almond, apricot, peach
Barley Sugar- and fodder-beet Rape, kale Cotton	Rye, wheat, oats Rice, sorghum Maize Potatoes, peas	Field beans Green beans

Bermuda and
   Rhodes grass
Bird's-foot trefoil
	Sweet clover
	Ryegrass
	Strawberry clover
	Lucerne
	Cocksfoot
		White, alsike and
		   red clover
		Ladino clover

pressure of the solution. The safe contents of salts in the soil can be expressed in other units. A soil is made up to about the sticky point with water, and then some of the solution removed by suction; if this solution contains up to 3,000 parts per million of salts, or has a specific conductivity at 25°C. of less than 4 millimhos per cm., no crop is likely to suffer from general salt injury, but if the salt content exceeds 5,000 parts per million, or the conductivity 8 millimhos per cm., then only salt-tolerant crops will grow, and even their yields are likely to be reduced, whilst if it exceeds 10,000 parts per million, or the conductivity exceeds 15 millimhos per cm., then no agricultural crops are likely to give economic yields.[1]

The Control of Soluble Salts in the Soil

Irrigation water is continuously adding soluble salts to the soil which, unless they are continuously removed, must soon accumulate to such an extent that no crop can grow on the land. Thus, no irrigation scheme can last long that does not ensure that the salts brought into the surface soil are removed from the root zone of the crop as fast as they are brought in, and that the salt content at which this equilibrium

[1] *Diagnosis and Improvement of Saline and Alkali Soils*, U.S. Regional Salinity Laboratory, 1954.

occurs is low enough not to harm the crops appreciably. That this is, in fact, often very difficult to ensure can be appreciated from the fact that crop yields are said to be reduced by 10 to 20 per cent over much of the twenty million acres of irrigated land in the Western United States by salts alone.

The general principles of salt control are to use water with as low a salt content as possible, to maintain the ground-water level at least 6 feet, and preferably deeper, below the soil surface, and to flush accumulations of soluble salts from the surface soil into the ground-water.

TABLE 137

Salt Contents of River Waters Used for Irrigation

	Parts per million in water			Tons per acre-foot			Ratio
	Sodium salts	Very soluble salts[1]	Total	Sodium salts	Very soluble salts	Total	Ca/Na as equiv.
Colorado at Yuma, Arizona[2] . . .	292	425	795	0·40	0·58	1·08	1·12
Gila at Florence Canal, Arizona[3] . . .	664	772	1023	0·90	1·05	1·39	0·37
Pecos at Barstow, Texas[2]	3080	4110	6200	4·20	5·60	8·45	0·57
White Nile at Khartoum[3] . . .	71	90	174	0·10	0·12	0·23	0·64
Murray at Cohuna, Victoria[4] . .	28	40	96	0·04	0·05	0·12	2·3
Indus at Sukkur[5] . .	12	99	300	0·02	0·14	0·41	16·0

The salt content of irrigation water depends on its source. Mountain-fed rivers usually have low salt contents, rivers that have traversed desert countries usually have a moderate salt content, and springs and ground-water in the desert a high salt content. Table 137 gives the salt contents of some representative rivers actually used for irrigation, where the salts are divided up into sodium salts, very soluble salts, which, in addition, include magnesium salts as well as any calcium chloride, and total salts, which in addition include calcium sulphate and bicarbonate, and the table gives both the salt content of the water in parts per million, or milligrams per litre, and in tons per acre-foot. Since 3 to 4 acre-feet of water may be evaporated or transpired a year, this often involves leaving from $\frac{1}{2}$ to 4 tons of very soluble salts and sometimes much more behind in the root zone of the crop.

[1] Excludes calcium sulphate and bicarbonate.
[2] Quoted by O. C. Magistad and J. E. Christiansen, *U.S. Dept. Agric.*, Circ. 707, 1944.
[3] Quoted by F. W. Clarke, *Data of Geochemistry*, 1924. For more recent analyses of the south-western rivers of the U.S.A., see *Diagnosis and Improvement of Saline and Alkali Soils*.
[4] J. W. Paterson, *Victoria J. Agric.*, 1913, **11**, 298.
[5] H. P. Paranjpe, *Bombay Dept. Agric.*, Bull. 96, 1920.

The problems of getting rid of these salts is obviously more difficult the higher the salt content of the water, the lower the rainfall, and the more impermeable the soil. Permeable soils with winter rainfalls of 10 to 15 inches will lose most of the salts they accumulated in the summer. But flushing down salts with rather salty irrigation water in rather impervious soils presents many difficulties, because this flushing must be done frequently, and during the process the soil is water-logged so that evaporation is proceeding rapidly and any crops growing on the land suffer from poor aeration. Further, the higher the salt content of the water, the greater is the proportion of the water that must be used for flushing, and therefore the smaller is the proportion that the crops can use for transpiration. Increasing salinity therefore puts down the efficiency, or the duty as it is often called, of the water used. This need of water for flushing down salts may cause great administrative difficulties in areas where it is not fully appreciated,[1] for it means that often one-quarter to one-third of the water entering the area must be used solely for washing down the salts and not for growing a crop, and in consequence the maximum area that can be irrigated must be reduced by this fraction compared to the area that could be irrigated if no flushing was necessary.

This problem of flushing salts down into the subsoil emphasises the importance of fairly rapid drainage, so the land remains water-logged for as short a time as possible—for, as pointed out on p. 451, poor aeration, which is the consequence of water-logging, is more harmful at high than at low temperatures. But the water must also leach through the soil at a uniform rate all over the surface of the land, for otherwise salts will be leached out of some places but not out of others, and, as pointed out on p. 386, once an area begins to get a higher salt content than the surrounding soil, it tends to draw salts to it. Thus, it is essential the land shall be as level and as uniform as possible during irrigation so that the water has a chance to seep through the whole area as uniformly as possible. It is not difficult to ensure this uniform leaching if the rate of entry of the irrigation water into the soil lies in the range 0·3 to 3·0 inches per hour, but if it falls below 0·1 inch great difficulties arise if the irrigation water is at all saline.

The problems of drainage and keeping the water table low usually concern the engineers of the irrigation authority. It should be kept so low that its capillary fringe is below the main root zone, so that roots do not bring up soluble salts either into the herbage, nor concentrate them in the root zone. Thus, depths exceeding 10 feet are desirable, although under some conditions of impermeability the water may only

[1] For examples from the Punjab, see E. McKenzie Taylor and M. L. Mehta, *Indian J. Agric. Sci.*, 1941, **11**, 137; M. L. Mehta, *Punjab Irrig. Res. Inst. Publ.*, 1940, **3**, No. 4.

be able to be removed from the subsoil by tile drains, and it is barely practicable to lay these deeper than 6 feet. But if the ground-water is not too saline it is often worth pumping it into the river or irrigation canals, diluting it with this better water and using this mixed water for irrigation lower down the valley. If this pumping is practised, so the ground-water is kept well below the surface, drainage is usually sufficiently good for no other precautions to be necessary.

It is of great importance to draw up a balance sheet of the salt and water movements in an irrigation area whenever possible, so that one can make an estimate of the net effect of present irrigation practice on the salt régime. C. S. Scofield[1] has done this for three areas in America, and his results for two, one lying immediately below the other on the Rio Grande, are given in Table 138. In the Mesilla

TABLE 138

Annual Salt and Water Balance in Two Irrigation Areas of the Rio Grande (New Mexico and Texas)

Water in thousand acre feet. Salts and ions in thousand tons

Area under irrigation	Mesilla Area About 80,000 acres			El Paso Area About 120,000 acres		
	Entering	Leaving	Per cent retained	Entering	Leaving	Per cent retained
Water	774·4	496·1	33·3	496·1	173·2	65·1
Concentration of salts in water, tons per acre foot	0·805	1·226		1·226	2·666	
Total Salts	599·4	608·1	−1·5	608·1	461·8	24·1
Ca	80·6	69·7	14·5	69·7	41·3	40·7
Mg	17·6	15·5	11·9	15·5	10·2	33·9
Na+K	102·0	122·6	−20·3	122·6	111·7	9·0
HCO_3,CO_3[2]	93·9	80·5	14·3	80·5	28·2	64·9
SO_4	233·4	208·0	10·9	208·0	108·7	47·7
Cl	71·3	111·1	−55·8	111·1	161·4	−45·3
NO_3	1·4	1·5	−3·0	1·5	0·5	34·8

area, which lies above El Paso, the salts are in balance—the same weight is leaving the area as is being introduced—whilst in the El Paso area, which uses the water leaving the Mesilla area, salts are accumulating at the rate of about 150,000 tons per year, of which about 100,000 tons are calcium and magnesium carbonates and calcium sulphate, and 50,000 tons, or about 0·4 ton per irrigated acre are readily soluble salts.

[1] J. Agric. Res., 1940, 61, 17.   [2] Computed as carbonate.

The table also shows the important point that the composition of the salts leaving the area differs from that of those entering, for the water leaving is relatively richer in sodium and chloride and poorer in calcium and sulphate than that entering. In the next section it will be shown that the higher the ratio of sodium to calcium the less desirable is the water for irrigation; hence the greater the proportion of the water that has been derived as drainage water from schemes higher up the river, the more care may have to be taken with it because of its sodium content. In the actual areas given in the table both are losing chlorides, but the El Paso area is gaining sodium derived from the Mesilla area, and both are gaining calcium, and to a less extent magnesium, from the soils and rocks higher up the river.

The farmer possesses various methods for controlling the distribution of salts in the field. Even if he cannot get rid of them all, he can reduce their concentration in the surface by giving a heavy irrigation, and this is usually necessary in saline soils before seed is sown, for young plants are injured more easily than established ones by salts. Again, if a young plant is very sensitive to salts, or the salt content of the soil is high, sowing the crop at the beginning of winter, or of the cool season, when transpiration and evaporation are at their lowest for the area, gives the crop a chance of establishing itself in a soil of relatively low salinity. There is another method available for crops grown on ridges, which depends on concentrating the salts in certain parts of the ridge, leaving other parts less saline. If the land is thrown up into ridges and water runs between them, the salts can be concentrated on the top of the ridges, leaving the furrows and the sides of the ridge just above the water-line at each irrigation lower in salts. W. T. McGeorge and M. F. Wharton[1] have developed this method in the Salt River Valley of Arizona for lettuces, which are planted on the sides of the ridges just above the water-line. The salts accumulate as a white band above them, and even down to 12 to 24 inches below the surface the salts are lower under the furrow than under the area where the salts accumulate.

Thus, in summary, salts in the surface soil are controlled by flushing them down into the subsoil. Provided the soil is reasonably permeable and well levelled, no great trouble arises, but the more salty the water, the greater the proportion of the water is needed for salt control and the smaller the proportion that can be used for transpiration, also the more frequently must the field be irrigated. Trying to economise water under these conditions, by giving small irrigations that only wet the top 2 to 3 feet of soil, are bound to lead to increased salt concentrations in the soil surface. It is one of the most difficult problems facing

[1] *Arizona Agric. Expt. Sta., Bull.* 152, 1936.

agricultural advisers to work out methods for making the optimum use of a limited amount of rather saline irrigation water in arid districts within the social framework of the district.

The Control of Alkalinity

For an irrigation scheme to be permanent, not only must the total salt content of the soil be kept below a certain figure, but the proportion of exchangeable sodium in particular, and possibly also of exchangeable magnesium, in the exchange complex must be kept below certain limits. If more than 12 to 15 per cent of the exchangeable ions are sodium, difficulties may be experienced in keeping the soil permeable, and if more than 40 to 50 per cent are sodium, not only may these difficulties become very great, but the plant may no longer be able to take up sufficient calcium for its needs.[1] Soils containing a high proportion of exchangeable magnesium ions also have their permeabilities reduced and plants growing on them their calcium contents,[2] but to a considerably less extent than would be caused by a corresponding proportion of exchangeable sodium ions.

The principal cause of the proportion of exchangeable sodium ions increasing in the soil during irrigation is through base exchange between the sodium ions in the downward-percolating soil water and the exchangeable calcium and magnesium ions. Now calcium ions are held more tightly than sodium, and in dilute solutions it appears that very little exchange of sodium for calcium takes place in normal soils if the solution contains equal equivalent concentration of sodium to calcium, and little occurs if the sodium ions are twice, and under some conditions even three times as concentrated as the calcium.[3] But since the calcium ions are divalent and the sodium monavalent, at constant ratio of sodium to calcium ions in the percolating solution, the higher the actual concentration of sodium ions, the greater is their entry into the exchange complex, as explained on p. 115. Hence, higher sodium to calcium ratios can be tolerated in irrigation waters of low than of high salinities. This can be seen from Fig. 51,[4] which shows on the right-hand curve the concentration and composition of salts in the percolating water that cause sodium ions to constitute 15 per cent of the exchangeable ions, and on the left-hand curve to constitute $7\frac{1}{2}$ per cent. Since soils containing over 15 per cent of exchangeable sodium

[1] E. I. Ratner, *Soil Sci.*, 1935, **40**, 459; J. S. Joffe and M. Zimmerman, *Proc. Soil Sci. Soc. Amer.*, 1945, **9**, 51.
[2] N. V. Orlovsky and A. M. Kupstova, *Pedology*, 1939, No. 9, 73.
[3] W. P. Kelley *et al.*, *Soil Sci.*, 1940, **49**, 95; W. P. Kelley, *Cation Exchange in Soils*, New York, 1948; N. G. Cassidy, *Queensland J. Agric. Sci.*, 1944, **1**, 140.
[4] Taken from H. Greene, *Using Salty Land*, F.A.O. Agricultural Studies No. 3, 1948. Other sets of curves are given in *Diagnosis and Improvement of Saline and Alkali Soils*.

usually have their properties very adversely affected by the sodium, waters lying to the right of the right-hand curve are unsuitable for irrigation, whilst if the exchangeable sodium constitutes less than $7\frac{1}{2}$ per cent of the exchangeable ions it has little effect on the soil properties, so that waters lying to the left of the left-hand curve are quite safe to use.

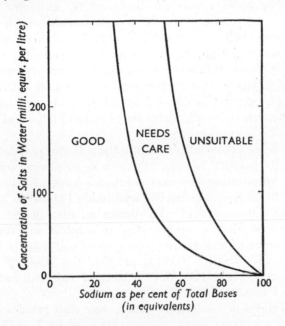

Fig. 51. The relation between the sodium content of water, its total concentration of salts and its suitability for irrigation.

Unfortunately the effective concentration of salts in the water is not that in the irrigation water itself, but that in the soil solution just before irrigation, for this is what leaches down on irrigation, and though this will be similar to the irrigation water on very permeable soils it may be up to ten times more concentrated in impermeable. Hence, the greater the impermeability of the soil, the lower must be the sodium content of the water for a given proportion of exchangeable sodium ions in the soil, and the more important it is that the proportion should remain low so the permeability, already poor, shall not be worsened.

Under present-day conditions when there is great pressure for increasing the acreage of land under irrigation, water must often be used that in time will cause the exchangeable sodium content of the soil to increase beyond the danger-point, if no precautions are taken to prevent it. Thus, water that is rather unsuitable for irrigation can still be used as long as the costs of keeping the exchangeable sodium down below a certain safe level are not too high. This involves, among other things, using the minimum possible amount of water for irrigation, to avoid unnecessary replacement of exchangeable calcium by sodium, though enough water must be used to wash down into the deep subsoil the salts that have accumulated in the root zone.

Exchangeable sodium can be replaced by calcium under field conditions either by adding a soluble calcium salt, such as gypsum, or a soluble acid such as sulphuric. Calcium carbonate is only useful if the pH is not too high, for whereas about 30 milli-equivalents of calcium as sulphate will dissolve in a litre of water, only about 1 milli-equivalent of calcium as bicarbonate or carbonate will dissolve at pH 8·6, though over 5 will dissolve at pH 7. Soils well supplied with gypsum can be irrigated with water that has too high a sodium content to be suitable for a gypsum-free soil.

Acids as such are not usually added to the soil, but powdered sulphur, which is rapidly oxidised in most arid soils to sulphuric acid, has been much used. Aluminium and iron sulphates have also been used, as both of these hydrolyse, leaving the hydroxide behind as a precipitate and liberating sulphuric acid. To obtain an idea of the amounts of these improvers needed, 1 ton per acre of sulphur will replace about 3 milli-equivalents of sodium per 100 gm. of soil from 1 foot of soil; and 5·4 tons of gypsum ($CaSO_4.2H_2O$), 6·9 tons of aluminium sulphate ($Al_2(SO_4)_3.18H_2O$), or 3·1 tons of calcium carbonate are equivalent to 1 ton of sulphur.

Routine methods of controlling alkali may thus involve the regular addition of an acidifying agent, in contrast to many humid soils which need the regular addition of calcium carbonate to counteract the normal increase of acidity due to leaching. If the soil is low in gypsum but well supplied with calcium carbonate it is always possible, in theory at least, to control the increase in exchangeable sodium, due to an unfavourable ratio of sodium to calcium in the irrigation water, by including in the rotation crops such as lucerne and some grasses that maintain a fairly high carbon dioxide content in the soil, since the solubility of the calcium in the carbonate increases rapidly with increasing carbon dioxide content. Farmyard manure and composts, and probably composts containing sulphur, may also be useful, as they release carbon dioxide when mixed with the soil, but how far this is the main cause of their beneficial action on irrigated land, and how far it is due to them maintaining the permeability of the surface soil is not known.

In many irrigation schemes there are areas of land that have been rendered infertile by alkalinity and which can be reclaimed and brought back to cultivation. The principles underlying the reclamation of such areas are: firstly, to ensure that their drainage is adequate and that saline water is not seeping into them from higher ground; and, secondly, to replace some of the exchangeable sodium by calcium.[1] If the soil contains gypsum, draining the land and flooding it with water is probably all that is required, although if the soil is heavy, it may initially be sufficiently impermeable for the cropping to have to be chosen very carefully. But if the soil is low in gypsum, the primary trouble, which is either present, or which will develop unless precautions are taken, is the impermeability of the surface soil to water, and one great danger in reclamation that must be guarded against is increasing the impermeability of the soil during the reclamation. Soils containing much exchangeable sodium, or free sodium carbonate, will deflocculate and become quite impermeable to water if wetted with pure water, or with rain, whereas if they contain much soluble salts, or the irrigation water has a high salinity, they may remain flocculated and permeable. Hence, the second great principle in reclaiming alkali soils is to maintain a fairly high salt content in the soil during the process of leaching out the exchangeable sodium. Provided the soil remains permeable, drainage, adding gypsum or sulphur, and flushing down the salts will remove exchangeable sodium without difficulty.

Many disused alkali soils are, however, almost impermeable to begin with, and the improvement in permeability is the primary problem.[2] Typically this is done by replacing the exchangeable sodium in the surface layer and so stabilising it, and then deepening this stabilised layer. Adding gypsum to the surface soil, or on some lighter soils working in farmyard manure or compost, and then letting it wet and dry a few times will be enough to give a few inches of stable permeable soil. The soil may then be flooded, provided an adequate drainage system has been installed, to allow the gypsum to wash down slowly into the subsoil, improving the permeability of every layer into which it penetrates, for rarely does a drained soil have a permeability of less than a few inches of water a month.[3] Fig. 52, taken from some experiments of H. Greene on an impermeable Gezirah clay, in which sodium constitutes 10 per cent of the exchangeable ions, shows this effect of gypsum of increasing the permeability of the subsoil.[4] The

---

[1] For illustrations of successful methods of reclamation, see W. P. Kelley, *J. Agric. Sci.*, 1934, **24**, 72; *Hilgardia*, 1934, **8**, 149; *Calif. Agric. Expt. Sta., Bull.* 619, 1937 (San Joaquin Valley, California); *The Diagnosis and Improvement of Saline and Alkaline Soils*; R. E. McKenzie and J. L. Bolton, *Sci. Agric.*, 1947, **27**, 193 (Val Marie, Saskatchewan); R. Aladzem, *Bull. Un. Agric. Egypte*, 1947, **45**, 37; R. S. Snyder et al., *Idaho Agric. Expt. Sta., Bull.* 233, 1940; W. L. Powers, *Oregon Agric. Expt. Sta., Bull.* 10, 1946.
[2] For an American bulletin on methods of doing this, see R. F. Reitemeier et al., *U.S. Dept. Agric., Tech. Bull.* 937, 1948.
[3] W. L. Quayle (*Wyoming Agric. Expt. Sta., Bull.* 243, 1941) quotes examples of the value of flooding some Wyoming soils for two months before a crop is taken.
[4] *J. Agric. Sci.*, 1928, **18**, 531. See also with O. W. Snow, *J. Agric. Sci.*, 1939, **29**, 1.

land was flooded in April, and shortly afterwards soil samples were taken for moisture content. The soil was left fallow and then flooded again in December and soil samples again taken. Without gypsum the water remained near the surface: with increasing dressings of gypsum it penetrated deeper and deeper into the soil. The drying out affected the first 5 feet equally whatever the gypsum treatment, but it did not equally affect the lower depths: the stores of water let down by the heavier dressings remained. The permeability of the soil can also sometimes be increased by very deep ploughing,[1] particularly if

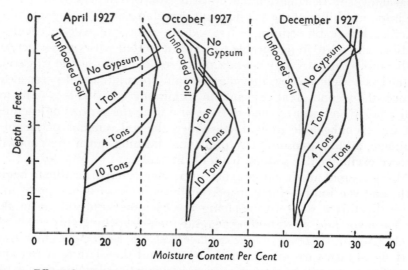

FIG. 52. Effect of gypsum on the permeability of soil. Percentage of moisture at different depths of unflooded soil (left-hand line) and of four flooded soils (right-hand lines) treated with different quantities of gypsum (tons per acre).

some gypsum is ploughed in at the same time or if gypsum is present in the subsoil. This is probably most efficacious if the subsoil has a compacted layer, for deep ploughing can bring this layer up to the surface, break it up to some extent, and expose it to the weather so its structure can be mellowed by drying and wetting in the hot season.

The second operation is to establish a crop on the land, either sown or of natural weeds, for the plant roots will continue the task of increasing the permeability of the subsoil, both by abstracting water from it, so causing cracks to develop which will let water down quickly, and also by respiring carbon dioxide there which will reduce the alkalinity somewhat. The choice of crop is, however, limited, for it

[1] V. A. Kovda, *Khim. Sotsial. Zemled.*, 1941, No. 4, 31; I. N. Antipov-Karataev and A. A. Zaitzev, *Dokuchaev Inst. Soils*, 1946, No. 14.

must be able to withstand the prolonged water-logging necessary for washing down as much sodium as possible into the deeper subsoil. Rice is an ideal crop, if other conditions are suitable, as it is kept water-logged throughout much of the season. Sweet clover and strawberry clovers are also suitable, so are many grasses and under some conditions so is lucerne, though lucerne will not stand water-logging so well as the others. Once these crops are established, they are encouraged to root deeply by being given heavy irrigations at as long intervals as possible, so the roots take as much water as they can from the subsoil before the next irrigation, though they must not be allowed to dry the soil so much that the soil solution becomes sufficiently concentrated to harm the roots. The first crop to be taken is often ploughed in as green manure, as the plant may contain too much salt for high feeding quality, and the green manure will not only produce carbon dioxide in the soil during its decomposition, but will also slowly set free plant nutrients such as phosphate, iron, manganese and zinc, which are very unavailable in alkaline soils.

Impermeable alkali soils can, therefore, be reclaimed and brought back into cultivation, though at the cost of much water, provided a water supply of good enough quality is available, for it must have a fairly low salt content because initially much of the water will have to evaporate from the soil surface, and the salt content must not build up enough to harm the crop.

A good crop rotation is an excellent insurance against alkali trouble, for grass, clover and lucerne leys can all build up the structure of a soil and improve its stability, and if these leys are consumed on the farm by dairy cattle, they will be returned to the land as farmyard manure, which again has a valuable action in maintaining the permeability of the surface soil.

Reclamation of Soils Damaged by Sea-water

Some interesting observations on the formation of a sodium clay by flooding with sea-water were made by T. S. Dymond in 1897-9.[1] The first effect of the flooding was to kill the vegetation by direct action of the salt. But when the flood subsided and the rain-water began to wash away the salt, an interesting sequence of events was observed. The soil was at first "in remarkably good condition, ploughing well and forming a capital seed-bed". But with further removal of the salt "this condition gradually altered until the soil became difficult to work and in dry weather hard and cindery". The clay became more

[1] T. S. Dymond and F. Hughes, *Report on Injury to Agricultural Land on the Coast of Essex by the Inundation of Sea Water on 29th November, 1897*, Chelmsford, 1899.

deflocculated, and would remain suspended for weeks in water while that from the unflooded land settled in a few hours.[1]

Dymond proved that the effect of the salt was to displace calcium and magnesium from the clay, and he argued that sodium had taken their place. He attributed the initial favourable physical conditions to the flocculation brought about by the small quantity of salt still left; when this was gone the clay became highly deflocculated.

TABLE 139

Influence of the Proportion of Divalent to Monovalent Bases on the Physical Conditions of Some Dutch Soils

Physical state	100 parts of replaceable bases contain:					
	Ca	Mg	Sum of divalent	K	Na	Sum of monovalent
Good, normal clay .	79·0	13·0	92·0	2·0	6·0	8·0
Fairly good . . .	65·8	17·6	83·4	4·0	12·6	16·6
Bad	42·1	25·0	67·1	6·5	26·4	32·9

The Dutch have had much experience in the last thirty years in reclaiming land from the sea, and their observations are in full accord with Dymond's. The soil starts very wet and sticky, but after a drainage system has been installed and some of the salt has been washed out, the surface soil acquires an excellent tilth. At this stage crops such as barley and mangolds will grow and yield well, and, in fact, the soil may have a high content of nitrate. It is in the following years, when the rain has removed still more salt so the clay becomes deflocculated, that troubles arise. The soils, however, usually contain enough calcium carbonate for calcium slowly to replace sodium. Once this has started, the soils can again be cultivated with care, though initially all cultivations must be very shallow so that the poor structural soil remains below.[2]

Table 139, taken from some of Hissink's work, shows how the proportion of exchangeable bases in the soil alters, starting off with the clay

[1] An interesting example occurred later at E. Halton, in North Lincs. The land was formerly very productive, being especially suited for wheat and beans; it was flooded by the sea in 1921 and became infertile. It has not since been flooded, but it remains very sticky when wet and hard as concrete when dry, so that cultivation is impossible; even wild plants make but little growth (H. J. Page and W. Williams, *J. Agric. Sci.*, 1926, **16**, 551). In 1931 it still showed signs of deterioration, but the wild white clover sown in the grass mixtures had done well. It appeared, however, that the under-drains were choked with deflocculated particles.

[2] For a detailed account of this work, see D. J. Hissink, *Rapporten met betrekking tot de bodemgesteldheid van de Wieringermeer en van den Andijker Proefpolder*, 1929, No. 1, 81; *Brit. Ass. Repts.*, 1931, 512; and several papers in *Trans. 6th Comm. Int. Soc. Soil Sci.*, Groningen, 1932, A, and 1933, B.

in very bad structure just after the salts have been washed out and finishing with the clay in good normal structure.

The Dutch, however, hastened this process when they set out to reclaim the land inundated with sea-water during 1944–5. Instead of waiting for the calcium carbonate to effect a replacement of the exchangeable sodium with calcium, which is slow because the sodium bicarbonate produced is alkaline and hence tends to keep the soil deflocculated, they added gypsum before the salt had been sufficiently washed out for the permeability of the soil to have been affected. This is much more soluble than the carbonate, and the sodium washes out as the neutral sulphate, hence has no tendency to reduce the permeability of the soil. By this means the soil can be kept permeable and cropped during the whole process of the replacement of sodium by calcium. The dressing of gypsum needed depends on the clay content of the soil, but it varies from 1 to 5 tons per acre.

CHAPTER XXXV

THE GENERAL PRINCIPLES OF SOIL MANAGEMENT

A GOOD SYSTEM of agriculture is required to produce as much food, either human or farm stock, as possible from the land at a reasonable cost without impairing its fertility. A farmer should always aim to leave the land in at least as productive a condition as when he acquired it. A good system of management must therefore ensure that the nutrient status of the soil is maintained; that all factors directly harmful to plant growth, such as high acidity, high alkalinity, or poor drainage are absent; that the land only grows the crops desired and not unwanted ones, that is, that weeds are kept under control; and that the soil particles themselves remain in place and are neither washed nor blown away.

The nutrient status of the soil is now very largely under the direct control of the farmer. If high-priced cash crops are being grown he can, if need be, buy all the plant food needed by the crop. But he should also aim at returning to the land all crop and animal residues that he can so as to minimise the loss of nutrients. Some soils, such as many semi-arid and desert, are naturally well provided with plant food; others, such as some tropical soils being derived from young, basic igneous rocks, are having their supplies of plant nutrients supplied by the weathering of the rock particles in the soil fast enough to meet the demands of the crops. Still others need to have nutrients added if they are to maintain good yields, and of these nutrients nitrogen and phosphate compounds are far the most important—nitrogen compounds wherever the water supply is sufficient to keep the plant growing all through its season, and phosphates in most parts of the world. These nutrients do not necessarily have to be added as fertilisers. The available nitrogen compounds in the soil can be greatly increased either by growing leguminous crops which contain nodules capable of fixing large quantities of atmospheric nitrogen, or by growing crops which return much nitrogen-poor organic matter to the soils under conditions in which decomposition can proceed rapidly and in which free-living nitrogen-fixing bacteria can flourish. The supply of other nutrients can also sometimes be increased by selecting crops which have a considerable power of extracting the nutrients in short supply from the soil minerals, or which have a particularly deep root system, and which can, therefore, concentrate the available soil supplies. In all these cases, however, if the crop is not ploughed in, it should be fed to animals and their dung and urine put back on the land in a way that gives the smallest possible losses.

The prevention of harmful factors, such as acidity and alkalinity, have already been dealt with, and both require that the calcium status of the soil shall remain satisfactory. Good drainage is also essential to allow the crops to root deeply, hence be able to withstand drought and possibly frost as well, and to prevent the accumulation of harmful substances produced biologically whenever the oxygen tension in the soil falls too low. The soil must also be kept permeable, so water can drain through it at a reasonable rate, and the carbon dioxide content of the air around the roots not rise too high, nor the oxygen content fall too low. To some extent these factors can be controlled by proper cultivations, a subject that will be discussed in a later section.

The Principles Underlying the Control of Soil Erosion

Soil particles can move by three processes: they may be blown away, they may be washed away, or the whole soil may slide or slump down a hill-side. Soil erosion can cause great troubles over large areas: dust storms, once started, may travel great distances; and conditions conducive to water erosion can lead to extensive flooding of valleys after storms, to silting-up of rivers, valleys and reservoirs, and to the great impoverishment of the land above the valley floor. Soil erosion is nearly always caused by an unsuitable method of agriculture being practised, and since among primitive peoples the system of agriculture affects their whole system life, methods of control involve not merely devising a system of agriculture which is better suited to the area and more productive, which is relatively easy, but also of altering the whole social outlook and sometimes even some of the religious beliefs or practices of the community, which is always an extremely difficult problem in sociology.

WIND EROSION AND SOIL DRIFTING

High winds can blow much material out of some bare soils, so that the wind itself becomes a dust storm, and soil material drifts across the land, forming dunes, filling up hollows and drifting against farm buildings and hedges. The physics of this action is now fairly well understood, as the principles have been clearly stated by R. A. Bagnold[1] and filled in in considerable detail for the particular case

[1] For a summary of his work, see his book *The Physics of Blown Sand and Desert Dunes*, London, 1941.

of soils by W. S. Chepil and R. A. Milne[1] at Swift Current, Saskatchewan.

Winds move soil and sand particles by three distinct processes: the finer particles are carried in suspension and may be transported as fine dust over very great distances; the coarser particles are rolled along the surface of the soil; and the medium-sized particles move by saltation. Bagnold has shown that saltation is, in fact, the primary process responsible for soil movement. The process of saltation is as follows. A strong eddy of wind at the soil surface picks up a sand grain and carries it up a few centimetres in the air where the wind has a much stronger horizontal component than at the soil surface itself. This wind then gives the sand grain a horizontal acceleration, and as the eddy which picked it up becomes dissipated, the sand grain falls back to the ground after having acquired considerable momentum. On impact it may cause some other sand grains to be shot a little way up in the air, and these in turn acquire momentum from the wind, and on hitting the ground may throw up other grains. Thus, the dust storm is due to this stream of sand particles which throw up others as they hit the ground. Soil movement by saltation thus requires a source of sand grains of a suitable size and a clear length of run for the wind to build up a sufficient density of sand grains moving in this way.

The size of particles taking part in saltation movement usually lies between 0·5 and 0·05 mm., with the grains in the size 0·1 to 0·2 mm. particularly active; and they need not be sand grains, but can equally well be soil aggregates or granules. Typically, the bulk of the grains do not rise more than an inch or so above soil-level, but a few rise to 3 to 6 feet; they rise steeply to their maximum height and then come down at an angle of between 10° and 16° with the horizontal. Typical paths for these grains are shown in Fig. 53, taken from R. A. Bagnold's *Blown Sand and Desert Dunes*. Grains smaller than about 0·1 to 0·05 mm., depending rather on the wind speed, do not take part in saltation, as they are sufficiently fine to be carried as dust in the turbulent motion of the wind, whilst grains larger than about 0·5 mm. are too heavy to be bounced into the air. Saltation thus brings the finer particles into the air and by bombarding the coarser particles rolls them along the surface of the soil.

The effects of soil blowing in the field are as follows. Soils containing a high proportion, that is, over 60 per cent of unaggregated sand grains and individual granules in the size range 0·1 to 0·5 mm., are very liable to blow, whilst those with less than 40 per cent do not usually blow easily. Such blowing soils are either fine sands, calcareous

[1] *Sci. Agric.*, 1939, **19**, 249; 1941, **21**, 479; 1942, **23**, 154; *Soil Sci.*, 1941, **52**, 417; 1945, **60**, 305, 397, 475; 1946, **61**, 167, 257, 331.

clays (for the calcium carbonate tends to give soil granules of this size) or fen soils containing well-rotted humus. The wind needs a run of from 50 to 500 yards to build up a large body of moving soil grains. At the windward end of the area the particles coarser than 0·5 mm. tend to accumulate; the sand dunes and drifts, which move mainly by saltation, are enriched in particles between 0·5 and 0·1 mm., and particles finer than 0·1 mm. are blown out of the area. The coarser of these particles, in the range 0·07 to 0·01 mm., are deposited on the outer fringes of the area as a loess.[1] Hence, the residual soils tend to become more sandy by this process. As one travels with the wind the grains fill up all hollows, and if there are no obstructions leave an

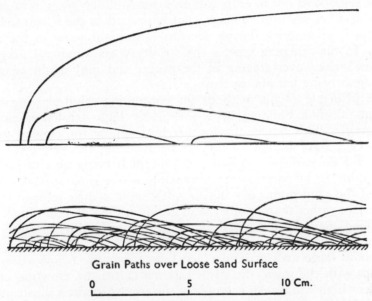

Grain Paths over Loose Sand Surface

0   5   10 Cm.

FIG. 53. *Upper*: Typical paths of sand grains moving by saltation.
Lower: Paths of sand grains moving over a loose soil surface.

almost level surface having shallow ripples across it. This smooth surface becomes resistant to further erosion as soon as the supply of incoming sand grains ceases. These effects are shown up most clearly in fine, sandy soils having few granules.

The effects are rather different for granulated clays, because the movement of different-sized granules does not necessarily involve any differential movement of the actual mineral soil particles. Further, the granules have not the abrasive action of sand grains, so typically they produce less dust to be blown out of the area, though they drift just as badly.

[1] F. E. Zeuner, *The Pleistocene Period*, Ray Soc. London, 1945.

The primary areas suffering from dust storms are on the edges of the desert, for blowing is only possible with dry soils. The desert and the fringes of the desert give this dryness and are also regions liable to strong winds. Because of the dryness, it is often difficult to keep vegetation growing on the soil during periods of droughts, so the soil is liable to have many bare patches, and it is in the bare patches that centres of blowing start. The primary problems of erosion control are only concerned with bare or partially bare soil, for soil well covered with vegetation never blows. Further, the type of agriculture practised in these semi-arid regions is either wheat growing with the necessary fallows for storing water, or ranching. In the former type there is always some land not in crop, and in a series of dry years most of the land will carry no crop. This is what happened in the wheat belt, or dust bowl, of America during the run of drought years in the mid-1930s. In the ranching type, a spell of dry years almost of necessity involves serious over-grazing of the range, and may again result in large areas being left almost bare.

The principle of all methods for controlling wind-blowing is to prevent saltation building up a sufficiently high density of moving sand grains. This can be done either by trapping the moving grains before they have become dense, or by reducing the velocity of the wind over the surface sufficiently to prevent it being able to pick up sand grains, or by covering the soil with a non-erodible surface so that most of the sand grains moving by saltation lose their momentum to this surface rather than to other sand grains in the saltation range.

Methods have been devised for reducing the liability of cultivated soils in the dry farming regions from blowing.[1] In the first place, no continuous large area of land is left fallow, but the fallow alternates as strips with the sown, the strips running across the direction of the prevalent high winds. An example of this from Alberta is illustrated in Plate XXXII. Fallow strips 100 to 200 yards wide, alternating with sown strips of the same width, normally blow very little, unless the soil is very erosive, for the wind cannot produce enough sand particles moving by saltation either to raise much dust or to cause much drifting before they are caught by the crop. However, this method by itself is only of limited value with soils very liable to blow, and at times of the year before the sown crop has germinated or grown large enough to prevent saltation. A modification of this method can be used in areas of adequate rainfall to protect areas of land liable to blow before the sown crop has grown enough to give protection. Comparatively

---

[1] For accounts of these methods, see E. S. Hopkins *et al.*, *Canada Dept. Agric.*, *Publ.* 568, 4th revision, 1946; A. E. Palmer, *Emp. J. Expt. Agric.*, 1945, **13**, 125; *U.S. Dept. Agric.*, *Farmers' Bull.* 1771, 1937; 1833, 1939; 1864, 1941.

narrow strips of permanent grass, if the herbage is 1 to 2 feet high, will stop saltation by entrapping the sand provided it is wide enough for the entrapped sand to be well away from its leeward side. This method, however, is only efficacious in areas where the rainfall is adequate to ensure a good crop of grass every year. In extreme cases the grass strip can be replaced by a narrow but thick hedge.

The second method of control, which is used in conjunction with strip cropping, is to reduce the velocity of the wind at the soil surface as much as possible, and do anything else that reduces the chance of the wind picking up any sand grains. Winds can be moderated by planting shelter belts, but the climate is often too dry and other conditions unfavourable for most trees to grow quickly,[1] and the effect of the shelter belt is small, limited to not more than five times its height on the windward or twenty to thirty times its height on the leeward side.[2] This method, however, is useful in the isolated areas of eastern England and Sweden,[3] for example, where soil-blowing can be serious.

W. S. Chepil[4] has given an example from Kaifeng in Honan Province, China, where this method is practised to stabilise a sandy soil. Single belts of willow, which grow to about 12 feet high, are planted in strips 50 to 60 feet apart across the direction of the prevailing wind and in strips 100 to 500 feet apart at right angles to this direction, leaving only small rectangular strips of field for cultivation.

Suitable cultivation methods can also reduce the chance of the wind picking up a sand grain. Obviously, if the soil structure can be made cloddy there will be no unaggregated sand particles of a suitable size to be picked up. Cultivating the soil when moist and never pulverising it helps, but it is not always possible to restrict cultivations to these times. Laying the soil down to drought-resistant grasses whose roots bind the soil together also improves the structure. Laying the soil up in ridges also reduces erosion through it preventing the build-up of particles moving by saltation.[5] It is also particularly important that any knoll or dune built out of erodible sand or soil particles should be very well stabilised, otherwise it will serve as a good source for particles to begin to drift by saltation at quite low wind speeds.

Another method, that has been used in parts of the Canadian prairies since 1915, is stubble mulch cultivation, described more fully on p. 634, in which the previous year's stubble is left anchored in the

---

[1] For an account of shelter belts, see, for example, *U.S. Dept. Agric., Farmers' Bull.* 1405, 1936; J. S. Yeates, *Farm Trees and Hedges, Massey Agric. Coll. (New Zealand) Bull.* 12, 1942.
[2] See, for example, J. W. Toumey, *Foundations of Silviculture*, New York, 1928; W. Nägeli, *Mitt. Schweiz. Anst. Forstl. Versuchsw.*, 1943, **23**, 223.
[3] G. Petersson, *LantbrHögsk. JordbrFörsöksanst. Medd.*, 1947, No. 20.
[4] *Agron. J.*, 1949, **41**, 127.
[5] W. S. Chepil and R. A. Milne, *Soil Sci.*, 1941, **52**, 417.

surface, and during the fallow period all cultivations are done below or on the surface in such a way that the previous year's stubble remains anchored in the surface but sticking out above it, as is shown in Plate XXXIII. Thus, weeds can be kept in control without the soil surface being left bare. Typically, in the wheat-growing areas where these methods were first developed, the wheat is harvested with the combine, a long stubble is left and the straw coming from the combine is also left on the ground. Thus, the wind velocity at ground-level is always very low because of the resistance of the stubble and straw, and the straw and stubble together reduce the chance of a moving sand grain throwing up others by saltation. Chepil[1] found, in fact, that as little as $\frac{1}{4}$ ton per acre of straw had an appreciable effect in reducing soil drifting. Stubble mulch farming may introduce some difficult problems in insect control, particularly the wheat stem sawfly and insects of the grasshopper-locust type, because they may be able to over-winter on the stubble, but so far few troubles of this type have arisen.[2]

All these methods used together as far as possible give good control of wind-blowing in most years, but it must be borne in mind that there are no methods of control yet available on cultivated land during periods of drought extending over several years. These lands cannot be sown down to grass or to anything else once the drought has started, though if one could forecast the onset of prolonged drought a year or so ahead they could be grassed down and left ungrazed over the dry period, and this might be enough to prevent the disastrous dust storms of the mid-1930s recurring.

EROSION BY RUNNING WATER

Water running over the surface of the soil is a far more serious cause of erosion in most parts of the world than is the wind. Water only runs off the soil surface when the rate of rainfall exceeds the rate of infiltration of the water into the soil, hence every factor that reduces the permeability of the soil increases the likelihood of water run-off. This run-off water has two consequences of great importance: the more the run-off the greater is the "flash" flood in the rivers draining the area after storms, and the greater is the amount of silt and soil the water is likely to pick up and hence the more silt will be deposited by the river after the floods have subsided. Hence, this type of run-off and erosion gives very difficult problems of flood control on the one hand and silt control on the other. As examples of silt trouble can be mentioned the burying of crops under silt in the flood plains of rivers,

---

[1] *Sci. Agric.*, 1944, **24**, 307.
[2] For an example of trouble of this type, see D. A. Wilbur *et al.*, *J. Amer. Soc. Agron.*, 1942, **34**, 16.

the rapid silting up of reservoirs, and the difficulty of keeping irrigation channels clear and irrigated fields level if the river supplying the irrigation scheme is silty.

Run-off can have a third consequence of very great importance, for the rain-water, instead of sinking into the soil, runs off the land and hence cannot be used by the vegetation. Run-off therefore increases the liability of the crop to damage by drought, and this effect is particularly serious in semi-arid regions and in all those parts of the tropics with a short, or uncertain rainy season, for even in these regions the rains that fall tend to fall in heavy storms of short duration.

The typical cause of serious erosion is that an unsuitable method of farming is being practised. Well-managed forests and pastures are almost immune from erosion troubles, whilst any system of agriculture that involves having large bare areas of soil during heavy rain storms are very susceptible. Thus, in many semi-arid parts of the world, liable to long drought and heavy storms and in which ranching is the natural method of land use, over-grazing in the dry season leaves the soil unprotected against the rain storms when they come, and hence very liable to serious soil erosion.[1] Over-grazed ranges are not only more liable to erosion but also may be more favourable habitats for rabbits and other rodents which themselves graze the range,[2] and hence will be an added cause for its decreased productivity. It is under just such conditions of limited water supply that water run-off is such a serious matter, because it causes the whole area to suffer unnecessary drought, and this is often a much more important factor than soil loss in semi-arid areas.

The erosive power of water, running over the surface of the soil, depends on its power of bringing soil into suspension and of carrying the soil load so brought in. These powers increase very rapidly with the velocity of flow and to some extent with the thickness of the water sheet.[3] Hence, the two fundamental principles in all methods of combating or reducing soil erosion by water are the maintenance of the permeability of the soil, to reduce the amount of run-off as much as possible, and ensuring that what run-off occurs takes place as thin sheets of slowly moving water. This latter point is difficult to achieve, for water running off a slope always tends to form runnels, in which the flowing water is concentrated and hence its power of erosion increased; and these runnels collect as fast flowing flood streams

[1] For examples, see H. Glover, *Erosion in the Punjab*, Lahore, 1944; K. B. Cumberland, *Soil Erosion in New Zealand*, Wellington, 1944; J. M. Holmes, *Soil Erosion in Australia and New Zealand*, Sydney, 1946.
[2] V. T. Vochies and W. P. Taylor, *Arizona Agric. Expt. Sta.*, *Tech. Bull.* 86, 1940; E. H. Graham, *The Natural Principles of Land Use*, New York, 1944; *J. Soil Water Conserv.*, 1946, 1, 55; R. L. Piemeisel, *U.S. Dept. Agric.*, *Tech. Bull.* 654, 1938.
[3] For some experiments showing this, see J. F. Lutz and B. D. Hargrove, *North Carolina Agric. Expt. Sta.*, *Tech. Bull.* 78, 1944.

which may soon begin to cut deep gullies. Hence, the need to keep the length of run of the water over the bare soil down to a reasonable length, for the longer the run the more the chance of runnelling. Thus, at Zanesville, Ohio, the amount of soil washed off runs of 36, 76 and 145 feet of soil continuously under maize having a 12° slope were 83, 99 and 117 tons per acre per year, yet the actual amount of water running off these three areas was the same.[1]

The effect of erosion on the particle size distribution of the soil left behind and the soil carried away depends on the velocity of the water running off the land. High velocities of run-off carry away all the soil particles, even stones, but at moderate velocities, when erosion is not very serious, the silt and clay particles tend to be removed and the sand particles to remain behind. Hence, land suffering from moderate erosion tends to become sandier, and the deposits left behind by the run-off water in the valleys more silty than the original soil.[2]

Various methods are employed to slow up the water and keep it flowing in as uniform a sheet as possible over the soil, of which strip cropping on the contour and the use of terraces are typical. In strip cropping, strips of land well covered with vegetation and hence resistant to erosion alternate with strips less well covered and hence more susceptible, whilst the terraces are banks of soil, often up to 18 inches high, running either on the contour or having a gentle fall, which intercept the water running off the land above them. The water either ponds up behind them if they are run on the contour, or runs off into well-protected waterways if they have a gentle fall. Hence, the base of the terrace must be able to withstand a stream of water running along it, so it is often necessary to grow a close-spaced crop, or a grass ley in it for this reason. Terraces can also be much lower structures, even only an upturned furrow, if they are run at frequent intervals on the contour across a grazing range. This slows up the water at regular intervals, and if the top of these small terraces are on the level, water cannot collect in streams, but spreads out uniformly each time it reaches one. The design of terrace systems and the proper width of close-cropping crops with wide-spaced ones in strip cropping are problems that lie outside the scope of this book.[3]

The maintenance of soil permeability can be extremely difficult, because the main cause of erosion is heavy rain storms. Thus, at Tyler,

[1] U.S. Dept. Agric., Tech. Bull. 888, 1945.

[2] For some examples of this, see L. A. Forrest and J. F. Lutz, Proc. Soil Sci. Soc. Amer., 1945, 9, 17.

[3] For detailed experimental results on different types of soils for different crops on which practical recommendations must be based, see the reports of the American Soil Erosion Research Stations, U.S. Dept. Agric., Tech. Bulls. 837, 1945; 859, 860, 873, 1944; 883, 888, 1945; 916, 1946; 959, 1948; and for details of the methods advised, H. H. Bennett, Soil Conservation, New York, 1939.

Texas, land under cotton lost on the average 21 tons of soil a year, but of this loss 12·5 tons were lost, on the average, in the two days in which the two heaviest storms occurred.[1] There are two reasons for this; one is that the heavy storm puts much water on the land very quickly, so unless the soil is very permeable a high proportion has to run off; but the second reason is that heavy storms fall as large, and hence fast-falling raindrops, which have a high momentum and kinetic energy when they hit the ground. M. L. Nichols and R. B. Gray[2] have calculated that 2 inches of heavy rain in which the drops fall at 20 miles per hour have to dissipate 6,000,000 foot-pounds of work per acre on hitting the ground—enough to raise the top 6 inches of soil 3 feet in the air if it all fell at once. Hence, the impact of the raindrops on a soil surface is to smash up all clods on the surface, and leave it level.[3] But in the process fine sand, silt and clay granules have become dispersed in the water, and splash up with the water droplets, so the percolating water becomes muddy. Another consequence of these water droplets containing fine soil particles is that if the land is on a slope this splashing moves these particles down the slope.

It has already been stressed that the infiltration of water into a soil, and its drainage through the soil, takes place in the wider pores, typically those between soil clods and crumbs, and down root and worm holes and other such discontinuities. The effect of a heavy rain on a bare soil is, therefore, to seal up the openings of these channels at the surface, both by soil from the disintegrated clods being knocked into them and by silt carried by the water settling out in them as the water percolates slowly down. Hence, shortly after the beginning of a heavy storm a bare soil surface will have become virtually impermeable to water, even though just below it there are channels running through into dry soil. The only ways the surface layer can be kept permeable in such conditions are to prevent the rain actually hitting the soil clods, for it is not possible to give the soil a crumb structure strong enough to withstand such impacts.

The soil surface can be protected from the raindrops either by growing a close-growing crop on it, so the leaves of the crop take the impact, or else by covering it with a straw, farmyard manure or leaf litter mulch. This again ensures that only clean, slowly moving water comes in contact with the surface of the soil, and hence causes a minimum reduction in the surface permeability. Even stubble left anchored in the soil, or the straw from the combine left on the soil,[4] as is done in

[1] U.S. Dept. Agric., Tech. Bull., 916, 1946.   [2] Agric. Engng., 1941, 22, 341.
[3] For examples and photographs, see J. O. Laws, Agric. Engng., 1940, 21, 431; W. D. Ellison, ibid., 1944, 25, 131, 181, and 1947, 28, 5 papers.
[4] For some details of the effectiveness of these methods, see F. L. Duley and L. L. Kelley, U.S. Dept. Agric., Circ. 608, 1941; J. C. Russel, Proc. Soil Sci. Soc. Amer., 1943, 7, 77.

stubble mulch cultivations, help considerably to maintain the permeability of the soil surface by taking much of the impact of the falling raindrops.

Ensuring that the water just after reaching the soil remains clear is, however, only part of the problem. It must remain as clear as possible as it runs over the surface, so impairing the permeability of the surface soil as little as possible. It is at this stage that a stable soil structure, obtained by proper use of farmyard manure, or grass or legume leys, can be so valuable. But even a good stable structure has only a limited effect on the clearness of the water, and close-growing crops, such as leys which cover the soil, or wheat drilled along the contour, or stubble anchored to the soil, or a surface mulch all help by slowing up the flow of the water, hence reducing its power to carry silt or soil. And it is for this reason that close-growing crops grown on the contour as strips between areas of wide-spaced crops, are such a valuable method of controlling soil and water losses, provided the slope of the land is not too steep and no gullying has begun.

The effect of various cropping practices on the amount of water and soil lost from strips of different crops has been measured in many experiments in America. An example from Zanesville, Ohio, will illustrate these points. Plots were laid out up a 12° slope on a silt loam soil. Over a nine-year period the average annual rainfall was 38 inches, and half the soil losses were caused by thirty-three rains during this period. The plots were cropped either to continuous maize, or to a four-year rotation of maize-wheat-two-year ley, or to permanent pasture, and the mean annual soil and water losses were:

	Average run-off of water		Soil loss, tons per acre
	Inches	As per cent of rainfall	
Continuous maize . . .	15	40·3	99·3
Crops in rotation:			
Maize	9	23·7	41·5
Wheat	9	24·8	11·4
First-year ley . . .	7	17·7	0·6
Second-year ley . . .	5	12·8	0·2
Permanent pasture . . .	1·6	4·3	0·02

These results show it is easier to reduce soil loss than water run-off by proper choice of crops, and that the better soil structure under maize following the two-year ley reduces both the soil and water loss very considerably compared with the soil with a poorer structure under continuous maize.

Strip cropping, like stubble mulch farming, may bring some difficult problems of insect control in its train, for it allows some of the plant-eating insects of the grasshopper-locust type to over-winter on the grass or cereal strips, so giving them the possibility of breeding quicker in the spring and so becoming a plague more easily. But the strips also allow the insects predaceous on these leaf-eaters to increase in numbers, and up to the present time the net effect of these covered strips on the plant-eating insects has been small.

CHAPTER XXXVI

PRINCIPLES OF THE METHODS OF SOIL CULTIVATION

THE GREAT CHANGES in technology that have taken place in the world during the last few centuries originated in north-west Europe, and this has been very apparent until a few decades ago in the improved methods of soil cultivation that were being practised by men of north-west European stock over the whole world. But though these methods have been very successful in temperate regions, they often had disastrous consequences in other areas. Thus, cultivations based on the mouldboard plough and weed-free soils are not universally appropriate. Unfortunately, at the present time there is still much controversy, particularly among successful farmers, about the consequences and necessities of different practices, and the account to be given here would be disputed by some of them.

There seems no question that the agriculture of north-west Europe has been centred on the mouldboard plough, an implement which when well used cuts and inverts a furrow and leaves the land completely bare of all vegetation. Mouldboard ploughing, therefore, buries all surface rubbish, and can be made to bury manure put on the surface, and in consequence can distribute relatively immobile fertilisers, such as phosphates, potash and lime, throughout the depth of ploughing; and it also loosens the layer of soil ploughed. The shallowest depth to which the surface of the soil is buried and the amount of comminution or aggregation of the soil clods depends on the shape of the mouldboard.

The ability of the mouldboard plough to kill weeds and prevent weed seeds germinating is undoubted, and under cool, humid conditions, such as the typical English late autumn to early spring, there appears to be no other implement that has anything like the ability to prevent weeds growing in the seed-bed; and the deeper the plough is set the more efficiently it prevents surface weeds from germinating and allows deep-rooting perennial weeds to be controlled by bringing up more of their root system to the surface.

The importance of distributing manure and fertilisers through a greater depth of soil than can be done merely by working them into the first few inches of surface soil is still under investigation. Obviously, if one is reclaiming land with a very acid subsoil, one will improve the drought resistance of a crop growing on it by spreading lime on the surface before ploughing, then ploughing as deeply as possible, and then spreading another dressing of lime on the surface; for this will neutralise the subsoil acidity more rapidly and allow the crop to become deeper rooting. But on soils in which roots can penetrate several feet quite easily, such as most agricultural soils, the occasions on which it is desirable to incorporate the manures and fertilisers deeply have not been well established, though general experience and general theory indicate that it should be in moderately dry years. For, as pointed out on p. 449, plant roots cannot extract nutrients from a dry soil, and tend to dry the soil from the surface downwards, hence the deeper the nutrients are incorporated, the longer after the onset of the drought will some of them remain in moist soil. It is probably for this reason that the practice of drilling part of the potash and phosphate, or in some conditions a complete fertiliser, on the bottom of an 8- to 10-inch deep plough furrow[1] has been spreading in regions subject to short but severe summer droughts.

The importance of the depth to which the soil is loosened has not been established yet. There are many progressive farmers in parts of Great Britain who are ardent advocates of deep ploughing, and it is not yet known just what benefits they derive from ploughing 15 to 18 inches deep. This deep ploughing naturally increases the permeability of the ploughed soil and the goodness of its aeration, and hence allows the soil to drain quicker provided the deeper subsoil is permeable or has an efficient drainage system; though if the drainage of the deeper subsoil is very impeded, deep ploughing merely increases the volume of the large pores that can become water-logged in wet weather, and hence helps to turn the land into a marsh. Subsoiling, that is, loosening the subsoil without bringing it to the surface, also improves permeability, and the point at issue between deep ploughing and subsoiling is the relative length of time that the improved permeability lasts. This improvement would be expected to be most beneficial on soils having a comparatively thin pan under the normal depth of ploughing, such as that produced by long-continued ploughing to a constant depth or by a tractor wheel running on the bottom of the furrow, and would most likely be seen on heavy soils.

There is, however, a very extensive body of experience and of experimental results that have shown deep ploughing to have no beneficial effects on the crop, and that, for as far as crop yields are concerned, ploughing depths of 4 inches appear to be quite satisfactory, though this is probably only true if the land is already free from weeds.

[1] For the results of many American experiments on the value of these practices, see the *Proceedings of the National Joint Committee of Fertiliser Application*.

Certainly, most of the Rothamsted experiments[1] have shown that 4-inch ploughing, or indeed any method of loosening the soil to a 4-inch depth, is all that wheat, barley and mangolds need, provided the land is clean, though the Rothamsted experience has been, as already stated, that deeper ploughing eases the task of keeping the land clean very considerably. The former part of this result has also been found by Swedish[2] and many American[3] workers.

The great limitation of the mouldboard plough is that, by leaving the soil surface completely bare, it leaves it in a condition very susceptible to erosion, and if the primary objective in mouldboard ploughing is to control weeds, particularly in the seed-bed and the early stages of the crop's growth, then the problem of replacing the mouldboard plough is that of finding alternative methods of weed control. The most likely line of development is to try and improve the methods developed six or more thousand years ago in the Middle East and Egypt, based on a plough that merely loosens the land without turning a furrow—a plough that is very like a cultivator tine. Such a plough will loosen the soil, will undercut all weeds and plants, but will leave them on the surface. Provided the weather is dry, particularly hot and dry, during or just after this operation, the surface weeds will be dried up and killed, but they will remain as a mulch anchored in the surface to help protect it against wind and rain. This is, in fact, the principle of stubble mulch farming being developed in the semi-arid parts of America. The methods being tried are to work the soil with wide sweeps attached to cultivator tines, such as is shown in Plate XXXIII or with rotary rod weeders, about 2 inches below the surface,[4] leaving all the dead weeds and last season's stubbles and crop residues lying on the surface, but anchored in it as is also shown in that plate. The next crop is sown by cutting a narrow band through this mulch and putting the seed into the seed-bed prepared below it. But this method is only successful in regions where cutting weeds about 1 to 2 inches below the surface is sufficient to kill them, and this needs dry weather and the absence of weeds that cannot easily be killed by this method. Duley and Russel have given an example of this for maize in Nebraska. In dry years the maize yielded relatively much better under stubble mulch cultivation than ploughing, 31 compared with 17 bushels per acre, but in wet years relatively worse, 62 compared with 72; the full causes of this difference have not been recognised.

[1] E. W. Russell and B. A. Keen, *J. Agric. Sci.*, 1941, **31**, 326.
[2] G. Torstensson and G. Enge, *Kgl. LantbrAkad. Tidskr.*, 1943, **82**, 296.
[3] See, for example, C. E. Millar and A. G. Weidemann, *Michigan Agric. Expt. Sta. Quart. Bull.*, 1947, **30**, 5.
[4] For a description of the machinery being developed, see F. L. Duley and J. C. Russel, *Agric. Engng.*, 1942, **23**, 39; M. B. Cox, ibid., 1944, **25**, 175; *U.S. Dept. Agric., Farmers' Bull.* 1797, 1938; 1997, 1948.

The correct implement to replace the mouldboard plough on erodable land in the humid tropics has not yet been developed. The native implement is the hand-hoe, and the area cultivated is divided into small, isolated patches. The methods being developed are taking advantage of the fact that in most tropical regions there is a wet and a dry season, and the object is to kill the weeds in the dry season, probably by some method such as the stubble mulch, and plant at the very beginning of the wet, so the land is covered with a crop as soon as possible.

A second series of cultivation operations that have been of great importance in the past, are the hoeings done between the rows of a wide-spaced crop, and it is probable that in England, at any rate, one of the principal reasons the seed drill was introduced was to allow the subsequent crop to be horse-hoed. These hoeings do two distinct things: they kill the weeds growing between the rows and they loosen the surface of the soil. At one time the agricultural scientists considered that the loose surface, the dust mulch as it is called, helped to reduce the amount of water lost by the soil, and though this is still believed by many farmers, field experiments all over the world have shown that this mulch does not normally have this effect.[1] The importance of this hoeing appears to lie in the weeds it kills and not in the loose tilth it creates,[2] and this is borne out by the practical experience that other methods of weed control that do not involve creating a soil mulch, such as using differential chemical weed killers and miniature flame throwers,[3] can benefit the crop as much as hoeing.

Surface hoeing may have, however, three undesirable consequences. The soil is left bare, the loose mulch is not stable enough to withstand a heavy storm, and the production of the loose mulch may involve harming the surface-feeding roots of the crop. This damage can be important in established crops of sugar-beet at Rothamsted,[4] and can be serious for shallow rooted plantation trees, such as tea and coffee.[5] The methods that must be adopted to control weed competition where these two consequences are really important will be discussed in the next section.

If the main effect of hoeing is to kill weeds, and its disturbing effect on the surface roots of the crop is undesirable, as with coffee, sugar-beet, and many market-garden crops,[6] chemical weed killers are likely

[1] H. C. Pereira (*Emp. J. Expt. Agric.*, 1941, **9**, 29) has collected together the results of several hundred experiments on this subject.

[2] For some modern experiments, see E. W. Russell *et al.*, *J. Agric. Sci.*, 1942, **32**, 330 (England); A. R. Saunders, *Farm. S. Africa*, 1944, **19**, 295; A. G. Weidemann, *Michigan Agric. Expt. Sta., Quart. Bull.* 1947, **29**, 320; G. H. Burvill *et al.*, *J. Dept. Agric. W. Aust.*, 1943, **20**, 244.

[3] For the use of this technique, see F. E. Farwell, *Sugar*, 1945, **40**, No. 2, 35; H. T. Barr, *Louisiana Agric. Expt. Sta.*, *Bull.* 415, 1947.

[4] E. W. Russell *et al.*, *J. Agric. Sci.*, 1942, **32**, 330.

[5] A. S. Thomas, *Emp. J. Expt. Agric.*, 1944, **12**, 191.

[6] R. D. Sweet, *Cornell Agric. Expt. Sta.*, *Bull.* 795, 1943.

to be of more benefit than weed killing by cultivation, and in fact with the range of differential herbicides now available, the amount of cultivation given to soils on which crops are growing is decreasing rapidly. But where hoeing is done, it should be as shallow as possible and at a time when it either kills most weeds or any particular pernicious weed, or when the weeds have a particularly depressing effect on crop growth. There is an increasing body of evidence, which has not yet been properly summarised, which indicates that weeds are usually most harmful to the crop during the early, and particularly the very early, stages of growth. Hence, the importance of clean weed-free seed-beds, and of beginning hoeing as soon as practicable. However, if deep-rooting perennial weeds are present, the best method of control may be to let them start growing and to wait until the food reserves in their root system are at a minimum before cutting down their aerial parts. J. C. Frazier[1] found that for bindweed in Kansas, this occurred about eight days after emergence, and that if the hoeing were delayed until this time, the weed was weakened much more than if the hoeing was done just after emergence.

There is also a close connection between the level of manuring, the amount of cultivations used and crop yield. Thus, E. W. Russell[2] found that on the Woburn light loam soil weed control was more important for sugar-beet growing under conditions of a low nitrogen supply than under a high one, as is shown in Table 140. Further, the high supply will often benefit the crop more than the weeds, so that it will grow faster than the weeds and smother them: it will, in fact, be its own weed controller.[3]

TABLE 140

The Effect of Weeds and Sulphate of Ammonia on the Yield of Sugar-beet

Woburn, 1939–43. Sulphate of ammonia at 3–4 cwt. per acre

Yield in tons clean beet per acre

Crop	No sulphate of ammonia	With sulphate of ammonia	Response to nitrogen
Clean weeded	11·1	15·0	3·9
Weedy	8·8	14·6	5·8
Depression due to weeds . .	2·3	0·4	—

[1] *Trans. Kansas Acad. Sci.*, 1941, **44**, 164. See also A. L. Bakke *et al.*, *J. Agric. Res.*, 1944, **69**, 137.
[2] *Proc. Inst. Brit. Agric. Engnrs.*, 1945, **3**, 99.
[3] For other examples of nitrogen fertilisers having this beneficial effect, see H. R. Cooper, *Indian Tea Assoc.*, Mem. 6, 1946 (for tea), and *Amer. Fert.*, 1947, **107**, No. 5, 12 (for maize).

Part of this effect is due, however, to the weeds removing nitrogen from the soil the beet would otherwise use. This effect has been found in experiments on stubble mulch cultivation methods in regions of rather high rainfall, for the method did not control weeds well and the crop, usually maize, responded better to nitrogen and sometimes potassium also than did that on clean ploughed land.[1]

However, this method of compensating for and controlling the harmful effects of weeds fails completely if the additional fertiliser benefits the weeds more than the crop. Thus, T. Eden[2] found that adding phosphate to tea on some soils increased the yield, but once a certain level of phosphate had been reached a weed that depressed the growth of tea began to respond better to the extra phosphate than did the tea. Hence, keeping the phosphate level in the soil under very careful control enabled the tea to get most of the phosphate it needed, whilst at the same time it prevented a weed that is difficult to eradicate from developing well.

This type of weed control is of particular importance for shallow rooting crops, such as tea and coffee, grown under conditions of high seasonal rainfall, for it is desirable to keep the soil between the bushes covered either with trash or vegetation, but the vegetation must not compete with the crop. Only recently has the importance of methods of weed control which obviate the necessity for cultivation been realised, so very few of such methods have yet been developed.

There is one common cultivation operation often done that is not connected with weed control, and that is rolling. This can be very valuable if the soil is rather dry, for by pressing the soil closer to the plant roots, or to the seed in the seed-bed, it also presses the water closer to the root or seed. Rolling, however, has a marked beneficial effect on some light soils and some thin soils over chalk. The benefit in the sands may be merely due to bringing the moisture closer to the root, but this certainly is not the cause of the benefit on the chalk soils. English experience is that compaction of these soils is essential, and though the cause of this has not yet been proved, it is possible that a part at least is due to the slightly poorer aeration, and hence higher carbon dioxide content of the soil air that it brings about; for, as was explained on p. 106, this will help to reduce the pH of the soil around the plant roots from 8·4, at which the plants will suffer from malnutrition due to the unavailability of phosphates and some trace elements, to a lower value at which these nutrients become more readily available.

[1] G. M. Browning *et al.*, *Proc. Soil Sci. Soc. Amer.*, 1944, **8**, 424; 1945, **9**, 142; C. L. Englehorn, *N. Dakota Agric. Expt. Sta.*, Bull. 341, 1946.
[2] *Emp. J. Expt. Agric.*, 1940, **8**, 269; *Tea Quart.*, 1947, **29**, 5; with T. E. T. Bond, *Emp. J. Expt. Agric.*, 1945, **13**, 141.

Mulches and Shade Trees

The practice of applying a layer of dead vegetable waste material, such as straw, hay or old grass, composts or farmyard manure, on to the surface of the soil around trees and bushes has been prevalent for a very long time in many parts of the world. These surface mulches can have very important effects on the conditions in the surface layers of the soil, and in consequence on the crops with shallow root systems. Thus, mulching has been widely used for many fruit trees and bushes and for tropical plantation crops with superficial root systems such as coffee and tea.

A surface mulch has two types of effect on the soil: a characteristic effect, from its being on the surface of the soil, and a general effect, which it would equally well have if it were ploughed into the soil, due to the plant nutrients set free as it decomposes. The primary specific effects of the mulch are confined to the superficial soil layers, which it keeps both cooler and at a more even temperature, and damper and more permeable to water than the unmulched soil.

The effect on soil temperature is shown most strikingly in tropical countries which have a very large diurnal temperature change. Thus, S. M. Gilbert,[1] working with coffee in Tanganyika, found that the temperature of the soil at 2 inches depth might vary by 12°C. during the day, whilst under a mulch it varied by 2° to 3°C. Some results of T. M. McCalla and F. L. Duley,[2] in Lincoln, Nebraska, also illustrate this effect. The average daily maximum temperature from June to September in the top inch of soil under maize was 31·2°C. if the soil was clean weeded, and 23·6°C. under a mulch of 8 tons per acre of straw, whilst the average daily minimum temperatures were 17·9°C. and 19·7°C. respectively, giving mean temperatures of about 24·5°C. and 21·6°C. respectively, with an average daily range of 13·3°C. and 3·9°C. respectively. The mulched soil is much cooler during the heat of the day and rather warmer during the night. This effect of a mulch in reducing the maximum temperature in the soil, without greatly affecting its minimum temperature, may also be shown by a dust mulch, that is, the loose surface layer of the soil produced by hoeing.[3]

The mulch slows down the rate of evaporation from a bare, wet soil very considerably for, as pointed out on p. 394, the rate of evaporation is controlled by the proportion of the energy absorbed by the soil which is used for evaporating water, and by the rate of removal of the water vapour from the region where it is being produced. So long as the wet

[1] *E. Afric. Agric. J.*, 1945, **11**, 75.
[2] *J. Amer. Soc. Agron.*, 1946, **38**, 75.
[3] I. de V. Malherbe, *Soil Fertility*, London, 1948.

soil is exposed to the air, the water vapour is rapidly removed by the general turbulence of the air, but if the water vapour must diffuse through a thin dry layer of soil, or through a mulch which keeps the air almost stationary, then the rate of diffusion limits the rate of evaporation, and this rate is about $\frac{1}{12}$ inch per week instead of $\frac{1}{8}$ to $\frac{1}{10}$ inch per day for normal hot days. Thus, whereas a wet, bare soil can lose $\frac{1}{2}$ inch of water in three to five days, it takes a mulched soil about six weeks to lose this amount, so that in hot climates a mulched soil can retain against evaporation much more of the water falling as rain than an unmulched.

The mulch also keeps the soil surface permeable. Rain-water can only reach the soil surface as a gentle stream of clear water, which causes a much smaller drop in permeability than if the soil surface itself was exposed to the beating rain. Thus, the mulch reduces the run-off of the rain and consequently reduces the amount of soil the water can carry away[1] and increases the proportion of the rain-water that percolates into the soil. Thus, not only is evaporation from the surface of the mulched soil reduced, but the amount of water infiltrating into it is increased. Hence, the water-supplying power of a soil can be considerably increased by mulching as is well illustrated by some of S. M. Gilbert's results on the mulching of coffee with banana leaves in Moshi, Tanganyika, given in Table 141.[2] The effect was large enough for the trees to be wilting on the clean weeded plots, but growing well on the mulched plots, at the time the first samples were taken.

The effect of mulches on the nitrate concentration in the soil is complex. During dry periods the increased moisture content under the mulch allows decomposition of the organic matter to continue with the production of nitrates for a longer time than in a bare soil, but once

TABLE 141

The Effect of Mulch on Conserving and Maintaining the Water Supply in the Soil

Percentage moisture in the soil on the oven-dry basis

Depth of soil in inches . .	After prolonged drought			After a rainy period		
	0–6	6–12	12–18	0–6	6–12	12–18
Mulched plots .	27·5	35·0	37·5	41·0	39·0	38·0
Clean weeded plots	15·5	22·0	26·0	30·0	33·0	32·5

[1] For an example of the effect of the weight of mulch applied on this control, see H. L Borst and R. Woodburn, *U.S. Dept. Agric., Tech. Bull.* 825, 1942.
[2] *E. Afric. Agric. J.*, 1945, **11**, 75.

the rains come the increased permeability of the soil may cause the nitrates to wash out rather more completely than from the unmulched. Again Gilbert's results on coffee soils in Tanganyika illustrate this, for during the dry season the mulched soils, in which coffee was growing, had nitrate nitrogen contents from 30 to 200 per cent more than on the clean weeded land, but had the same, or even less, during the rains. However, these results are not always found, particularly when wheat or maize straw is used as mulch, as is becoming customary in the Great Plains and the prairies of North America, for on the whole these mulches reduce the nitrate content of the soil there.[1]

Mulches can have an important influence on the weeds growing in the soil. Thus, Gilbert found that banana trash reduced the labour required each year for weeding coffee from the thirty-five to forty days per acre needed for clean weeding, to eight to fourteen days, and further that undesirable grasses, which needed forking out, did not establish themselves under the trash as they did on the clean weeded areas.

The mulch also has certain general effects on the soil due to its organic matter decomposing. The moister conditions under the mulch favour the soil micro-organisms and probably the smaller animals as well, and the decomposition they bring about improves and stabilises the soil structure, as described on p. 445. This again helps to maintain the permeability of the superficial soil layer. The animals by their activity in the surface soil will also increase the number of the larger channels through which the water can leach. Further, the decomposition continuously sets free plant nutrients in the surface soil whenever it is moist. This decomposition must not, however, go on too fast, nor, in tropical regions where termites are common, should they consist of materials with too high a cellulose content, otherwise the mulch will soon disappear. Thus, relatively slowly decomposable material should be used, such as straw, for example. Gilbert has shown that, for coffee in Tanganyika, some grasses have little value as a mulch for this reason, whilst coarse material, such as banana slashings, are very valuable.

A further effect of mulches is that they increase the amount of exchangeable potassium in the soil, although the reason for this has not been established. Thus, I. W. Wander and J. H. Gourley[2] found that it was increased considerably to a depth of 8 inches in two years under a heavy straw mulch, and to a depth of 24 inches in twenty to

[1] T. M. McCalla and J. C. Russel, *Nebraska Agric. Exp. Sta., Res. Bull.* 131, 1943; C. A. Mooers *et al., Soil Sci.,* 1946, **66**, 307.

[2] *J. Amer. Soc. Agron.,* 1938, **30**, 438; *Proc. Amer. Soc. Hort. Sci.,* 1943, **42**, 1; 1945, **46**, 21. For similar results in short periods, see R. E. Stephenson and C. E. Schuster, *Soil Sci.,* 1945, **59**, 219; 1946, **61**, 219.

thirty years. In the latter examples the soil under the mulch contained about 490 parts of exchangeable potassium per million of soil to about this depth, but fell rapidly to about a fifth of this value below it, whilst the exchangeable potassium in the unmulched soil fell to this value after a few inches. The extra potassium may have come from the straw, but potassium is the only mineral element showing this strong downward percolation. Further, a grass mulch, made by putting land down to grass and mowing it with a gang mower, such as is used on golf greens, and leaving the grass cuttings in place, also increases the available potassium in the soil. This method is used in many apple orchards, both in this country and overseas, and it causes the apple trees to take up much more potassium, and also more phosphate, from the soil than if the orchard is kept either clean weeded or sown to annual cover crops which are ploughed in.[1] Hence, this extra uptake of potassium, and possibly also of phosphate, appears to be a specific effect of the mulch due to some cause yet unrecognised.

These effects of mulches show the reasons why they are so valuable with shallow rooting crops in hot weather, for all these effects help to maintain the surface layers of the soil as a suitable environment for root growth. Indeed, for some of the very shallow rooting crops the root system tends to develop from the soil surface into the base of the mulch.

A surface mulch can have another very important function for use in helping to establish small seeded crops in hot climates, for the surface inch of soil is a very poor medium for seed germination if exposed to the heat of the tropical sun. This technique can be very useful in getting a grass or legume cover established on eroded or bare soils.[2]

Some of the benefits of a mulch can be obtained by growing shade trees which will protect the surface of the soil and low-growing crops from the direct heat of the sun and will to some extent break the fall of the raindrops before they hit the soil. Plate XXXIV gives a good idea of the kind of intensity of shade used, in this case for coffee growing at 5,000 feet elevation in Kenya. The benefits from this practice of shade trees is difficult to assess, as several other factors besides shade are often involved. Thus, shade trees are commonly leguminous plants and hence they help to enrich the soil in nitrogen—if not through their roots, then through their leaf fall—and the practice of growing shade trees is often bound up with that of regularly slashing them and using the slashings as a surface mulch. Again, shade trees often act as windbreaks, and will therefore reduce the rate of transpiration from the

[1] See, for example, M. B. Davis and H. Hill, *Dom. Canada Dept. Agric.*, Publ. 802 (*Tech Bull.* 65), 1948; C. Bould *et al.*, *Long Ashton Ann. Rep.*, 1948, 37.
[2] B. H. Hendrickson and R. B. Crowley, *J. Amer. Soc. Agron.*, 1941, **33**, 690 (lespedeza in Georgia); G. E. Glendening, ibid., 1942, **34**, 797 (grasses in Arizona).

protected crop during periods of strong drying winds, they probably raise the night minimum temperatures over the shaded crop somewhat, and they may reduce the incidence of insect pests, but they compete for water with the crop. More work must be done before the detailed circumstances in which shade trees benefit such crops as tea, coffee and cocoa plantations are known.

CHAPTER XXXVII

THE CONTROL OF SOIL FERTILITY IN PRACTICE

PROBLEMS IN THE control of soil fertility have been discussed in passing all through this book, and in this final chapter a few of the more essential conditions for fertility will be summarised.

The object of trying to increase, or to conserve, fertility is to obtain as large a yield as is economic, or as is possible, of whatever crops are grown; but high fertility often has the further consequence that it increases the range of crops a farmer can grow. Soil fertility naturally only plays a small part in the choice of crops, for the climate is the most important factor, and, in particular, the rainfall, the length of the frost-free period, and minimum night temperatures during the growing season. The control exercised by the first two are very severe. Drought and prolonged frost prevent large areas of the earth's surface being cultivated, whilst night frosts merely restrict the choice of crop. Again, unless there is a certain depth of soil, crop production becomes precarious, and this, together with the low temperatures and often high winds and heavy rainfall, prevents or severely limits the cultivation of large areas of mountain land over the world. These areas show how climate or depth of soil prevents crops from making use of whatever fertility is stored in these soils.

A soil can only be fertile if it is a favourable environment for root growth. The roots of most agricultural crops need the following conditions for good development: they must have an adequate supply of oxygen and a low concentration of carbon dioxide; and the pH of the soil must lie in a fairly definite range, bounded on the upper side by the root's ability to extract nutrients from the soil, and usually on the lower by the concentration of certain cations such as aluminium and manganese, which are adsorbed under these conditions in sufficiently large quantities to harm the roots or the plant itself.

The oxygen and carbon dioxide needs of the root system depend on the soil temperature and the activity of the root system. There is no evidence that the root system is ever harmed by too high an oxygen content in the soil air, but it will most definitely suffer if the oxygen content falls too low. The principal exception to this rule is rice, whose roots need only very little oxygen in the soil air, for they appear to be supplied with it through special tissues in the stem and root. Most root systems do not seem to need carbon dioxide in the soil air, and most are harmed if it rises to more than a few per cent. But a moderate carbon dioxide concentration, up to 1 to 2 per cent in extreme cases, can be very desirable in soils containing free calcium carbonate or much exchangeable sodium, for this helps to reduce the pH of the soil to below 8, or even below 7·5, at which pH the root systems of most plants can extract the phosphates and other minor elements they need. The actual carbon dioxide concentrations plant roots can tolerate depends to some extent on the root, but it also depends on the soil temperature, for the higher the temperature the lower is the concentration that begins to harm them.

A low oxygen content of the soil air, or a very low air content in the soil can have other undesirable consequences, for the microbial population in the subsoil will set up strong reducing conditions there, maintaining a high carbon dioxide concentration and producing reduced compounds, such as sulphides, which are very toxic to most roots. Thus, water-logging, a high water table, or a soil with such a fine texture that it has a very restricted air space are all undesirable; and most crops can only be profitably grown on soils in which water-logging is prevented, and a high water table lowered by drainage. One can do little to improve fine textured soils with a very small air space, except restrict the cropping to those crops that suffer least from this condition.

Low oxygen and high carbon dioxide concentrations in the soil air and water also affect the composition of the organisms inhabiting the soil, for only groups tolerant of anaerobic conditions can make active growth, or even exist at all, and these groups are mainly confined to the bacteria. The more general aerobic population will be confined to the surface of such soils, and the composition of its larger members will be restricted because they cannot escape unfavourable climatic conditions of heat, cold or drought by penetrating into the subsoil. Thus, most species of earthworms are absent from such soils.

Another harmful consequence of poor drainage in arid regions is that the quantity of salts in the soil begins to become sufficiently high to affect plant growth, and often to restrict very considerably the species of plants which can grow. Not only may the salt content rise, but so may the content of exchangeable sodium ions, with the consequence that the soil may become very alkaline, badly aerated and difficult to drain.

The pH of the soil affects the root system mainly indirectly, for the root or plant suffers from consequences of the pH before the actual hydrogen- or hydroxyl-ion concentration has any harmful effect. Thus, few roots can absorb enough phosphate, iron, zinc or manganese from the soil with a pH much above 8 for the plant's needs. And at low pHs the root system suffers from poisoning by soluble aluminium and manganese ions on the one hand, and from shortage of available calcium ions on the other, before the hydrogen-ion concentration begins to be harmful.

Thus a soil can only be a suitable environment for plant roots if it is adequately drained and aerated, if its salt content and content of exchangeable sodium ions is low, and if its *p*H falls in a suitable range. Hence, drainage and dressings of lime or of sulphur or gypsum may be necessary to bring a soil into a suitable condition for good root development. If these conditions are not properly fulfilled the choice of crop will be unduly restricted, and so will its root system. Hence, it will be liable to suffer from frosts, droughts and high temperatures that would not affect a deeper root system, and these harmful effects are all more serious in hot regions than in cool, and particularly in moist, cool regions, for under such conditions a shallow root system may be able to carry a full crop because at no time will it have to build up an appreciable water deficit in the soil.

The root system needs not only a suitable environment in which to grow, it must also take up enough water and nutrients for the crop to give a good yield of whatever part is required. Of the nutrient shortages that limit crop yields over the world as a whole, nitrogen and phosphorus are the most important, though lack of available calcium and potassium is also important.

Lack of water probably limits the total food production in the world more than any other single factor, although it is relatively unimportant in a humid country such as Great Britain. It is directly responsible for the sterility of the deserts, and for the very low yields and restricted choice of crops in the semi-deserts and steppes.

Drought only begins to affect plant growth appreciably when the root system has extracted all the readily available water from the soil in the root zone, by which time it has also extracted some from the soil below. The deeper the root system, and the more thoroughly it ramifies through the soil, the greater is the amount of water it can withdraw from the soil, and the longer the crop can withstand a drought without suffering. There are very few methods available for deepening the root system of the plant. Lowering the water table and incorporating lime in the subsoil are both helpful if water-logging or acidity limit the depth of root penetration. Breaking up a hard pan is also helpful, but just how indurated or compact a pan must be before the roots cease to be able to penetrate it is uncertain. A pan may harm the root system more by impeding the drainage of water, and hence allowing reducing conditions to prevail and the carbon dioxide content to rise to too high a level, than by its actually preventing the roots penetrating through it.

Again, in heavy clay soils the root system cannot always ramify through the clay uniformly enough to extract all the available water in the root zone, and it is possible that in such circumstances deep tillage may encourage this ramification, but the technique for doing this has not yet been established.

Very little can be done to increase the water-holding power of the soil, for even large additions of bulky organic manures have little effect, and probably can never have an effect greater than would correspond to deepening the root zone by 6 inches. But they can have a very important local effect, for an extra small amount of water, in the neighbourhood of a seed or a young plant during a drought, may allow it to rapidly deepen its root system at this critical time.

But the removal of water from the soil by the crop is only one side of the water régime: it is equally important to allow sufficient water to penetrate into the soil for crop growth. This is the problem of maintaining the surface of the soil in such a condition that rains, even if they fall as torrential storms, shall be able to penetrate into the soil whenever necessary. This maintenance of surface permeability is undoubtedly one of the most difficult problems farmers have to face in regions subject to such storms. This does not mean that, for as far as the farmer is concerned, all the rain must enter the soil, for as soon as the water deficit in the soil has been made good it may be desirable for most of the remainder of the water to run off, provided it does not remove too much soil, for unnecessary leaching of water through the root zone removes the nitrates from the soil, and hence wastes some of the soil's store of available nitrogen. Run-off may complicate the job of the engineers in the river catchment boards, in that flood control is the more difficult the quicker the surplus water finds its way into the rivers. However, efficient drainage systems may give them just the same problems, for storm-water rapidly percolates through most well-drained soils into the drains.

Nitrogen and phosphate probably are the two plant foods that most limit crop yields in regions where water is not the limiting factor. Phosphate shortage occurs in areas all over the world, and may limit yields even in dry areas, as, for example, in the wheat-growing districts of Australia. Shortage of available nitrogen is characteristic of the humid regions, although A. E. V. Richardson[1] considers that even in some semi-arid regions shortage of nitrogen is as important a factor as shortage of water in causing the low yields obtained. Recent field experiments all over the world have consistently shown how once water is plentiful, crop yields can be increased, sometimes very markedly, by adding available nitrogen compounds to the soil. In fact, in many

[1] With H. C. Gurney, *Emp. J. Exp. Agric.*, 1933, **1**, 193, 325.

soils and for many crops, the nitrogen level in the soil is the most important factor controlling the crop yield.[1] But nitrogen differs from phosphates in that if the phosphate status of the soil is low, a phosphate fertiliser must in general be added, whilst if the nitrogen status is low, either leguminous crops can be grown, which directly increase the amount of available nitrogen compounds in the soil, or nitrogen-poor but otherwise readily decomposable organic matter can be added so that the nitrogen-fixing bacteria in the soil can increase the supply, or the soil surface can be left wet so nitrogen-fixing blue-green algae can develop. Of these three mechanisms, the first is of very great agricultural importance, the second is probably mainly of importance in forests and in some pastures, and the third probably only in paddy rice fields. But it is not always profitable to rely entirely on biological methods for increasing the nitrogen supply of the soil, and the need for nitrogen fertilisers is rapidly being appreciated all over the world. There is little doubt that crop yields in the humid regions could be considerably increased if the farmers could be persuaded to adapt their systems of farming for making the best use of these nitrogen fertilisers.

The conservation of fertility usually involves, on the one hand, putting back into the soil the nutrients removed by the crop or leached out by drainage water, and on the other preventing any appreciable movement of the soil. Fertility cannot necessarily be maintained merely by putting back all the crop residues even if this is possible, for this does not replace the losses by leaching. But proper conservation, and the return of all crop residues and of the excreta of animals feeding on the crops, reduces the drain on the reserves of plant food. In areas where the temperature and rainfall are high, and the minerals composing the soil particles are weathering fast enough to provide much of the minerals needed by the crop, a stable system of farming, for as far as nutrients are concerned, can be assured if an adequate number of leguminous crops are taken.

Another method of ensuring stability of nutrient status, which can only be practised in the valleys of certain rivers, is to allow fertile silt carried by the river to be deposited on the land. Thus, much Egyptian soil has been kept fertile for several millennia by plant nutrients derived from the weathering and erosion of rocks in the Abyssinian highlands. Here is a case where the most efficient way of tapping the plant nutrients produced may not be to grow crops on the site of their production, that is, on the thin soils of the high mountains, but to let these materials be washed down into the deep alluvial soils of the valley.

[1] See, for example, H. L. Richardson, *Emp. J. Exp. Agric.*, **14**, 1, 109, 175.

The prevention or at least the control of water erosion on agricultural lands depends on keeping the soil surface permeable, and ensuring that whatever water cannot penetrate the soil runs off the surface slowly as a thin uniform sheet. This control may involve developing a suitable method of farming to ensure that the soil surface is protected from the actual falling raindrops, and that enough decomposable organic manure is used, or long enough leys are taken, to ensure the water-stability of the crumb is as high as possible. Strip cropping on the contour, sometimes with terraces, is often the method to be used, and here, as in the prevention of wind-blowing, the mouldboard plough can be a very undesirable cultivation implement because of the bare soil surface it leaves.

The prevention of wind-blowing consists in preventing the wind blowing across long lengths of bare, unprotected soil. The soil can be protected by planting quite narrow strips of crops across the direction of the strongest winds, of cultivating the soil so that as much as possible of the previous year's crop residues are left on the surface of the soil, or are anchored into the soil with most of the residues being above the soil. Or it can be protected, but not very effectively, by running ridges across the direction of the wind. None of these methods, however, give much protection if the land is subjected to a drought lasting several years.

Soil organisms and soil organic matter usually only affect crop growth indirectly. One of the principal consequences of the soil organisms feeding on the soil organic matter is the continuous conversion of nutrients from a form in which they are relatively immobile and unavailable into one in which they are mobile and available to the plant. The organic matter is an excellent reservoir of all plant nutrients, and in this form they are relatively immobile in the soil, and the soil organisms slowly release the plant nutrients from the organic matter into a mobile form that is available for the growing crop. Besides this primary function, some organisms have other functions, such as the mixing of the dead plant litter that falls on to the surface of uncultivated soil with the superficial layers of the soil—one of the principal functions of the surface-feeding earthworms.

The soil organisms have another function, the details of which are not fully understood, which is the mellowing of the soil crumbs in clay soils, and the binding together of sand particles in light soils. They either produce, as a by-product of their metabolism, chemical substances that bind the soil particles together, or they bring the soil particles and organic substances into intimate contact with each other. This increases the stability of the distribution of pore sizes during wetting, and the resistance of the soil crumbs and clods to break-up by slaking. Hence, they help to improve and maintain the permeability of the surface soil and the goodness of aeration in the subsoil during wet periods. By mellowing the tilth of the clay soils, the clods crumble more easily, and by binding together the sand and silt particles, sandy soils are less liable to blow and to cap.

The general soil organisms have another important action in that they tend to kill any organism not adapted to life in the soil, and since few of the plant pathogenic organisms are so adapted, the general population plays an important part in the control of many plant diseases.

The Management of Sandy Soils in England

The general problems facing the light- and heavy-land farmers in England will serve as an illustration of the principles just discussed. The great problems facing the light-land farmer are to obtain enough water in the seed-bed for the crop to get started, to provide an adequate amount of plant food in such a way that it will not get washed out of the soil too quickly, and, in some places, to prevent the soil from blowing.

The best way of increasing the water-holding power of the seed-bed, and also of maintaining an adequate supply of nutrients without too great a loss by leaching, is to maintain as high a level of organic matter in the surface soil as possible. The old method of doing this was to fold sheep over the land. Between two and four green crops might be taken during twelve to twenty-four months, and each would be eaten off by sheep and then this was followed by two or more years in arable crops. The sheep and the green crops not only added organic matter to the soil, but the sheep compacted and often puddled the surface layer of the soil. This somewhat increased the carbon dioxide content of the soil air, which is of importance on all light soils containing free calcium carbonate, as it helps to reduce the pH of the soil, and hence increase the availability of some of the plant nutrients.

The main problem at the present time on many of these soils is to develop a system of farming which is adapted to present-day economic conditions and which is technically as satisfactory as the sheepfold. Leys left down for several years and grazed with cattle are technically as satisfactory as the sheepfold, but they often involve fencing and watering large areas of land, sometimes in districts where water is scarce. The fibrous roots of the ley will often bind soil particles together for three to four years after it has been ploughed out.

Another aspect of the problem of conserving water at sowing or planting time is weed control, for light land encourages both deep-rooting weeds and weeds that multiply from a spreading root system or from underground rhizomes. Weed control may be particularly troublesome during winter on light land compared with heavy, because light soils are so much better aerated than heavy that weeds grow in them for a long period in the late autumn and early winter, and start growing again earlier in late winter and early spring; and in a number of years weeds will, in fact, make appreciable growth throughout the whole winter. These weeds can be killed or set back by suitable cultivation before the seed is sown, but in a dry spring the process of doing this may dry out the surface soil so much that the seed cannot germinate until after the drought has broken. An important principle in weed control in areas of adequate rainfall is to keep the land cropped, for the crop, even if only quite small, discourages many weeds. These catch crops not only help to control weeds, but they also prevent the leaching out of nutrients, reduce the liability of the soil to blow, and add a little more organic matter to the soil, when they are ploughed in. Catch-cropping is therefore an integral part of light-land husbandry whenever the rainfall is sufficient, and is, in many parts of the country, confined to light land. In the days of the sheepfold these would always have been fed off, but now they are often ploughed in.

The secret of light-land farming is therefore to prevent weeds multiplying on the land, for it is much easier to get a moist seed-bed in dry weather when there is no necessity to have to use weed-killing operations such as ploughing or deep harrowing—operations that cause a large loss of water from the surface soil by evaporation.

Finally, light land can suffer from over-liming very easily. Ideally light land should have a pH between 6 and 6·5, and whenever it is necessary to lime it should be given in small dressings, at frequent intervals if necessary, but one should never aim at bringing the pH up to 7.

Thus, one can summarise the problems of the light-land farmer as maintaining the humus content of the surface soil as high as possible, keeping a growing crop on the land for as large a part of the year as possible, and keeping the land so clean that the absolute minimum of cultivations are necessary to get a seed-bed free from weeds whenever the weather is dry.

The Management of the English Clay Soils

These soils present an entirely different set of problems from the sands. The two great difficulties in clay-land farming are to keep the soil as dry as possible during the winter six months when transpiration is low, and to obtain a suitable tilth for drilling seeds at the appropriate times of the year. The effect of improving the drainage on the stand of young wheat or beans through a wet winter can be most striking, and an efficient drainage system and deep cultivations help to ensure that the surface soil is well drained and well aerated throughout this season. The importance of this is obvious, for, on the one hand, water-logging keeps the root system very shallow and poorly developed, and hence causes the young plant to be partially starved of nutrients, and, on the other, water-logged soils heave badly during frosts and so break a large proportion of these poorly developed roots.

The English clay soils fall into two sharply contrasting classes with respect to their ease of drainage. The genuine clays have normally a fairly good stable subsoil structure, and a properly installed drainage system will function efficiently for a long time, since there are a large number of stable drainage channels. The silty clays, which may easily be mistaken for the true clays on a cursory inspection, are so high in silt that they do not possess a stable subsoil structure nor stable drainage channels through the subsoil. Hence, it is much more difficult to get the water into the drains, and the water that enters is silty, so that the drains will soon be blocked with silt unless proper steps are taken to trap the silt. These soils are probably some of the most difficult to manage in the country, and the only way it seems possible to improve them is to lay them down to long leys and then to take a few arable crops while the subsoil is still well supplied with drainage channels formed by the roots of the ley.

Clays also differ from the sands in the case of cultivation. Sands can be cultivated on almost any day of the year, and rarely are there any problems in getting a tilth suitable for sowing, provided there is enough moisture for the seed to germinate. Clays, on the other hand, can only be cultivated when the moisture content of the soil lies between comparatively narrow limits, and if it is cultivated at the wrong time, or in the wrong way, the surface will be composed of large lumps that are plastic when wet and hard when dry, and that cannot be com-minuted into crumbs of a suitable size for a seed-bed. Hence, the primary problem of the clay-land farmer is to choose the right time and the right implement to do his cultivations, and since there are only a limited number of days during which cultivations are possible, he needs more and heavier cultivating machinery per 100 acres than his light-land colleague. Cultivating heavy land when it is moist, and leaving the clods exposed to the sun, wind, and rain, and in particular to the frost, help to produce a crumbly layer of soil on the surface; and if one wants to prepare a seed-bed, it is essential that no deep cultivations be done once this tilthy layer has begun to form.

Most of the English clay soils are naturally low in phosphate. Thus, even if the surface soil has received generous dressings of phosphate, deep ploughing, by bringing up fresh subsoil, may cause crop failures unless the phosphate deficiency of this subsoil is rectified. Again, much of the clays had been in pasture for many years before the 1939–45 war, during which time they received very little phosphate. As a consequence, they were so short of phosphate that, when the pastures were ploughed out during the war, arable crops would fail unless generous dressings of phosphate were given, much to the surprise of many farmers who had expected to cash the fertility stored up by the grass. Even the pastures themselves would have been improved if they had received adequate dressings of phosphate, as is shown in Plate XXXV, which illustrates the effect of adding, in this case, ground rock phosphate to a typical phosphate-starved acid pasture on the London Clay in Essex.[1] The phosphate encouraged the development of wild white clover and the good pasture grasses at the expense of such poor grasses as the bents (*Agrostis*) and *Aira caespitosa*.

Heavy land holds much more available water than very light land, but, even so, seed-beds in the spring can easily be dried out if they are over-cultivated during drying periods. Hence, again, the great value of preventing weeds growing or germinating in the seed-bed, and the value of general good management which helps to ensure this.

Nutrient levels can be maintained more easily in clays than sands, for they hold the nutrients much more retentively against drainage. Clay soils also are never as well aerated as sands, so the pH of even a calcareous clay never rises high enough to affect the availability of phosphates or of trace elements. Hence, clay soils cannot be over-limed, and in fact the mellowness of the tilth is often said to be improved by very heavy dressings of chalk. Again, the humus content of heavy soils is less important than that of light, for whereas it is practically impossible to farm many sands without regard to the humus and fibre content of their surface soils, it is perfectly feasible to farm clays, apparently indefinitely, without the use of farmyard manure or leys.

The importance of farmyard manure, leys, and lime or chalk in helping to improve the crumbliness or mellowness of clay clods or crumbs in practice is still undecided. Farmers have successfully farmed clay lands without adding humus or fibre to the soil, and without ensuring the presence of free calcium carbonate in the soil, though this success may only have been achieved by men who are very skilful cultivators.

[1] G. Scott Robertson, *J. Min. Agric.*, 1922, **29**, 519, 600.

Clay lands are often spoken of as cold soils, and certainly crops make much less growth during the six winter months on clay soils than they do on sandy soils in the same district. Thus, catch-cropping is impracticable on clays, and winter-sown crops must often be sown one or even two months earlier on clays than on sands if they are to make enough growth to stand the winter frosts. In the same way, spring-sown crops must often be sown considerably later on clays, because they are still too cold and wet for seeds to germinate, although conditions on the lighter soils are passable. But the cause of this shorter growing season may be the poorer aeration rather than the lower temperatures of wet clays compared with sands.

Clay soils have had rather a chequered agricultural history. Originally covered with oak forest and hazel undergrowth, they were early reclaimed for agriculture purposes by draining, applications of lime[1] and, later, of ground bones. Wheat and beans were the great clay crops, and in the early part of the last century, under the combined influence of high prices, large drainage schemes and artificial stimulus to enclosure, great areas came into cultivation, so that now only little unreclaimed clay remains, excepting where the forest was preserved for hunting. Crops grew well but ripened late; a wet harvest was a terrible calamity. Bare fallowing was always necessary once in four years, and any of the intervening years might, if wet, be lost by the difficulty of getting on the land to sow the crop. When the price of wheat fell in the eighties of the last century many of these soils went out of cultivation and became covered with a mixed growth of grass and weed, which was grazed by stock and gradually deteriorated as the old drains choked up and the land became more and more waterlogged. *Aira caespitosa*, bent grass (*Agrostis vulgaris*), yellow rattle (*Rhinanthus Crista-galli*), and in drier places the quaking grass (*Briza media*) and ox-eye daisy (*Chrysanthemum leucanthemum*) are among the commoner plants on these neglected fields; after continued neglect thorns and other trees spring up and the land reverts to wild woodland; the only relics of the past are the field names and the high ridges or "lands" made years ago to facilitate drainage. But much of this rough land has recently been improved and converted into useful pasture or arable land by attending to the drainage, and to the lime and phosphate status of the soil on the one hand, and by the introduction of the crawler tractor and heavy cultivating implements on the other.

Thus, the problems of clay-land farming are keeping the surface soil well drained during the winter, and having an adequate amount of machinery available so that as much of the land as possible can be

[1] For example, see *The Inrichment of the Weald of Kent*, by R.I., 1625 (attributed in the 1636 and later editions to Gervase Markham).

cultivated when it is in a condition to fall down easily to a crumbly condition. Heavy-land farming should, therefore, be power-farming wherever possible.

Some Principles Involved in the Management of Tropical Soils

The management of tropical soils involves quite different sets of principles from that of English soils: both the climate and the soils are different. In the tropics there are no marked seasonal changes of temperature, such as occur between winter and summer in the higher latitudes, so the soils there usually have a more even, and a considerably higher average temperature. The rainfall, again, in the tropics has a different distribution from that in the temperate regions, for the rain tends to fall in heavy storms, and to be confined to one or to two rainy seasons in the year, with intervening dry seasons of severe drought. Further, as the annual rainfall increases, so usually does the length of the rainy season with a corresponding shortening of the dry.

The leached soils of the tropics differ from those in the temperate regions by the much higher proportion of kaolinite clay they contain. If the parent material is low in iron and aluminium, and the site is ancient and uneroded, kaolinite clay may be practically the only mineral present in the soil, and such soils will have a poor, unstable structure and a very low base exchange capacity. But if the parent material contains much iron or aluminium, then the soil will contain their oxides and hydroxides, which will cement clusters of kaolinite particles into firm and larger aggregates, thus improving the soil structure and permeability, though often at the cost of increasing the power of the soil to fix phosphates. Further, the subsoil of such soils may contain these hydroxides in such a form that it is fairly soft and plastic in its natural condition, but dries out into hard bricks that only weather down very slowly to a friable soil when exposed to the sun.

The basic principle of managing these soils is, therefore, to devise a system of farming that involves the minimum of clean cultivation—for this leaves the soil bare—and that maintains a high organic matter content in the surface soil—for this not only helps to hold bases against leaching and phosphate against fixation by the active iron and aluminium compounds present, but it is also a source of plant nutrients in itself and it helps to maintain the structure and permeability of the surface soil.

The problems involved in cultivating a soil with a minimum amount of clean cultivation are still largely unexplored in the humid tropics. Methods of soil cultivation under a surface mulch, similar to the stubble mulch techniques that are being developed in the wheat lands of

Canada and America, may be found applicable; but the best basis for future developments may be that underlying traditional native agriculture, namely, mixed cropping, in which the land carries crops planted and coming to maturity at different times, and of dibbling or planting the crop into a soil that has only received a very shallow cultivation with a hoe.

Soil organic matter and soil structure can be maintained in some areas by the use of farmyard manure and composts, but the dressings of manure needed are so high, up to 30 tons per acre annually,[1] that this method is mainly confined to vegetable gardens. However, it can also be maintained in land under permanent plantation crops by leaving, as a mulch on the soil surface, slashings from trees or crops grown and cut largely for this purpose.

The usual method of maintaining soil organic matter is, however, to use an alternation of a few years of tillage crops with a few of soil-resting crops, that is, crops not requiring any cultivation. This method is therefore similar in principle to that of alternate husbandry in England, but it differs greatly in detail. It may be very similar, for provided the soil is adequately supplied with nutrients, or adequate amounts of fertiliser are used, and there is an adequate rainfall, then the land can be put down to grass for a period of years. These leys are usually planted, not sown, but they differ from temperate leys in that there are not yet any tropical pasture legumes corresponding to the clovers and lucerne of the temperate regions. In East Africa, grasses of the *Pennisetum* and *Cynodon* genera are often used, including elephant (*P. purpureum*) and kikuyu (*P. clandestinum*) grasses. These leys are down for 3 to 6 years and their primary function is to restore the structure of the soil: they are most valuable if they are planted before the structure has deteriorated too badly.[2]

The much more common way of putting land down to a resting crop is to let it revert to natural vegetation, which will be a grass or savannah (grass with bush) type in the drier[3] and a forest type in the wetter regions—a practice commonly known as *shifting cultivation*. The problems of importance here are to ensure that a desirable type of natural vegetation is quickly established, that is, one which covers the soil surface, increases the organic matter content and nutrient status of the soil and improves its structure as quickly as possible, and one which can easily be killed when the land next comes into arable. On the

---

[1] For an example of the efficacy of dressing of this order in Kenya, see M. D. Graham, *E. Afric. Agric. J.*, 1945, **11**, 3.

[2] M. D. Graham, *E. Afric. Agric. J.*, 1945, **11**, 3, has given an example from Kenya of a rotation based on leys like this.

[3] This practice is sometimes referred to as fallowing, but is entirely different from the European practice of bare fallowing which, naturally, must not be practised in these regions.

whole a desirable type of vegetation usually regenerates if the land was well managed and its condition was still reasonable at the end of the arable break, whereas undesirable species, such as the *Imperata* type of grass, come in if the land is left in too poor a condition. Further, the last crop planted may influence the rate of establishment of the desirable species. Thus C. E. Kellogg[1] quotes the findings of workers in the Belgian Congo that in some areas bananas and cassava encourage the rapid regeneration of forest, which is wanted, whilst groundnuts encourage sparse, and therefore inferior savannah that is only slowly invaded by the forest.

The re-establishment of the natural vegetation takes place quicker if the cultivated areas are either small plots or narrow strips surrounded by the natural vegetation. Small plots are customary in much native agriculture, but long narrow strips allow a more systematic and intensive use of the land, and at the same time can give better protection against erosion. Kellogg, in the F.A.O. bulletin already quoted, has described such an improved system of shifting cultivation that is being developed in parts of the Belgian Congo, and two of his photographs illustrating stages in this system are reproduced in Plate XXXVIII. The first shows a mixed crop of cassava and bananas, with the natural forest in the background and the second shows the forest invading a strip after the last harvest has been taken.

The number of years the land must be left in a resting crop depends on the poverty of the soil and the goodness of management during the tillage period. Very impoverished soils, such as occur in the wetter areas where forest is the natural vegetation, need a longer rest than soils with a higher reserve of plant nutrients, such as often occur in the drier areas where grass or savannah is the natural vegetation. Hence 3 to 6 years in grass is often sufficient, whilst 10 to 20 years in forest may be necessary. Such short periods in grass are, however, only effective if its grazing or burning is controlled, for if the grass is grazed too heavily, it cannot develop a deep or extensive root system, hence cannot bring up plant nutrients from the deeper layers of the subsoil, nor add sufficiently large quantities of organic matter to the superficial layers of the surface soil to improve the structure. These methods therefore can only be effective if the land is neither over-populated with stock nor human beings, for over-grazing renders the resting period largely ineffective in restoring the soil condition, and over-population prevents the land from being kept out of cultivation long enough for this restoration to take place.

The problem of bringing land back into cultivation after the resting

[1] *Soil Conservation*, F.A.O. Agricultural Studies No. 4, 1948. This bulletin describes some of these shifting cultivation practices.

Plate XXXV

Poor grass pasture on acid London Clay, untreated (*top*) and dressed with 10 cwt. per acre of ground rock (Gafsa) phosphate (*bottom*). Phosphate given February 1918, pasture photographed August 1919 at Horndon-on-the-Hill, Essex

(*p. 652*)

Plate XXXVI

The Ross Lowlands from the slopes of Linton Hill, looking west towards Penyard Hill and Ross
(p. 657)

Plate XXXVII

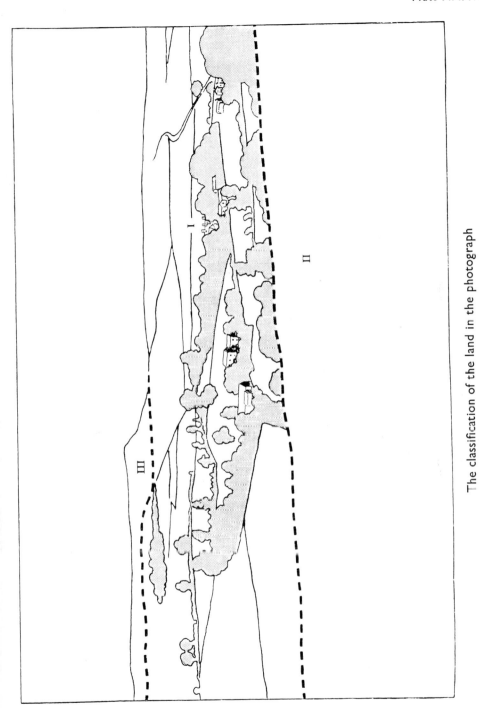

The classification of the land in the photograph

Category I: The large arable fields with sandy loam soils on gentle rolling topography
Category II: The foreground shows land having rather a steep slope and a shallow soil, which is carrying a patchy crop probably because of drought

Category III: The steep wooded slopes of Penyard Hill, in the background

(p. 657)

Plate XXXVIII

Mixed cropping with cassavas and bananas in an improved agricultural rotation in the Congo

Forest invading an old cassava and banana field, to begin the forest fallow which will last for several years. Some forest trees are allowed to remain on the land to give shade and regeneration (Congo)

(p. 656)

period is usually solved by firing the vegetation when it is dead, preferably at the beginning of the rains, if it is mainly grass; and cutting it down and burning it, if it is forest. Presumably burning the vegetation, particularly the grass, is rather a wasteful operation, but the problems involved in composting it are considerable. In the first place it mainly consists of cellulose and lignin, a great proportion of which must be oxidised away before the nitrogen content of the compost is high enough for it to be put on the land, and in the second place termites may use much of the more cellulosic material as food, so becoming much too numerous.

The two general aims of crop husbandry in the tropics thus seem to be to keep the soil surface protected from the sun and rain for as long as possible each year, and to choose a system of management in which some of the crops grown will enrich the surface soil in plant nutrients and allow its structure to regenerate after it has begun to deteriorate under tillage crops. The former is achieved by mixed cropping, by methods of planting not involving much cultivation, by methods of weed control based on suitable rotations rather than on clean weeding, and by the use of mulches, cover crops and shade trees. The second is achieved by converting the maximum amount of unwanted plant and animal refuse into manure and compost, by the use of adequately manured leguminous crops, and by the control of the rate of regeneration of the natural vegetation, and its type, through the use of suitable rotations and a proper lay-out of the cultivated and resting areas.

Soil Fertility and Productivity: A Summary

The preceding discussions have shown that the agricultural uses to which land can be put are largely controlled by factors such as the climate of the area, the topography of the land, the depth of the soil, the chemical processes of its formation and certain of its properties which are directly dependent on the parent material from which it has been derived. Some of these factors restrict the yield of all crops in the area, and others restrict the range of crops which will give good growth or economic returns. One of the most thankless and difficult tasks of an agricultural adviser or research officer is to tell farmers that they are trying to grow a crop on a soil quite unsuited to it, when they can see it growing very profitably elsewhere in their area.

Plate XXXVI is a photograph of a typical Herefordshire landscape, which illustrates the control that topography and soil depth together can have on the productivity and range of cropping of that area. The large arable fields in the centre of the photograph are situated on deep, fairly level and well-drained soils, so this area is obviously well suited to large-scale arable farming. The field in the foreground, which is on a moderate slope and has a shallow, stony soil, is also in arable but is less suited to arable farming than the lower lands, both because its ability to supply water to the crop during dry periods is strictly limited and also because cultivations are more expensive, particularly if precautions were to be taken to control soil and water erosion. In the background, the steep slopes of Penyard Hill are in woodland, because the land is much too steep for cultivation and the soil is too shallow for pasture. There is very little a farmer can do to ameliorate the restriction these factors of topography and soil depth exert on the choice of crops or their yields.

The control which some of the other factors exert on the choice of crops and their yield need not be so strict as that of topography and soil depth. Thus shortage of water due to lack of rain can sometimes be made good by irrigation, and the harmful effects of too high a water-table in the soil, particularly if its height fluctuates too much, can be reduced by a suitable drainage scheme. In some areas irrigation and drainage involve large capital works and control over very considerable areas of land, and at the present time can usually only be undertaken by governments or with strong government backing. Hence these methods of reducing the dependence of cropping on environment are beyond the control of the individual farmer.

The individual farmer, however, can reduce the control exerted by a number of factors. Thus if yields are limited by lack of plant nutrients, he can apply these as fertilisers; if by unfavourable tilth, he can choose suitable crop rotations or use adequate amounts of farmyard manure; if by soil acidity, he can use lime. Further, if there is an adequate drainage scheme for his district, he can, if necessary, improve the aeration of his soils by draining his fields; and if he has water available, he can reduce the harmful effect of short periods of drought by the use of supplementary irrigation.

To conclude this chapter, it is worth emphasising an obvious point. A potentially fertile soil and a good climate will not of themselves ensure high crop yields. The potentiality of the land can only be realised if it is farmed by men and women with the necessary energy, skill and money to make use of the resources which are now at their disposal. But all these resources are of only limited value to the farmer if his standard of farming is low. Unfortunately, one has only to compare the yields obtained by the best farmers with the average for that district to realise that the level of skill and industry of a large part of the farming community has now become the principal factor limiting crop yields on most of the agricultural soils of the world.

Conversion Factors for Units used in the Text

Length

1 inch = 2·540 cm.
1 foot = 12 in. = 30·48 cm.
1 yard = 3 ft. = 91·44 cm.

Area

1 sq. yd. = 0·8361 sq. m.
1 acre = 4840 sq. yd. = 0·4047 hectares

Weight

1 ounce = 28·35 gm.
1 pound = 16 oz. = 453·6 gm.
1 hundredweight = 112 lb. = 50·80 kg.
1 ton (2240 lb.) = 20 cwt. = 1016 kg.

Volume

1 gallon = 4·546 litres.
1 bushel = 1·031 American bushels = 36·37 litres.
1 cubic foot = 28·32 litres.

1 lb. per acre = 1·121 kg. per ha.
1 cwt. per acre = 125·5 kg. per ha.
1 ton per acre = 2510 kg. per ha.
1 bu. per acre = 89·87 litres per ha.

1 acre foot of water = 271×10^3 gall. and weighs 1210 tons (approx.).
1 cusec = a flow of 1 cubic foot of water per second
1 cusec per day (24 hours) = 1·98 acre ft.
1 part per million (p.p.m.) of salts in water = $1·21 \times 10^{-3}$ tons per acre ft.

To convert K into K_2O multiply by 1·20.
P into P_2O_5 multiply by 2·29.

1 bushel of wheat weighs about 60 lbs. (27 kg.).

AUTHOR INDEX

SUBJECT INDEX

Absorption by soils, of anions, 99 *et seq.*
 of gases and liquids, 128
Acids, excreted by plant roots, 537
Acid clays, 93 *et seq.*
 heat of neutralisation, 95
Acid of humus, 272–5
Acidity of soil,
 control of, 528–32
 due to aluminium ions, 94
  ammonium sulphate, 118
 effect on C/N ratio, 276
  composition of pastures, 527
  nitrogen fixation by legumes, 329
  phosphate states, 494, 504
  plant growth, 523–8
  soil population, 219
 methods of increasing, 614
 tolerance of crops to, 524
  of plant pathogens to, 526
 See also, pH of soils.
Acrasieae, 167, 214
Actinomycetes, in soil, 154
 effect of moisture content, 216
Aeration of soil,
 effect of earthworms, 185, 187
 effect of nitrification, 302
 effect on nutrient uptake, 450
 processes involved in, 363–5
Aggregates in soils, *see* Clods, Crumb.
Agrobacter, 150
Air,
 absorption by soils, 129
 space in soil, 361–3
  determination of, 362
 in soil, composition of, 363–9
 supply in soil, effect on nutrient uptake, 412, 450
Alder, nitrogen fixation by, 325
Algae,
 effect on oxygen content of soils, 162
 nitrogen fixation by blue-green, 163, 323
 number in soils, 162
 in paddy soils, 162, 263
 types of in soil, 160
Alkali soils, types of, 598
 reclamation of, 612
Alkalinity in soil,
 effect on plant growth, 532
 methods for controlling, 534, 614
Allophane in soils, 80
Aluminium compounds,
 movement in soil formation, 553, 563, 570–6, 586
Aluminium hydroxide,
 forms present in soils, 79
 as residual product of weathering, 553, 559, 505–6

Aluminium ions,
 cause of soil acidity, 94 *et seq.*
 effect on plant growth, 523
  soil pH, 109
 fixation of phosphate by 481
 reaction with humus, 282–5
Amino acids,
 excretion from leguminous nodules, 226, 348
 in humus, 270
Amino sugars, in humus, 269
Ammonia,
 inhibitor of nitrification, 299, 301
 level in soils, 309–11
 oxidation to nitrate, 296–303
 production from humus, 296
 volatilisation from soil, 311
Ammonium ions,
 level in soil, 303–11
 oxidation to nitrate, 296–303
 production from humus, 222, 289, 304
 reversion into non-exchangeable form, 114
Ammonium sulphate, effect on calcium status of soils, 118
Amoebae in soil, 164–8, 200
 giant forms, 168, 214
Amorphous constituents in soils, 79
Amphoteric behaviour of soil, 101
Anaerobic respiration, 143
Animal nutrition, trace elements in, 54
Animals in soil, *see* Fauna.
Anion-holding power of soils, 99 *et seq.*
Anionic exchange, in soils, 103
Antagonism, ionic in plants, 66
Antibiotics, produced by micro-organisms, 144, 159, 221, 230
 effect on microbial population, 210
 for controlling plant pathogens, 230
Ants in soils, 190–4
Apatite, presence in soils, 486
 solubility of, 483
 structure of, 476–9
Arbuscules, 238
Arthropods in soil, *see* Fauna.
Ash analysis, as guide to manuring, 13, 15
 constituents in plants, 390, 536, 563
  as affected by water supply, 390
Atmosphere in soil, *see* Air.
Autochthonous bacteria, 151
Autotrophic organisms, definition of, 138
Autoxidation of humus, 265, 271–2
Auxins,
 in composts, 252
 as plant nutrients, 25
Available nutrients in the soil, 467–71, 492, 512

675